# EVOLVING GENES AND PROTEINS

# EVOLVING GENES AND PROTEINS

*A SYMPOSIUM*

Held at the Institute of Microbiology
of Rutgers · The State University
*with support from the*
NATIONAL SCIENCE FOUNDATION

*Edited by*

Vernon Bryson and Henry J. Vogel

1965

Academic Press · New York and London

ACADEMIC PRESS INC
111 Fifth Avenue, New York, New York 10003


United Kingdom Edition published by
ACADEMIC PRESS INC. (LONDON) LTD.
Berkeley Square House, London W.1


LIBRARY OF CONGRESS CATALOG CARD NUMBER: 65-23644

PRINTED IN THE UNITED STATES OF AMERICA.

*This volume is dedicated to the memory of David Mahlon Bonner, distinguished teacher of one of us (H. J. V.) and cheerful friend.*

# List of Participants

ABELSON, PHILIP H., Geophysical Laboratory, Carnegie Institution of Washington, Washington, D.C.

AJL, SAMUEL, Albert Einstein Medical Center, Philadelphia, Pennsylvania

ALBRECHT, ALBERTA M., Walker Laboratory, Sloan-Kettering Institute for Cancer Research, Rye, New York

ALSTON, R. E., Department of Botany, University of Texas, Austin, Texas

ANDERSON, THOMAS F., Institute for Cancer Research, Philadelphia, Pennsylvania

ANFINSEN, CHRISTIAN B., National Institutes of Health, Bethesda, Maryland

ARNOW, PETER M., Squibb Institute for Medical Research, New Brunswick, New Jersey

AUSTRIAN, ROBERT, Department of Research Medicine, University of Pennsylvania School of Medicine, Philadelphia, Pennsylvania

AVERS, CHARLOTTE J., Department of Biological Sciences, Douglass College, Rutgers University, New Brunswick, New Jersey

BACON, DONALD F., Institute of Microbiology, Rutgers University, New Brunswick, New Jersey

BARD, RAYMOND C., University of Kentucky Medical Center, Lexington, Kentucky

BARKULIS, S. S., Ciba Pharmaceutical Products, Summit, New Jersey

BARRATT, RAYMOND W., Department of Biological Sciences, Dartmouth College, Hanover, New Hampshire

BASSIN, ROBERT H., Institute of Microbiology, Rutgers University, New Brunswick, New Jersey

BAUMBERG, SIMON, Institute of Microbiology, Rutgers University, New Brunswick, New Jersey

BAUTZ, E. K. F., Institute of Microbiology, Rutgers University, New Brunswick, New Jersey

BAUTZ, FRIEDLINDE A., Institute of Microbiology, Rutgers University, New Brunswick, New Jersey

BECKER, BENJAMIN, Institute of Microbiology, Rutgers University, New Brunswick, New Jersey

BENDICH, AARON, Sloan-Kettering Division, Cornell University, Sloan-Kettering Institute, New York, New York

BENNETT, JOHN, Box 14, Bennett Hall, University of Pennsylvania, Philadelphia, Pennsylvania

BLOCH, KONRAD, Department of Chemistry, Harvard University, Cambridge, Massachusetts

BLUM, HAROLD F., Department of Biology, Princeton University, Princeton, New Jersey

BODE, WERNER, Department of Physics, Kansas State University, Manhattan, Kansas

BOLLUM, F. J., Biology Division, Oak Ridge National Laboratory, Oak Ridge, Tennessee

BOLTON, ELLIS T., Department of Terrestrial Magnetism, Carnegie Institution of Washington, Washington, D.C.

BORENFREUND, ELLEN, Sloan-Kettering Division, Cornell University, Sloan-Kettering Institute, New York, New York

BOYDEN, ALAN A., Department of Zoology, Rutgers University, New Brunswick, New Jersey

BRAUN, WERNER, Institute of Microbiology, Rutgers University, New Brunswick, New Jersey

BRAUNITZER, G., Max-Planck-Institut für Biochemie, Munich, Germany

BRIODY, BERNARD, Department of Microbiology, New Jersey College of Medicine and Dentistry, Jersey City, New Jersey

BRITTEN, ROY J., Department of Terrestrial Magnetism, Carnegie Institution of Washington, Washington, D.C.

BROWN, WILLIAM E., E. R. Squibb and Sons, New Brunswick, New Jersey

BRUCH, CARL W., Bioscience Programs Office, National Aeronautics and Space Administration, Washington, D.C.

BRYSON, VERNON, Institute of Microbiology, Rutgers University, New Brunswick, New Jersey

BUETTNER-JANUSCH, JOHN, Department of Anthropology, Yale University, New Haven, Connecticut

BUETTNER-JANUSCH, VINA, Department of Anthropology, Yale University, New Haven, Connecticut

BURNETT, J. PAUL, Lilly Research Laboratories, Indianapolis, Indiana

CALVIN, MELVIN, Department of Chemistry, University of California, Berkeley, California

CARTA, GUY R., Institute of Microbiology, Rutgers University, New Brunswick, New Jersey

CHARNEY, WILLIAM, Schering Corporation, Bloomfield, New Jersey

CHYTIL, F., Institute of Microbiology, Czechoslovak Academy of Science, Prague, Czechoslovakia

CIRILLO, VINCENT P., Department of Biological Sciences, State University of New York, Stony Brook, Long Island, New York

CLEGG, JOHN, Department of Biophysics Johns Hopkins University, School of Medicine, Baltimore, Maryland

COHEN, EDWARD P., Institute of Microbiology, Rutgers University, New Brunswick, New Jersey

COHEN, SEYMOUR S., Department of Biochemistry, University of Pennsylvania School of Medicine, Philadelphia, Pennsylvania

COPELAND, JAMES C., Institute of Microbiology, Rutgers University, New Brunswick, New Jersey

CORA-FIGUEROA, MARIA E., Institute of Microbiology, Rutgers University, New Brunswick, New Jersey

COREY, EILEEN, Institute of Microbiology, Rutgers University, New Brunswick, New Jersey

CRONQUIST, ARTHUR, New York Botanical Garden, Bronx Park, New York, New York

DANIELSON, PATRICIA, Institute of Microbiology, Rutgers University, New Brunswick, New Jersey

DATTA, PRASANTA, Henry Shaw School of Botany, Washington University, St. Louis, Missouri

DAVIS, FRANK F., Department of Physiology and Biochemistry, Rutgers University, New Brunswick, New Jersey

DAVIS, ROWLAND H., Department of Botany, University of Michigan, Ann Arbor, Michigan

DEBUSK, A. GIB, Department of Biological Sciences, Florida State University, Tallahassee, Florida

DELUCA, M., Department of Biology, Johns Hopkins University, Baltimore, Maryland

DEMAIN, ARNOLD L., Merck, Sharp and Dohme Research Laboratories, Rahway, New Jersey

DEMEREC, M., Department of Biology, Brookhaven National Laboratory, Upton, Long Island, New York

DEMOSS, J. A., Department of Biology, University of California, La Jolla, California

DISHON, THEODOR, Department of Experimental Medicine, Hebrew University, Hadassah Medical School, Jerusalem, Israel

DONOVICK, RICHARD, Squibb Institute for Medical Research, New Brunswick, New Jersey

DOTY, PAUL, Department of Chemistry, Harvard University, Cambridge, Massachusetts

DOUDNEY, C. O., M. D. Anderson Hospital, Texas Medical Center, Houston, Texas

DOUGHERTY, H. W., Department of Biochemistry, Duke University Medical Center, Durham, North Carolina

DURANT, DAVID, Institute of Molecular Evolution, University of Miami, Coral Gables, Florida

DUTCHER, JAMES D., Squibb Institute for Medical Research, New Brunswick, New Jersey

EAGLE, HARRY, Department of Cell Biology, Albert Einstein College of Medicine, New York, New York

ELLIS, LILLIAN, Douglass College, Rutgers University, New Brunswick, New Jersey

FEDERMAN, MICHELINE, Department of Biological Sciences, Douglass College, Rutgers University, New Brunswick, New Jersey

FILOSA, MICHAEL, Institute of Microbiology, Rutgers University, New Brunswick, New Jersey

FIRSHEIN, WILLIAM, Wesleyan University, Middletown, Connecticut

FLAVIN, MARTIN, National Institutes of Health, Bethesda, Maryland

FOWLER, A., Department of Molecular Biology, Albert Einstein College of Medicine, New York, New York

FOX, SIDNEY W., Institute of Molecular Evolution, University of Miami, Coral Gables, Florida

FREESE, ERNST, National Institutes of Health, Bethesda, Maryland

FRESCO, JAQUES, Department of Chemistry, Princeton University, Princeton, New Jersey

FUKUI, GEORGE, Wallace Laboratories, Cranbury, New Jersey

GARCIA, ETHEL A., Institute of Microbiology, Rutgers University, New Brunswick, New Jersey

GEORGIADAS, M., Institute of Microbiology, Rutgers University, New Brunswick, New Jersey

GERBER, NANCY, Institute of Microbiology, Rutgers University, New Brunswick, New Jersey

GEST, HOWARD, Adolphus Busch III Laboratory of Molecular Biology, Washington University, St. Louis, Missouri

GILES, NORMAN H., J. W. Gibbs Research Laboratory, Yale University, New Haven, Connecticut

GILLESPIE, HAZEL B., Department of Bacteriology, Douglass College, Rutgers University, New Brunswick, New Jersey

GILLIS, ROBERT E., Department of Microbiology, New Jersey College of Medicine and Dentistry, Jersey City, New Jersey

GILVARG, CHARLES, Department of Chemistry, Princeton University, Princeton, New Jersey

GOLDTHWAITE, C. D., Department of Biochemistry, Albert Einstein College of Medicine, New York, New York

GRANICK, S., Rockefeller Institute, New York, New York

GRAPPEL, SARAH F., Institute of Microbiology, Rutgers University, New Brunswick, New Jersey

GREEN, JAMES W., Department of Physiology, Rutgers University, New Brunswick, New Jersey

GUNSALUS, I. C., Biochemistry Division, University of Illinois, Urbana, Illinois

GUTTMAN, HELENE N., Department of Biology, New York University, New York, New York

HANABUSA, K., Department of Biochemistry, Duke University Medical Center, Durham, North Carolina

HANDLER, PHILIP, Department of Biochemistry, Duke University School of Medicine, Durham, North Carolina

HARE, P. EDGAR, Geophysical Laboratory, Carnegie Institution of Washington, Washington, D.C.

HARRIS, HENRY, Sir William Dunn School of Pathology, University of Oxford, Oxford, England

HARTMAN, HYMAN, Department of Biology, University of California, La Jolla, California

HARTMAN, PHILIP E., Department of Biology, Johns Hopkins University, Baltimore, Maryland

HASHIMOTO, T., Department of Biochemistry, Duke University Medical Center, Durham, North Carolina

HECHTEL, MAUREEN A., Institute of Microbiology, Rutgers University, New Brunswick, New Jersey

HEIDELBERGER, MICHAEL, Department of Pathology, New York University Medical School, New York, New York

HELINSKI, DONALD R., Department of Biology, Princeton University, Princeton, New Jersey

HENDLIN, DAVID, Merck, Sharp and Dohme, Research Laboratories, Rahway, New Jersey

HENLEY, DAVID, Department of Chemistry, Princeton University, Princeton, New Jersey

HENNEMAN, DOROTHY, Squibb Institute for Medical Research, New Brunswick, New Jersey

HILL, ROBERT L., Department of Biochemistry, Duke University School of Medicine, Durham, North Carolina

HOROWITZ, NORMAN H., Biology Division, California Institute of Technology, Pasadena, California

HOTCHKISS, ROLLIN D., Rockefeller Institute, New York, New York

HOUSEWRIGHT, RILEY D., U.S. Army Biological Laboratories, Fort Detrick, Maryland

HOYER, BILL H., National Institutes of Health, Bethesda, Maryland

HUTCHISON, DORRIS J., Sloan-Kettering Institute for Cancer Research, Rye, New York

INMAN, JOHN, Department of Biophysics, Johns Hopkins School of Medicine, Baltimore, Maryland

JENNINGS, ROBERT K., Biochemistry Branch, Office of Naval Research, Washington, D.C.

JOHNSTON, JAMES A., Department of Agricultural Biochemistry, Rutgers University, New Brunswick, New Jersey

JONES, EVAN E., Institute of Microbiology, Rutgers University, New Brunswick, New Jersey

JOSHI, J. G., Department of Biochemistry, Duke University Medical Center, Durham, North Carolina

JUKES, THOMAS H., Space Sciences Laboratory, University of California, Berkeley, California

KABAT, ELVIN, Neurological Institute, College of Physicians and Surgeons, Columbia University, New York, New York

KALF, GEORGE, Department of Biochemistry, New Jersey College of Medicine and Dentistry, Jersey City, New Jersey

KAPLAN, NATHAN O., Graduate Department of Biochemistry, Brandeis University, Waltham, Massachusetts

KAUZMANN, WALTER, Department of Chemistry, Princeton University, Princeton, New Jersey

KESSEL, R. W. I., Institute of Microbiology, Rutgers University, New Brunswick, New Jersey

KIESLICH, KLAUS, Schering A.-G., Berlin, Germany

KITTO, G. BARRIE, Graduate Department of Biochemistry, Brandeis University, Waltham, Massachusetts

KLEIN, DEANA T., Department of Microbiology, Albert Einstein College of Medicine, New York, New York

KLEIN, RICHARD M., New York Botanical Garden, Bronx Park, New York, New York

KOFT, BERNARD W., Department of Bacteriology, Rutgers University, New Brunswick, New Jersey

KORNBERG, ARTHUR, Department of Biochemistry, Stanford University School of Medicine, Palo Alto, California

KRAEMER, KENNETH, Institute of Microbiology, Rutgers University, New Brunswick, New Jersey

KRAMPITZ, LESTER O. Department of Microbiology, School of Medicine, Western Reserve University, Cleveland, Ohio

KUCHAYEVA, ALEKSANDRA, Institute of Microbiology of the Academy of Sciences of the U. S. S. R., Moscow, U. S. S. R.

LAMANNA, CARL, Army Research Office, Department of the Army, Washington, D. C.

LAMPEN, J. OLIVER, Institute of Microbiology, Rutgers University, New Brunswick, New Jersey

LANDMAN, OTTO, Department of Biology, Georgetown University, Washington, D. C.

LANGLYKKE, ASGER F., Squibb Institute for Medical Research, New Brunswick, New Jersey

LASKIN, ALLEN I., Squibb Institute for Medical Research, New Brunswick, New Jersey

LEATHEM, JAMES H., Nelson Biological Laboratory, Rutgers University, New Brunswick, New Jersey

LECHEVALIER, HUBERT A., Institute of Microbiology, Rutgers University, New Brunswick, New Jersey

LECHEVALIER, MARY P., Institute of Microbiology, Rutgers University, New Brunswick, New Jersey

LENGYEL, PETER, Department of Biochemistry, New York University School of Medicine, New York, New York

LEVERE, R., Rockefeller Institute, New York, New York

LEWIS, HERMAN W., Genetic Biology Program, National Science Foundation, Washington, D C.

LINDENMAYER, A., Department of Biology, Queens College, Flushing, New York

LIVINGSTON, LAURA R., Department of Biology, Yale University, New Haven, Connecticut

LURIA, S. E., Department of Biology, Massachusetts Institute of Technology, Cambridge, Massachusetts

MARGOLIASH, EMANUEL, Abbott Laboratories, North Chicago, Illinois

MARGOLIN, PAUL, Cold Spring Harbor Laboratory of Quantitative Biology, Cold Spring Harbor, New York

MARMUR, JULIUS, Department of Biochemistry, Albert Einstein College of Medicine, New York, New York

MARSHECK, WILLIAM J., Jr., Institute of Microbiology, Rutgers University, New Brunswick, New Jersey

MAXWELL, R. E., Parke-Davis Research Laboratories, Ann Arbor, Michigan

MAYR, ERNST, Museum of Comparative Zoology, Harvard University, Cambridge, Massachusetts

McAUSLAN, BRIAN, Department of Biology, Princeton University, Princeton, New Jersey

McCARTHY, BRIAN J., Departments of Microbiology and Genetics, University of Washington, Seattle, Washington

McDANIEL, LLOYD E., Institute of Microbiology, Rutgers University, New Brunswick, New Jersey

McELROY, WILLIAM D., Department of Biology, Johns Hopkins University, Baltimore, Maryland

McLELLAN, WILLIAM L., JR., Institute of Microbiology, Rutgers University, New Brunswick, New Jersey

MENON, MIRA, Institute of Microbiology, Rutgers University, New Brunswick, New Jersey

MILLS, STANLEY E., Department of Biology, University of California, La Jolla, California

MOSES, VIVIAN, Lawrence Radiation Laboratory, University of California, Berkeley, California

NAGY, STEVEN, Department of Agricultural Biochemistry, Rutgers University, New Brunswick, New Jersey

NAKANO, MASAYASU, Institute of Microbiology, Rutgers University, New Brunswick, New Jersey

NASON, ALVIN, Department of Biology, Johns Hopkins University, Baltimore, Maryland

NATHANS, DANIEL, Department of Microbiology, Johns Hopkins University School of Medicine, Baltimore, Maryland

NAYLOR, AUBREY W., Department of Botany, Duke University, Durham, North Carolina

NEMER, MARTIN, Institute for Cancer Research, Philadelphia, Pennsylvania

NEUMANN, NORBERT P., Institute of Microbiology, Rutgers University, New Brunswick, New Jersey

NICKERSON, WALTER J., Institute of Microbiology, Rutgers University, New Brunswick, New Jersey

ORTIGOZA-FERADO, JORGE A., Institute of Microbiology, Rutgers University, New Brunswick, New Jersey

OTSUJI, NOZOMU, Department of Molecular Biology and Biophysics, Yale University, New Haven, Connecticut

PALCZUK, NICHOLAS C., Department of Zoology, Rutgers University, New Brunswick, New Jersey

PAPPENHEIMER, A. M., JR., Biological Laboratories, Harvard University, Cambridge, Massachusetts

PAULING, LINUS, Division of Chemistry and Chemical Engineering, California Institute of Technology, Pasadena, California

PÈNE, JACQUES J., Department of Biochemistry, Albert Einstein College of Medicine, New York, New York

PERLMAN, D., Squibb Institute for Medical Research, New Brunswick, New Jersey

PERRY, ROBERT, Institute for Cancer Research, Philadelphia, Pennsylvania

PIENTA, ROMAN J., Institute of Microbiology, Rutgers University, New Brunswick, New Jersey

PLESCIA, OTTO J., Institute of Microbiology, Rutgers University, New Brunswick, New Jersey

PONNAMPERUMA, CYRIL, Exobiology Division, National Aeronautics and Space Administration, Ames Research Center, Moffet Field, California

POTTER, VAN R., McArdle Memorial Laboratory, University of Wisconsin Medical School, Madison Wisconsin

PRAMER, DAVID, Department of Agricultural Microbiology, Rutgers University, New Brunswick, New Jersey

PRICE, CARL A., Department of Plant Biology, Rutgers University, New Brunswick, New Jersey

RANCOURT, MARTHA W., Department of Biological Sciences, Douglass College, Rutgers University, New Brunswick, New Jersey

RAO, C. V. N., Institute of Microbiology, Rutgers University, New Brunswick, New Jersey

REILLY, EUGENE E., Institute of Microbiology, Rutgers University, New Brunswick, New Jersey

RICH, ALEXANDER, Department of Biology, Massachusetts Institute of Technology, Cambridge, Massachusetts

RINALDINI, L., University of Cordoba, Cordoba, Argentina

ROBERTS, RICHARD B., Department of Terrestrial Magnetism, Carnegie Institution of Washington, Washington, D. C.

ROGERS, PALMER, Department of Microbiology, University of Minnesota, Minneapolis, Minnesota

ROUSE, HARRIET, Rutgers Medical School, New Brunswick, New Jersey

RUDKIN, GEORGE, Institute for Cancer Research, Philadelphia, Pennsylvania

RUTTER, WILLIAM J., Department of Chemistry, University of Illinois, Urbana, Illinois

SAGER, RUTH, Department of Zoology, Columbia University, New York, New York

SALTHE, STANLEY, Graduate Department of Biochemistry, Brandeis University, Waltham, Massachusetts

SANDERSON, K. E., Department of Biology, Brookhaven National Laboratory, Upton, Long Island, New York

SANTER, MELVIN, Haverford College, Haverford, Pennsylvania

SANTER, URSULA, Haverford College, Haverford, Pennsylvania

SAUNDERS, GRADY F., Department of Microbiology, University of Illinois, Urbana, Illinois

SAUNDERS, PRISCILLA, Department of Dairy Science, University of Illinois, Urbana, Illinois

SCHER, BARBARA, Department of Molecular Biology, Albert Einstein College of Medicine, New York, New York

SCHER, WILLIAM I., JR., Rockefeller Institute, New York, New York

SCHLESINGER, R. WALTER, Rutgers Medical School, New Brunswick, New Jersey

SCHULTZ, JACK, Institute for Cancer Research, Philadelphia, Pennsylvania

SCHWARTZ, STANLEY A., Institute of Microbiology, Rutgers University, New Brunswick, New Jersey

SELIGER, H. H., Department of Biology, Johns Hopkins University, Baltimore, Maryland

SHILO, M., Department of Microbiological Chemistry, Hebrew University, Hadassah Medical School, Jerusalem, Israel

SHIMURA, YOSHIRO, Department of Microbiology, Johns Hopkins University School of Medicine, Baltimore, Maryland

SHOCKMAN, GERALD D., Department of Microbiology, Temple University School of Medicine, Philadelphia, Pennsylvania

SHULL, GILBERT, E. R. Squibb and Sons, New Brunswick, New Jersey

SIEGEL, ELI C., Institute of Microbiology, Rutgers University, New Brunswick, New Jersey

SIEKEVITZ, PHILIP, Rockefeller Institute, New York, New York

SIMPSON, MELVIN V., Department of Biochemistry, Dartmouth Medical School, Hanover, New Hampshire

SMITH, EMIL L., Department of Biological Chemistry, University of California School of Medicine, Los Angeles, California

SMITH, LUCILE, Department of Biochemistry, Dartmouth Medical School, Hanover, New Hampshire

SNELL, J. F., Department of Biochemistry, Ohio State University, Columbus, Ohio

SONNEBORN, TRACY M., Department of Zoology, Indiana University, Bloomington, Indiana

SPETNER, L. M., Applied Physics Laboratory, Johns Hopkins University, Silver Spring, Maryland

SPEYER, JOSEPH F., Cold Spring Harbor Laboratory of Quantitative Biology, Cold Spring Harbor, New York

SPIEGELMAN, SOL, Department of Microbiology, University of Illinois, Urbana, Illinois

SPRINSON, DAVID B., Department of Biochemistry, College of Physicians and Surgeons, Columbia University, New York, New York

STETTEN, DeWITT, JR., Rutgers Medical School, New Brunswick, New Jersey

STETTEN, MARJORIE R., Rutgers Medical School, New Brunswick, New Jersey

STEVENS, THOMAS M., Rutgers Medical School, New Brunswick, New Jersey

STONEHILL, ELLIOTT H., Walker Laboratory, Sloane-Kettering Institute for Cancer Research, Rye, New York

STOUDT, T., Merck, Sharp and Dohme Research Laboratories, Rahway, New Jersey

STRAMPP, ALICE, Institute of Microbiology, Rutgers University, New Brunswick, New Jersey

STRASSMAN, MURRAY, Albert Einstein Medical Center, Philadelphia, Pennsylvania

STRAUS, DAVID B., Department of Chemistry, Princeton University, Princeton, New Jersey

STROHL, WILLIAM A., Rutgers Medical School, New Brunswick, New Jersey

STRUMEYER, DAVID H., Department of Agricultural Biochemistry, Rutgers University, New Brunswick, New Jersey

SUBBAIAH, T. V., Department of Biochemistry, Albert Einstein College of Medicine, New York, New York

SUEOKA, NOBORU, Department of Biology, Princeton University, Princeton, New Jersey

SUSKIND, SIGMUND R., Department of Biology, Johns Hopkins University, Baltimore, Maryland

SWARTZ, H. E., Institute of Microbiology, Rutgers University, New Brunswick, New Jersey

SYMINGTON, E. BLAND, Institute of Microbiology, Rutgers University, New Brunswick, New Jersey

SZUCHET, SARA, Department of Chemistry, Princeton University, Princeton, New Jersey

TAGO, KATSUHIKO, Institute of Microbiology, Rutgers University, New Brunswick, New Jersey

TALMAGE, DAVID W., Department of Microbiology, University of Colorado School of Medicine, Denver, Colorado

TATUM, E. L., Rockefeller Institute, New York, New York

TAUB, S. R., Department of Biology, Princeton University, Princeton, New Jersey

TAYLOR, M. WIGHT, Department of Agricultural Biochemistry, Rutgers University, New Brunswick, New Jersey

THIMANN, KENNETH V., Biological Laboratories, Harvard University, Cambridge, Massachusetts

THOMAS, CHARLES A., Department of Biophysics, Johns Hopkins University, Baltimore, Maryland

UMBREIT, WAYNE W., Department of Bacteriology, Rutgers University, New Brunswick, New Jersey

UNGER, LEON, Institute of Microbiology, Rutgers University, New Brunswick, New Jersey

VAN NIEL, C. B., Hopkins Marine Station, Pacific Grove, California

VOGEL, HENRY J., Institute of Microbiology, Rutgers University, New Brunswick, New Jersey

VOGEL, RUTH H., Institute of Microbiology, Rutgers University, New Brunswick, New Jersey

WARD, JOHN M., Metabolic Biology Program, National Science Foundation, Washington, D. C.

WARNER, JONATHAN R., Department of Biochemistry, Albert Einstein College of Medicine, New York, New York

WEINREB, EVA L., Department of Biology, New York University, New York, New York

WEISSMANN, CHARLES, Department of Biochemistry, New York University School of Medicine, New York, New York

WHITE, DAVID, Exobiology Division, National Aeronautics and Space Administration, Ames Research Center, Moffet Field, California

WILLIAMS, CURTIS A., Rockefeller Institute, New York, New York

WINTERSTEINER, OSKAR, Squibb Institute for Medical Research, New Brunswick, New Jersey

WOODRUFF, H. BOYD, Merck, Sharp and Dohme Research Laboratories, Rahway, New Jersey

WRIGHT, BARBARA KALCKAR, Huntington Laboratory, Massachusetts General Hospital, Boston, Massachusetts

YAMANE, TETSUO, Department of Chemistry, Princeton University, Princeton, New Jersey

YANKOFSKY, SAUL A., Department of Microbiology, University of Illinois, Urbana, Illinois

YANOFSKY, CHARLES, Department of Biological Sciences, Stanford University, Stanford, California

YČAS, MARTYNAS, Department of Microbiology, Upstate Medical Center, State University of New York, Syracuse, New York

YOSHIDA, AKIRA, National Institutes of Health, Bethesda, Maryland

ZUCKERKANDL, EMILE, Laboratoire de Physico-Chimie Colloidale, Montpellier, France

# Preface

Recent accomplishments in biochemistry and genetics have drawn evolution into the context of molecular biology. Such a development was foreseen by the pioneer evolutionists. Darwin, although organismally oriented, spoke of "natural selection among the molecules." Huxley, in 1869, frankly linked evolution to biochemistry: "It is a probable hypothesis that what the world is to organisms in general each organism is to the molecules of which it is composed. Multitudes of these, having diverse tendencies, are competing with one another for opportunity to exist and multiply; and the organism, as a whole, is as much the product of the molecules which are victorious as the Fauna, or Flora of a country is the product of the victorious organic beings in it." Views of molecular evolution in relation to organismal evolution are thus time-honored. What opens up an entirely new perspective is the information, now emerging in remarkable detail, as to structural and functional features of proteins and nucleic acids.

A symposium on "Evolving Genes and Proteins" was held at the Institute of Microbiology of Rutgers, The State University, September 17 and 18, 1964, with support from the National Science Foundation. A four-page summary of the symposium proceedings has appeared in *Science* **147**: 68, 1965. The full proceedings are contained in this volume.

We wish to express our warm appreciation to Dr. E. L. Tatum for his delivery of the Opening Address. The contributions of the session chairmen, Dr. K. V. Thimann, Dr. C. B. van Niel, Dr. C. B. Anfinsen, Dr. E. L. Smith, Dr. D. Stetten, Jr., Dr. P. H. Abelson, Dr. P. Doty, Dr. W. Braun, and Dr. R. D. Hotchkiss, and of Dr. T. M. Sonneborn, who made his presentation as an Evening Lecture, are also gratefully acknowledged.

For their fine assistance in connection with many details of the meeting, we thank Mr. E. R. Isaacs and the other staff members of the Institute of Microbiology who were involved.

*April, 1965*
               VERNON BRYSON
               HENRY J. VOGEL

# Contents

# PART IV
## EVOLUTION OF PROTEINS II

# PART V
## EVOLUTION OF PROTEINS III

# PART VI
## EVENING LECTURE

# PART VII
## EVOLUTION OF GENES I

# PART VIII
## EVOLUTION OF GENES II

# PART IX
## EVOLUTION OF GENES III

# EVOLVING GENES AND PROTEINS

# Introductory Remarks

J. Oliver Lampen

*Director, Institute of Microbiology*

It is a pleasant privilege that I have to welcome all of you on behalf of the Institute of Microbiology. We are continuing our series of symposia emphasizing aspects of modern biology and biochemistry in which recent experimental findings have provided new means of contact among the various formal disciplines. Our ability to compare with new comprehension certain features of enzymes, "active sites," and pathways from a broad variety of organisms has provided precisely such an opportunity. This is evidenced by the kaleidoscopic array of specialties represented both by our speakers and by our general participants. As the Symposium continues, we trust that the interactions will prove to be powerful but not explosive.

We hope that you will enjoy the sessions and the opportunities for personal discussion that they will provide.

## Opening Address

# Evolution and Molecular Biology

### E. L. Tatum

*The Rockefeller Institute, New York, New York*

This Symposium in a certain sense is a milestone on our travels along uncharted paths of molecular biology. Not too many years ago it would have been presumptuous to have undertaken a serious discussion of the molecular bases of the evolution of metabolic pathways, of proteins, and of genes. Today, however, a hasty glance at the program for this meeting should convince even the most skeptical that the situation has changed. We are now in the position of having maps, if as yet only fragmentary and vague in spots, indicating some of the guiding landmarks along the road leading to an understanding of the molecular events involved in the evolution of pathways, proteins, and genes. It can confidently be anticipated that this Symposium will add more useful guideposts along this route and thus speed our travels to the goal of understanding the molecular bases of evolution of living organisms. It is tempting to try framing our possible travels toward this goal, in terms of analogy, as a "Biologist's Pilgrims Progress"! However, neither time nor my ability permits this attempt.

Rather, I want to take a brief look at our present location and to try to place it in perspective in terms of the paths we have already traveled, and the signposts which have guided our way hither. Thus, rather than anticipating the content of this Symposium, let us consider the evolution of our understanding of the underlying concepts of molecular biology.

The evolution of molecular genetics can be classified roughly into several periods, which might be designated, corresponding to periods in the history of civilization, or of art, as the primitive period, the classic period, the renaissance, and the modern.

The primitive period would be the pre-Mendel times, and the classic the period of Morgan during which the primary emphasis was on the material basis of heredity and the mechanism of inheritance via genes and chromosomes. The renaissance would be the period during which

3

emphasis shifted toward gene action, the period initiated to a significant extent by the recognition of the potentialities and utility of microorganisms, and during which the concepts of gene action in terms of biochemistry of the cell were developed, as symbolized by the "one gene–one enzyme" concept.

The modern period, symbolized as that of "molecular biology" or "The Age of DNA," now in full flower of rapid, exponential development, is characterized by the gratifyingly successful attempt to delineate in detail the molecular structures, processes, and forces which underly the specificity, replication, and functioning of hereditary material (16). Although this approach is indeed ostensibly characterizable as a mechanistic or materialistic approach to life, in a true sense our closer understanding only accentuates and intensifies our appreciation of the beauty and order of Nature and of the natural processes of Life itself—hence is the antithesis of Materialism.

But enough of philosophizing—let us consider in more detail the origin and status of some of the concepts of this modern period. The general thesis which seems to hold, as I hope to bring out, is that, as in most areas of knowledge and science, advances are not often made by great quantum jumps involving completely new ideas or principles, but in a continuous, more or less smooth curve marked by interrelated ideas and concepts, each based on earlier or related advances or concepts. The whole resembles the growth of a living organism, or the processes of metabolism, in that its orderly development results from a complex series of interrelated events, regulated and stimulated by informational feedback systems, and catalyzed by and dependent on the enzymes of new technical methods and approaches and conceptual formulations. In connection with this curve of progress, it may also be worth pointing out that each sophisticated technique and concept of each today tends to develop into the simple, taken-for-granted technique and concept of each tomorrow. It behooves us only to avoid the dangers of too readily accepting glib sophistication and intellectual satisfaction as necessarily establishing, per se, the validity of a concept.

Let us now be more specific in illustration of my thesis. What I have called the renaissance period was concerned with the more general aspects of gene action. It was initiated with the recognition of the experimentally useful characteristics of microorganisms, notably *Neurospora*, for the verification of generalized principles which had previously been formulated from specific and more limited instances of inborn errors of metabolism of man, from plant and insect pigments, and from a few isolated animal and yeast enzymes. The finding, predicated on vitamin and growth-factor studies in the nutrition of both animals and microorganisms, that biosynthetic reactions in *Neurospora* were under specific genetic control (1) was very soon extended to other microorganisms, bacteria, yeast, and algae. This extension supported the generalization that all biochemical reactions of all cells are gene-determined, and conversely that genes act primarily in controlling biochemical, i.e., enzymatic reactions. Hence the dictum "one gene–one enzyme."

During this period, also, the use of specific auxotrophic mutations in bacteria as marker genes led to the discovery of new genetic systems in bacteria, bacterial conjugation, and transduction, and, in fungi, of parasexuality and somatic recombination. These new genetic systems in turn functioned as feedback systems, adding new experimental approaches to the gene–enzyme relation, and leading directly to comparative studies on metabolic pathways and to consideration of the evolution of these pathways.

With these new discoveries of genetic systems in bacteria, detailed knowledge of these systems, of linkage, of gene replication and recombination, and of chromosome passage in conjugation progressed very rapidly. Also, the study of these systems, of induction, repression, and inhibition of enzyme synthesis and activity soon led to important new concepts of the regulation of gene activity—notably the now almost classical concepts of "feedback regulation," the "operon," and "allosteric regulation." I cannot resist recalling that feedback regulation systems were probably first observed, but not so named, in early studies on the effects of nutrient levels on the accumulation of biosynthetic intermediates in *Neurospora*.

We might say that the modern age of molecular genetics was conceived by the recognition of DNA as the genetic material of the transforming principle in pneumococcus and as the hereditary material in bacteriophage. During its gestation period its development was marked by the overthrow of the tetranucleotide structure of DNA by the experimental findings of Chargaff, anticipating the base-pairing hypothesis, and by the recognition of the helical structure of DNA by X-ray and other studies by Pauling and by Wilkins. It was delivered and christened by the formulation of the now universally accepted Watson-Crick model. I need not remind this audience of its rapid growth and development during infancy and childhood, with all its ramifications, as for example into mechanisms of gene replication and transcription, and its implications for all areas of biology and genetics.

I would like only to recall that during this period of development and growth of the DNA age some of these implications and inferences led, by posing certain questions related to the specificity, replication, and functioning or transcription of DNA, to the development of new techniques for answering these questions. The answers in turn fed back new knowledge and understanding of gene nature and functioning and raised new significant questions. I might mention a few of the more striking examples.

The technique of cesium gradient centrifugation was developed (12) to isolate DNA fractions of differing densities resulting from the incorporation of heavy isotopes, and hence to examine the replication of DNA, which was found in *Escherichia coli* to be semi-conservative, as predicted from the Watson-Crick model.

The technique of DNA melting, or double-strand separation and reconstitution on cooling (4), stemmed from the concepts of H-binding in DNA double helices and has proved extremely valuable in the detection of binding of other substances such as actinomycin to DNA, and in the detection by hybridization of molecular homologies between different DNA molecules, and between DNA and RNA.

These principles have been effectively and ingeniously used to determine molecular and, by inference, evolutionary relationships between DNA's from different organisms (2), as well as to isolate specific messenger RNA. The latter use with virus mRNA has made possible direct, most ingenious analysis of the processes of virus DNA transcription and replication (15), now considered as dependent *in vivo* on double-stranded, circular DNA.

The development of techniques of determining amino acid sequences in proteins, and of the fingerprinting technique for screening for peptide differences, led with human hemoglobins to the first identification of a single amino acid substitution as the consequence of gene mutation, a result supplying the first experimental verification of theory. The expansion and extension of such findings with other hemoglobinopathies, and enzymes such as tryptophan synthetase, are familiar to all of us. Sequence differences in single enzymes, notably such as cytochrome *c*, from different species, are now being fruitfully interpreted in terms of evolutionary changes in proteins during speciation (11), and extended by inference to the primary mutational changes in DNA base sequence and hence to considerations of the evolution of DNA in these species. These problems and findings will be presented and discussed in detail later in these sessions.

Direct experimental evidence of mutational changes in base-pair sequences in DNA is so far unavailable. However, considerable indirect evidence of various sorts supports the general thesis. Mutations are indeed produced by the incorporation of base analogs into replicating DNA *in vivo*, presumably by causing faulty pairing and hence base-pair substitutions. Results of fine structure genetic analysis of mutation within single loci can most simply be interpreted in terms of mutation as involving single base-pair changes. The comparison of genic fine structure changes with function, as with the rII locus of phage or tryptophan synthetase of *E. coli* and *Neurospora*, has led to a satisfying correlation of mutational changes in DNA with changes in the phenotype, consistent with the hypothesis of colinearity of base triplet sequence in DNA with amino acid sequence in the protein end product.

Electrophoretic and chromatographic techniques have permitted the demonstration that many if not most enzymes exist in more than one molecular form (isoenzymes), often as different aggregates of several different polypeptide monomers (5). This concept, applied to the one-time confusing and obscure phenomenon of intra-allelic complementation between different genetic subunits or cistrons, has led to the refinement, but not to crucial modification, of the "one gene–one enzyme" hypothesis to the generalization "one cistron–one polypeptide chain."

The most direct evidence so far available as to DNA sequence structure in relation to function is of course that coming from studies on the amino acid code. Before the experimental system of Nirenberg and Matthaei was available, most of us considered the direct experimental relation of DNA structure with protein structure to be many years away, and that it would require the establishment, by methods yet to be developed, of complete amino acid sequences of proteins, and the isolation of single homogeneous gene DNA preparations, with the determination of their complete base sequences. This route of attack was bypassed when it was shown that enzymatically synthesized RNA polymers of different known base content had specific functions as messengers in amino acid incorporation into protein in an *in vitro* system (14). With continued refinement and definition, we are rapidly getting closer to complete knowledge of the precise RNA triplet code designations of all the protein amino acids. From base-pairing principles the primary DNA triplet code is directly deducible from the RNA code. The extension of this information to systems from many organisms and species into considerations of universality of the code, and of coding redundancy, is of obvious importance in relation to evolution.

It might here be appropriate to inject a few words of caution against the assumption that all cellular activity falls within the same genic DNA–RNA template–protein–synthesis framework. The syntheses of certain specific polypeptide molecules, such as the antibiotics gramicidine and tyrocidine, have been shown not to involve RNA messengers with the same instability and properties as protein mRNA, and to lack the complete amino acid specificity characteristic of protein synthesis (10).

Such "atypical" or "nonclassic" modes of synthesis may well apply to other polypeptides of biological significance.

Another area for caution is in regard to the phenomenon of extra-chromosomal or cytoplasmic inheritance, which may be of considerable and general importance in organisms other than the microorganisms, bacteria, algae, and fungi from which some of the most well-studied examples come.

If I may, I would like to describe briefly some recent pertinent experiments involving *Neurospora*. For several years Dr. Garnjobst and I have been studying two slow-growing, morphologically characteristic similar strains of spontaneous origin. Genetic examination proved that chromosomal factors were not involved in a primary way, and that the distinctive abnormality, similar in some ways, but more marked than in *poky*, could be transferred to other genetic strains via cell anastomosis and protoplasmic exchange. Using the ingenious techniques he had already developed for *Neurospora* microinjection, Dr. J. F. Wilson was able to transmit the abnormal character to other susceptible strains by injection of protoplasm from the abnormal strain, even without demonstrable transfer of nuclei (17). Even more interestingly, Dr. E. G. Diacumakos in our laboratory has recently been able to show that the abnormal characteristics could be transmitted by microinjection of sucrose-gradient-purified mitochondria from the abnormal strain (3). She also showed that strains so altered by injection possessed, to varying extents, the cytochrome abnormalities of the original abnormal strain from which the mitochondria were derived.

This work shows the definitive association of a nonchromosomal characteristic with a subcellular entity, the mitochondrion. The inferential biological continuity of the mitochondrion in *Neurospora* is in satisfying accord with Luck's finding, based on isotopic evidence, that mitochondria in *Neurospora* do indeed reproduce by division (8). In accord with theoretical expectations for a self-perpetuating cytoplasmic factor, it should be recalled that plastids have clearly been shown to contain DNA. Although the presence of DNA in mitochondria has until recently been indicated only by somewhat indirect methods, Drs. Luck and Reich have now provided definitive evidence (9). They have shown that *Neurospora* mitochondria bind labeled actinomycin and possess an actinomycin-sensitive RNA polymerase. They have also isolated DNA from mitochondria by preparative centrifugation in cesium chloride. This DNA binds actinomycin, and its buoyant density differs from that of nuclear DNA. It should be mentioned that similar DNA has also been shown to be associated with animal cell mitochondria (13). An electron photomicrograph, prepared by Dr. Stoeckenius, of the *Neurospora* mitochondrial DNA shows regular long filaments consistent with double-stranded high-molecular-weight DNA. Thus, in *Neurospora*, the evidence seems clear that one type of nonchromosomal character is carried in mitochondria, and that these mitochondria contain DNA which differs in base ratio from nuclear DNA. This evidence strongly suggests that in *Neurospora* mitochondrial DNA is involved in the replication and biological functioning of the mitochondria.

So much for our discussion of some of the high points of the development of molecular biology through its childhood and early adolescence. Can we make any predictions as to what its youth and maturity will bring?

Certainly one area, which is already opening up in an exciting manner, will be that of the regulation and control of gene action during differentiation and development. I need only cite the recent evidence that histones are involved in gene expression, and that hormone action may similarly be involved. Already, the insect hormone ecdysone, several mammalian steroid sex hormones, and even the plant hormone auxin (6) have been implicated in gene activity via mRNA synthesis. In a very recent report, for example, Kidson and Kirby (7) describe the different and possibly specific effects of a number of hormones, even including insulin and thyroxine, on the pattern of presumptive mammalian mRNA synthesis.

Another area which has not yet actually been opened up, but which undoubtedly soon will be, is that of morphological differentiation and development.

Both of these areas will certainly, in due course of time, provide opportunities for studies on their evolutionary aspects and implications and should provide exciting material for rewarding consideration in a symposia such as this one.

Even more remotely, in full maturity of this period of biology perhaps we should anticipate studies on controlled evolution, including genetic engineering, on the evolution of life on other planets and in other solar systems, and even on the origin of life itself.

Now, a few concluding remarks more directly related to this Symposium. The three areas to be considered—the evolution of metabolic pathways, the evolution of proteins, and the evolution of genes—are of course intimately and causally interrelated. It is also obvious that their order in this Symposium is the chronological order in which the three areas have been observed and studied at the molecular level as well as the order of increasing intrinsic difficulty of their experimental approach.

From orthodox evolutionary theory, and from the causal interrelationships of pathways, proteins, and genes, a number of questions suggest themselves. Some of the most difficult and intriguing are analogous to that of the old chicken-and-the-egg query. Which came first in the evolution of life? On which system have selective forces been most effectively exerted during evolution? And last, but not least, have changes as a consequence of gene mutation always been random, preceding selection and evolution, as evolutionary theory would predict? Or, is it possible that among the complex feedbacks not yet recognized there are conditions under which such feedbacks have functioned or still function?

Let us keep in mind that this Symposium, in answering those questions we are conceptually ready to ask, may be supplying clues to concepts we have not yet dreamed of, or seen, even "as in a glass, darkly."

## REFERENCES

1. BEADLE, G. W., AND TATUM, E. L., *Proc. Natl. Acad. Sci. U.S.*, **27**, 499 (1941).
2. BOLTON, E. T., AND HOYER, B. H., this volume.
3. DIACUMAKOS, E. G., GARNJOBST, L., AND TATUM, E. L., *J. Cell Biol.*, in press.
4. DOTY, P., *Harvey Lectures*, **55**, 103 (1959-60).
5. KAPLAN, N. O., this volume.
6. KEY, S. L., Abstract, Plant Physiol. Meetings, Boulder, Colo., Aug. 24-27, 1964. *Plant Physiol.*, **39**, *Suppl.*, in press.
7. KIDSON, C., AND KIRBY, K. S., *Nature* **203**, 599 (1964).
8. LUCK, D. J. L., *Proc. Natl. Acad. Sci. U.S.*, **49**, 233 (1963).
9. LUCK, D. J. L., AND REICH, E., *Proc. Natl. Acad. Sci. U.S.*, in press.
10. MACH, B., AND TATUM, E. L., *Proc. Natl. Acad. Sci. U.S.*, in press.
11. MARGOLIASH, E., AND SMITH, E., this volume.
12. MESELSON, U., AND STAHL, F. H., *Proc. Natl. Acad. Sci. U.S.*, **44**, 671 (1958).
13. MARMUR, J., personal communication.
14. NIRENBERG, M. W., AND MATTHAEI, J. H., *Proc. Natl. Acad. Sci. U.S.*, **47**, 1588 (1961).
15. SPIEGELMAN, S., this volume.
16. TATUM, E. L., *Proc. Natl. Acad. Sci. U.S.*, **51**, 908 (1964).
17. WILSON, J. F., GARNJOBST, L., AND TATUM, E. L., *J. Cell Biol.*, in press.

PART I

# EVOLUTION OF PATHWAYS I

# Chairman's Remarks

KENNETH V. THIMANN

*The Biological Laboratories,*
*Harvard University,*
*Cambridge, Massachusetts*

I think we can, as Dr. Tatum indicated, look forward to a very exciting Symposium.

Our program this morning concerns the evolution of pathways. This is a rather difficult subject to introduce in a brief space of time. Obviously I cannot say anything about evolution in the presence of this distinguished gathering of evolutionists. It would be equally silly to say anything about pathways when we are just going to hear about them in detail, so I will content myself with an historical remark at this stage.

I think it was Alfred the Great who first studied the passage of time in short periods. He observed that a candle flame burning in a protected space moved down a considerable distance in the course of a half hour, and he hit on the idea of marking the candle to indicate half-hour periods. I believe this was the first recorded occasion on which short periods of time were precisely measured. I have made similar researches under somewhat different circumstances, and I have observed that the flame of an audience's interest dies down a considerable distance in half an hour.

I should like to suggest, therefore, that our speakers try not to trespass on each other's time or to use up that precious safety valve of time which is available to the rest of the audience, namely the discussion, by going over their half-hour period.

# The Evolution of Biochemical Syntheses – Retrospect and Prospect

N. H. HOROWITZ

*Biology Division, California Institute of Technology,
Pasadena, California*

Biology at the present time is entering a period of renewed interest in problems of evolution. The major impetus for this revival comes from the borderline area between genetics and biochemistry called molecular biology. This discipline promises—and, in fact, has begun to deliver—a complete description of the genes, their activities, and their products at the molecular level of resolution. These advances are giving new meaning to the classical evolutionary problems, and they are opening new areas of evolutionary research that were not accessible before. Even that greatest of evolutionary puzzles, the origin of life, has acquired a new significance and vocabulary in the past two decades; and it is taking on new immediacy as we enter the age of exploration of the moon and planets by means of rockets from the earth.

## THE GARDEN OF EDEN

In this paper, I should like to discuss some questions related to the evolution of biosynthetic reaction sequences in the light of recent developments. Nearly twenty years ago, I proposed a mechanism for the evolution of biosynthetic pathways which took into account the evidence, then being accumulated in Beadle and Tatum's laboratory, which indicated that a given gene controls the formation of just one protein. The latter finding, which become known as the "one gene, one enzyme"—later modified to "one gene, one polypeptide chain"—theory, implied that each biosynthetic pathway is governed by a constellation of functionally related genes. The discovery of such groups of genes posed a perplexing evolutionary problem: Each gene of a constellation presumably arose by an independent mutation and was maintained in the population by selection pressure; but the constellation has selective value only when considered as a whole, since, in general, only the end product is useful. Intermediate stages in the synthesis of an amino acid, for example, have no value per se, and the corresponding genes should therefore be selectively neutral or even disadvantageous. The solution proposed for this problem was that the first organisms arose in an environment rich in organic materials and that evolution began with the end product of the biosynthetic pathway and worked backward, one step at a time, toward the beginning of the reaction chain. By evolving backward in this way, each mutation would confer a selective advantage on its possessor, since it would make a new source of the end product available (11).

The model for this seemingly implausible environment was derived from Oparin's theory of the origin of life, according to which a long period of nonbiological synthesis of organic matter preceded the appearance of life on the earth (24). A novel feature of Oparin's view was that the atmosphere of the primitive earth was in a reduced state, its carbon present as hydrocarbons and its nitrogen as ammonia. Previous authors had assumed an oxidized atmosphere for the primitive earth, its carbon in the form of carbon dioxide, and the first organisms were usually assumed to be capable of photosynthesis. According to Oparin's theory, however, the organisms should have been completely heterotrophic, living effortlessly in what Hawkins has aptly called "an aquatic Garden of Eden" (10). Growth of the primitive organisms would in time, however, deplete the Garden of Eden of essential end products; with that crisis, the process of backward evolution, or "retroevolution," would begin.[1]

### THE UREY-MILLER EXPERIMENT

An important series of confirmations of Oparin's view came in the 1950's. Urey arrived independently at the conclusion that the primordial atmosphere of the earth had been reducing and, on the basis of thermodynamic arguments, deduced its probable qualitative composition (34). Soon afterward, Miller showed that when this mixture of gases—methane, ammonia, water, and hydrogen—is subjected to a spark discharge, a variety of biologically important organic compounds, including $\alpha$-amino acids, is produced (22). This finding, which now forms one of the main supports of the Oparin theory, has been confirmed and extended in impor-

---

[1] Haldane, in an essay first published in 1929, independently put forward suggestions concerning the origin of life which contained some of the elements of Oparin's theory and of my backward evolution proposal (9). H. J. Muller has informed me that he lectured along similar lines to university classes in the twenties, having arrived at the conclusion that the most primitive organisms were heterotrophic from his considerations on the gene as the basis of life (23).

tant ways by many investigators. Of particular interest is the fact that adenine, which was not found among the products of the original Miller synthesis, has recently been detected in similar experiments (25, 27).

It has to be kept in mind, of course, that not every so-called "simulated primitive earth" experiment can be accepted at face value. Especially is this true when the synthesis depends on the reaction of chemically pure reagents in concentrations and conditions which could never obtain outside the laboratory. Because a biologically interesting substance is formed in such an experiment, it does not follow that the same process occurred in nature.[2] Even credible experiments, such as that of Miller, leave plenty of room for debate about the timing of events and the exact composition of the atmosphere. Our knowledge of conditions on the primitive earth is uncertain and, as the history of the subject shows, is liable to drastic revision from time to time as new data are obtained. Despite all this, it now seems as certain as anything can be in such a subject that reducing conditions prevailed on the earth at some time in the remote past and that an extensive synthesis of organic matter took place. Life presumably originated at this time, but we are still far from understanding how this came about (13). It is a long way from an aqueous mixture of amino acids, purines, and pyrimidines to a living organism. Nevertheless, many, including Oparin, believe that the origin of life was virtually inevitable in the circumstances. Whether this was so, or whether the origin of life was an event of vanishingly low probability—almost an unrepeatable accident—is impossible to say at the present time. This is one of the major scientific questions that the exploration of Mars might answer, since there is reason to believe that the early development of Mars was similar to that of the Earth (34).

## The Evolution of "Operons"

The evolution of new biosynthetic pathways in primitive organisms must, in general, have necessitated an increase in the size of the genome. How did the new genes originate? A possible clue to this problem is to be found in the linkage relations of genes controlling biosynthetic reactions in bacteria. As Demerec and co-workers first showed, genes involved in the biosynthesis of the same amino acid are often closely linked in *Salmonella* and *Escherichia coli* (5). Of the known examples, the histidine cluster has been one of the most intensively studied. This cluster involves the nine genes which govern the synthesis of histidine starting from ATP and phosphoribosyl pyrophosphate (2). No gene concerned

---

[2] For a critical discussion of some of these experiments, see the review by Horowitz and Miller (13).

with histidine biosynthesis is outside the cluster, and no gene uncon-
cerned with histidine synthesis is in it. The genes of the cluster are
under a common control mechanism and constitute an "operon" (15).
The same state of affairs holds for the smaller constellations of genes
involved in the synthesis of leucine (20) and tryptophan (30). I should
like to consider two questions with regard to these clusters: First, how
did they arise? And second, why are the genes controlling the same pathways in *Neurospora* not clustered?

As regards the first question, two possibilities have to be considered:
either the individual genes of an operon originated in different regions
of the chromosomes and were transposed to their present positions, or
they originated at their present sites. In the former case, the genes have
different ancestries—i.e., they arose from different antecedent genes—
while in the latter case all the genes of an operon are descendants of a
common ancestral gene. In either case, they are presumed to have originated by tandem duplication, followed by functional differentiation, as
elaborated by Lewis (18).

A number of considerations suggest that the genes of an operon have
a common origin. In the first place, the enzymes of an operon form a
reaction chain, the product of one enzyme being the substrate of the
next. This implies overlapping specificities, which in turn suggest structural homology and common ancestry.

Next, there are inherent difficulties in the alternative view. Events
that bring about reshuffling of genes—inversions and translocations—are
rare. In *Drosophila*, where they have been extensively studied, they
occur with frequencies no higher than mutation rates. Rearrangements
involving multiple breaks, such as would be required to remove a segment from one region of a chromosome and insert it in another, are
probably extremely rare. Comparisons of the map locations of homologous genes in different species of *Drosophila* have shown that inversions are the chief cause of gene shuffling in natural populations (32).
The inversion of a segment of a bacterial "chromosome," however, introduces a special difficulty. In order to preserve polarity in double-
stranded DNA, the inverted segment must be rotated around its long
axis (Fig. 1). The result is a strand interchange. If, as now seems
established, only one DNA strand is read *in vivo* (21), this would
result in chaos, except if the inverted segment begins with and ends
at an operator locus, the latter being defined as a specialized region
at which reading begins (15). But an operon has, by definition, only
one operator region. It follows that existing operons cannot have been
assembled from previously scattered genes unless a series of what appear to be exceedingly improbable events occurred. I have assumed here

that while only one DNA strand is read in any given region, this need not be the same strand in all regions. If further investigation shows that the same strand is read throughout the entire bacterial "chromosome," this would make the rearrangement of genes by inversion an impossibility in bacteria.

Finally, there is the phenomenon of allosteric inhibition, in which the product of the last enzyme in the chain inhibits the activity of the first enzyme (33). This remarkable effect is consistent with the idea that the pathways evolved by retroevolution, and that the first enzyme carries a memory of its origin.[3] It is interesting to note that the genes controlling the first and last enzymes of histidine synthesis are found side by side

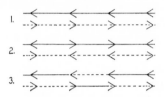

FIG. 1. Inversions in double-stranded DNA. (1) Normal sequence. (2) Inversion. (3) Inversion with rotation.

on the *Salmonella* map (Table I), and the same thing has been noted in the leucine operon (20). If these clusters evolved backward by tandem duplication and mutation, then the map orders imply that the gene controlling the last step in both operons is the one that gave rise to the gene controlling the first step, since the latter is located at the end of the map.

It should be mentioned at this point that the genes within an operon are not necessarily linked in the order of the corresponding biosynthetic reactions, as they appeared to be at first. Linkage-in-order is not found in either the histidine or the leucine operon, although it is found in the four reactions of the tryptophan operon; this may be due to chance. As long as one thought that the ordering was restricted in this way, one could not explain the evolution of the cluster on the basis of the kind of hypothesis I have outlined. One would have had to assume that the most recent gene in the sequence was always the last in line and was always the one which gave rise to the next gene. Alternatively, one had to suppose that considerable reshuffling of the gene order occurred in the course of evolution, with a selective advantage attaching to the order that paralleled the reaction sequence. In the latter connection, the genes controlling the arginine pathway in *E. coli* are of interest. Important studies of the arginine system have been made by Vogel (35),

---

[3] I am indebted to Dr. Robert L. Metzenberg for pointing this out to me.

Gorini *et al.* (6), and Maas (19). The genes controlling this pathway
are not organized in an operon, although certain features, such as their
map locations and feedback inhibition and repression, suggest that they
may have originated as one. They demonstrate that clustering of biosynthetic genes is not essential in bacteria and suggest that such clustering, where it occurs, is to be interpreted as a sign of common descent.

TABLE I

HISTIDINE GENES IN *Salmonella* AND *Neurospora*[a]

| Salmonella genes (in order) | Enzymatic step | Neurospora genes | Neurospora linkage group[b] |
|:---:|:---:|:---:|:---:|
| E | 2 | *hist-3B* | I-R[c] |
| I | 3 | *hist-3A* | I-R[c] |
| F | 6 | | |
| A | 4 | *hist-7* | III-R |
| H | 5 | | |
| B | { 7 | *hist-1* | V-R |
|   | { 9 | *hist-4* | IV-R |
| C | 8 | *hist-5* | IV-R |
| D | 10 | *hist-3D* | I-R[c] |
| G | 1 | *hist-2* | I-R |
| (operator) | | | |

[a] Based on Ahmed *et al.* (1) and on B. N. Ames, and R. G. Martin, *Ann. Rev. Biochem.*, 33, 235 (1964).

[b] Roman numerals = linkage group; R = right arm.

[c] These genes are in a cluster with the properties of an operon. None of the other *Neurospora* genes are clustered.

## THE SCATTERING OF FUNCTIONALLY RELATED GENES IN *Neurospora*

One of the most puzzling aspects of the operon problem is the general absence of close linkage of functionally related genes in *Neurospora*. Although some exceptions have been found, it is the usual rule
that genes controlling different reactions of the same biosynthetic pathway are only loosely linked in *Neurospora*, or not linked at all. The
contrast with bacteria is especially striking because the respective pathways are, in general, completely homologous. Specifically, the pathways
of leucine (4, 8, 16), tryptophan (17), and histidine (1) synthesis are
the same in *Neurospora* and bacteria; yet in bacteria the genes that
control them are grouped into operons, whereas in *Neurospora* they
are largely scattered among the chromosomes. A noteworthy exception
is the *hist-3* cluster in Linkage Group I that governs three reactions in
histidine synthesis (Table I). More characteristic, however, is the case
of the β-carboxy-β-hydroxyisocaproic acid isomerase of the leucine pathway. This enzyme is controlled by two genes in both *Salmonella* and

*Neurospora* and is probably built out of two different kinds of polypeptide chains (7). In *Salmonella*, the two genes occupy contiguous positions (20), but in *Neurospora* they are on different chromosomes.

If the genes of these pathways evolved in the manner I have described, then the bacterial arrangement is clearly the more primitive one. The *Neurospora* arrangement is presumably a later development, and the fragments of operons which are found in *Neurospora* would then be vestiges of the original condition. The most obvious physical difference between the genetic apparatus of *Neurospora* and the bacteria is the fact that *Neurospora* possesses seven small, but typical, chromosomes, whereas in bacteria this apparatus may consist of a single Watson and Crick double helix. The haploid DNA content of *Neurospora* is about four and one-half times that of *E. coli* (12). It seems reasonable to suppose that the scattering of functionally related genes in *Neurospora* is related to the development of the chromosomal apparatus. It is possible that the evolution of chromosomes brought with it a more elaborate genetic control system which eliminated the need for the operon mechanism.

Another possibility is that operons would be unstable in higher organisms, owing to the occurrence of unequal crossing over within them, an event that would be less important in predominantly asexual bacteria. It is well known that tandem duplications undergo unequal crossing over with a relatively high frequency in *Drosophila* (31), and the same should be true of sequences of genes which, by virtue of their common origin, bear sufficiently strong structural resemblances to one another. An excellent example of this is provided by the recent work of Baglioni (3) on a mutant human hemoglobin, Hemoglobin Lepore. Baglioni shows that it is likely that this hemoglobin has resulted from unequal crossing over between the genes for the $\beta$ and $\delta$ subunits of normal hemoglobins A and $A_2$. These genes are known to be linked (28), and the $\beta$ and $\delta$ subunits are very similar, their sequences differing in about 10 amino acid residues out of 146 [see Baglioni (3) for references]. Ingram and Stretton (14) have suggested that $\delta$ appeared relatively recently in evolution, since it is not found below the primates, and have proposed that it arose by duplication and differentiation of the $\beta$ gene. This case may thus serve to illustrate both the origin of a gene cluster and the instability of such a cluster in higher organisms.[4] An interesting

---

[4] The frequency of unequal crossing over would presumably be reduced in the case of a tandem duplication if the duplicated segment were reversed with respect to the original segment—i.e., (CD)(DC) instead of (CD)(CD). This would not hold for clusters larger than two, however. For further discussion, see E. B. Lewis, *Genetics*, **30**, 137 (1945).

discussion of the possible role of unequal crossing over in evolution has also been given by Smithies *et al.* (29).

## CONCLUSION

The point on which we lack sufficient evidence is the assumption that the genes of a biosynthetic pathway are, in fact, related in the manner I have proposed. To my knowledge, no new enzyme has ever been produced by mutation in the laboratory, nor do we know enough about enzyme structure to say how many mutations would be needed to pass from one enzyme to another. Modern enzymes are undoubtedly too highly evolved to permit us to obtain an answer to this question by direct comparison of enzyme structures. What is needed is a fundamental understanding of the relation between structure and function of protein molecules—a subject on which other participants in this Symposium are better qualified to speak than I. It seems just possible that a comparison of the amino acid sequences of the enzymes of a bacterial operon would yield evidence bearing on the relatedness of the enzymes.[5] This is one of the more formidable tasks for the future. In the meantime, I like to recall a comment that G. W. Beadle once made: "It's hard to make a good theory," he said, "—a theory has to be reasonable, but a fact doesn't."

## ACKNOWLEDGMENTS

I have had informative discussions on the topics considered in this paper with Drs. A. H. Sturtevant, E. B. Lewis, and E. Zuckerkandl. I am indebted to Dr. Norman H. Giles for permission to quote data from his laboratory in advance of publication.

## REFERENCES

1. AHMED, A., CASE, M., AND GILES, N. H., *Brookhaven Symp. Biol.*, **17**, 53 (1964).
2. AMES, B. N., AND HARTMAN, P. E., *Cold Spring Harbor Symp. Quant. Biol.*, **28**, 349 (1963).
3. BAGLIONI, C., *Proc. Natl. Acad. Sci. U.S.*, **48**, 1880 (1962).
4. BURNS, R. O., UMBARGER, H. E., AND GROSS, S. R., *Biochemistry*, **2**, 1053 (1963).
5. DEMEREC, M., AND HARTMAN, P. E., *Ann. Rev. Microbiol.*, **13**, 377 (1959).
6. GORINI, L., GUNDERSEN, W., AND BURGER, M., *Cold Spring Harbor Symp. Quant. Biol.*, **26**, 173 (1961).
7. GROSS, S. R., *Proc. Natl. Acad. Sci. U.S.*, **48**, 922 (1962).
8. GROSS, S. R., BURNS, R. O., AND UMBARGER, H. E., *Biochemistry*, **2**, 1046 (1963).
9. HALDANE, J. B. S., "The Inequality of Man," p. 148, Chatto & Windus, London, 1932.

---

[5] The same suggestion has been made by Pauling and Zuckerkandl (26) in a paper which came to my attention while I was preparing this talk.

10. HAWKINS, D., "The Language of Nature," p. 270, W. H. Freeman, San Francisco, 1964.
11. HOROWITZ, N. H., *Proc. Natl. Acad. Sci. U.S.*, **31**, 153 (1945).
12. HOROWITZ, N. H., AND MACLEOD, H., *Microbial Genet. Bull.*, **17**, 6 (1960).
13. HOROWITZ, N. H., AND MILLER, S., *Fortschr. Chem. org. Naturstoffe*, **20**, 423 (1962).
14. INGRAM, V. M., AND STRETTON, A. O. W., *Nature*, **190**, 1079 (1961).
15. JACOB, F., AND MONOD, J., *Cold Spring Harbor Symp. Quant. Biol.*, **26**, 193 (1961).
16. JUNGWIRTH, C., GROSS, S. R., MARGOLIN, P., AND UMBARGER, H. E., *Biochemistry*, **2**, 1 (1963).
17. LESTER, G., *J. Bacteriol.*, **85**, 468 (1963).
18. LEWIS, E. B., *Cold Spring Harbor Symp. Quant. Biol.*, **16**, 159 (1951).
19. MAAS, W. K., *Cold Spring Harbor Symp. Quant. Biol.*, **26**, 183 (1961).
20. MARGOLIN, P., *Genetics*, **48**, 441 (1963).
21. MARMUR, J., AND GREENSPAN, C. M., *Science*, **142**, 387 (1963).
22. MILLER, S. L., *Science*, **117**, 528 (1953).
23. MULLER, H. J., *Proc. 1st Intern. Congr. Plant Sci., Ithaca, 1926*, **1**, 897 (1929). Banta Publ., Menasha, Wisconsin.
24. OPARIN, A. I., "The Origin of Life" (trans. by S. Morgulis), Macmillan, New York, 1938.
25. ORO, J., AND KIMBALL, A. P., *Arch. Biochem. Biophys.*, **94**, 217 (1961).
26. PAULING, L., AND ZUCKERKANDL, E., *Acta Chem. Scand.*, **17**, S 9 (1963).
27. PONNAMPERUMA, C., LEMMON, R. M., MARINER, R., AND CALVIN, M., *Proc. Natl. Sci. U.S.* **49**, 737 (1963).
28. RANNEY, H. M., JACOBS, A. S., BRADLEY, T. B., AND CORDOVA, F. A., *Nature*, **197**, 164 (1963).
29. SMITHIES, O., CONNELL, G. E., AND DIXON, G. D., *Nature*, **196**, 232 (1962).
30. SOMERVILLE, R. L., AND YANOFSKY, C., *J. Mol. Biol.*, **8**, 616 (1964).
31. STURTEVANT, A. H., *Genetics*, **10**, 117 (1925).
32. STURTEVANT, A. H., AND NOVITSKI, E., *Genetics*, **26**, 517 (1941).
33. UMBARGER, H. E., *Cold Spring Harbor Symp. Quant. Biol.*, **26**, 301 (1961).
34. UREY, H. C., "The Planets," Yale Univ. Press, New Haven, 1952.
35. VOGEL, H. J., *Cold Spring Harbor Symp. Quant. Biol.*, **26**, 163 (1963).

# Lysine Biosynthesis and Evolution

HENRY J. VOGEL

Institute of Microbiology, Rutgers, The State University, New Brunswick, New Jersey

To be useful in the detection of evolutionary relationships, a biochemical character must be suitably poised between the extremes of biochemical unity and diversity (cf. van Niel, 31). A character that would seem to meet this requirement is the mode of biosynthesis of the amino acid lysine. The two distinctive lysine pathways known to occur in nature can be considered molecular organelles that serve as "biochemical fossils" (Vogel, 40).

α,ε-Diaminopimelic acid (DAP) is a key intermediate in one of the pathways, and α-aminoadipic acid (AAA), in the other. The major features of these biosynthetic systems, particularly, the origins of each carbon atom in the lysine synthesized, have been definitely established; some details remain to be clarified. The present knowledge of the DAP-lysine path (Gilvarg, 10; Farkas, Yugari, and Gilvarg, 8) and of the AAA-lysine path (Strassman, 30; Broquist, 3; Sagisaka and Shimura, 25) is schematically represented in Figs. 1 and 2, respectively. Various aspects of lysine formation, not explicitly considered here, have been discussed previously (1, 41, 42, 44).

## DIAGNOSTIC RADIOCARBON TRACERS

The occurrence of the two lysine pathways in the biological world could be conveniently explored with the aid of certain specifically-labeled radioactive tracers (Vogel, 34, 36). The general procedure consisted in allowing the organisms to utilize the desired tracer (in the presence of an unlabeled main carbon source), and measuring the relative specific radioactivity of the lysine, threonine, and aspartic acid from the protein of the cultures obtained. The radiocarbon tracers used were 3- and 4-labeled aspartic acids, 1-labeled alanine, and 2-labeled acetate. With these tracers, the mode of lysine synthesis is revealed through characteristic labeling patterns. In the case of the DAP-lysine path, protein aspartic acid, threonine, and lysine tend to approximate the same relative specific radioactivity with either the 3- or the 4-labeled aspartic acid, or with the acetate-2-$C^{14}$; with alanine-1-$C^{14}$, the specific radioactivity of the lysine tends to be comparatively high. In the case of the AAA-lysine path, lysine is not appreciably labeled with either as-partic-4-$C^{14}$ acid or alanine-1-$C^{14}$, whereas acetate-2-$C^{14}$ tends to result in relatively heavy labeling. The two labeling patterns are exemplified (36, 41) in results with a fern (which has the DAP path) and with a mushroom (which has the AAA path), as shown in Table I.

TABLE I

INCORPORATION OF TRACES INTO PROTEIN AMINO ACIDS OF A FERN
(*Azolla caroliniana*) AND A MUSHROOM (*Coprinus radians*)[a]

| Organism | Tracer | Asp | Thr | Lys |
|----------|--------|-----|-----|-----|
| | Labeling Pattern of DAP-Lysine Path | | | |
| A. caroliniana | As-3 | 100 | 98 | 92 |
| | As-4 | 100 | 80 | 91 |
| | Al-1 | 100 | 83 | 223 |
| | Ac-2 | 100 | 81 | 101 |
| | Labeling Pattern of AAA-Lysine Path | | | |
| C. radians | As-3 | 100 | 95 | 112 |
| | As-4 | 100 | 115 | 0 |
| | Al-1 | 100 | 103 | 0 |
| | Ac-2 | 100 | 116 | 262 |

[a] Data from Vogel (36, 41). The results are expressed as specific radioactivity (on a molar basis) relative to the respective protein aspartic acid values taken as 100. A value of 0 indicates that no radioactivity was found. Radioactivity corresponding to a value of 5 could have been detected. Abbreviations: As-3, DL-aspartic-3-$C^{14}$ acid; As-4, DL-aspartic-4-$C^{14}$ acid; Al-1, DL-alanine-1-$C^{14}$; Ac-2, sodium acetate-2-$C^{14}$; Asp, protein aspartic acid; Thr, protein threonine; Lys, protein lysine.

The labeling patterns are thought to arise as follows (Table II; cf. 41). In the DAP path, lysine is formed by decarboxylation of this seven-carbon acid, which contains four carbons derived from aspartate (via aspartic β-semialdehyde) and three carbons derived from pyruvate (see Fig. 1). Thus, the 3- and 4-carbons of aspartate are introduced into the carbon skeletons of DAP and lysine through aspartic β-semialdehyde. The 1-carbon of α-alanine can label lysine, via L- and *meso*-DAP, in a twofold manner: through pyruvate as such, and through the sequence, pyruvate, oxaloacetate, and aspartate. The 2-carbon of acetate is incorporated into lysine via the citric acid cycle, oxaloacetate, and aspartate.

In the AAA path, the carbon skeleton of lysine is constructed of four carbons derived from the succinyl moiety of α-ketoglutarate and two carbons derived from acetate (see Fig. 2). The 3-carbon of aspartate labels lysine via oxaloacetate, part of the citric acid cycle, α-ketoglutarate, and AAA. The 4-carbon of aspartate is not incorporated into lysine, since this carbon becomes the 1-carbon of α-ketoglutarate

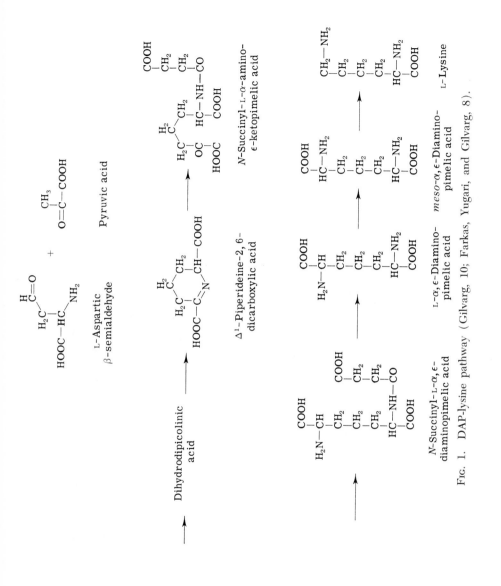

Fig. 1. DAP-lysine pathway (Gilvarg, 10; Farkas, Yugari, and Gilvarg, 8).

and is lost on the way to AAA. Lysine also receives no radiocarbon from 1-labeled alanine, which gives rise to 1-labeled pyruvate and oxalo-acetate, but to unlabeled α-ketoglutarate (because the 1-carbon of ox-aloacetate is removed in the formation of α-ketoglutarate through the citric acid cycle). The 2-carbon of acetate contributes to lysine in two

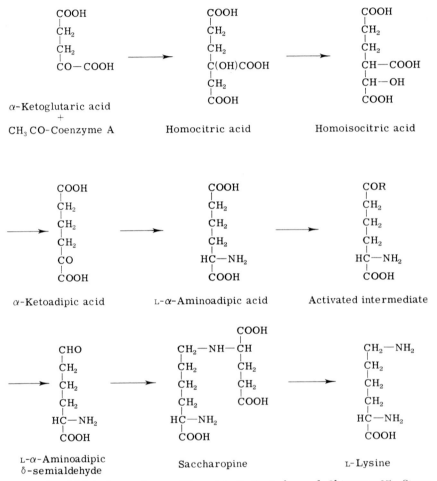

Fig. 2. AAA-lysine pathway (Broquist, 3; Sagisaka and Shimura, 25; Strass-man, 30).

ways: this carbon labels the two-carbon moiety of lysine (in the α-carbon) and the four-carbon moiety via part of the citric acid cycle and α-ketoglutarate.

When protein lysine is thus labeled in two ways, the two contributions of $C^{14}$ to the lysine (due to channeling-type effects) need not be equivalent in a given organism, nor constant in ratio from organism to organism. Therefore, in organisms having the AAA pathway, protein lysine will show a variable relative specific radioactivity, with acetate-2-$C^{14}$ as tracer. A similar argument applies to organisms having the DAP path, when alanine-1-$C^{14}$ is the tracer used.

Data on protein threonine serve as a kind of control. With all tracers employed, protein threonine and protein aspartate tend to exhibit the same relative specific radioactivity, regardless of the organism or of the mode of lysine synthesis. Hence, in the various organisms, aspartate is indicated to be a precursor of threonine. Moreover, the labeling data are consistent with the existence of a citric acid cycle in all the organisms examined.

TABLE II

FATE OF SPECIFICALLY-LABELED TRACERS[a]

| Tracer | Result | Route |
|--------|--------|-------|
| | | DAP-Lysine Path |
| As-3 | Labels lysine | Via aspartic β-semialdehyde, DAP |
| As-4 | Labels lysine | Via aspartic β-semialdehyde, DAP |
| Al-1 | Labels lysine | (i) via pyruvate, DAP; (ii) via pyruvate, oxaloacetate, aspartate, DAP |
| Ac-2 | Labels lysine | Via citric acid cycle, oxaloacetate, aspartate, DAP |
| | | AAA-Lysine Path |
| As-3 | Labels lysine | Via oxaloacetate, part of citric acid cycle, α-ketoglutarate, AAA |
| As-4 | Does not label lysine | Label lost between α-ketoglutarate and AAA |
| Al-1 | Does not label lysine | Label lost between oxaloacetate and α-ketoglutarate |
| Ac-2 | Labels lysine | (i) via acetyl-CoA, AAA; (ii) via acetyl-CoA, part of citric acid cycle, α-ketoglutarate, AAA |

[a] See the text and Figs. 1 and 2. For abbreviations of tracers, see Table I. Cf. Vogel (41).

For the tracer incorporation experiments, the organisms were grown in suitable (usually, chemically defined) test media supplemented with the desired specifically-labeled radiochemical (cf. 41). At the end of the incubation period, the organisms were harvested, dried *in vacuo*, and subjected to appropriate extraction, hydrolysis, paper chromatography, radioautography (see Fig. 3), and counting procedures (Roberts *et al.*, 23). The relative specific radioactivity (on a molar basis) of the protein lysine, threonine, and aspartic acid was then determined. The relative molar abundance of these three amino acids in the protein of the various organisms (which had to be known

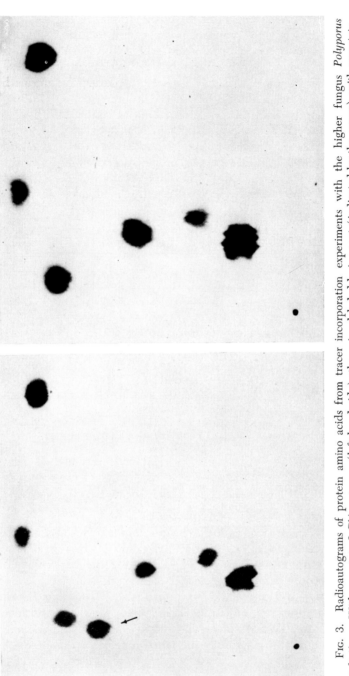

FIG. 3.  Radioautograms of protein amino acids from tracer incorporation experiments with the higher fungus *Polyporus tulipiferus*. With aspartate-3-C14 as tracer (left-hand side), there is a labeled-lysine spot (indicated by the arrow); with aspartate-4-C14 as tracer (right-hand side), no labeled lysine is detected (cf. 41).

for the computation of specific activity) was ascertained in experiments in which uniformly $C^{14}$-labeled major carbon sources but no specifically-labeled tracers were used.

## DISTRIBUTION OF THE TWO LYSINE PATHS

### Bacteria

Among the organisms initially examined in this study were various bacteria, including representatives of the pseudomonads, eubacteria, and actinomycetes (Vogel, 34, 35). These organisms, as well as all additional bacteria tested (see Table III), exhibited the labeling pat-

TABLE III
LYSINE SYNTHESIS IN BACTERIA: DAP PATH

| Species | Family |
|---------|--------|
| Pseudomonadales | |
| Rhodopseudomonas spheroides | Athiorhodaceae |
| Hydrogenomonas facilis | Methanomonadaceae |
| Pseudomonas fluorescens | Pseudomonadaceae |
| Eubacteriales | |
| Azotobacter agilis | Azotobacteraceae |
| Agrobacterium radiobacter | Rhizobiaceae |
| Alcaligenes faecalis | Achromobacteraceae |
| Escherichia freundii | Enterobacteriaceae |
| Aerobacter aerogenes | Enterobacteriaceae |
| Erwinia carotovora | Enterobacteriaceae |
| Serratia marcescens | Enterobacteriaceae |
| Proteus rettgeri | Enterobacteriaceae |
| Salmonella typhimurium | Enterobacteriaceae |
| Micrococcus denitrificans | Micrococcaceae |
| Micrococcus lysodeikticus | Micrococcaceae |
| Streptococcus bovis | Lactobacillaceae |
| Arthrobacter globiformis | Corynebacteriaceae |
| Bacillus subtilis | Bacillaceae |
| Actinomycetales | |
| Mycobacterium smegmatis | Mycobacteriaceae |
| Streptomyces griseus | Streptomycetaceae |
| Actinoplanes philippinensis | Actinoplanaceae |

tern of the DAP-lysine path. Table III lists bacteria that are rod-shaped, coccal, or mycelial; Gram-positive or Gram-negative; and spore-forming or non-spore-forming. Some of the bacteria contain DAP as a structural component of their cell wall, and some do not; nevertheless, DAP is indicated to be an intermediate of lysine synthesis in all cases studied. This finding is of interest, particularly, in view of data on the distribution of DAP as a structural component: this distribution shows a dichotomy among the bacteria that splits the otherwise relatively homogeneous lactobacilli (Work and Dewey, 43; Cummins and Harris, 7). It is note-worthy (see Table III) that organisms capable of anaerobic growth by photosynthesis (*Rhodopseudomonas*) or of deriving energy from the oxidation of hydrogen (*Hydrogenomonas*) behave like other bacteria, as far as lysine synthesis is concerned.

## Blue-green and Green Algae

The well-known relationship between bacteria and blue-green algae (see, for example, Bloch, 2) had led to the expectation that this group of algae would use the DAP-lysine path. The expectation was fulfilled: *Plectonema boreanum* and a *Nostoc* species gave a labeling pattern like that given by the bacteria tested (Vogel, 39). It seemed of particular interest, though, when it was found that the green algae, *Chlorella vulgaris* and *Chlorella pyrenoidosa*, also exhibited the labeling pattern of the DAP-lysine path (35).

## Higher Plants

In view of the results with the green algae, the problem of lysine synthesis in vascular plants invited attention. At that time, no detailed results bearing on this problem appeared to be available. Several higher

TABLE IV
Lysine Synthesis in Higher Plants: DAP Path[a]

| Organism | Plant material tested |
|---|---|
| Flowerless Plant | |
| *Azolla caroliniana* (a fern) | Whole plant |
| Flowering Plant: Gymnosperm | |
| *Ginkgo biloba* (maidenhair tree) | Pollen tissue |
| Flowering Plants: Angiosperms (Monocotyledons) | |
| *Lemna minor* (duckweed) | Whole plant |
| *Agave toumeyana* (century plant) | Leaf parenchyma tissue |
| Flowering Plants: Angiosperms (Dicotyledons) | |
| *Melilotus officinalis* (sweet clover) | Habituated root tissue |
| *Helianthus annuus* (sunflower) | Petiole crown gall tissue |

[a] From Vogel (36). See Table I.

plants were, therefore, examined in aseptic culture. In two cases, the tracer experiments were carried out with the intact plants, and in the remaining cases, with pollen, leaf, root, and petiole tissue cultures (Table IV). Consistently, the labeling pattern of the DAP-lysine path was obtained (Vogel, 36). These observations have been supported by enzymatic studies with *Lemna*, *Agave*, and maize (26, 27).

## Euglenids

The findings with *Rhodopseudomonas*, the blue-green and green algae, the fern, and the flowering plants show that the DAP-lysine path is broadly distributed among organisms capable of photosynthesis. It seemed intriguing, therefore, when it was found that *Euglena* has the AAA-lysine path (Vogel, 35). This organism was subjected not only to incorporation experiments with specifically-labeled tracers but also to "isotopic competition" experiments with a uniformly-labeled tracer. L-Aspartate-$C^{14}$ labels the lysine, aspartic acid, and threonine in the protein of *Euglena*; however, with this tracer and an unlabeled supplement of either AAA or hexahomoserine [which is convertible to α-aminoadipic δ-semialdehyde (44)], the radioactivity in the protein lysine, but not in the protein aspartic acid or threonine, is almost completely suppressed (Vogel, 35). An efficient utilization of these characteristic unlabeled supplements in the synthesis of lysine in *Euglena* has thus been demonstrated. From experiments with a different strain and $C^{14}$-labeled AAA, it was concluded that *Euglena* uses the AAA pathway of lysine synthesis exclusively (Rothstein and Saffran, 24). In harmony with these results, *Euglena* was shown to lack DAP decarboxylase but to contain saccharopine dehydrogenase, which is characteristic of the AAA-lysine path (Vaughan and Broquist, 33).

## Fungi

Since euglenids and fungi may, to some extent, be related (for example, through having certain animal-like traits; cf. Hutner and Provasoli, 13; Martin, 19), particular interest attached to the mode of lysine synthesis in the broad assemblage of the fungi.

Among the phycomycetes, the so-called algal fungi, the two lysine pathways were found to have a remarkable dichotomous distribution (Vogel, 37, 38, 41; see Table V), which correlates with mode of spore flagellation (cf. Couch, 5; Koch, 15). Organisms having biflagellate (*Achlya, Thraustotheca, Sapromyces, Sirolpidium, Pythium*) or anteriorly uniflagellate (*Hyphochytrium, Rhizidiomyces*) spores show the DAP path and go with bacteria, blue-green and green algae, and higher plants, whereas organisms having posteriorly uniflagellate (*Phlyctochytrium, Rhizophlyctis, Allomyces, Monoblepharella*) or nonflagellate (*Cunninghamella, Rhizopus, Syncephalastrum*) spores show the AAA path and go with euglenids, as far as lysine synthesis is concerned (41). The observed correspondence, in the phycomycetes, between mode of lysine synthesis and mode of spore flagellation reinforces the view that the spore flagellation of the lower fungi is a most useful phylogenetic marker (Sparrow, 29; cf. Cronquist, 6).

With higher fungi belonging to various orders of ascomycetes and basidiomycetes, uniform results were obtained, as listed in Table VI. Represented are hemiascomycetes and euascomycetes (plectomycetes, pyrenomycetes, and discomycetes), as well as heterobasidiomycetes and homobasidiomycetes (hymenomycetes and gasteromycetes). In all cases, these higher fungi exhibited the AAA-lysine path (41), as did the phycomycetes producing posteriorly uniflagellate or nonflagellate spores: a monophyletic assemblage is thus indicated.

TABLE V

CORRELATION BETWEEN MODE OF LYSINE SYNTHESIS AND TYPE OF SPORE FLAGELLATION AMONG PHYCOMYCETES[a]

| Species | Order | Lysine path | Spore flagellation |
|---|---|---|---|
| *Achlya bisexualis* | Saprolegniales | DAP | —o— |
| *Thraustotheca clavata* | Saprolegniales | DAP | —o— |
| *Sapromyces elongatus* | Leptomitales | DAP | —o— |
| *Sirolpidium zoopthorum* | Lagenidiales | DAP | —o— |
| *Pythium ultimum* | Peronosporales | DAP | —o— |
| *Hyphochytrium catenoides* | Hyphochytriales | DAP | o— |
| *Rhizidiomyces* sp. | Hyphochytriales | DAP | o— |
| *Phlyctochytrium punctatum* | Chytridiales | AAA | —o |
| *Rhizophlyctis rosea* | Chytridiales | AAA | —o |
| *Allomyces macrogynus* | Blastocladiales | AAA | —o |
| *Monoblepharella laruei* | Monoblepharidales | AAA | —o |
| *Cunninghamella blakesleeana* | Mucorales | AAA | o |
| *Rhizopus stolonifer* | Mucorales | AAA | o |
| *Syncephalastrum racemosum* | Mucorales | AAA | o |

[a] Data from Vogel (41). Symbols: —o—, biflagellate; o—, anteriorly uniflagellate; —o, posteriorly uniflagellate; o, nonflagellate.

## A Protozoon-Bacterium Complex

The presence of the AAA path in higher fungi and in euglenids raised the question of lysine synthesis in organisms with more frankly animal-like characteristics. Although animals, in general, appear to require lysine as an "essential" amino acid and not to synthesize it, a suitable test organism seemed to present itself in the protozoon *Crithidia oncopelti*. This trypanosomatid flagellate, in contrast to close relatives that are nutritionally exacting, can be cultivated on a comparatively simple, chemically defined, lysine-free medium (Newton, 21; Nathan, 20).

Various lines of evidence showed that the atypical nutritional behavior of *C. oncopelti* reflects the synthetic activities of a symbiotic bacterium present within the protozoan cell (Gill and Vogel, 9). Tracer experiments revealed that *C. oncopelti* has the DAP-lysine path. The characteristic *meso*-DAP decarboxylase proved to be associated with a fraction (prepared from disrupted protozoa) that contains particles of bacterial morphology (9). Ultrathin-section electron micrographs of the inferred endosymbiote present a typically bacterial appearance (Fig. 4): there are structures consistent with a cytoplasmic membrane, membrane septa, a cell wall, and nuclear zones (9).

TABLE VI
LYSINE SYNTHESIS IN HIGHER FUNGI: AAA PATH[a]

| Species | Order |
|---|---|
| Ascomycetes | |
| Dipodascus uninucleatus | Endomycetales |
| Taphrina deformans | Taphrinales |
| Penicillium chrysogenum | Plectascales |
| Venturia inaequalis | Pseudosphaeriales |
| Neurospora crassa | Sphaeriales |
| Gibberella fujikuroi | Hypocreales |
| Morchella crassipes | Pezizales |
| Sclerotinia fructicola | Helotiales |
| Basidiomycetes | |
| Ustilago maydis | Ustilaginales |
| Polyporus tulipiferus | Polyporales |
| Coprinus radians | Agaricales |
| Calvatia gigantea | Lycoperdales |

[a] From Vogel (41). The imperfect fungus *Candida utilis* (36), like the yeast *Saccharomyces cerevisiae* (41), also gives the labeling pattern of the AAA-lysine path, with the four specifically-labeled tracers used.

In collaboration with the laboratory of Dr. J. Marmur, DNA samples from endosymbiote-containing *C. oncopelti* and isolated cells of the endosymbiote were compared as to their buoyant density in a cesium chloride gradient (Marmur, Cahoon, Shimura, and Vogel, 17). Bands of density 1.709 g/cc and 1.691 g/cc (Fig. 5) were attributed to DNA from the protozoan nucleus and from the endosymbiotic bacterium, respectively. A third DNA band (density, 1.699 g/cc; see Fig. 5) was also observed, and was concluded to correspond to DNA from specialized structures (presumably kinetoplasts) or from a virus. On the basis of their buoyant density, the bacterial, inferred kinetoplastic, and protozoan nuclear DNA's have a calculated mole per cent guanine plus cytosine composition (Marmur and Doty, 18) of 32, 40, and 50, respectively.

As far as lysine synthesis is concerned, it seems clear that the endosymbiotic bacterium, like other bacteria, has the DAP path and that the protozoon, like some other protozoa and metazoa, cannot produce its own lysine. In view of known protozoon-bacterium complexes (cf. Kirby, 14; Sonneborn, 28; van Wagtendonk, Clark, and Godoy, 32), the present case is of interest, since it reveals a definite biochemical and

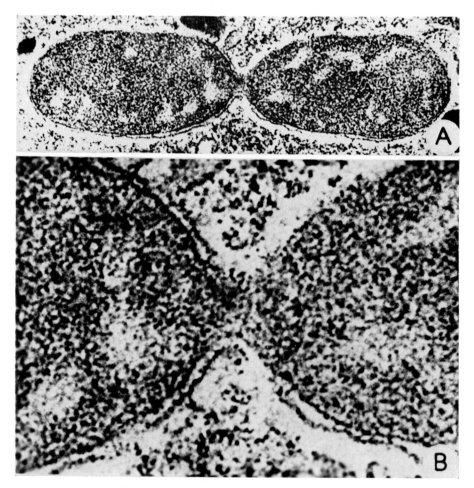

Fig. 4. (A), electron micrograph of dividing endosymbiotic bacterium surrounded by cytoplasm of *Crithidia oncopelti*. × 29,000. (B), detail of (A). × 101,000. From Gill and Vogel (9).

nutritional relationship between the protozoon and its endosymbiote. Presumably, the bacterium also furnishes other metabolites to the complex; the protozoon provides the bacterium with the protection of an intracellular environment.

## ON THE DESCENT OF THE LYSINE PATHS

The two paths of lysine synthesis seem to be quite unusual in the consistency of their dichotomous distribution over a wide range of biological forms. This consistency suggests that these paths did not arise sporadically and that their distribution pattern was not disturbed by genetic exchange. It appears probable that neither path emerged in an organism possessing the other, since a partial appearance of either path in the presence of the other may well have been selected against, and an appearance *in toto* is thought unlikely in view of the number of enzymes involved in each path. It is, therefore, assumed that the

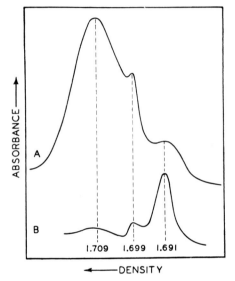

FIG. 5. Banding patterns of DNA from cells of endosymbiote-containing *Crithidia oncopelti* (A) and from isolated cells of the endosymbiote (B). From Marmur, Cahoon, Shimura, and Vogel (17).

two lysine paths arose individually in organisms incapable of lysine synthesis. Quite possibly, the DAP-lysine path is the more ancient, because it occurs in the relatively simple bacteria (as well as in more complex plants). The AAA-lysine path has so far been found only in fungi and euglenids, which are more complex than bacteria. It seems attractive to postulate a common ancestor of organisms having the AAA-lysine path (Vogel, 41).

These considerations are incorporated in a working hypothesis on the evolutionary descent of the lysine paths, as represented in Fig. 6. Ancestral Group I having no lysine path is pictured as precursor of

Ancestral Group II having the DAP path, in line with the idea of the evolution of biosynthetic capabilities following primitive heterotrophy (Horowitz, 11, 12; Oparin, 22). Ancestral Group II is thought to have given rise, characteristically with retention of the DAP path, to modern plants: bacteria, the so-called water molds and related forms (including phycomycetes producing biflagellate or anteriorly uniflagellate spores), blue-green and green algae, and vascular plants. Additionally,

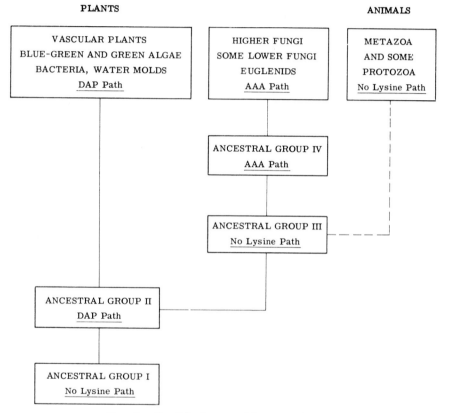

Fig. 6.    Possible descent of lysine pathways.

Ancestral Group III, having lost the ability to synthesize lysine, is believed to have arisen out of Group II. Such loss of synthetic ability would be in harmony with the views expressed by Lwoff (16). A novel pathway of lysine synthesis, namely the AAA path, appears to have emerged in the evolution of Ancestral Group IV out of Group III. Such emergence may be regarded as a "biochemical innovation" in the sense of Cohen (4). Modern higher fungi and related lower fungi (including phycomycetes producing posteriorly uniflagellate or nonflagellate spores), as well as euglenids, are postulated to have a common evolutionary precursor in Ancestral Group IV. Some modern protozoa and metazoa, which cannot synthesize lysine, may have descended from Group III, as indicated by the dashed line (Fig. 6). This possibility would be consonant with animal-like qualities noted in fungi (cf. Martin, 19) and euglenids (cf. Hutner and Provasoli, 13). Alternatively, independent losses of ability to produce lysine may have occurred in lines leading to Group III on the one hand and to metazoa on the other. (Fig. 6 is not intended to imply that all members of an assemblage for which lysine synthesis is indicated can indeed produce lysine; rather, the paths appear to be characteristic for the assemblages, as shown.)

## CONCLUSION

The impression is thus gained that the descent of the lysine paths correlates with major lines of evolution. The DAP path would seem to be a plant-like organelle; the consistent inability to produce lysine may be an animal-like quality; the AAA path is indicated to be a feature of organisms (such as fungi and euglenids) that have veered from the main stream of evolution of the plant kingdom in the direction of animality. These results would recommend the character *lysine synthesis* as a phylogenetic tracer that complements other "biochemical fossils" as well as nonbiochemical characters of useful scope.

## ACKNOWLEDGMENTS

This work was aided by grants from the National Science Foundation, and by a contract between the Office of Naval Research, Department of the Navy, and Rutgers, The State University. Excellent technical assistance was rendered by Mrs. Helen Carnevale. Many valuable discussions with Dr. Ruth H. Vogel are gratefully acknowledged.

## REFERENCES

1. ABELSON, P. H., AND VOGEL, H. J., *J. Biol. Chem.*, **213**, 355 (1955).
2. BLOCH, K., this volume.
3. BROQUIST, H. P., *Abstr., 6th Intern. Congr. Biochem.*, New York, Vol. V, 363 (1964).
4. COHEN, S. S., *Science*, **139**, 1017 (1963).
5. COUCH, J. N., *Am. J. Botany*, **28**, 704 (1941).
6. CRONQUIST, A., *Botan. Rev.*, **26**, 425 (1960).
7. CUMMINS, C. S., AND HARRIS, H., *J. Gen. Microbiol.*, **14**, 583 (1956).
8. FARKAS, W., YUGARI, Y., AND GILVARG, C., *Federation Proc.* **22**, 243 (1963).
9. GILL, J. W., AND VOGEL, H. J., *J. Protozool.*, **10**, 148 (1963).
10. GILVARG, C., *Federation Proc.*, **19**, 948 (1960).
11. HOROWITZ, N. H., *Proc. Natl. Acad. Sci. U.S.*, **31**, 153 (1945).

12. HOROWITZ, N. H., this volume.
13. HUTNER, S. H., AND PROVASOLI, L., in "Biochemistry and Physiology of Protozoa" (S. H. Hutner and A. Lwoff, eds.), Vol. II, p. 17, Academic Press, New York, 1955.
14. KIRBY, H., JR., in "Protozoa in Biological Research" (G. N. Calkins and F. M. Summers, eds.), p. 1009, Columbia University Press, New York, 1941.
15. KOCH, W. J., Am. J. Botany, 43, 811 (1956).
16. LWOFF, A., "L'Évolution physiologique. Étude des pertes de fonctions chez les microorganismes" Hermann et Cie., Paris, 1944.
17. MARMUR, J., CAHOON, M. E., SHIMURA, Y., AND VOGEL, H. J., Nature, 197, 1228 (1963).
18. MARMUR, J., AND DOTY, P., J. Mol. Biol., 5, 109 (1962).
19. MARTIN, G. W., Mycologia, 47, 779 (1955).
20. NATHAN, H. A., J. Protozool., 5, 194 (1958).
21. NEWTON, B. A., Nature, 177, 279 (1956).
22. OPARIN, A. I., "The Origin of Life," Macmillan, New York, 1938.
23. ROBERTS, R. B., ABELSON, P. H., COWIE, D. B., BOLTON, E. T., AND BRITTEN, R. J., "Studies of Biosynthesis in Escherichia coli," Carnegie Institution of Washington Publication 607, Washington, D.C., 1955.
24. ROTHSTEIN, M., AND SAFFRAN, E. M., Arch. Biochem. Biophys., 101, 373 (1963).
25. SAGISAKA, S., AND SHIMURA, K., J. Biochem. (Tokyo), 51, 398 (1962).
26. SHIMURA, Y., AND VOGEL, H. J., Federation Proc., 20, 10 (1961).
27. SHIMURA, Y., AND VOGEL, H. J., unpublished data.
28. SONNEBORN, T. M., in "Perspectives in Virology" (M. Pollard, ed.), Vol. II, p. 5, Burgess Publishing Co., Minneapolis, 1961.
29. SPARROW, F. K., Mycologia, 50, 797 (1958).
30. STRASSMAN, M., Abstr. 6th Intern. Congr. Biochem., New York, Vol. V, 373 (1964).
31. VAN NIEL, C. B., Bacteriol. Revs., 13, 161 (1949).
32. VAN WAGTENDONK, W. J., CLARK, J. A. D., AND GODOY, G. A., Proc. Natl. Acad. Sci. U.S., 50, 835 (1963).
33. VAUGHAN, S. T., AND BROQUIST, H. P., Federation Proc., 24, 218 (1965).
34. VOGEL, H. J., Federation Proc., 18, 345 (1959).
35. VOGEL, H. J., Biochim. Biophys. Acta, 34, 282 (1959).
36. VOGEL, H. J., Proc. Natl. Acad. Sci. U.S., 45, 1717 (1959).
37. VOGEL, H. J., Biochim. Biophys. Acta, 41, 172 (1960).
38. VOGEL, H. J., Nature, 189, 1026 (1961).
39. VOGEL, H. J., Genetics, 47, 992 (1962).
40. VOGEL, H. J., in "Evolutionary Biochemistry" (A. I. Oparin, ed.), Vol. III, Proc. 5th Intern. Congr. Biochem., p. 341, Pergamon Press, Macmillan, New York, 1963.
41. VOGEL, H. J., Am. Naturalist, 98, 435 (1964).
42. VOGEL, H. J., AND BONNER, D. M., in "Encyclopedia of Plant Physiology" (W. Ruhland, ed.), Vol. 11, p. 1, Springer-Verlag, Berlin, 1959.
43. WORK, E., AND DEWEY, D. L., J. Gen. Microbiol. 9, 394 (1953).
44. YURA, T., AND VOGEL, H. J., J. Biol. Chem., 234, 339 (1959).

# Discussion of Part I

K. V. THIMANN, N. H. HOROWITZ, E. L. TATUM, L. SPETNER, H. J. VOGEL,
R. SAGER, W. BRAUN, O. E. LANDMAN, S. W. FOX, K. BLOCH,
N. H. GUTTMAN, P. H. ABELSON, C. B. VAN NIEL,
C. PRICE, C. PONNAMPERUMA

CHAIRMAN THIMANN: The papers presented are now open for discussion.

DR. HOROWITZ: I would like to ask Dr. Tatum two questions: First of all, I wasn't sure whether your cytoplasmic slow grower, which Wilson has used for injection experiments, was *poky* or not?

The second question is, do you know how much DNA is present per mitochondrion in *Neurospora*?

We have made some calculations from Luck's paper at the Biochemistry Congress which I would like to compare with yours.

DR. TATUM: I can't give you an answer to the second question. I am not sure that the calculations have all been carried through precisely. We can check on that later. The two strains, *poky* and ours, seem to have many differences in extremeness and constancy. Ours is not curable during division and growth, and we feel that it has some other differences in the cytochrome picture from *poky*. It was of independent origin.

DR. SPETNER: My question is directed to both Dr. Horowitz and Dr. Vogel. In the original development of pathways by the backward process as discussed by Dr. Horowitz, could there have been many alternative pathways available, of which only one or two were achieved?

The probability of the kind of backward evolution that Dr. Horowitz described would increase if many possible pathways were available in the original organic soup. Otherwise, I feel, the probability would be intolerably small. The occurrence of a few of these many possibilities would explain the alternative pathways now found in the higher organisms. I would like to hear comments on this from either of the speakers.

DR. HOROWITZ: I think there could have been alternative routes to these end products. Your knowledge of organic chemistry is possibly better than mine, but even I could think of various ways of arriving at, say, histidine or lysine or arginine. Urey has calculated that the primitive seas contained ten per cent organic matter. If this was the case, the possibilities could have been virtually infinite.

I am not quite so sure about your second statement, that this would be a possible explanation of the alternative pathways in higher organisms, since this would imply that two or more pathways were develop-

41

ing simultaneously. One would think that if one pathway got a little bit ahead of another, it would have eventually outstripped the other one.

One thing about biochemistry that always strikes me is its monotony. Biochemistry is the same wherever you look at it—the same 20 amino acids, the same four or five bases of DNA, and pathways that are very similar. I would, therefore, prefer to think that the differences in biosynthetic reaction sequences are the result of subsequent evolutionary changes which have been arrived at for special purposes and special adaptations.

CHAIRMAN THIMANN: I just had a thought during Dr. Vogel's speech. I think that the solution-feeding protozoa—many flagellates, after all, and at least one ciliate can be grown in this way—have probably not been surveyed for their ability to dispense with lysine and to use α-amino-adipic or diaminopimelic acid instead. Maybe this would be worth while doing.

DR. VOGEL: Yes. I think this would be a very interesting thing to look at. We intend to do so. This raises the general question of the possibility of the existence of partial or fragmentary pathways.

DR. SAGER: Since both chloroplasts and mitochondria are being shown to contain DNA's, one is led to speculate on the genetic function of these nucleic acids. I should like to ask Dr. Tatum how he feels about the possibility that organelle DNA may be sequestered from the chromosomes for regulatory purposes—in other words, that it may be advantageous for the organism to control organelle formation in a manner somewhat independent of the chromosomal regulatory mechanisms.

DR. TATUM: More power to it! I wouldn't doubt it, but we will see in the future, maybe in the next symposium.

DR. HOROWITZ: I wonder if I could ask Ruth Sager a question. How much DNA is there per chloroplast in *Chlamydomonas*?

DR. SAGER: Our best estimate of the amount of chloroplast DNA comes from isolating total cell DNA and then fractionating it according to buoyant density in a cesium chloride density equilibrium gradient. We have found about 5% of the DNA in a satellite band associated with the chloroplasts. The DNA obtained from isolated chloroplasts is greatly enriched for this fraction, but of course there are losses in preparation, and the final values of DNA per chloroplast by this method are about 1% of the cell DNA. Since *Chlamydomonas* has about 0.2 picograms of DNA per cell, or 20 times the DNA of *E. coli*, the amount of chloroplast DNA would be approximately that present in a bacterial cell.

DR. BRAUN: I wonder, in connection with Dr. Sager's suggestion, whether we might not have a very interesting case of having watched this sort of evolution in the last ten years. I am referring to the very interesting resistance transfer factor of bacteria, where the sudden development of an independent circular DNA replicon, in the Jacob terminology, seems to have taken place. This appears to have given these resistance transfer factor elements an enormously high survival value because they have spread very rapidly, as most of you know, in the *Salmonella* and the *Escherichia coli* population of Japan. It seems to me that this might be a very interesting recent example of the evolution of an independently replicating circular DNA structure, which apparently endows the carrier with an unusual selective survival value.

DR. LANDMAN: Dr. Sager's postulate is, I believe, that in evolution, DNA was perhaps originally located only in the nucleus, and then, as organelles developed, DNA controlling the structure of these organelles might have made itself independent.

We have been studying an organelle in bacteria, the mesosome, which may represent an intermediate stage in this hypothetical transition from remote control by nuclear DNA to direct control by local DNA. The mesosome is a bundle of membranes which can be lost to the bacteria in its entirety. Its loss may then be perpetuated over many generations. Alternatively, the mesosomes can be induced to reappear at any time. The kinetics and general characteristics of the loss and the induction are such that it is quite clear that no DNA is lost or gained [O. E. Landman and S. Halle, *J. Mol. Biol.* **7**, 721 (1963)].

In this case, you could say definitely that the genes that are involved in the control of this organelle have not yet detached themselves from the general genome of the bacterium, but are still located in the nucleus. On the other hand, the organelle is sufficiently autonomous, so that the genes cannot easily initiate it.

DR. FOX: The remark that I would like to make is probably better made by Dr. Abelson. In fact, some years ago he did make it [P. H. Abelson, *Ann. N.Y. Acad. Sci.*, **69**, 274 (1957)].

The geological evidence for a primitive, so-called reducing atmosphere is, I believe, quite compelling. However, results of experiments which use a simulated reducing atmosphere, though consistent with that premise, should not be construed as *proof* of a geologically primitive reducing atmosphere.

A review of the quasigeochemical experiments permit us the inference that, if there is enough carbon in any of the various forms, enough hydrogen, oxygen, and nitrogen, and enough of any kind of energy of various types, then amino acids are inexorable products (S. W. Fox, in I. Breger, ed., "Organic Geochemistry," Pergamon Press, 1963, p. 39).

CHAIRMAN THIMANN: I suppose this could occur under oxidizing conditions, to some extent?

Dr. Fox: I think some experiments show organic matter produced under oxidizing conditions to some extent.

Dr. Bloch: I have a comment and a question for Dr. Vogel. I think it is of interest to mention another example of amino acid metabolism in which the higher plant pattern is the same as the bacterial pattern, namely nicotinic acid biosynthesis.

Higher plants, in contrast to the fungi, use a *de novo* synthesis for nicotinic acid, not the breakdown of tryptophan.

My question is whether the euglenids you examined were grown under photosynthetic conditions or heterotrophic conditions, because the various biosynthetic patterns in euglenids depend critically on growth conditions.

If your organisms were grown as strict phototrophs, perhaps you would have obtained the plant pattern.

Dr. Vogel: We grew the euglenids with illumination, in the presence of organic carbon sources.

Dr. Guttman: In reference to what Br. Bloch said, I think we have obtained relevant results from some of our experiments. We were looking for differences in biotin metabolism in *Euglena gracilis* grown either photoautotrophically or under a variety of heterotrophic conditions. We reasoned that there would be an increased requirement for biotin when autotrophic metabolism came into play because of the involvement of biotin coenzymes in early stages of $CO_2$ fixation.

*Euglena* has no exogenous biotin requirement for growth under most conditions we can impose in the laboratory. However, biotin avidity, i.e. uptake of biotin from an incubation medium, occurs only under conditions where all cellular carbon comes from $CO_2$ fixation. That is, cells grown heterotrophically (in the dark) or in the light in the presence of organic substrates (mixed auto- and heterotrophy) are indifferent to biotin offered in the medium (none is taken up by the cells). But when growth is completely dependent on $CO_2$ fixation and good cell crops are being produced, apparently the biotin enzyme reactions become limiting and biotin offered in the medium is taken up.

It seems that autotrophic versus heterotrophic conditions can be very strong metabolic determining factors and the cell responds by trying to make a living via the most efficient way. We have been accustomed to thinking of induction, derepression, etc. of key enzymes as indicators of the metabolic changeovers but these are gross changes involving substrates. Our experiments point to metabolic fine controls involving coenzymes.

Dr. Vogel: This is an interesting example of a metabolic change, as a function of autotrophy and heterotrophy. As you point out, this change seems biochemically understandable. It does not appear too likely, though, that two different synthetic paths leading to a particular amino acid would come into play, depending on these cultural conditions. However, such a duality is not inconceivable. I might add that our methods of testing for the two lysine paths are such that we could have expected to detect a simultaneous functioning of these paths in an organism. We have never obtained evidence for more than one lysine path in any one organism.

DR. GUTTMAN: This comment has to do with nucleic acids in *Crithidia oncopelti*.

I believe that your work, Dr. Vogel, and the work you did with Dr. Marmur showed that there were three DNA peaks, one of which would be nuclear DNA, one symbiote DNA, and a third one.

It is probable that the third peak is kinetoplastic DNA and, if not beyond the resolving power of the analytical ultracentrifuge, a potential fourth peak would be mitochondrial DNA—if mitochondria do not have the same kind of DNA as do kinetoplasts.

In some other trypanosomatids (which lack endosymbiote), it has been established which is the kinetoplastic DNA peak [see for example the abstract by du Buy *et al.*, *J. Cell. Biol.*, 23, 26A (1964)].

By analogy with the finding that chloroplast DNA's from algae and higher plants are very similar, we might expect that kinetoplast DNA from all trypanosomatids ought to be very similar and should therefore peak at approximately the same place. Viral DNA would then be easy to identify—though I doubt very much whether it will be found.

DR. VOGEL: In the paper I believe you have in mind [J. Marmur, M. E. Cahoon, Y. Shimura, and H. J. Vogel, *Nature*, 197, 1228 (1963)], it was suggested that the third peak corresponds to DNA from specialized homogeneous structures or from a virus. It was, in fact, our working hypothesis that the third peak represents kinetoplast DNA.

The possibility of a virus, though not considered likely, would have been consistent with the narrow width of the band involved. However, even if no virus is found, we have a set of remarkable ecological relationships: at their base is a milk weed with which the *Oncopeltus* bug is specifically associated; the bug is the host for the protozoon *Crithidia* which, in turn, harbors its endosymbiotic bacterium.

DR. HOROWITZ: I would like to answer the comment that Dr. Fox made. I was listening to two people at once. I may have missed some points, but I believe he said that under oxidizing conditions one could still get amino acids, if sufficient energy was fed into the system.

Calvin and collaborators [W. Garrison, D. Morrison, J. Hamilton, A. Benson, and M. Calvin, *Science*, 114, 416 (1951)], you know, did an experiment in which they irradiated a mixture of water and carbon dioxide with 40 mev helium ions from a cyclotron, and they obtained very low yields of simple organic compounds, such as formic acid, but not the rich synthesis found under reducing conditions.

There is a question of whether the primitive atmosphere was in thermodynamic equilibrium. Dr. Abelson probably should be saying what I am going to say, that I believe that his own experiments have shown that you will get synthesis of organic materials, including amino acids, if the carbon is present as $CO_2$, rather than methane, but you always have to have an excess of hydrogen. The net conditions have to be reducing. It is obvious, as Wald has pointed out, that if you have oxidizing conditions, you will end up with a combustion, not with a synthesis of organic compounds.

DR. Fox: Perhaps the problem here is one of semantics, how you define a reducing atmosphere, oxidizing atmosphere, etc. The answer is different if you have a completely oxidizing, or completely oxidized, atmosphere than if you have one which is oxidizing to some extent.

Of course, if you are going to have amino acids, you must have a sufficient proportion of hydrogen as well as the other elemental components of the amino acids.

Calvin's historical experiments do not prove that a carbon dioxide-rich atmosphere fails to give amino acids, inasmuch as no nitrogen compounds were present in the reaction. The interpretation of those experiments is a corollary of the statement about the need for sufficient amounts of each of four elements for the formation of amino acids. One could hardly expect nitrogen-containing compounds in Calvin's 40 mev products when no nitrogen compounds were present in the reaction.

DR. HOROWITZ: Nobody has claimed that $CO_2$ would prevent syntheses. The point is simply that net reducing conditions must prevail.

DR. ABELSON: Both speakers are right. The point is that the environment must have a certain degree of reducing character in order for organic compounds to be formed in substantial amounts. I performed experiments in which there were no reducing components—using $CO_2$, nitrogen—and found that no amino acids were formed.

In the presence of free oxygen, organic matter is destroyed rather quickly, so that one would not expect any real accumulation of organic matter in the presence of an appreciable concentration of free oxygen in the atmosphere.

CHAIRMAN THIMANN: I would like to ask Dr. van Niel if he knows whether the biotin requirements of purple bacteria have been carefully studied under heterotrophic and autotrophic conditions.

DR. van NIEL: Present information on the vitamin requirements of

purple bacteria indicates that only one type requires biotin; this is
*Rhodospirillum rubrum*. The vitamin is needed for growth in light, by
photosynthesis, as well as for growth in darkness, by an ordinary oxidative metabolism. But since *Rh. rubrum* cannot be grown as a strict
autotroph, this does not really answer your question.

DR. PRICE: Dr. Vogel made a very interesting point about the need
in selecting the correct span in looking for diversification to avoid finding
either monotony or triviality. In the lactate oxidation of *Euglena*, there
is perhaps this kind of diversification. The cells possess a soluble NAD-
dependent D-lactate dehydrogenase, and also a mitochondria-linked
NAD-independent lactate dehydrogenase. This may be of some generality among algae—*Euglena* is an alga—because diatomes, for example,
are able to utilize lactate as one of the very few carbon sources for
heterotrophic growth.

Another interesting point, perhaps a generalization, is that while one
typically doesn't find two separate pathways leading to the same end
product, when one has organelles, the situation might be greatly changed.

For example, again, in *Euglena*, there seem to be two completely
independent pathways for porphyrin synthesis, one of which is in the
chloroplasts of autotrophic *Euglena*, and one of which is extra-chloroplast
—probably mitochondria plus soluble.

CHAIRMAN THIMANN: Maybe organelles are parasites, after all. I
always liked Josh Lederberg's remark about the effect of streptomycin
on green plants:—It "cures" plants of their chloroplasts.

DR. PONNAMPERUMA: I would like to comment on the discussion concerning the nature of the reducing atmosphere. The equilibrium constant
at 25° for the formation of methane from carbon dioxide and hydrogen
is $8 \times 10^{22}$. Starting with carbon dioxide in the presence of hydrogen,
is no different from starting with methane. Urey's calculations have
shown that the amount of carbon dioxide which can exist in equilibrium
with one atmosphere of methane is $10^{-8}$ atmospheres.

CHAIRMAN THIMANN: We have arrived at the end of our allotted time.

# PART II

# EVOLUTION OF PATHWAYS II

# Chairman's Remarks

## C. B. van Niel

*Hopkins Marine Station, Pacific Grove, California*

Ladies and Gentlemen!

In order to keep to the time schedule, I shall dispense with the introductory remarks. I shall ask Dr. Bloch to present his paper.

# Lipid Patterns in the Evolution of Organisms

KONRAD BLOCH

*Department of Chemistry,*
*Harvard University,*
*Cambridge, Massachusetts*

Biochemical unity, in the broadest sense, prevails for many if not all of the processes that are common to all organisms and constitute the essential and minimal manifestations of life. Biochemical diversity, on the other hand, is the molecular expression of cellular differentiation and specialization of function. An important element in evolutionary diversification is the invention of novel and often unprecedented chemical structures, and, as I intend to show, many of these novel molecules are lipid in nature. Lipids are not generally considered to be especially relevant to evolutionary development and diversification, nor have they received much attention as phylogenetic markers or as diagnostic aids to taxonomy. Yet a survey of the vast body of information provided by comparative lipid biochemistry shows striking differences in the lipid patterns of various phylogenetic groups and leads to the conclusion that the inventions of certain lipid molecules were decisive events in evolutionary diversification.

It seems generally agreed that lipids function universally as structural components of cytoplasmic and intracellular membranes. Lipids, and specifically phospholipids, have been isolated from all cell fractions which are—with varying degrees of certainty—regarded as membranes: the mitochondrial membrane, red cell ghosts, endoplasmic reticulum, the myelin sheath, and the protoplast membranes of bacteria. The existence of a lamellar lipid bilayer is a central postulate of all membrane structures and membrane models that have been proposed (42). All cells have confining membranes, and since the chemistry of the lipid varies so widely from organism to organism these differences must find some expression in the properties which membranes from different organisms and cells exhibit.

Students of evolutionary diversification are placing increasing emphasis on membrane structures as features distinguishing the more advanced from the more primitive cell types. This point of view emerges with particular clarity from a discussion of Stanier and van Niel (47) dealing with the organizational patterns of two cellular prototypes, the procaryotes and the eucaryotes. As stated by these authors, "in the pro-caryotic cell the cytoplasmic membrane is the only bounding element which can be structurally defined," while in the eucaryotic cell (all organisms except the bacteria and the blue-green algae) the membrane-bound cytoplasm contains organelles (nuclei, mitochondria, endoplasmic reticulum, chloroplasts) which are themselves enclosed by membranes. The evolutionary step from the procaryotes to the eucaryotes, surely a decisive one in the evolution of organisms, thus resulted in the segregation of the subunits of physiological function and their multienzyme assemblies into discrete organelles, separated by physical barriers from the surrounding cytoplasm.

More by accident than by systematic investigation, the lipids of pro-caryotic and eucaryotic cells have been found to differ strikingly with respect to two classes of compounds. Firstly, sterols occur universally in eucaryotic cells, but they are absent in all the procaryotes examined. Secondly, polyunsaturated fatty acids do not occur in the bacterial phylum, yet they are ubiquitous in eucaryotic cells.

## Sterols in Bacteria and Blue-Green Algae

Occasional reports claiming the isolation of sterols from bacteria have not been substantiated. Whenever bacterial lipids have been care-fully analyzed, particularly from organisms grown on synthetic media, the evidence for the presence of sterols has been entirely negative (1, 3, 23). None of the organisms listed in Table I contains sterol in amounts greater than 0.001% of their dry weight, whereas in eucaryotic cells the sterol content is generally 0.2% or more. The early literature indicated also the scarcity if not the complete absence of steroids in the cyanophy-tae, the most primitive of the algal groups. Carter et al., in a systematic survey of the algal lipids, were able to isolate sterols from all representa-tives of the major algal divisions but failed to find these substances even in traces in the blue-green algae (11). Because of the special taxonomic position of the blue-green algae we have re-examined several representa-tives of this group with the aid of more sensitive modern techniques (36) and have fully confirmed the negative findings of Carter et al. The fact that the blue-green algae, in contrast to all other lower and higher plants, lack what is otherwise a universal cell constituent greatly strengthens the morphological argument for placing these primitive organisms into the same taxonomic group as the bacteria. Though one can set only lower analytical limits on the occurrence of a cell constituent and cannot exclude its presence with absolute certainty, it seems safe to accept the lack of sterols as a real and significant phylogenetic marker of the pro-caryotic cell.

As pointed out already, the major morphological basis for distinguishing the procaryotic and eucaryotic cell types is the presence or absence of membrane-bound intracellular organelles, the functional units carrying the enzyme assemblies for oxidative phosphorylation, for photosynthesis, and for the biosynthesis of macromolecules. Membrane fractions

TABLE I

DISTRIBUTION OF STEROLS

| Organism | Synthesis | Requirement | Reference |
|---|---|---|---|
| A. Procaryotes | | | |
| *Escherichia coli* | — | — | ( 1) |
| *Lactobacillus arabinosus* | — | — | ( 1) |
| *Azotobacter chroococcum* | — | — | ( 1) |
| *Rhodospirillum rubrum* | — | — | (23) |
| Actinomycetes | — | — | (23) |
| *Pseudomonas testosteroni* | — | — | ( 1) |
| PPLO group | — | + | (44) |
| *Anacystis nidulans* | — | — | (36) |
| *Anabena variabilis* | — | — | (36) |
| *Nostoc muscorum* | — | — | (36) |
| B. Eucaryotes | | | |
| Red algae and higher forms except: | + | | (11, 48) |
| Anaerobic yeast | — | + | ( 2, 38) |
| *Labyrinthula* sp. | — | + | (30) |
| *Trichomonas* sp. | — | + | (30) |
| *Tetrahymena* sp. | — | + | (30) |
| Most invertebrates | — | + | (13) |

prepared from these organelles are in general rich in lipids, and these lipids always include sterols though in varying amounts (15). Membranes with a high sterol content are the endoplasmic reticulum, the red cell membrane, and the myelin sheath, whereas in membrane preparation from mitochondria, chloroplasts, or nuclei relatively little sterol is found. Thus, it would seem that the appearance of certain functionally specialized membrane structures of the eucaryotic cell and the invention of the biosynthetic pathways leading to the sterol molecule were concurrent events and possibly causally related.

For deciding whether the sterol molecule is a specific component of only one or of several of the intracellular organelles, the following facts seem pertinent. Sterols occur in the unicellular nonflagellated red algae

(11, 48), organisms which are more advanced than the cyanophytae but are still relatively primitive. According to Dougherty and Allen (17) and Pitelka (40) they contain some but not all of the intracellular features of the eucaryotic cell. In particular, the marine red algae lack mitochondria, and it therefore seems unlikely that sterols are of significance for the membrane structure of this organelle. The sterol requirement of anaerobic yeast (2, 38) points to the same conclusion. Strictly anaerobic yeast contains no mitochondria (50), yet since a sterol is an essential nutrient under these conditions it is obviously needed for some non-mitochondrial function. In the mammalian cell the bulk of cholesterol is localized in the endoplasmic reticulum (9), while in animal mitochondria (5) and liver nuclei (27) sterol is a minor and perhaps adventitious lipid constituent. The eucaryotic cytoplasmic membrane and its endoplasmic extensions thus emerge as the most likely candidates for structures requiring sterol as an essential component.

The mode of action of certain antifungal agents, the polyene antibiotics nystatin and filipin, provides independent evidence for the essential nature of sterols in the eucaryotic membrane. The polyene antibiotics are effective agents against a variety of higher protists (26, 31, 35), acting apparently by combining with sterol or by causing sterol to leak from the cytoplasmic membrane. Sterol added to the culture medium antagonizes the antibiotic effect. Bacteria and blue-green algae, the two sterol-less groups of organisms, resist the action of these agents, in agreement with the presumed mode of antibiotic action, i.e., interaction with the sterol component of the cytoplasmic membrane.

One final remark about sterols in the context of procaryotic and eucaryotic cells. The presence of mucopeptide is a generally accepted biochemical character of the procaryotic cell (52), and this structure is held responsible for the mechanical strength of the bacterial cell wall. Organisms which have discontinued the synthesis of mucopeptide—the eucaryotes—may have compensated for this loss by synthesizing sterol which is also believed to function by strengthening and stabilizing the membrane structures that surround the cytoplasm (24). Nature has carried out an experiment which may be cited in support of this line of reasoning. The Pleuropneumonia organisms are regarded as natural L-forms of bacteria which are capable of survival in spite of their inability to synthesize mucopeptide. However, they are viable only when a sterol is incorporated into their growth media (44), and the sensitivity of their plasma membrane appears to be inversely related to their sterol content (41). This unique behavior of the PPLO group provides perhaps a preview of one of the functions that sterols came to play as components of eucaryotic membranes.

Direct information on the relation between the detailed molecular structure of sterols and the properties of sterol-containing membranes is not available. If we assume, however, that the sterol requirements of anaerobic yeast (2, 38), of insects (12, 13), and of certain sterol-deficient protozoa (30) are valid measures of sterol utilization for membrane synthesis, then certain essential features for the fitness of the sterol molecule can be defined. To judge from nutritional experiments, biological activity depends critically on the planarity of the entire tetracyclic ring system, on the equatorial orientation of the 3-hydroxy group, and on the presence of an aliphatic side chain, six to eight carbon atoms long. Like the long-chain fatty acids, the sterols are strongly hydrophobic molecules. However, the fused ring system of the steroids is a very rigid planar structure, in contrast to the great flexibility of the aliphatic fatty acid chain. This additional feature, i.e., the rigid planarity of a hydrophobic molecule, could conceivably be the element which distinguishes the eucaryotic from the procaryotic membrane and confers on it novel properties.

## POLYUNSATURATED FATTY ACIDS

The second conspicuous feature of bacterial lipid chemistry is the absence of fatty acids containing two or more double bonds (45). In the various bacterial species so far examined one finds a diversity of saturated, branched, and monounsaturated acids but none of the di- or polyenoic acids which are so widely distributed in higher forms. Though a generalization on the basis of the small number of organisms analyzed is perhaps premature, it does appear that the lack of polyunsaturated acids is as typical of bacterial lipids as is the absence of sterols. For the reasons cited earlier it is a point of interest to know whether this biochemical deficiency is a typical character of all procaryotic cells. Analyzing the lipids of the blue-green algae *Anabena variabilis*, we have found substantial amounts of linoleic and linolenic acids in this procaryotic organism (37), and therefore the generalization does not apply. Significantly, however, the polyunsaturated fatty acids are localized in the chromatophores of *Anabena*. In the remaining cytoplasm their concentration is very low.

The chromatophores of the blue-green algae are functionally equivalent to the internal lamellae of the photosynthetic apparatus in eucaryotes, but unlike the chloroplasts they are not bounded by an external membrane. The presence of polyunsaturated fatty acids in the algal chromatophores, therefore, implies a connection of these molecules with activities other than those residing in the procaryotic membrane. Removal of the cyanophytan chromatophores should, therefore, leave lipids with a bacterial fatty acid pattern. This point has been tested and demonstrated by analysis of sulfur bacteria, organisms that have been designated as apochlorotic blue-green algae. In *Beggiatoa*, a member of this group, fatty acid synthesis follows the bacterial pattern, producing monounsaturated but none of the polyunsaturated acids, including α-linolenate (21). With the provision that the generalization does not include the photosynthetic machinery of the blue-green algae, we may add the lack of polyunsaturated acids to the list of biochemical characters by which procaryotic cells may be defined.

The acquisition of the biosynthetic pathways to polyunsaturated fatty acids can be related to novel physiological activities which the bacterial cell does not possess. Because it is a constituent of the cyanophytan chromatophore, α-linolenic acid is likely to play some role in photosynthesis. In specifying this role note must be taken of the fact that the photosynthetic bacteria display the fatty acid pattern typical of other bacterial groups and not that of the blue-green algae (45). If polyunsaturated fatty acids are to play a role in photosynthesis and if on the other hand these molecules are missing in one distinctive group of photosynthetic organisms, then there must be some features which distinguish photosynthesis in one group from that in the other. It is known from the classical work of van Niel that photosynthetic bacteria, uniquely among photosynthetic organisms, fail to use water as a reductant and hence do not evolve molecular oxygen (49). The occurrence of α-linolenic acid in blue-green algae, the universal presence of this acid in chloroplast lipids, and its absence in the photosynthetic bacteria thus direct attention to oxygen evolution as the process in which α-linolenic acid may be involved (18). Evidence along several lines for a role of α-linolenic acid in green plant photosynthesis has been furnished by various laboratories including our own. In general, α-linolenic acid seems to be localized in the photosynthetic apparatus: in the chromatophores of the blue-green algae and in the chloroplasts or "quantasomes" of green plant cells (16, 53). In the phytoflagellate *Euglena gracilis*, which becomes etiolated when grown heterotrophically in the dark, α-linolenate disappears along with the chloroplast (19). Quite generally there seems to be a correlation between the extent of photosynthetic activity and the concentration of α-linolenic acid (14).

Not only the intracellular localization but also the chemical linkage form of α-linolenic acid shows a high degree of specificity. It is known, primarily from the work of Benson (6), that mono- and digalactosyl glycerides, the glycolipids discovered by Carter *et al.* (10), are major and typical chloroplast lipids. It is not definitely established that these substances occur elsewhere, either in plants or in animals. The galactosyl glycerides contain unusually high concentrations of polyunsaturated fatty acids and account in fact for the major portion of these acids in the chloroplasts. In *Euglena gracilis* the galactolipids as well as the unsaturated fatty acids disappear when the organism is adapted to growth in the dark (10, 29, 43), and they reappear when dark-grown cells are exposed to light. A specific association of galactolipids rich in polyunsaturated acids with plant photosynthesis is thus strongly indicated. Since the galactosyl glycerides are found in the chromatophores of *Anabena*, particles which lack an enclosing or confining membrane, these lipids are probably part of the lamellar matrix associated with the pigments and electron carriers and are not components of an outer membrane.

The galactosyl glycerides, the carriers for α-linolenate, are associated with the photosynthetic machinery in those organisms in which photosynthesis is of the advanced type, i.e., in blue-green algae as well as in higher algae and in plants, but they are missing in the photosynthetic bacteria (J. Lascelles and J. Szilagyi, private communication). It appears, therefore, that in the evolution of photosynthetic systems the invention of mechanisms for the photolysis of water occurred in parallel with the biosynthesis of novel lipid types as well as of multiply-unsaturated acids. The remarkably high degree of unsaturation of the fatty acids in these plant-specific lipids may be an important clue to the specific function of these molecules in photosynthetic electron transport.

## POLYUNSATURATED FATTY ACIDS IN PLANTS AND ANIMALS

Fatty acids containing more than two double bonds are found in natural sources in wide variety, their structures differing in the length of the carbon chain, the degree of unsaturation, and the location of the double bonds. Klenk (33) and Mead (39) have been able to assort the more abundant of these fatty acids into two structural types and biosynthetic lineages. They have postulated and partly shown by experiment the divergence of two major pathways at the stage of linoleic acid (9,12-octadecadienoic acid), one leading to α-linolenic acid (9,12,15-octadecatrienoic acid) and the other to γ-linolenic acid (6,9,12-octadecatrienoic acid) and arachidonic acid (5,8,11,14-eicosatetraenoic acid). In discussing the relation of polyunsaturated fatty acids to photosynthesis I made mention only of α-linolenic acid which contains the third double bond near the methyl terminus of the chain. By contrast, γ-linolenate and arachidonate, the products of the second pathway, arise characteristically by extension of the double-bond system of linoleate in the opposite or carboxyl direction, either before or after the carbon chain has been lengthened. The reasons for grouping polyunsaturated fatty acids into two types, "animal" and "plant," will be apparent from Table II. Listed

TABLE II

OCCURRENCE OF POLYUNSATURATED FATTY ACID IN PROTISTS

| Organism | α-Linolenate | γ-Linolenate and (or) arachidonate | Reference |
|---|---|---|---|
| Blue-green algae: | | | |
| Anabena variabilis | + | − | (36) |
| Red algae: | | | |
| Porphyridium cruentum | + | + | (34, 21) |
| Rhodomelia subfusca | | | |
| Chrysomonads: | | | |
| Ochromonas sp. | + | +++ | (28, 22) |
| Phytomonads: | | | |
| Chlamydomonas reinhardi | + | +++ | (21) |
| Euglenids: | | | |
| Euglena gracilis | + | − | (29) |
| Green algae: | | | |
| Ankistrodesmus braunii | + | | (34, 21) |
| Chlorella pyrenoidosa | | | |
| Scenedesmus obliquus | | | |
| Ameba: | | | |
| Hartmanella rhysodes | − | +++ | (22) |
| Ciliates: | | | |
| Tetrahymena sp. | − | + | (20) |
| Phycomycetes | | | (46) |
| Ascomycetes | ± | − | (46) |

here are three categories of organisms, those containing exclusively α-linolenic acid, those forming only γ-linolenic acid and arachidonic acid, and a third group in which both fatty acid types occur side by side. In the leaf tissues of higher plants and in the green and blue-green algae α-linolenate predominates, and, as already mentioned, this acid is found primarily in the galactolipids of the photosynthetic apparatus. In the metazoan group only the lipids of vertebrates have been thoroughly analyzed. From the available data it seems quite clear that arachidonic acid is the major polyunsaturated fatty acid component of the lipids associated with the various intracellular organelles. Particularly high is the arachidonic acid content of mitochondrial phospholipids and of the membranes prepared from these organelles (5). In general the fatty acid patterns of animal lipids are complex and difficult to interpret because they represent both the materials of endogenous origin and the composition of absorbed dietary acids which can be either of animal or of plant origin. Nutritionally controlled experiments and studies with labeled precursors have nevertheless established that in the metazoa as well as in a number of animal protists the synthesis of polyunsaturated fatty acids proceeds exclusively from linoleic acid to γ-linolenate and to arachidonate (33, 39). There is no evidence that the α-isomer of linolenate can be synthesized in higher animals nor that this acid serves as a source of the essential fatty acids which most animal species require. The position of entry of one of the three double bonds—15,16 versus 6,7—is, therefore, critical in determining the structural fitness of a fatty acid for either photosynthetic or heterotrophic metabolism. The fatty acid patterns of the physiologically diverse phytoflagellates are particularly revealing in this regard. Members of the nutritionally and physiologically versatile chrysomonads, phytomonads, and euglenids, organisms that can meet their energy requirements by phototrophic as well as by heterotrophic metabolism, contain α-linolenate side by side with γ-linolenate and arachidonate, a biochemical expression of their dual physiological potential (22, 28). On the other hand some of the specialized strictly "animal" descendants of the chrysomonads, the ciliates (20), and the ameba (22) appear to have retained only the γ-linolenate pathway.

In the phytoflagellate *Euglena gracilis* the degree of phototrophic and heterotrophic metabolism is variable and subject to environmental influences that are readily controlled in the laboratory (51). In these adaptable organisms the lipid patterns change drastically, depending on the presence or absence of light and on the availability of organic carbon sources (18-20). Conditions favoring photosynthetic activity raise the cellular content of α-linolenate and of galactosylglycerides at the expense of arachidonate and phospholipids. Conversely, in green cells adapting to growth in the dark the shift is from galactolipids containing α-linolenate to phospholipids containing arachidonate, events that parallel the disappearance of the chloroplasts and the increase in the number of mitochondria. In wild-type *Euglena* these shifts reflect quantitative adjustments to a changing environment without change of genotype. However, in colorless mutants of *Euglena gracilis* produced either artificially by physical agents or by antibiotics, or in natural mutants, the loss of plant-type lipids appears to be complete and irreversible (18, 19).

It was stated earlier that the ability to synthesize α-linolenic acid is a unique property which distinguishes blue-green algae from the bacteria and that the appearance of this fatty acid occurred in parallel with a major advance in the evolution of photosynthetic systems. The red algae, the protists which are presumed to occupy the next higher step in algal evolution (17, 40), are the earliest organisms in which γ-linolenate and arachidonate, the polyunsaturated fatty acids of the animal type, are found side by side with α-linolenate. If the red algae are indeed the most primitive eucaryotic cells, then the appearance of pathways to this novel fatty acid type, along with sterol synthesis, may mark the beginning evolution of separate membrane-bound units of cell function. At any rate, both their morphology and their lipid chemistry make the red algae exceptionally interesting organisms from the point of view of organic evolution.

The available data on the lipid composition of the higher protists suggest that the biosynthetic route to γ-linolenate and arachidonate persisted throughout the evolution of the major protistan lines. This fatty acid type became associated with the heterotrophic energy metabolism of eucaryotic cells, just as α-linolenate appears to have been selected as an advantageous component for the oxygen-evolving type of photosynthesis. As long as the protists were physiologically diversified they contained polyunsaturated fatty acids of both the α and γ type, but with increasing specialization of function there is a trend to retain only one or the other of the two pathways.

Several deletions of fatty acid biosynthesis seem to have occurred in protistan evolution, some of which are indicated in Table III. Among the descendants of the chrysomonads, the branch leading to the lower fungi (phycomycetes) retains the ability to synthesize γ-linolenate but not α-linolenate (7, 46), while in the ascomycetes and basidiomycetes only the plant pathway is preserved (46). In an ameba species which we have analyzed fatty acid biosynthesis is of the "animal" type producing γ-linolenate and arachidonate as in the chrysomonads (22), while in various ciliated protozoa the sole polyunsaturated fatty acid is γ-linolenate (20). In all the vertebrates examined arachidonate is a major product of polyunsaturated fatty acid synthesis, but the biosynthetic chain is incomplete because one of the intermediate steps, the conversion of oleate to linoleate, has been deleted in this phylum (39). Linoleate, the precursor of arachidonate, is, therefore, an essential nutrient for higher animals. Apparently none of the metazoan species has retained the enzyme systems for converting oleate to linoleate. The same step appears to have been deleted in the insecta, but in these invertebrates dietary linoleate is not converted to more highly unsaturated acids (4), indicating that an additional mutation has eliminated the further desaturation of linoleate. The evidence, though very incomplete,

TABLE III

DELETIONS IN POLYUNSATURATED FATTY ACID SYNTHESIS

| | |
|---|---|
| Ciliates, phycomycetes | $9\text{-}C_{18} \longrightarrow 9,12\text{-}C_{18} \longrightarrow 6,9,12\text{-}C_{18}\text{-}\mathbin{\Vert}\rightarrow 5,8,11,14\text{-}C_{20}$ |
| Vertebrates | $9\text{-}C_{18}\text{-}\mathbin{\Vert}\rightarrow 9,12\text{-}C_{18} \longrightarrow 6,9,12\text{-}C_{18} \longrightarrow 5,8,11,14\text{-}C_{20}$ |
| Invertebrates (Insecta) | $9\text{-}C_{18}\text{-}\mathbin{\Vert}\rightarrow 9,12\text{-}C_{18}\text{-}\mathbin{\Vert}\rightarrow 6,9,12\text{-}C_{18}\text{-}\mathbin{\Vert}\rightarrow 5,8,11,14\text{-}C_{20}$ |

suggests that in this invertebrate order the dienoic acid per se may serve as an essential fatty acid.

The functional consequences of these mutations are difficult to assess, and it is perhaps unwise to overemphasize their significance. It seems unlikely, however, that the formation of specific fatty acid types is vestigial and without physiological significance. In the vertebrates at least, the omission of polyunsaturated fatty acids from the diet leads to deficiencies including impaired mitochondrial function (32).

A survey of the kind attempted here suffers from several weaknesses. First of all, the number of organisms so far analyzed is insignificant compared to the available sample, and there is always the specter that investigation of additional organisms will invalidate the generalizations. Second, comparative analysis relies of necessity on arbitrarily selected data that often apply only to the special conditions under which the organisms were cultivated. Analyzing the lipid composition of microorganisms, one soon recognizes the marked influence of environmental conditions such as temperature, composition of growth medium, and light intensity on these biochemical parameters. In some situations the lipid patterns are affected so profoundly that what appears to be a phenotypic character may in fact represent a physiological or metabolic extreme (25). This variability must be kept in mind before the presence or absence of a particular lipid constituent can be interpreted as a distinctive genotypic expression.

In this discussion it has been suggested that the sterol molecule and two structural types of polyunsaturated fatty acids played a decisive role in the evolutionary progression of protistan cells. The biochemical mechanisms that currently operate in the synthesis of these lipids have the very notable feature that they require molecular oxygen as a direct electron acceptor (8). This is true for the successive introduction of double bonds into the fatty acid chain as well as for the cyclization of squalene and numerous later steps in sterol synthesis. The absolute requirement for oxygen in several of the reactions of lipid biosynthesis can be rationalized on mechanistic grounds, the argument being that only a strong oxidant can bring about these chemically unique transformations. By the same token it seems reasonable to ascribe the limited potentialities of anaerobic forms of life to the unavailability of reagents that compare with oxygen in oxidizing potential. The advent of molecular oxygen in the atmosphere during evolution not only facilitated the development of a vastly superior machinery for energy production and transformation but also provided a unique reagent for biosynthetic innovations which in turn may have paved the way for the specialization and differentiation of cells.

## REFERENCES

1. AMDUR, B., AND BLOCH, K., unpublished observations.
2. ANDREASEN, A. A., AND STIER, T. J. B., *J. Cellular Comp. Physiol.* **43**, 271 (1954).
3. ASSELINEAU, F., AND LEDERER, E., *in* "Lipide Metabolism" (K. Bloch, ed.), Wiley, New York, 1961.
4. BADE, M., *J. Insect Physiol.*, **10**, 333 (1964).
5. BALL, E. G., AND JOEL, C. D., *Intern. Rev. Cytol.*, **13**, 99 (1962).
6. BENSON, A. A., *Ann. Rev. Plant Physiol.*, **15**, 1 (1964).
7. BERNHARD, K., AND ALBRECHT, H., *Helv. Chim. Acta*, **31**, 977 (1948).
8. BLOCH, K., *Federation Proc.*, **21**, 6 (1962).
9. BUCHER, N. L. R., AND MCGARRAHAN, K., *J. Biol. Chem.*, **222**, 1 (1956).
10. CARTER, H. E., OHNO, K., NOJIMA, S., TIPTON, Z. L., AND STANAZEV, N. Z., *J. Lipid Res.*, **2**, 215 (1961).
11. CARTER, P. W., HEILBRON, I. M., AND LYTHGOE, B., *Proc. Roy Soc.*, **B128**, 82 (1939).
12. CLARK, J., AND BLOCH, K., *J. Biol. Chem.*, **234**, 2578 (1959).
13. CLAYTON, R. B., *J. Lipid Res.*, **5**, 3 (1964).
14. CONSTANTOPOULOS, G., AND BLOCH, K., unpublished observations.
15. COOK, R. P., *in* "Cholesterol" (R. P. Cook, ed.), Academic Press, New York, 1958.
16. DEBUCH, H., *Z. Naturforsch.*, **16b**, 246 (1961).
17. DOUGHERTY, E. C., AND ALLEN, M. B., *in* "Comparative Biochemistry of Photoreactive Systems" (M. B. Allen, ed.), Academic Press, New York, 1961.
18. ERWIN, J., AND BLOCH, K., *Biochem. Z.*, **338**, 496 (1963).
19. ERWIN, J., AND BLOCH, K., *Biochem. Biophys. Res. Commun.*, **9**, 2 (1962).
20. ERWIN, J., AND BLOCH, K., *J. Biol. Chem.*, **238**, 1618 (1963).

21. ERWIN, J., AND BLOCH, K., unpublished observations.
22. ERWIN, J., HULANICKA, D., AND BLOCH, K., *Comp. Biochem. Physiol.*, **12**, 191 (1964).
23. FIERTEL, A., AND KLEIN, H. P., *J. Bacteriol.*, **78**, 738 (1959).
24. FINEAN, J. B., *Experientia*, **9**, 17 (1953).
25. FULCO, A., AND BLOCH, K., *J. Biol. Chem.*, **239**, 998 (1964).
26. GOTTLIEB, D., CARTER, H. E., SLONEKER, J. H., AND AMMANN, H., *Science*, **128**, 361 (1958).
27. GURR, M. I., FINEAN, J. B., AND HAWTHORNE, J. N., *Biochim. Biophys. Acta*, **70**, 406 (1963).
28. HAINES, T. H., AARONSON, S., GELLERMANN, J. L., AND SCHLENK, H., *Nature*, **194**, 1282 (1962).
29. HULANICKA, D., ERWIN, J., AND BLOCH, K., *J. Biol. Chem.*, **239**, 2778 (1964).
30. HUTNER, S. H., AND HOLZ, G. G., *Ann. Rev. Microbiol.*, **16**, 189 (1962).
31. KINSKY, S. C., *J. Bacteriol.*, **82**, 889 (1961).
32. KLEIN, P. D., AND JOHNSON, R. M., *J. Biol. Chem.*, **211**, 103 (1954).
33. KLENK, E., *Experientia*, **17**, 199 (1961).
34. KLENK, E., KNIPPRATH, W., EBERHAGEN, D., AND KOOF, H. P., *Z. Physiol. Chem.*, **334**, 44 (1963).
35. LAMPEN, J. O., ARNOW, P. M., BOROWSKA, Z., AND LASKIN, A. I., *J. Bacteriol.*, **84**, 1152 (1962).
36. LEVIN, E. Y., AND BLOCH, K., *Nature*, **202**, 90 (1964).
37. LEVIN, E. Y., LENNARZ, W. J., AND BLOCH, K., *Biochim. Biophys. Acta*, **84**, 469 (1964).
38. MASTERS, R., Ph.D. Thesis, Harvard University, 1964.
39. MEAD, J., *in* "Lipide Metabolism" (K. Bloch, ed.), Wiley, New York, 1960.
40. PITELKA, D. R., "Electron-Microscopic Structure of Protozoa," p. 101, Macmillan, New York, 1963.
41. RAZIN, S., *J. Gen. Microbiol.*, **33**, 471 (1963).
42. ROBERTSON, J. D., *Progr. Biophys. Biophys. Chem.*, **10**, 343 (1960).
43. ROSENBERG, A., *Biochemistry*, **2**, 1148 (1963).
44. ROTHBLAT, G. H., AND SMITH, P. F., *J. Bacteriol.*, **82**, 479 (1961).
45. SCHEUERBRANDT, G., AND BLOCH, K., *J. Biol. Chem.*, **237**, 2064 (1962).
46. SHAW, R., *Biochim. Biophys. Acta*, in press.
47. STANIER, R. Y., AND VAN NIEL, C. B., *Arch. Mikrobiol.*, **42**, 17 (1962).
48. TSUDA, K., AKAGI, S., AND KISHIDA, Y., *Science*, **126**, 927 (1957).
49. VAN NIEL, C. B., *Advan. Enzymol.*, **1**, 263 (1941).
50. WALLACE, P. G., AND LINNANE, A. W., *Nature*, **201**, 1191 (1964).
51. WOLKEN, J. J., "Euglena: An Experimental Organism for Biochemical and Biophysical Studies. Rutgers Univ. Press, New Brunswick, New Jersey, 1961.
52. WORK, E., *Biochem. J.*, **49**, 17 (1951).
53. ZILL, L. P., AND HARMON, E. A., *Biochim Biophys. Acta,* **53**, 579 (1962).

# Evolution of Heme and Chlorophyll

S. GRANICK

*The Rockefeller Institute, New York, New York*

## INTRODUCTION

The functions of respiration and photosynthesis in protoplasm serve to provide energy for maintenance and renewal. In this paper I wish to present some hypotheses on how these functions may have been accomplished in a primitive form in inorganic mineral catalysts, how organic molecules came to take over these functions, and how these organic molecules were modified as the biosynthetic chains developed. Finally, I should like to discuss the recent appearance in evolution of a heme oxidative enzyme.

## THE TWO FUNCTIONS OF THE PORPHYRIN BIOSYNTHETIC CHAIN

One of the problems that fascinated me as a student was whether the two major pigments of protoplasm, heme and chlorophyll, were related. This was an old problem. It had its roots in the realization of the basic unity of protoplasm which became evident when the cell theory was proposed about 125 years ago. The philosophical question of the unity of protoplasm on a molecular level was also being considered at that time, since some of the biologically occurring molecules had already been synthesized by organic chemists. There is a paper in the *Comptes Rendus* of about 1850 which stated that the two major pigments were indeed related, since both contained iron. The author of the paper should have been given an A in philosophy but a zero in qualitative analysis.

By the 1940's, the massive and difficult work on the structural chemistry of heme and chlorophyll was almost complete (14). The methods of organic chemistry had shown that heme and chlorophyll were constructed on the same porphyrin plan (Fig. 1), but there were a number of differences. It was only through a biochemical approach that the reason for their similarity was found about fifteen years ago (10). It was then shown that both pigments arise from the same precursor, protoporphyrin. To make heme, iron is inserted into protoporphyrin. To make chlorophyll, magnesium is inserted into protoporphyrin; then in a number of steps the side chains, i.e., the fringes around the porphyrin ring, are modified. One propionic acid group is esterified with methanol

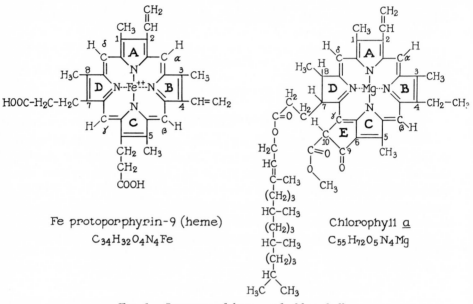

Fɪɢ. 1.   Structure of heme and chlorophyll.

and oxidized to form the cyclopentanone ring; one vinyl is reduced to an ethyl group; one pyrrole is reduced by addition of two H atoms; and finally, the other propionic acid group is esterified with phytol. Thus, it is seen that the basic plan of the two pigments is essentially the same, but in chlorophyll there are fringe benefits.

Heme and chlorophyll are related not only because they are two end products of the same biosynthetic chain. They are also related in function. Heme serves as the catalyst for respiration to release the energy stored in organic bonds to be used for useful work. Chlorophyll serves as a catalyst to convert the energy of sunlight into the stored chemical energy of organic bonds. The basic energetics of protoplasm are thus catalyzed by these two pigments derived from the same biosynthetic chain (10).

When we examine the structures of heme and chlorophyll and attempt to relate them to their functions, a simple relation is evident. The redox activities of heme which are responsible for its catalytic function reside in the properties of the iron atom; the properties of the porphyrin surrounding the iron atom merely modify the properties of the iron atom. On the other hand the porphyrin or chlorophyll molecules are dyestuffs that have properties suitable for photochemical reactions; these dyes absorb light and fluoresce intensely in the visible region of the spectrum.

A number of biological pigments are known which can act photochemically, e.g., derivatives of flavins or carotenoids. However, the ability of the porphyrin to do two jobs, i.e., both redox and photochemical reactions, gave it such an advantage that it easily preempted the biological stage.

## Possible Starting Conditions for Life on Earth

Before we discuss evolution it would be nice to know the starting conditions at the time the earth was formed. However, our knowledge of this early part of the process is on a par with our knowledge of the expanding universe for which Shapley wrote: "Already the various theoretical cosmogonists give confident answers to cosmogonical questions; the answers, however, are rarely in agreement."

But let us take one of the latest hypotheses as proposed by Fowler *et al.* (7) and see where it leads us. According to this hypothesis, before the planets were formed from the condensing mass around the sun, the molecules $H_2O$, $NH_3$, $CH_4$, and $H_2$, along with ultraviolet light, were abundant. In addition, there were fine solid particles which presented a large area for adsorption. It was during this time that prebiotic carbonaceous material could have been formed. [The work of Miller, Oro, and others has shown that irradiation with ultraviolet light or spark discharges on the above molecular ingredients leads to trace amounts of amino acids, purines, etc. (23, 29).] As condensation proceeded at 130° to 200°K, planetesimals, several meters in extent, were formed, consisting mainly of metal silicates and oxides embedded in an icy matrix. After the planetesimals had aggregated to form the earth, Whipple (31) suggests that most of the volatile constituents including C, N, and O were lost. Actually, the primitive atmosphere and oceans may have been derived secondarily by a squeezing-out process from the residual solid matter of the earth.

So, at the beginning we may have had on the earth's surface traces of residual organic matter which provided material to start life processes in an atmosphere consisting mainly of $CO_2$, $N_2$, and $H_2O$. The geochemists (18, 24) tell us that there then occurred a gradual separation of the earth into a dense inner core of iron and nickel with a lighter metal sulfide phase above it and a surface of which we are a part, representing the slag heap of this process or, if you prefer, the upper crust.

In connection with the start of life, carbonaceous-containing meteorites like the Orgueil meteorites (29) are of great interest because they may have been part of the original planetesimals (Table I). The main components of the meteorites are hydrous-layer lattice silicates, magnetite, and carbonaceous substances ranging from 0.2% up to as high as 4.8%. According to Anders (1) the components $SO_4^{--}$, $Fe_3O_4$, FeS, $CO_3^{--}$, and S consist of oxidized and reduced species close to a chemical equilibrium that would be attained at a pH of 8 to 10 and a redox potential, $Eh$, of —0.2 volt. The organic contents of the meteorite are in dispute be-

TABLE I
SOME IMPORTANT DATES

| Event | Billion years |
|---|---|
| Age of earth | 4.5–5.0 |
| Carbonaceous chondrites[a] | >4.0 |
| Oldest crustal rocks[b] | 3.3 |
| Lime-secreting organisms[c] | ~2.7 |
| Absence of atmospheric $O_2$[d] | ~2.0 |
| Presence of atmospheric $O_2$[e] | ~1.0–2.0 |
| Fossiliferous chert[f] | |
|   Blue-greens? | |
|   Iron bacteria? | 1.6 |
|   Coelenterates? | |
| Chlorophyll derivatives | |
|   and isoprenoid hydrocarbons[g] | 1.1 |
| Precambian living bacteria[h] | >0.6 |
| Graptolites (Prechordates?) | <0.6 |

[a] Anders (1).

[b] Oldest yet dated (Rutten, 26).

[c] Limestone and dolomite deposited by lime-secreting organisms found in Rhodesia by MacGregor (26).

[d] The weathering of minerals such as FeS, $FeS_2$, etc., left them unoxidized.

[e] Red beds of quartz silty sediments with limonite (hydrated ferric oxide) found at this time but not earlier.

[f] Silicified fossils in chert from Greenflint Iron Formation of Southern Ontario found by Tyler and Barghoorn (26).

[g] From Nonesuch shale (21).

[h] Reported by Dombrowski (6).

cause of possible contamination with earth impurities. (For example, it has been claimed that 2 mg of dust can have all the amino acid components found in 1 g of the meteorite.) Whether this is the complete explanation of the seventeen amino acids found there by Kaplan *et al.* (15) remains to be fought out.

These carbonaceous meteorites are a prize package for various evolutionary hypotheses. They contain organic carbon which will support the thick or thin organic soup hypothesis for the origin of life as first proposed by Oparin and by Haldane. They contain the hydrous-layer lattice silicates proposed by Hendricks and by Bernal for adsorption of substrates and for ion exchange and catalysis. They also contain the minerals magnetite and iron sulfide proposed by Granick (11) for a photovoltaic unit that would perform a crude photosynthesis.

### A PHOTOVOLTAIC MINERAL UNIT AS THE POWERHOUSE UNIT OF PREPROTOPLASM

If we consider the functions of the iron protein catalysts of present-day protoplasm we find that they may be classified under several headings such as electron transport (i.e., the cytochromes), activation of $O_2$ (cytochrome oxidase), and activation of $H_2O_2$ (peroxidase). These catalysts are efficient, they have a high turnover rate, and are specific in function and stable. However, ferrous and ferric ions or their inorganic hydroxides possess all of these catalytic functions, although their turnover rate is comparatively low, and there is little specialization of function. Thus, the same iron hydroxide molecule may act as electron transporter or oxidase, or peroxidase. The versatile beauty of iron is that (a) depending on the pH and anions present such as hydroxide, phosphate, carbonate, or sulfide, the redox potential may be varied from the level of the hydrogen potential toward that of the oxygen potential; (b) iron may form coordination complexes using the $3d$, $4s$, and $4p$ orbitals and may have three different magnetic states for ferrous and for ferric complexes (14).

This comparison between the activities of iron catalysts of protoplasm and inorganic iron compounds suggests that the ubiquitous inorganic iron minerals may have been the primitive respiratory catalysts. If we generalize this idea of an evolutionary derivation we see that we have a method to explore origins. That is: examine present-day functions of protoplasm and seek to relate them to inorganic materials that have similar functions (10).

On the basis of this postulate, what would one look for in the inorganic realm that would serve for photosynthesis? About seven years ago at another conference on evolution, I proposed a model for photosynthesis based on the properties of iron compounds (11) like the ones found in carbonaceous meteorites, e.g., magnetite, FeO, FeS.

The diagram on the right in Fig. 2 shows a modification of this model, and the diagram on the left represents the current ideas on photosynthesis as postulated by Witt, Duysens, Arnon, and others. We think of photosynthesis in terms of two units, each possibly representing a cluster or packet of several enzymes. These units are mediated by a plastoquinone molecule which can transfer an electron from unit II to unit I. I like to think of the plastoquinone as a metronome with its long (70-A) isoprene tail anchored in a lipid phase and the quinone head making contact between the two units. A light quantum absorbed by any chlorophyll molecule is funneled into unit II so that an electron is released from a hydroxyl group. The electron is raised up the potential hill to plasto-quinone which is thereby reduced. Then the electron falls a short distance downhill to cytochrome $f$ of unit I. This fall is coupled with the formation of a high-energy phosphate bond. Now another light quantum is funneled into unit I and raises the potential of the electron further. This electron can be used to reduce TPN or to form $H_2$. The over-all reaction to convert $2H_2O$ to $O_2$ + TPNH + 4ATP requires 8 quanta. Manganese is required in unit II if $O_2$ is to be released. So we see that the cooperation of a number of enzymes in two packets and a number of photons is required.

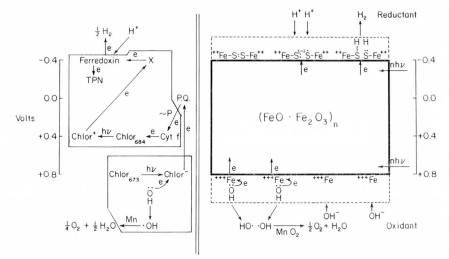

Fig. 2. *Left*—Diagram of model of photosynthesis. The upper portion represents unit I, and the lower portion, unit II. *Right*—Diagram of a photovoltaic model for carrying out a primitive photosynthesis.

Let us contrast this present-day model of photosynthesis with the hypothetical inorganic photovoltaic model on the right. This diagram shows a mineral magnetite which has an inverse spinel structure. It can act as an $n$-type semiconductor. On the upper surface it is con-taminated with a monolayer of FeS and $FeS_2$, and on the lower surface with a monolayer of ferric hydroxide and some $MnO_2$. This blackish mineral unit may be only several hundred atoms in size, but sufficiently large to absorb a number of light quanta which can generate a number of electrons. The central portion is an excellent trap for several electrons. The model would work in the following way: Light quanta impinging on the mineral would cause electrons to flow through a rectification layer at the bottom. This would create an OH radical which could either serve as oxidant, be converted to a peroxide which could serve as oxidant, or be decomposed by $MnO_2$ to $O_2$ and $H_2O$. On the upper surface the absorption of other light quanta would cause electrons to flow across another rectification layer and reduce an S–S bond to SH; and hydride ions could be formed to generate $H_2$. The decomposition of water requires 1.2 volts. If at each rectification layer an electron could be raised by 0.6 volt, then water would be decomposed. If only 0.2 to 0.3 volt could be generated, this would be enough to form a pyrophosphate bond which could be stored as inorganic polyphosphate. The mineral postulated is essentially an impure magnetite ($FeO \cdot Fe_2O_3$). In the inverse spinel 8 ferric ions are tetrahedrally surrounded by oxygen anions, and 8 ferric ions and 8 ferrous ions are octahedrally surrounded by oxygen anions. Such a mineral absorbs light intensely because of the resonance between the ferrous and ferric ions; and because of resonance it is a good semiconductor of the $n$ type. In this mineral some of the divalent and trivalent iron atoms may be replaced by a number of divalent or trivalent ions of similar radii. The exact distribution of the cations is of secondary importance, so there may be excess negative or excess positive charge in localized regions. Even the absence of metal ions is possible as in the $\gamma$ iron oxides.

Two recent discoveries of iron compounds that function in photosynthesis appear to be compatible with the model as proposed a number of years ago. One is the iron compound ferredoxin (30), first isolated from some bacteria and then shown to function in chloroplasts to reduce TPN with the aid of a flavin enzyme. The potential of reduced ferredoxin is such that it can generate $H_2$ if a hydrogenase is present. Analyses of *Clostridium* ferredoxin show that it is a primitive protein, lacking several amino acids, and has a molecular weight of only 6000. But this is what is exciting. This small protein contains 7 Fe atoms complexed with 7 cysteine residues and 6 inorganic sulfide atoms. Blomstrom and co-workers (30) suggest that the iron atoms in ferredoxin are linearly arranged and complexed with the cysteine sulfur and inorganic sulfur bridges. This structure fits the hypothetical inorganic model at the upper surface. What about the lower surface of our model? Another discovery, that by Gewitz and Völker (8), is of an iron (not heme) enzyme which Warburg suggests may be the one concerned with $O_2$ production in photosynthesis.

If this inorganic photosynthetic unit could work it might serve as a "powerhouse" unit for respiration and photosynthesis. Various organic compounds could be formed and concentrated on the oxidant and reductant surfaces. What I am suggesting, then, is the *de novo* formation, by sunlight and a photovoltaic mineral, of organic compounds concentrated around this colloid unit. Such a photovoltaic unit could have remained a component of a primitive cell even for some time after DNA and proteins were synthesized. Probably later, the basic functions of respiration and photosynthesis in the cell were gradually taken over by organic compounds which were more specific and more efficient.

## ELABORATION OF THE PHOTOCHEMICAL FUNCTION

The evolution of a biosynthetic chain is perhaps more clearly envisioned in the steps of heme-chlorophyll synthesis than in other biochemical syntheses because it leads unidirectionally to two end products, one serving to catalyze the conversion of the sun's energy into chemical energy and the other to release this energy to do the work of the cell. Above, we have suggested that these "powerhouse" functions were first found in inorganic catalysts. Only later, concomitant with the elaboration of DNA and proteins, do we consider that the evolution of the heme-chlorophyll chain took place (Figs. 3 and 4).

The useful step in this biosynthetic chain was reached only when uroporphyrinogen and its oxidation products were formed. Uroporphyrin is an intensely absorbing, fluorescent, photoactive dye which can carry out photochemical reactions. Uroporphyrin can also form a tight chelate complex with iron which can serve as a redox catalyst.

But why did this biosynthetic chain not stop with the formation of uroporphyrin? It is evident from the ten or more additional steps to chlorophyll that uroporphyrin was just one step in an evolutionary process to seek out the compounds and mechanisms that would function most efficiently for redox and photosynthetic reactions. In general, these elaborations proceeded from more water-soluble products to more lipid-soluble products which then became organized in lipoprotein membranes (mitochondria and chloroplasts).

The concept of a stepwise evolution of a biosynthetic chain implies that at one time each step had to be an end product of the biosynthetic chain and serve a useful function. Later, an additional step would be elaborated to produce an end product that could carry out the same function more efficiently, but the previous step would still be essential, for it would serve as an intermediate. The end product of the chain to serve a useful function would have to become part of a more elaborate complex of enzymes. The rate of evolution of the heme-chlorophyll biosynthetic chain would depend on the intermeshing of evolutionary developments in other chains. For example, elaboration of more lipid-soluble porphyrins would become useful when lipoprotein membranes for their organization had evolved. The longer the biosynthetic chain and the more elaborate the structure-function organization at the end of the chain, the more restricted would become the chances for the exploration in evolution of new biosynthetic chains to carry out the same function.

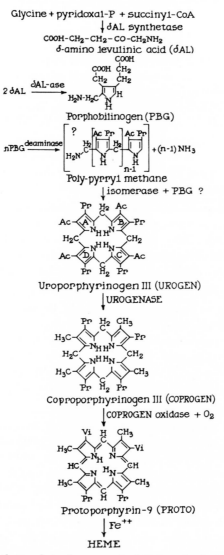

Glycine + pyridoxal-P + succinyl-CoA

$\downarrow$ δAL synthetase

COOH-CH$_2$-CH$_2$-CO-CH$_2$NH$_2$

δ-amino levulinic acid (δAL)

2 δAL $\xrightarrow{\text{δAL-ase}}$

Porphobilinogen (PBG)

nPBG $\xrightarrow{\text{deaminase}}$ + (n-1) NH$_2$

Poly-pyrryl methane

$\downarrow$ isomerase + PBG ?

Uroporphyrinogen III (UROGEN)

$\downarrow$ UROGENASE

Coproporphyrinogen III (COPROGEN)

$\downarrow$ COPROGEN oxidase + O$_2$

Protoporphyrin-9 (PROTO)

$\downarrow$ Fe$^{++}$

HEME

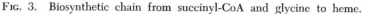

FIG. 3.   Biosynthetic chain from succinyl-CoA and glycine to heme.

Evolution is a one-way road. If heterochromatin were to store temporarily discarded genes, this might lessen the unidirectionality of evolution.

As mentioned above, once uroporphyrin had been formed, it could have been used as a photochemical catalyst. As the chain evolved, other end products were formed and explored for various uses. Certain of these intermediates or products formed from them are known to take part in photochemical reactions today. For example, the plant protein-bile pig-

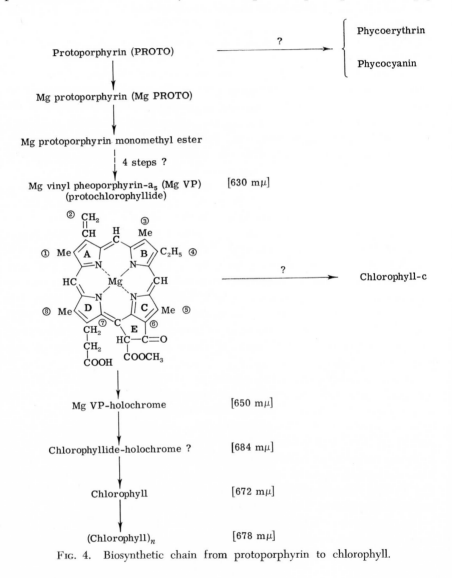

FIG. 4.   Biosynthetic chain from protoporphyrin to chlorophyll.

ments, phycocyanin and phycoerythrin (Fig. 4), which are found in red and blue-green algae, are possibly derived from protoporphyrin or iron protoporphyrin by opening up of the ring. These compounds are combined with protein to form intensely fluorescent pigments. At present, these pigments serve as antennae to catch the light and transfer it to chlorophyll *a* 674 mμ. Another protein thought to contain a bile pigment is phytochrome; it undergoes a photochemical change, triggering a biochemical reaction that leads to important physiological changes in plants. Near the apex of the biosynthetic chain is the greenish pigment protochlorophyllide. This pigment in the presence of light and an unknown reductant is converted to chlorophyllide. In this photochemical reaction, pyrrole ring IV is reduced by the addition of two H atoms. There is no evidence that this photoreduction is a reversible reaction at present. However, it may have been the basis for a photosynthetic mechanism in the past. In the brown algae is a pigment, chlorophyll *c*, which is related to protochlorophyllide in structure; chlorophyll *c* serves, like the phycobilins, as an accessory pigment to transmit energy from sunlight to chlorophyll *a* 674 mμ.

Why did the plants go on to vary the porphyrin until they arrived at chlorophyll? The answers must lie in the chemistry and photochemistry of these pigments of which we know so little.

Uroporphyrin must have been the first compound of the heme-chlorophyll biosynthetic chain to serve in protoplasm in a photochemical capacity. If we search through the plants we find no remnant of uroporphyrin photochemical activity. Probably too many of the coupling enzymes that were required to make it work have long since gone. But the photochemical properties of uroporphyrin can be examined today. Because of the recent beautiful work of David Mauzerall of our laboratory we have begun to learn of some of the remarkable properties of uroporphyrin (19, 20).

When uroporphyrin is illuminated it will react with EDTA, a mild reductant, and pull out an electron from the EDTA. Thus a radical of uroporphyrin is formed. Two of these radicals can disproportionate to form a molecule of dihydroporphyrin (phlorin) and a molecule of porphyrin. Two molecules of dihydroporphyrin can disproportionate to form one molecule of tetrahydroporphyrin and one of porphyrin (Fig. 5). The absorption spectra of these reduced porphyrins are shown in Fig. 6. The dihydroporphyrin has an absorption band at 735 mμ. The tetrahydroporphyrin has an intense band at about 500 mμ.

By the action of light, uroporphyrin can be excited to accept and store up to four electrons. If these electrons are on a potential level of the hydrogen electrode, then with the correct coupling enzymes $H_2$ may be generated. This reaction is analogous to the over-all reaction that occurs in the absence of $O_2$ in purple photosynthetic bacteria. When these bacteria are provided with a rich organic nutriment in the presence of light, they generate $H_2$.

At present we do not know whether the light energy in this uro-

$$\text{Porphyrin + EDTA} \xrightarrow{h\nu} \text{[Porphyrin radical·] + EDTA oxidized}$$

$$2\ \text{[Porphyrin radical·]} \rightleftharpoons \text{Dihydroporphyrin + Porphyrin}$$

$$2\ \text{Dihydroporphyrin} \rightleftharpoons \text{Tetrahydroporphyrin + Porphyrin}$$

Fig. 5.   Photochemical steps in the reduction of porphyrin to tetrahydroporphyrin.

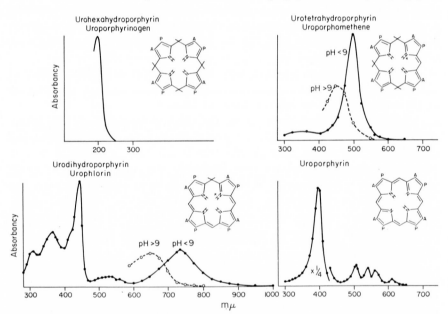

Fig. 6.   Absorption spectra of the various steps of reduction of uroporphyrin (19, 20).

porphyrin reaction is used merely as energy of activation, that is, to catalyze electron transfer, or whether the energy of light can be stored in the form of chemical energy.

Even if uroporphyrin in the presence of light only activated an electron transfer from organic compounds, and $H_2$ was generated, this might be a useful mechanism. It could have served to remove $H_2$ from the highly reduced "organic soup" of Urey. The $H_2$ would have escaped into the atmosphere and eventually into outer space, thus leaving the lithosphere less reducing.

The photochemical properties of uroporphyrin and the number of steps of reduction, i.e., of electron storage, that are possible in the identical molecule make this an exciting molecule to play with. When we know more about it we may have a better idea of what primitive photosynthesis in protoplasm may have been like.

Although protoporphyrin was the last step in development for the iron chelate prosthetic group of plants and animals, the insertion of Mg into protoporphyrin began a new series of adventures into photochemistry. One apparent function that may be assigned to Mg is that it makes the pyrrole nitrogens more negative and possibly facilitates the ejection of an electron from light-excited Mg protoporphyrin, i.e., makes it a better electron donor. Further steps up the biosynthetic chain convert Mg protoporphyrin to a more lipophylic pigment. Chlorophyll, in addition to its photochemical function of converting light to chemical energy, is concentrated in lipoprotein monolayers in a rather close-packed array. This enhances its ability to transmit the energy of captured photons to the active chlorophyll site where it is converted to the energy of chemical bonds. The long phytol chain in the chlorophyll serves not only to make the pigment lipophylic but sterically hinders the formation of crystalline chlorophyll in the monolayer so that the absorption is not shifted to the infrared (2).

The chlorophylls in $CCl_4$ appear to behave as though there was an affinity of the cyclopentanone ring oxygen of one chlorophyll molecule for the Mg of an adjacent molecule (16). If this occurs in the chloroplast, then the function of the cyclopentanone ring might be that it provides for the correct stacking of chlorophylls for energy transmission. The conversion of protochlorophyllide to chlorophyllide by the addition of two H atoms at pyrrole ring IV shifts the absorption toward the red; therefore, less light energy is required to excite the molecule.

Evolutionary inventions which have modified the photochemistry of chlorophyll are suggested by the fact that two units of photosynthesis are present (Fig. 2). At the active sites of these two units, chlorophyll a molecules function with different redox potentials. This indicates that, in addition to chlorophyll structure, specific coupling factors and enzymes may have to be considered in explaining function.

Geochemical evidence for the presence of chlorophyll-like pigments 1.1 billion years ago is provided by the finding of vanadium porphyrins with specific side chains in certain oil shales. However, lime-secreting organisms, presumably algae with photosynthetic pigments, were already present 2.7 billion years ago (Table I).

## ELABORATION OF THE REDOX FUNCTION

As noted above, it was only when the biosynthetic chain had developed to the stage of uroporphyrinogen with its oxidized form, uroporphyrin, that a molecule appeared that could chelate iron. At present there is no evidence for iron uroporphyrin or iron coproporphyrin in animal or plant tissues. In animal tissues we think we know why. It is because several mechanisms have been developed to prevent this formation: (a) The intermediates of the biosynthetic chain are the porphyrinogens which do not chelate iron. (b) The low $K_m$ values for the enzymes from uroporphyrinogen to protoporphyrinogen indicate that only traces of porphyrinogens are present at any one time. (c) Uroporphyrinogen and coproporphyrinogen are formed outside the mitochondria, whereas the iron-insertion mechanism for iron porphyrin formation appears to be localized in the mitochondrion. In the mitochondrion coproporphyrinogen is oxidized to protoporphyrinogen and thence to protoporphyrin. The iron is then inserted into protoporphyrin to form heme.

The formation of iron protoporphyrin appears to be the end of the line for iron chelate pigments as far as the biosynthetic chain which we are considering is concerned. There appear to be no iron pigments related to the Mg series. The phycobilin pigments in plants may represent a decomposition of iron protoporphyrin. The present-day enzymes that contain iron protoporphyrin as prosthetic group are the various $b$ cytochromes, catalase, and peroxidase. Cytochrome $c$ heme is also derived from iron protoporphyrin; there is suggestive evidence that the apocytochrome $c$ peptide can condense with protoporphyrinogen to form thioether bonds (27) (perhaps while the polypeptide is being synthesized on the ribosomes?), and then iron is inserted. The cytochrome $a$ porphyrin differs from iron protoporphyrin; it has a formyl group in side-chain position 8, and the vinyl at side chain 2 is coupled with farnesol. Whether cytochrome $a$ is derived from protoporphyrin or iron protoporphyrin is not known.

Although $b$-type cytochromes and certain $c$-type cytochromes may function with oxidants other than $O_2$ to provide high-energy phosphate, cytochrome oxidase together with cytochrome $c$ functions in conjunction with molecular oxygen as oxidant. Did cytochrome oxidase (i.e., cytochrome $a$) appear at the time the biosynthetic chain had evolved to the protoporphyrin step, or did it appear much later? If cytochrome oxidase appeared at the protoporphyrin step it would mean that the photochemistry at the protoporphyrin level was providing sufficient atmospheric oxygen for the existence of animal life.

The geochemical evidence based on the lack of oxidation of sediments containing FeO, FeS$_2$, and pitchblende suggests that atmospheric O$_2$ was scarce 2 billion years ago (26) and became plentiful only between 1 and 2 billion years ago (Table I). However, lime-secreting organisms, presumably algae which could fix CO$_2$ from CaHCO$_3$ and thus cause deposition of CaCO$_3$, were present some 2.7 billion years ago. These algae may have already generated oxidant and perhaps even O$_2$. In a colloidal quartz mineral of 1.6 billion years ago, silicified remains of simple plants and microbes have been reported. These findings suggest that, sometime less than 2 billion years ago, molecular oxygen became sufficiently plentiful to permit animal life. Certainly before this time, cytochrome $c$ and a cytochrome oxidase with a great affinity for O$_2$ must have evolved.

## Some Properties of Evolving Genes

Before the evolution of the genes of the porphyrin biosynthetic chain is considered, some general properties of evolving genes will be discussed.

1. Existing genes can be duplicated as first suggested by Bridges. The frequency of duplications may be high as judged by somatic pairing between regions of homologous and nonhomologous chromosomes in *Drosophila* (17).

2. If a duplicate gene arises and is functional, too much of a product may be produced, resulting in a physiologic imbalance. One mechanism to repress the activity of the duplicate gene is to convert it to a tightly coiled form, i.e., equivalent to a "silent form."

3. Heterochromatin (4) may represent regions of tightly coiled chromosomes which contain numerous duplicate genes. The function of heterochromatin may be to act as a reservoir for the silent genes. Some of these genes may mutate, lose the property of heterochromatization, and then be used to add a new step to a biosynthetic chain or start a new chain.

4. A gene that codes for a functional protein has built-in sequences of certain nucleotides that must be conserved to conserve function. This statement may be best appreciated by comparing the different globins. The discovery that myoglobin and the α, β, and γ chains of hemoglobin are isomorphous with each other on the basis of three-dimensional folding of their polypeptide chain is of prime importance. It suggests that functioning of hemoglobin requires a specific alignment of the correct amino

acids, leading to the folding of the polypeptide chain which provides a "mold" for the heme. Although I do not wish to burden the DNA with more "-on" words, the word "moldon" may prove useful. We shall define as "moldon" the appropriate sequences of nucleotides in a gene that will code for the appropriate sequences in the polypeptide that will fold to provide the mold. The "moldon" represents an evolutionary discovery that is stringently conserved because it codes for a functional protein.

5. Evolution by duplication of a moldon will occur far more readily than the creation of a new moldon. For example, it is highly probable that enzymes with the same prosthetic group, e.g., DPN, are derived from the same gene by duplication. Indeed, the amino acid sequences of three DPN dehydrogenases have recently been shown to be related to each other (33). X-Ray studies will probably show that these enzymes are isomorphous in three-dimensional structure.

6. The juxtaposition and fusion of two or more moldons resulting from crossing over or translocation may be expected to produce a polypeptide of greater molecular weight containing several different prosthetic groups. An example of stages in the evolution of the enzyme tryptophan synthetase is suggested by the studies of Yanofsky (32) and Bonner et al. (3). In Escherichia coli, two adjacent cistrons A and B are present which code for enzymes A and B that together catalyze the synthesis of tryptophan from indole glycerol-P and serine. However, in Neurospora, the adjacent cistrons have fused and the individual functions of the A and B enzymes are incorporated into a single polypeptide chain.

### Evolution of Genes of the Porphyrin Biosynthetic Chain

Having examined some properties of genes, let us see how these properties may be applied to an interpretation of the development of the porphyrin biosynthetic chain. Although answers require questions, hypotheses require facts. Many facts are unknown about this biosynthetic chain. None of the enzymes have been obtained in a crystalline form, and only some of the properties of the enzymes of the biosynthetic chain to heme have been studied. Yet because of the beauty and symmetry of the stepwise synthesis of the intermediates a pattern of evolution may be surmised more readily in this than in other biosynthetic chains (Fig. 3).

Let us review these steps briefly (14). The first product of this biosynthetic chain is built up of two simple, basic ubiquitous molecules, succinate and glycine, both of which are activated and then combined to form the straight-chain 5-carbon amine, δ-aminolevulinic acid (δALA). Then two of the δALA molecules are placed side by side and condensed to form a small five-membered pyrrole ring, called porphobilinogen

(PBG). Four of these pyrrole rings are fitted together to form a large tetrapyrrole ring, i.e., a reduced porphyrin; then the side chains on the outer portions of the porphyrin ring are trimmed and modified in a series of steps leading to chlorophyll.

Why did this biosynthetic chain proceed to evolve in such a manner once the cell found a way to form δALA? The earlier repetitive joining together of similar units, i.e., δALA and PBG, and the later successive stepwise modifications of the porphyrin ring suggest an evolution of the biosynthetic chain based primarily on the concept that genes are capable of duplicating and mutating.

Evolutionary relations are probably to be most readily found between adjacent structural genes of the same operon. The biosynthetic chain to heme possibly consists of three or more operons, as deduced from the amounts of enzymes formed and their distribution in the cell. The first operon codes for the enzyme δALA-synthetase, the second codes for the enzymes that convert δALA to coproporphyrinogen, and the third codes for the enzymes that convert coproporphyrinogen to heme. In the mammalian liver and in the chick embryo blastoderm, a suppressor mechanism for the operon of the first enzyme, δALA-synthetase, is postulated from the available data (12, 13). The amount of this enzyme appears to limit the rate of heme synthesis. In these tissues the enzymes converting δALA to coproporphyrinogen are only slightly repressed if at all, which suggests that they belong to another operon. The distribution of the enzymes of the heme biosynthetic chain inside and outside the mitochondria suggests three operons. The soluble enzymes that convert δALA to coproporphyrinogen are found outside the mitochondria, but the first and the last two enzymes to heme are found inside the mitochondria. Whether the enzymes found in the mitochondria are coded by mitochondrial DNA remains to be determined.

At first sight there appears to be no relation between the mold of the complicated enzyme that synthesizes δALA and the one that converts two δALA molecules to PBG. In the case of δALA-synthetase, two co-enzymes, CoA and pyridoxal-P, are required as well as two substrates, succinate and glycine. It is not known whether this enzyme consists of two separate polypeptide chains, i.e., coded by two genes, or whether the enzyme is a single polypeptide chain, one that may have been formed by juxtaposition of a gene coding for the CoA mold and the gene coding for the pyridoxal-P mold. What is of interest here is the finding by Shemin et al. (28) that δALA-synthetase is somewhat inhibited by its product δALA ($K_i = 0.05\ M$). This fact suggests that there is a "mold" for δALA in this enzyme.

The genes of the operon coding for the conversion of δALA to

COPROGEN may be derived from each other by repetition of moldons. For example, the enzyme to form PBG might be formed by the juxtaposition of two molds for δALA. In addition to an accurate placement of the molds, some amino acids would have to be changed to furnish a push-pull mechanism for dehydration. The next step, to convert 4PBG to a tetrahydroporphyrin (uroporphyrinogen isomer I), might come about by the juxtaposition of four moldons of the previous gene to form a porphyrinogen moldon; the resulting polypeptide then should have four times the molecular weight of the δALA-dehydrase polypeptide. On this enzyme there must be postulated at least one spot for deamination which will result in methane bridge formation between two pyrroles, perhaps catalyzed by the appropriate location of a basic and acidic amino acid. This enzyme and an additional one act in concert to form uroporphyrinogen isomer III.

Next let us examine the question: Why was isomer III selected out of the four possible isomers, not only for the synthesis of heme and chlorophyll but also for vitamin $B_{12}$? When PBG is heated in acid solution all four isomers are obtained. When PBG is heated in neutral or alkaline solution only isomers I and III are obtained. Let us consider the early time when the biosynthetic chain ended with the enzyme that formed PBG and the environment was slightly basic. PBG might spontaneously form small amounts of the I and III uroporphyrins. If these compounds represented an advantage to the cell, then an enzyme would be developed to do the job more efficiently. This leads to the question of whether there is a general tendency in evolution to select an enzyme to carry out a step that may take place spontaneously in neutral or alkaline but not in acid solution. In addition, is there selection for stability of compounds that are stable in neutral or alkaline rather than in acid solution, e.g., DNA? These events would follow from an evolution in a somewhat basic environment like that of sea water.

Why did the cell decide to use the III instead of the I isomer? It is possible that a "decision" was not made until the stage had been reached when coproporphyrinogen was converted to protoporphyrinogen and possibly reacted with apocytochrome $c$ peptide (27). One will have to await a detailed knowledge of how cytochrome $c$ functions in phosphorylation and electron transfer before the necessity for this particular linkage to the type III isomer is understood.

Once a moldon for porphyrinogen was produced, a subsequent mutation to the moldon for porphyrin with its flat rigid structure could be envisioned. Then slight successive modifications of the porphyrin moldon leading to chlorophyll were feasible.

## DNA in Cytoplasmic Organelles

Another major step in evolution appeared with the formation of specific membranes to surround the nucleus, the chloroplasts, and the mitochondria. This step marks an evolutionary development which separates the bacteria, including photosynthetic bacteria and the blue-green algae, from all other plants and animals. Along with this segregation went a DNA strand (9) to code for some as yet unknown materials specific for chloroplasts and for mitochondria, in part, possibly structural lipoproteins. It remains to be determined whether any of the genes of the heme-chlorophyll biosynthetic chain were incorporated into this DNA. Because there were multiple numbers of these DNA units per cell, mutations could occur in one or another unit and be carried along until a drastic environmental change selected for the mitochondria or plastids that best responded to the new environment.

In higher plants and animals the possibility of carrying along mutant genes in cytoplasmic organelles and in heterochromatin of the nucleus provided for a more rapid evolutionary development.

## An Example of the Recent Evolution of a Heme Enzyme and Its Control Mechanism

Some 400 million years ago, when fishlike creatures were hesitantly beginning to explore the land, a new heme enzyme arose in the microsomal fraction of the liver together with mechanisms to control the synthesis of this new enzyme. We became interested in this heme enzyme, "P-450," and its control in a roundabout way. For a number of years we have been trying to understand the human inherited disease called acute porphyria. In this disease the patient excretes large amounts of porphyrin precursors in the urine. Accompanying this disease are acute abdominal pains. Physicians who gave barbiturates to such patients found that instead of sedating the patient, the patient would become much worse. Later it was found that compounds like barbiturates, when given in large doses to animals, would also cause a porphyria to develop. In studies of this chemically induced porphyria we found that it was primarily the liver that was involved. In the normal liver the first enzyme of the heme biosynthetic chain is the one that makes δALA from succinyl-CoA and glycine (Fig. 3). The effect of the barbiturate was to derepress the control so that more of this enzyme (δALA-synthetase) was made—in fact, forty to one hundred times as much. Because this enzyme is the limiting one— all the other enzymes of the chain are present in adequate concentrations —the rate of porphyrin and heme synthesis in the liver is controlled by the amount of this first enzyme. Therefore a compound like a barbiturate will cause the first enzyme to increase in the liver, and more porphyrin and heme will be made (13).

What is the significance of making more heme in the liver? It is known that there is a microsomal heme enzyme, "P-450," in liver which requires TPNH and $O_2$ (22). This enzyme acts to hydroxylate benzene rings and to hydroxylate aliphatic chains—in general to hydroxylate foreign, relatively insoluble chemicals and drugs. The liver does this to make the drugs and chemicals more soluble so that they can be excreted by the kidney. This type of hydroxylation is one of the important mechanisms for the detoxication of foreign chemicals and drugs.

The excellent studies of Brodie and his co-workers at the National Institutes of Health (5) have shown that detoxication reactions of this kind are found in all mammals, birds, and reptiles, but not in fishes or certain amphibians. In fishes the gills serve as dialysis membranes to get rid of fatty foreign substances. In frogs the skin serves as such a dialysis membrane. When animals began to migrate onto land, they became encased in waterproof leathery skins to conserve water. At the same time they had to evolve mechanisms for removing unwanted lipid-soluble materials from the body. One detoxication mechanism which evolved was a mechanism to hydroxylate these chemicals and make them more soluble so that they could be discarded into the urine. For this purpose a new heme enzyme was invented, "P-450," which resided in the fatty membranes of the endoplasmic reticulum of the liver where the fatty foreign molecules concentrated on their arrival from the intestinal tract. To make this an efficient mechanism, the liver learned to react to foreign small chemicals, just as the plasma cells learned to respond to foreign proteins by generating antibodies. The liver responds to a barbiturate by making more of the microsomal heme enzyme, as Remmer has shown (25), and by making more δALA to make more heme for the heme enzyme, as we have shown (12).

Thus, 400 million years ago, the stage was set for twentieth-century man to cope with our age of chemicals and drugs. What a wonderful foresight.

## Summary and Conclusions

Several topics have been considered which relate to the development of the processes of photosynthesis and respiration and the evolution of heme and chlorophyll.

1. A photovoltaic mineral model is proposed that may convert the energy of sunlight into chemical energy. This photosynthetic unit would thus serve as a primitive powerhouse unit of preprotoplasm around which organic molecules would be formed. Such a model can be tested.

2. Uroporphyrin may represent the earliest organic photochemical catalyst. Further studies of its properties may give us an insight into the early beginnings of photosynthesis in protoplasm.

3. The progressive evolution of the porphyrin biosynthetic chain is considered to occur by duplication and mutation from each successive last gene of the chain. Some properties of evolving genes are examined and applied to an analysis of the genes of this chain.

4. In higher plants and animals the presence of multiple alleles in cytoplasmic organelles and in the heterochromatin of the nucleus suggests that mutations in these alleles may occur that will not greatly affect the physiologic balance; accumulation of these mutations may provide for a more rapid evolutionary development.

5. An example of the evolution of a heme enzyme with its controls is described, which developed when animals progressed onto the land.

These examples discussed from the viewpoint of evolutionary biology show the usefulness of such an approach. They also illustrate our naïveté. What each of us in his separate way has been trying to do in this Symposium, to develop the story of the evolution of genes and proteins, reminds me of the story of the five blind men of India who examined an elephant for the first time. One of their major problems, you will recall, was to recognize whether this creature had two tails or whether there was a true front end and which it was. Like them, each of us has a grasp of a few facts from which we attempt to infer the complete entity. We do not know the front end of the problem from the back end, i.e., whether life originated as a thin or thick soup, or made its own soup essentially from inorganic beginnings, nor whether the biosynthetic chain evolved in a backward or forward fashion, nor which came first, the proteins or the genes. Perhaps when we get more facts and surer interpretations we may be able to disentangle the tales in this problem. With this, I come to the end of my tale.

## Acknowledgments

I wish to acknowledge my gratitude to Dr. R. D. Levere, Dr. D. Mauzerall, and Dr. A. Gibor for their criticisms of this paper. This paper was supported in part by Research Grant GM-04922 from the Division of Research Grants and Fellowships, U.S. Public Health Service.

## References

1. ANDERS, E., Ann. N.Y. Acad. Sci., 108, 514 (1963).
2. BELLAMY, W. D., GAINES, G. L., AND TWEET, A. G., J. Chem. Phys., 39, 2528 (1963).
3. BONNER, D. M., SUYAMA, Y., AND DeMoss, J. A., Federation Proc., 19, 926 (1960).

4.  BRINK, R. A., *Am. Naturalist*, **98**, 193 (1964).
5.  BRODIE, B. B., AND MAICKEL, R. P., *Intern. Pharmacol. Meeting, 1st, Stockholm 1961*, Vol. 6, p. 299 (1962). Macmillan, New York.
6.  DOMBROWSKI, H., *Ann. N.Y. Acad. Sci.*, **108**, 453 (1963).
7.  FOWLER, W. A., GREENSTEIN, J. L., AND HOYLE, F., *Am. J. Phys.*, **29**, 393 (1961).
8.  GEWITZ, S., AND VOLKER, W., *Z. Naturforsch.*, **18b**, 649 (1963).
9.  GIBOR, A., AND GRANICK, S., *Science*, **45**, 890 (1964).
10. GRANICK, S., *Harvey Lectures*, **44**, 220 (1948-49).
11. GRANICK, S., *Ann. N.Y. Acad. Sci.*, **69**, 292 (1957).
12. GRANICK, S., *Proc. 9th Congr. European Soc. Haematol.*, *Lisbon*, Vol. VI, 596 (1963). Karger, Basel.
13. GRANICK, S., AND LEVERE, R. D., *Progr. Hematol.*, **4**, 1 (1964).
14. GRANICK, S., AND MAUZERALL, D., *in* "Metabolic Pathways" (D. Greenberg, ed.), Vol. II, p. 526, Academic Press, New York, 1960.
15. KAPLAN, J. R., DIGENS, E. T., AND REUTER, J. H., *Geochim. Cosmochim. Acta*, **27**, 805 (1963).
16. KATZ, J. J., CLOSS, G. L., PENNINGTON, F. C., THOMAS, M. R., AND STRAIN, H. H., *J. Am. Chem. Soc.*, **85**, 3801 (1963).
17. KAUFMAN, B., AND IDDLES, M., *Carnegie Inst. Wash. Year Book*, **47**, 153 (1947-48).
18. MASON, B., "Principles of Geochemistry," Wiley, New York, 1952.
19. MAUZERALL, D., *J. Am. Chem. Soc.*, **82**, 2601 (1960).
20. MAUZERALL, D., *J. Am. Chem. Soc.*, **84**, 2437 (1962).
21. MEINSCHEIN, W. G., BARGHOORN, E. S., AND SCHOPF, J. W., *Science*, **145**, 262 (1964).
22. OMURA, T., AND SATO, R., *J. Biol. Chem.* **239**, 2370 (1964).
23. ORO, J., *Ann. N.Y. Acad. Sci.*, **108**, 464 (1963).
24. RANKAMA, K., AND SAHAMA, T. G., *Geochemistry*, Univ. Chicago Press, Chicago, 1952.
25. REMMER, H., AND MERKER, H. J., *in* Evaluation of Mechanisms of Drug Toxicity. *Ann. N.Y. Acad. Sci.*, **123**, 79 (1965).
26. RUTTEN, M. G., "Geological Aspects of the Origin of Life on Earth," Elsevier, Amsterdam, 1962.
27. SANO, S., AND KAYUKO, T., *J. Biol. Chem.*, **PC239**, 3109 (1964).
28. SHEMIN, D., KIKUCHI, G., AND ABRAMSKY, T., *in* "Les Maladies du Metabolisme des Porphyrines," p. 173, Presses Univ. France, Paris, 1962.
29. Symposium on the "Life-Like Forms in Meteorites and the Problems of Environmental Control on the Morphology of Fossil and Recent Protobionta." *N.Y. Acad. Sci.*, **108**, 339-611 (1963).
30. Symposium on "Ferredoxin." *Abstr. 148th Meeting Am. Chem. Soc.*, *Chicago*, 14C-17C (1964).
31. WHIPPLE, F. L., *Proc. Natl. Acad. Sci. U.S.*, **52**, 565 (1964).
32. YANOFSKY, C., *in* "Cytodifferentiation and Macromolecular Synthesis" (M. Locke, ed.), p. 15, Academic Press, New York, 1963.
33. YOSHIDA, A., AND FREESE, E., *Abstr. 6th Intern. Congr. Biochem.*, New York, Vol. III, p. 69 (1964).

# Discussion of Part II

C. B. van Niel, J. O. Lampen, N. H. Horowitz, P. Siekevitz,
K. Bloch, H. Gest, O. E. Landman, R. Sager

Chairman van Niel: It seems to me that the last two papers should provide ample opportunity for discussions on various levels. Who would like to begin?

Dr. Lampen: Dr. Bloch has suggested that the polyenic antifungal antibiotics be used to remove sterol from the cell membrane and thus obtain some idea of the function of membrane sterols. Present information on the polyenes indicates that it is the combination of the antibiotic with the sterol of the membrane which is the critical damaging event, rather than any eventual loss of sterol from the membrane (which may not occur). The complexing of polyenic macrolide and sterol probably causes sufficient distortion and alteration of the membrane to disrupt various transport systems and eventually bring about leakage of critical metabolites (and death).

One would predict that the growth of yeast would be as sensitive under anaerobic as under aerobic conditions. Yeast requires exogenous sterol for anaerobic growth, and this sterol should be present in its membrane. The polyenes could presumably complex with this sterol in the usual fashion and kill the cell.

I should note that at least one bacterial species, a pleuropneumonia-like organism which requires sterol for growth, is inhibited by the polyenic antibiotics. Its relative sensitivity to the various polyenes is quite different, however, than that of yeast or other fungi. The organism seems to respond only to those polyenes which have a rather drastic action and cause rapid lysis, and not to those which have more specific effects on permeability. The role of the sterol in membrane structure may be less critical in PPLO than in yeast. Thus, the mere combination of polyene and membrane sterol might not be sufficient to damage the membrane significantly. Only those polyenes with detergent-like action would then be inhibitory.

Dr. Horowitz: I would like to comment briefly on Dr. Granick's mention of the recent paper by W. A. Fowler, J. L. Greenstein and F. Hoyle [*Am. J. Phys.*, **29**, 393 (1961)].

These authors proposed a new origin of the solar system in which, for theoretical reasons, they require that most of the hydrogen cloud was dissipated before the earth and the planets were actually formed.

As Dr. Granick pointed out, they envisioned the early stages consisting of clusters of planetesimals, objects of the order of a meter in size, which later aggregated to form the earth.

These authors suggest that the primary organic material on the earth was actually formed in this cloud before the earth was formed. As a matter of fact, they go on and suggest very hesitantly, being nonbiologists, that life itself may have originated before the earth was formed. This is a fascinating idea.

If their model is taken at face value, the primitive earth would not have had much free hydrogen in its atmosphere, but, as Stanley Miller and I have pointed out [N. H. Horowitz and S. L. Miller, *Fortschr. Chem. org. Naturstoffe,* **20**, 423 (1962)], one would expect that as the earth aggregated from the planetesimals, the organic matter that had accumulated in the planetesimals would have undergone decomposition due to the heating from the release of gravitational energy, and this decomposition would have formed a reducing atmosphere.

Another point I ought to mention about the Fowler model is that the water in the planetesimals was in the form of ice, not exactly a favorable condition for the origin of life. However, I would not want to be dogmatic about the events that occurred in an epoch that is totally beyond our recall.

Dr. SIEKEVITZ: I would like to ask a question of Dr. Bloch, namely, whether he implied that the presence of galactolipids in chloroplasts, of phospholipids in mitochondria, and of different kinds of fatty acids in chloroplasts and mitochondria signifies the syntheses of these components within the respective organelles. We do know in the case of the phospholipids that some of the enzymes involved in their synthesis are made in the microsome fraction; thus, it is possible that mitochondrial phospholipids are synthesized elsewhere and then deposited, as it were, in the mitochondria. This may be important because of the possibility that the mitochondria and chloroplasts, in view of their content of DNA, are self-replicating organelles.

Dr. BLOCH: The only information I am aware of is Neufeld's demonstration that galactolipids are synthesized in chloroplasts, and not in the soluble cytoplasm. I am not familiar with the various partial reactions in phospholipid synthesis, but I would agree that certainly the mitochondrion is not autonomous in this respect.

Dr. GEST: I would like to make a few comments on the iron protein ferredoxin, that Dr. Granick mentioned in his talk.

First of all, I think it is worth while reminding the audience that the general function of this protein in photosynthetic electron transfer was mainly elucidated by the work of San Pietro in this country and by Hill in England, who called the protein by different names. The protein was isolated from green plants and characterized before ferredoxin was discovered in microorganisms.

The second point concerns the fact that one nowadays sees schemes in which the same type of protein is implicated as an electron carrier in the formation of molecular hydrogen in photosynthetic systems. As far as we know, green plants do not make molecular hydrogen, whereas a number of photosynthetic bacteria do.

The difficulty with ascribing a role to ferredoxin in the bacterial process is that some photosynthetic bacteria, such as *Rhodospirillum rubrum*, which make enormous quantities of hydrogen photochemically, do not appear to contain ferredoxin, at least as far as Bose and I have been able to determine. I think a number of other investigators have also failed to find significant amounts of this protein in *Rhodospirillum*.

On the other hand, certain other photosynthetic bacteria, such as *Chromatium*, do contain ferredoxin. Recent work in Dr. Fuller's laboratory at Dartmouth, however, indicates quite clearly that *Chromatium* is able to make hydrogen by a dark process using pyruvic acid as the substrate. Apparently, the ferredoxin participates as an electron carrier in the decomposition of pyruvate to molecular hydrogen and other products, and so this system seems to be very similar to the one that occurs in clostridia and certain other nonphotosynthetic bacteria.

DR. LANDMAN: I wanted to comment on Dr. Bloch's statement that procaryotes do not have any internal membrane systems. I think that idea is based on older work, but in more recent times, electron microscopists who examine thin sections of bacteria find very extensive internal membrane systems. These systems are easily detected in Gram-positive bacteria (reviewed by W. Van Iterson, in "Recent Progress in Microbiology," N. E. Gibbons, ed., University of Toronto Press, 1963). They can also be found in Gram-negative bacteria when special techniques of cell breakage are used, and the broken cells are sectioned [S. A. Robrisch and A. G. Marr, *J. Bacteriol.*, **83**, 158 (1962)]. The idea that there are no internal membrane systems in procaryotes must therefore be revised. I think this does not detract at all from the notion that the membranes of procaryotes are chemically, and possibly functionally, quite different from those of higher organisms.

DR. SAGER: I wanted to ask you, Dr. Bloch, whether you have had an opportunity to examine any of the green algae which are blocked in the Hill reaction, that is, presumably in the oxygen release mechanism. Mutants of *Chlamydomonas* and of *Scenedesmus* have been reported of this type, but so far it has been very difficult to pinpoint the position of the mutant block. I was wondering whether linolenic acid had been looked for in these strains.

DR. BLOCH: We have looked at various Hill-less mutants of *Scenedesmus* and *Chlamydomonas* and have found some quantitative but no qualitative differences between mutants and wild-type cells.

CHAIRMAN VAN NIEL: Are there any further questions? If not, I would like to thank the speakers at this point in the program.

PART III

# EVOLUTION OF PROTEINS I

# Chairman's Remarks

## CHRISTIAN B. ANFINSEN

*National Institute of Arthritis and Metabolic Diseases,*
*National Institutes of Health,*
*Bethesda, Maryland*

Since we have a fairly tight schedule this afternoon, we might as well get under way. We shall discuss, this afternoon, the evolution of proteins. I'm sure some of the evolutionists will object to that title. Evolution as reflected in changes in the structure of proteins is perhaps more accurate.

# Evolutionary Divergence and Convergence in Proteins

EMILE ZUCKERKANDL

*Laboratoire de Physico-Chimie Colloidale du C. N. R. S.,*
*Montpellier, France*

AND

LINUS PAULING

*California Institute of Technology,*
*Pasadena, California*

## I. THE MOLECULAR APPROACH TO THE ANALYSIS OF THE EVOLUTIONARY PROCESS

Exponents of chemical paleogenetics have been faced at the present meeting by two disapproving scientific communities, the organismal evolutionists and taxonomists on the one hand, and some pure (very unorganismal) biochemists on the other hand. Some of the biochemists point out, or imply, that the interest in the biochemical foundation of evolutionary relationships between organisms is a second-rate interest. According to them (and to us), what most counts in the life sciences today is the uncovering of the molecular mechanisms that underly the observations of classical biology.

The concept of mechanism should, however, not be applied exclusively to short-timed processes. The type of molecules that have been called informational macromolecules (68) or semantides (75) (DNA, RNA, proteins) has a unique role in determining the properties of living matter in each of three perspectives that differ by the magnitude of time required for the processes involved. These processes are the short-timed biochemical reaction, the medium-timed ontogenetic event, and the long-timed evolutionary event. Although the slower processes must be broken down into linked faster processes, if one loses sight of the slower processes one also loses the links between the component faster processes.

Why are semantides to play a privileged role in the understanding of living matter? For Simpson (60), "the most truly causative element in the adaptive system" is to be located at the organismal level. There may be no such thing as the most truly causative element. Yet there is no greater concentration of causal factors than in informational macromolecules. There is indeed no greater concentration of information. Here the concept of information replaces to advantage the concept of cause, since it is a better tool in the analysis of reality.

An organism is, by virtue of its genome, what one might call an informostat, by analogy with a chemostat or a thermostat. It keeps nearly constant the information that it contains and that it passes on. Its main memory banks are those polynucleotides that are capable of self-duplication. In order to accept the special importance of the analysis of informational macromolecules, it is sufficient to subscribe to the following propositions: (a) The level of biological integration that contains the greatest concentration of "causal factors" will further our understanding of life more than any other. (b) A concentration of information is a concentration of "causal factors." (c) The largest concentration of information present in an organism, and perhaps also the largest amount of information, and the only organically transmissible information, is in its semantides.

This last proposition has been discussed elsewhere (75) and will not be re-examined here. It suggests the decisive importance of studying all processes of life at the level of their macromolecular foundation, including long-timed processes (evolution). It also suggests that semantides are potentially the most informative taxonomic characters and not, as has been contended at this meeting, just one type of characters among other, equivalent types.

No organism would be apprehended as such if it were not for the nontransient character (through survival or reproduction) of a certain, complex constellation of traits whereby it is defined. The factors of constancy that define the organism as a nontransient organization are all in the informational macromolecules, and in that sense the essence of the organism is there and not at any level of the environment of these molecules.

Since taxonomy tends, ideally, not toward just any type of convenient classification of living forms (in spite of a statement to the contrary made at this meeting), but toward a phyletic classification, and since the comparison of the structure of homologous informational macromolecules allows the establishment of phylogenetic relationships, studies of chemical paleogenetics have a bearing on taxonomy. The taxonomic competence of this nascent discipline is, in fact, only a by-product in relation to the main concern, which is not a classification of organisms, but is the modes of macromolecular transformations retained by evolution, types of changes in their information content, consequences of these changes for molecular function and for the organism as a whole, and the history of evolution as seen from these points of view. The evidence with a specifically taxonomic bearing, in the phyletic sense, that is to be derived from studies in chemical paleogenetics has been considered by some biochemists as uninteresting. It has the measure of interest one is willing to grant to progress in knowledge of the biochemical nature of extinct organisms, progress in knowledge of the course evolution has actually taken at a particularly important level of biological integration, and progress in the as yet nonexistent knowledge about phases of evolution that have left no trace among fossils. Certainly we cannot subscribe to the statement made at this meeting by a renowned biochemist that comparative structural studies of polypeptides can teach us nothing about evolution that we don't already know.

It is more important to understand the general than the particular, but the first is achieved only through the second. By what precise channels of molecular transformations evolution probably proceeded on earth is indeed particular (and at the same time only one of the possible achievements of chemical paleogenetics). The full value of this type of knowledge will be apparent only if and when terrestrial evolution can be compared with evolution on other planets and organic evolutions become a class of phenomena to which general laws will apply. Only then, presumably, will it become known whether certain general trends of anagenesis (progressive evolution), such as the appearance of central nervous systems and of their higher stages of development, occasionally culminating in hominoids, are in their essential features the necessary result of a relatively small number of definable factors (as we believe on the basis of the numerous cases of independent parallel evolution on earth), or the result of such a large number of accidents that, for all practical purposes, the trend is not expected to be reproducible (Simpson, 61; Dobzhansky, 15).

The relative importance of the contributions to evolution of changes in functional properties of polypeptides through their structural modification on the one hand, and of changes in the timing and the rate of synthesis of these polypeptides on the other hand, constitutes a further important problem that in itself would justify the study of evolution at the level of informational macromolecules. The evaluation of the amount of differences between two organisms as derived from sequences in structural genes or in their polypeptide translation is likely to lead to quantities different from those obtained on the basis of observations made at any other, higher level of biological integration. On the one hand some differences in the structural genes will not be reflected elsewhere in the organism, and on the other hand some differences noted by the organismal biologist may not be reflected in structural genes. The first propositon should hold on account of the degeneracy of the genetic code (Zuckerkandl and Pauling, 75; see also Itano, 34, and, especially, T. Sonneborn, this volume); the second proposition—concerning the existence of phenotypic differences not reflected in the base sequence of structural genes—should hold if all regulator genes are not at the same time structural genes active in putting out a metabolically functional polypeptide product. Many phenotypic differences may be the result of changes in the patterns of timing and rate of activity of structural genes rather than of changes in functional properties of the polypeptides as a result of changes in amino acid sequence (69). Consequently, two organisms may be phenotypically more different than they are on the basis of the amino acid sequences of their polypeptide chains, and they may be phenotypically less different than they are on the basis of the base sequence of their structural genes. Quantitatively, prominent enzymes and structural proteins that are likely to be investigated from the point of view of their amino acid sequences may not, as a rule, be controlled by structural genes that are at the same time regulator genes in relation to other structural genes. If this supposition is correct, the compounded results of sequence studies in polypeptides will give a measure of phyletic distance that is unique in kind. The type of measure of differences at the polypeptide level will take into account basic constituents of the organism only, whereas other types of measure, at higher levels of biological integration, will include modifications in the interaction patterns between these constituents. By subtraction, an evaluation of the contribution of the latter processes to the over-all difference between two organisms may be possible. If no significant difference is found, the implication is that most structural genes are also controller genes, and that amino acid substitution in one type of polypeptide chain is in general reflected by changes in rate or period of synthesis of other polypeptide chains.

Another justification for putting time and effort into comparative structural studies of homologous polypeptide chains was quoted at this meeting as though in opposition to the perspective we are developing here, namely the interest to correlate differences in amino acid sequence with differences in physicochemical, functional properties of a given type of protein. Of the primary importance of such studies we have, of course, been fully aware (49, 75); efforts in that direction have led to results of which a few have already been published (72), and others are included in this article. By furnishing probable structures of ancestral proteins, chemical paleogenetics will in the future lead to deductions concerning molecular functions as they were presumably carried out in the distant evolutionary past. Progress in laboratory methods of polypeptide synthesis, already partly accomplished, will permit the study of the functional properties of ancestral polypeptide chains directly.

There is yet an ultimate reason, of a more philosophical nature, for interest in the paleogenetic approach. Whereas the time dependence of evolutionary transformations at the molecular level (see Section III) can be established only by reference to extraneous sources, the topology of branching of molecular phylogenetic trees should in principle be definable in terms of molecular information alone. It will be determined to what extent the phylogenetic tree, as derived from molecular data in complete independence from the results of organismal biology, coincides with the phylogenetic tree constructed on the basis of organismal biology. If the two phylogenetic trees are mostly in agreement with respect to the topology of branching, the best available single proof of the reality of macro-evolution would be furnished. Indeed, only the theory of evolution, combined with the realization that events at any supramolecular level are consistent with molecular events, could reasonably account for such a congruence between lines of evidence obtained independently, namely amino acid sequences of homologous polypeptide chains on the one hand, and the findings of organismal taxonomy and paleontology on the other hand. Besides offering an intellectual satisfaction to some, the advertising of such evidence would of course amount to beating a dead horse. Some beating of dead horses may be ethical, when here and there they display unexpected twitches that look like life.

Simpson (60) believes that, for studying affinities between organisms, characters that are far removed from the genes are better than characters of the genes themselves or of the closely related polypeptide chains. By a character that is "far from the genes" one is apparently to understand a character that is determined by the interaction of numerous genes, with the implicit specification that the consequences of this interaction are apprehended at a high level of biological integration. It seems to us, however, that this specification is not really relevant to establishing a difference between the effect of the action of numerous genes and the effect of the action of a single gene. The cellular, tissular, systemic, organismal consequences of a single gene mutation are also "far removed" from the gene. The "length of the functional chain from the genes to the character selected for or against" (Simpson, 60) is always considerable, for instance from the structural change in the single gene responsible for phenylketonuria to the feeble-mindedness of the affected individual. Furthermore, although characters observed by the organismal biologist are determined by many genes at a time, any *change* in such characters is presumably determined by discrete single gene mutations, and it is on such *changes* that natural selection is expected to act. The effect of natural selection should therefore be correlated, not exceptionally, as Simpson proposes, but generally, with single mutations in single genes. Evidently, the further we are from the gene, the better we usually understand why selection occurred, since the function of the gene is definable only in terms of the interaction of direct and indirect products of the gene with direct and indirect products of other genes and with factors from the environment of the organism. At the level of the individual gene itself we find no basis for selection, since we find no basis for defining function. Selection occurs wherever function occurs. Although it is in the nature of function to be understood in terms of events at a lower level of integration in relation to events at a higher level, this fact seems to have little bearing on the question whether, in living matter, there is any level of organization as informative for tracing phyletic affinities as that of the informational macromolecules.

To the extent to which differences in gene regulation are not reflected in amino acid sequences of polypeptides, the analysis of levels "far from the gene" provides information that is not to be obtained at a level as close to the gene as that of the polypeptides. If so, the reason, in this case, is that the polypeptide level is not quite close enough to the gene. It is almost unavoidable to postulate that differences in gene regulation must correspond to differences in nucleotide sequences in self-duplicating polynucleotides, or in the order along the genetic chromosomal or extrachromosal units of the functional subunits—again a matter of sequence.

Although we disagree with some of the views put forward by Simpson in his recent article (60), the ability of this author to state important issues in clear terms offers rewarding opportunities for thought and discussion. A further objection of organismal "evolutionists" to chemical paleogenetics will be dealt with in Section III.

## II. Patterns of Amino Acid Substitution

Various aspects of this topic have been examined by others, notably by Šorm and his group (64), by Lanni (39), and by Pattee (48). In the present treatment we shall examine some effects of divergent evolution on the amino acid sequence of a number of homologous globin chains. We make the likely assumption that, except in regions of the molecule where the comparison between the chains reveals a deletion or an addition, the differences noted are attributable to successive single amino acid substitutions. The globin chains whose amino acid sequence has been available to us in whole or in part are the sperm whale myoglobin chain (58),[1] the human myoglobin chain (23), the human hemoglobin

---

[1] The sequence of sperm whale myoglobin used is one that was kindly com-

α, β, γ, and δ chains (58, 22), the horse α and β chains (12, 62), the cattle α and β chains (53, 3), the cattle fetal chain (3), the pig α and β chains (10), various Primate β chains (24), the gorilla α and β chains (76, 77), the carp "α" chain (11), and a lamprey hemoglobin chain (52).

The different residues are so numbered that homologous residues in different chains carry the same numbers. The numbering system used is that introduced by Kendrew et al. (cf. Cullis et al., 13). Capital letters refer to helical regions, and pairs of capital letters refer to regions between the corresponding helices. The general use of this numbering system, although perhaps not strictly rational, since the system applies specifically to the sperm whale myoglobin chain, allows one to visualize easily the region of the molecule in which a given residue is located. Abbreviations are used as by Cullis et al. (13), except that asn stands for asparagine, glm for glutamine, and ilu for isoleucine.

### 1. Invariant Molecular Sites

Until very recently it seemed that 16 homologous sites of hemoglobins and myoglobins were strictly invariant. This figure, which represents about 11% of the total number of residues per polypeptide chain of this type, had already been decreased in the light of new information on amino acid sequences in comparison to the figure of 13% given earlier (69). The sequence analysis of the cattle fetal chain by Drs. Donald Babin and W. A. Schroeder (3) has removed one further residue from the list of the invariant ones (phe in the cattle chain instead of try at position A12), and the partial sequence analysis of a lamprey hemoglobin chain by Drs. V. Rudloff and G. Braunitzer (52) has removed four further residues from this list (in the lamprey chain, lys instead of arg at B12; met instead of leu at CD7; arg instead of lys at E5; ilu instead of val at E11). At this writing we are left with 11 invariant sites in hemoglobin and myoglobin polypeptide chains, representing about 8% of the total number of sites.

One may wonder how far this progressive shrinkage of the number of apparent invariant sites will eventually go. It is unlikely that this number will decrease to zero, because it is unlikely that the function of hemoglobin and myoglobin can be maintained if the iron atom of the heme is linked to a residue other than histidyl. But the "final" number of invariant residues may indeed turn out to be 1 or 2. Not even in the immediate environment of the heme group is invariance assured any

---

municated to us by Dr. L. Stryer in March 1964 as including that latest corrections made by Drs. Edmundson and Kendrew. This sequence is not always identical as to the nature of the residues and the exact location of helical sections with the sequence published by Dr. Perutz in his book in 1962 (50).

longer. At the writing of Kendrew's 1963 article (38), of 11 residues of globin that interact with the heme group, 8 appeared invariant on the basis of the information available to him. At present the count is reduced to 4, one of which is the so-called proximal histidine, the one to which the iron atom is linked. Another of these residues that still appears invariant evolutionarily, the so-called distal histidine, situated at the opposite site of the heme group, has been shown to be substituted in a functional, although somewhat unstable, abnormal human hemoglobin, Hb Zurich (44). It is not very probable, but possible, that arginine will be found at this site in some normal globin, i.e., one that has become widespread in a species by natural selection. The two remaining invariant residues in contact with the heme group are C4 (threonine) and CD1 (phenylalanine). The threonine is shown by Kendrew to interact with one of the vinyl groups of heme, and the phenylalanine with one of the pyrrole rings. The residue that interacts with the other vinyl side chain (H14) and the two residues (FG5 and E11) that interact each with one other pyrrole ring (the fourth pyrrole ring is not reported to be in contact with any amino acid residue) all have been shown to be variant residues. Consequently, the two remaining invariant residues may also eventually be found to be substituted in some hemoglobin or myoglobin chain that is distantly related to the one whose sequence is presently known.

The other remaining invariant sites in the polypeptide chains are A14 (lys), B6 (gly), B10 (leu), C2 (pro), GH5 (phe), H9 (lys), and H22 (tyr). At A14, valine is substituted by aspartic acid in the α chain of the abnormal human hemoglobin I (45). Even though the substitution is probably an unfavorable one in man (a HbI homozygote has not yet been found, and therefore the "seriousness" of the condition in man cannot be evaluated), HbI is recognizable as a functional hemoglobin. It is therefore not unlikely that a substitution at site A14 will be found to occur in some as yet unknown normal hemoglobin or myoglobin. The invariant glycyl residue at position B6 has been shown by Kendrew and his collaborators to interact with another glycyl at position E8. The two glycyls meet at a point of crossing between two helices, the helices B and E. It has been surmised by some that the invariance of these glycyl residues is critical for the structure of hemoglobins and myoglobins, since any other residue at these sites would not permit an equally short contact between the two helical segments. It has, however, turned out that the glycine at E8 is replaced by alanine in the cattle α chain and in a lamprey hemoglobin chain. Consequently it is also possible that the glycine at position B6 will be found to be replaced by alanine in some forms.

It is worth noting that the majority of the remaining "invariant" residues in globin chains—namely those that appear evolutionarily invariant—are neutral. This is especially the case if we do not consider the two histidines at E7 and F8, which have special functional roles, with respect not to the general structure of the globin, but to the property of reversible oxygenation of the heme iron. In that case we count 8 neutral residues out of 9, and of these 8, 6 are apolar. As will be mentioned again later, at sites where charged residues occur replacements are found more frequently than at sites where apparently only apolar residues occur. Over and above the sites that appear to be invariant in both hemoglobins and myoglobins, we count at present 15 sites that are invariant in hemoglobin chains only. This brings the total number of invariant sites, for the hemoglobins alone, to 26, a figure that will no doubt decrease further. Of the 15 sites mentioned, 12 are apolar (E4, FG5, G2, G5, G7, G8, G12, G17, H1, H5, H14, H18), 1 is polar and noncharged (F5), and 2 are charged (EF3, G1). Of the nonpolar residues only one, the residue at G17, is found to be replaced by a different type of residue, namely a charged residue, in a myoglobin chain.

Even when a residue is seen to remain strictly invariant in forms very far removed from each other on the evolutionary scale, it cannot be deduced from such an observation that none of the other nineteen amino acids would be compatible with the maintenance of the functional properties of the molecule. It is possible, in particular, that some favorable substituent cannot be reached through a single mutational step, nor through two steps one of which represents an isosemantic substitution (74). Any of the possible intermediate substituents may be unfavorable. Furthermore, some residues may remain invariant, not because they are intrinsically necessary, but because any change would have to be coordinated immediately with one or more changes in other parts of the molecule. For example, residue H22 (tyrosine) is known to interact (13) with residue FG5 (valine or isoleucine). This interaction may be critical for keeping helix H in position and for assuring the stability of the whole molecule. Conceivably, two or more simultaneous changes would be required here to reach a different, functionally satisfactory state. The time allotted to evolution on earth may not be long enough for such an event to occur. This consideration is of some consequence in relation to the problem of molecular convergence (cf. Section V). It is remarkable that most globin residues can presumably be changed—sometimes, as we shall see, only within narrow limits—without any simultaneous adjustments in other parts of the molecule. The question is often asked why only twenty different amino acids are provided for proteins by the genetic code, since sixty-four different triplet code words are available, and many more than twenty different amino acids are produced metabolically. Without going into a discussion of this question here, we may note that, in the case of most globin sites, more different amino acids appear to be coded for than are necessary for achieving a certain molecular function.

The residues common to all known globin chains are unlikely to be engaged in specific interactions between polypeptide chains, since the vertebrate myoglobins exist as single chains. These residues should rather be instrumental in intrachain stabilization, i.e., in the stabilization of the tertiary rather than of the quaternary structure, or in allowing the heme to carry out its basic function. We saw that only one or two residues may play this latter role, and that the number of the other invariant residues may eventually decrease to zero or to a very small number. This means that no, or almost no, amino acid residue is specifically needed for stabilizing a given tertiary structure. Conversely, if absolute invariance is observed, on the basis of what is becoming apparent in the case of the globin chains it would seem that this invariance, in most instances, is probably not necessary for the stabilization of the tertiary structure of the polypeptide. This statement may be valid also for proteins with little or no helical content, since in hemoglobins and myoglobins the amino acid sequence in interhelical regions is also highly variable. The progressive shrinkage of the number of invariant sites in globin chains brings into relief the fact, first strongly suggested by a comparison of myoglobin and hemoglobin polypeptide chains (50), that what function is associated with and what nature selects for is a tertiary more than a primary structure. A restriction to this statement will be discussed in the next subsection. The fact is that most interactions between helices and most sequential devices for stabilizing nonhelical regions are not strictly linked to the presence of one unique amino acid residue at one unique site.

These observations on globin structure are spectacularly at variance with observations on the primary structure of cytochromes c. In these cytochromes about 50% of the residues seem to have remained evolutionarily immutable since the time of the common ancestor of yeast and man (41). The question arises whether this difference with the globins is due to the presence in cytochrome c of a large proportion of residues of intrinsic absolute evolutionary stability, while the remaining residues change evolutionarily at a rate comparable with the rate of evolutionary change in hemoglobins; or whether in cytochromes c evolutionary changes are so slow throughout the molecule that the time elapsed between the epoch of the common ancestor of man and yeast and the present, although enormous (presumably 1 to 2 billion years), is insufficient for a high percentage of the residues to be substituted.

If we compare human polypeptide chains with the corresponding chains in horse, cattle, pig, and rabbit we find, on the average, 22 differences between the adult major component hemoglobin chains (cf. Section III.4) and 10 differences between the cytochromes $c$. These figures represent, respectively, 15% and 10% of the total numbers of residues in the chains. Thus in mammalian evolutionary history the difference in rate of change of the two types of proteins seems to have been small. This difference can be totally eliminated if, on the basis of available information, certain plausible assumptions are made about the number of strictly invariant residues in tetrahemic hemoglobins and in cytochromes $c$, and if the number of changed residues is related to the probable number of changeable residues rather than to the total number of residues.

If no such assumptions are made, the application of the quantitative relation to be described in Section III of this article to the case of cytochrome $c$ leads to an unacceptable value for yeast. The common ancestor of yeast and man appears at an epoch that is implausibly recent. In other words, during a plausible span of time too few residues have been changed in cytochrome $c$. This incongruence encourages one, in answer to the question formulated above, to assume the absolute evolutionary immutability of an important proportion of residues in cytochrome $c$.

It has been proposed that the observed invariance could be due to the presence of mutational "cold spots," to a local lack of mutability of the genic DNA. According to this tentative interpretation the mutation rate would be the limiting factor in the rate of evolutionarily effective mutations. This is very unlikely. If a reasonable value of total mutation rate and of interbreeding population size is assumed, one finds that the probable number of mutations per amino acid site and per line of descent is far larger (by 100 to 1000 times) than the average number of evolutionarily effective mutations that show up in the hemoglobin $\alpha$ chain–non-$\alpha$ chain comparison. This should apply to proteins generally, at least in organisms with a generation time up to an order of magnitude of one year. Furthermore, from what is now known about globin chains, it is certain that 94% of the coding triplets are mutable. This percentage is slightly higher than would correspond to the 8% evolutionarily unchangeable polypeptide sites referred to earlier. Indeed, although the replacement of the "proximal" and "distal" histidines (E7 and F8) has never been evolutionarily effective, so far as we know, these residues have been found to be replaced through point mutation in abnormal human hemoglobins: Hb $M_{Boston}$, Hb $M_{Emory}$ (20), Hb Zurich (44), Hb $M_{Kankakee}$ (35). Another evolutionarily "unchangeable" residue has been replaced in the abnormal human hemoglobin I, as already mentioned. This reduces the possibly immutable sites to 8, i.e., to 6% of the molecule. There is reason to think that the apparent absolute stability of 6% of the coding triplets is caused not by the absence of mutation but by the action of natural selection. It is not plausible that a small number of base triplets, known to make sense in terms of an amino acid, and scattered over the molecule, should radically differ in mutational behavior from the overwhelming majority of triplets. Moreover, a very slow rate of evolutionarily effective substitutions at certain molecular sites does not imply a slow mutation rate. In hemoglobins and myoglobins, at molecular sites that are substituted very rarely during evolutionary history, substituents are nearly exclusively confined to functionally closely similar residues. It is true that according to Eck's proposal for a complete genetic code nearly all transitions between functionally closely related amino acids can be brought about by one single mutational step. This fact could be quoted as evidence in favor of the plausible hypothesis that the genetic code, as it stands today, was evolved at early times of the history of life through the action of natural selection. The evidence cannot at present be so construed, because Eck's code was based in part on considerations of functional similarity between amino acids, so that there would be an element of circularity in this reasoning. One must await the establishment of a definitive complete code before settling this matter. However, even if the present impression should then be confirmed, namely that indeed the code provides one-step transitions between functionally related amino acids by a statistically significant bias, this would not mean that other one-step transitions do not also occur. It would be unreasonable to assume that, at highly but not absolutely invariant molecular sites, only those transitions occur that are evolutionarily effective and actually observed, namely between functionally closely related amino acids. We conclude that there is no reason to suppose that, in hemoglobins and myoglobins the residues that are only rarely substituted successfully during evolution undergo, on the average, fewer mutational changes, including the evolutionarily noneffective ones, than the residues that are changed during evolution with a relatively high frequency. Mutational hot spots and cold spots may exist, but the relative frequency of evolutionarily effective substitutions at different molecular sites gives no clue as to the distribution of such hot spots and cold spots. From the evidence that has become available, it seems highly unlikely that any cold spot in globin genes is cold enough to prevent mutational changes altogether during the time allotted to evolution.

There is no reason to assume that mutation rates in cytochromes should differ radically from those that obtain in globins, in that one half of the residues represent cold spots so icy that no mutations occur at all, whereas the other half of the residues mutate at a normal rate. The improbability of such a view is obvious.

How is the high resistance to evolutionarily effective mutation of part of the cytochrome c molecule to be explained? A decrease in the rate of evolutionarily effective substitutions may be brought about by the aging of the molecule: the phase of the most active molecular transformation is expected to be the incipient phase, just after a polypeptide chain has become established in a new function (49). Cytochrome c may have gone through this phase even before the epoch of the common ancestor of yeast and man. However, the type of stability obtained through the aging of a molecule should not be absolute. Conservative (41) (= isogenetic, ref. 72) evolutionarily effective mutations are expected to occur occasionally within the limits of relative evolutionary stability (cf. Section III). Such conservative substitutions are found in cytochrome c at most of the changeable molecular sites (see Section II.3). Their occurrence does not indicate that, at these changeable sites, cytochrome c has not yet reached its optimal state in relation to any given set of circumstances. If the substitution is strictly indifferent, a shift between closely related residues may nevertheless spread in the population through genetic drift. The assumed indifference of the substitution implies, in that case, a satisfactory adaptation of the original residue to molecular function, because an identical degree of inadaptation of two residues is unlikely to occur. Alternatively, one may assume that the substitution of one residue by another even closely related one never has a selective value of exactly zero. In that case the occurrence of either one of two closely related residues in different lines of descent suggests that each of the residues is better adapted than the other to certain conditions of the external and internal environment of different organisms. In each form the best-adapted residue presumably occurs, and the observed variation is again compatible with satisfactory molecular adaptation in any given set of circumstances. The apparent absence of substitutions from nearly one-half of the molecular sites of cytochrome c cannot be taken as evidence for stability obtained through progressively improved adaptation in the course of evolution, if the presence of conservative substitutions at other sites is, at any given time, compatible with a fully adapted state. The measure of stability in amino acid sequence that one may expect to be reached by virtue of a relatively rapid phase of initial molecular adaptation should not be absolute.

Absolute stability can hardly be attributed to evolutionary old age of the molecule. It should more probably be due to very stringent functional requirements.

What type of stringent functional requirement in relation to numerous molecular sites can one conceive for cytochrome $c$ that does not also obtain for hemoglobins and myoglobins? This question is being discussed by Margoliash and Smith in their contribution to this volume. As these authors point out, by analogy with globins, one would expect that few, if any, residues are absolutely required for the maintenance of a given tertiary structure. To be sure, a larger number of residues than in globins, where it is perhaps 1 or 2, may be required for preserving the basic functional properties of the cytochromes. On the other hand, from what is known today about the structure–function relationship in proteins it is not to be expected that the absolute stability of a large number of residues is required for maintaining the basic functional properties of a prosthetic group or of an active site. The most plausible explanation of absolute stability over and above that of the residues associated with the prosthetic group or the active site might be restrictions imposed on structural variation by specific interactions between molecules or molecular subunits. This effect, which may be called the Ingram effect (32; cf. Section III), is expected to lead to complete structural invariance of a section of a polypeptide chain only if the interacting molecule is itself invariant, or if the number of variable interacting molecules is sufficiently large. The stable sites of cytochrome that are not concerned in preserving the basic function of the prosthetic group may be required to interact with several other macromolecules or (Margoliash and Smith, this volume) with some evolutionarily invariant organic molecule such as a coenzyme. Alternatively, the stable regions not directly associated with the prosthetic group may be required to interact with a single type of macromolecule, which, however, is in turn required to interact with a number of others. This latter situation might obtain for the cytochromes because of their association with a cellular organelle, the mitochondrion. As was also mentioned independently by a participant at the present meeting, requirements for the stability of the primary structure of a polypeptide may not be the same for proteins that are normally in free solution and proteins associated with cellular organelles. Surface structures that reversibly interact with soluble proteins in such organelles may display a high structural constancy. If so, the interacting regions on the soluble proteins should be equally invariant. If this consideration applies to cytochrome $c$, the stable sequences should be found at the outside of the molecule, or in parts that move to the outside if the molecule becomes reversibly bound and perhaps reversibly denatured within the mitochondrion. It will be of interest to see whether some of the stable sequences in cytochrome $c$ are found again in other mitochondrial enzymes.

One further suggestion may be made tentatively. The reduced form of cytochrome $c$ is completely resistant to proteolysis, whereas the oxidized form is susceptible to attack by proteolytic enzymes (40a, 63). This observation suggests that oxidation and reduction are accompanied by an intramolecular rearrangement. Since cytochrome $c$ contains one polypeptide chain per molecule, the rearrangement could not be compared to the one that is observed upon oxygenation and deoxygenation in hemoglobins (43), which seems to be primarily one in quaternary structure. For cytochrome $c$ a probable change in tertiary structure may be inferred. The cytochrome polypeptide chain should therefore have well-defined kinetic properties for the conformational rearrangement to occur properly, and some severe restrictions may thus be imposed on sequence. This hypothetical feature of cytochrome $c$ might in particular explain the evolutionary stability of some of the glycine residues, if reversible bending movements have to occur in some nonhelical regions of the molecule. At certain sites any residue other than glycine might be in the way of such movements of the main chain.

Whatever the reason for the stability of one-half of the cytochrome $c$ molecule, it helps one realize how exceedingly old proteins, and therefore structural genes, may be. It is possible that this will be found to apply to a large proportion of the proteins, including the globins, and that living matter has changed less in the last 1 to 2 billion years than morphological comparisons suggest. No doubt biochemical evolution has added new proteins to old ones and has, in the process, dispensed with some of the latter. But a significant proportion of the oldest proteins and genes may have been preserved, if we consider as oldest, in relation to life as we know it today, an epoch not much further removed in time than that of the common ancestor of yeast and man.

## 2. Variable Molecular Sites

What is called the evolution of a given type of protein molecule amounts in general to the introduction of the greatest structural changes compatible with the smallest functional changes. It seems that the greatest functionally tolerable changes in tertiary structure are small, whereas the greatest tolerable changes in primary structure will affect, according to the type of protein, part of the molecule or its near totality.

The different types of mutational changes that may occur in proteins have often been enumerated. Deletions or additions of one to several amino acid residues are expected to be eliminated by natural selection in a high proportion of cases. Those that are preserved should be mostly found at either end of a chain, at the end of helices, in short helices, or in nonhelical regions, notably in loops that may be shortened or lengthened without affecting the steric relationships in the rest of the molecule. A deletion or addition in the middle of a long helix would result in so many simultaneous alterations in side-chain interactions that it is highly unlikely that the tertiary structure and the function of the molecule could survive such an event. The deletions or additions found in hemoglobin and myoglobin chains are compatible with these generalities.

The outlook for survival of the molecule should be likewise poor if two or more adjacent amino acid residues are replaced by an equal number of residues. No evidence of such an event in globins has as yet been forthcoming, and it would not be easy to ascertain.

A major conformational rearrangement of the molecule, while leading to the disappearance of one molecular function, might of course be accompanied by the appearance of a new molecular function. In that case, however, the molecule is no longer of the type under consideration, and it may not be recognized or isolated readily.

Perhaps the most frequently occurring type of mutational event and, at any rate, the most frequently observed and preserved type is the replacement of one single amino acid residue by one other amino acid residue. As we saw, such substitutions can occur mutationally anywhere along the globin chain. In general one may expect natural selection to act against the following effects of such substitutions:

1. At the inside of the molecule, against a notable increase in bulk (there would mostly be no space for such an increase) and against an increase in polarity (this would destabilize the structure; cf. Schachman, 54).

2. At the outside of the molecule, against a notable change in polarity (because the solubility characteristics of the protein would be altered).

3. At bends, against substitutions that destabilize them and tend to turn the regional sequence into a straight helix.

4. At helices, against substitutions that destabilize *them* (cf. Schellman and Schellman, 55).

5. At sites where conformational specificity requirements are particularly high, namely at "active sites," or at sites of binding of prosthetic groups, or at sites of binding of coenzymes and of molecules that act through allosteric effects (42), or at sites of binding of associated polypeptide chains, or at sites remote from these, but whose modification directly affects one or the other of them.

If any of these restrictions are ignored by an amino acid substitution, the functional properties of the molecule should be partly or totally impaired, while its tertiary structure, in many cases, may not be, or may be only slightly affected. Single amino acid substitutions, precisely because the tertiary structure of the molecule has a fair chance not to be greatly changed, are expected to lead to the appearance of a new molecular function in a smaller proportion of cases than the more radical mutational changes considered above. Typically, they lead to impairment of function, not to the evolvement of a new function.

The restrictions to functional amino acid substitutions enumerated on a priori grounds seem stringent. Yet the degrees of liberty, for amino acid substitutions, on the basis of the limited number of globin chains that are at present available to us for comparison, are already as high as 6 or 7 at some sites (7 or 8 different residues found at these sites), and as high as 2.0 per site, on the average, for the whole molecule (3.0 different residues found on the average per site). This situation is expressed in the well-known fact that the differences in amino acid sequence between mammalian hemoglobin chains and myoglobin chains are very numerous indeed. For instance, between the human hemoglobin α chain and the sperm whale myoglobin chain—two chains that are very similar in tertiary structure and function—there seem to be 107 differences in amino acid sequence, over the 141 molecular sites that are common to the two chains. Thus the two chains differ over 76% of their sites.

How is one to reconcile the considerable plasticity of the primary structure within the limits of a given type of tertiary structure and of function with what appear to be good reasons for expecting stringent restrictions with regard to evolutionarily effective amino acid substitutions? These two features are compatible principally on the following two grounds.

Firstly, from the evidence derived from the comparison of different globin chains it appears that the presence of a certain residue at a certain site is only exceptionally required for "absolute" functional reasons, as apparently in the case of the heme-linked histidine in globins. Most of the time residues are needed at some sites in relation to other residues at other sites. What seems to count, most often, from the functional standpoint, is a system of interactions between two or more residues and not the chemical nature of any single residue per se. As more extensive data will be forthcoming about the interactions between the different side chains in hemoglobins and myoglobins, evolutionary changes will best be analyzed in terms of changes in these interactions, rather than simply in terms of changes in amino acid sequence. Since the changes in primary structure are introduced most of the time residue by residue, groups of interacting residues may be transformed progressively. When more than two residues are involved in such a group, the alteration of one does not necessarily compromise the local stability of the molecule, and this first alteration may make possible subsequent ones, at other sites, that heretofore were not permissible.

Secondly, numerous amino acid substitutions are possible because many of the amino acid residues found in proteins are so similar in structure and chemical properties to at least one other type of residue that transitions from one amino acid to the most closely related ones will usually represent a very small modification indeed. These are the "conservative" transitions. We shall see that their list is extensive and, in effect, includes couples that have not been considered, on a priori grounds, as candidates for conservatism.

However, even in globins, whose amino acid sequence proves to be so variable, the plasticity of the primary structure in relation to the tertiary structure is by no means unlimited. Although we saw that the number of strictly invariant sites is dwindling, a number of sites are nevertheless of high evolutionary stability in that the only substituents tolerated at these sites are residues most closely related to those usually found. Even this very restricted type of transition can be extremely rare. Thus, at residue B12, arginine, found in all known globin chains, is replaced by lysine in lamprey hemoglobin; and, similarly, at E11, valine by isoleucine, and at CD7, leucine by methionine. (The transition leucine–methionine is a very common one, as the data in Tables I and II show, and their functional kinship is thereby strongly suggested, in spite of the fact that methionine is somewhat polar, whereas leucine is not.) There are 41 sites in normal globins at which so far only one substituent amino acid has been found. This figure represents 28% of the 148 globin sites under consideration here, each of which is shared by at least some type of hemoglobin chain with the mammalian myoglobin chain. The most frequent conversions at these sites occur between leucine and phenylalanine (5 times), between lysine and arginine (3 times), and between valine and leucine (3 times). At 20, i.e., one half of these sites, the transitions are of the type defined here as "very conservative" (see Section II.3). At the 21 remaining relatively stable sites, the expectancy of finding some other substituent in the future is highest. However, the sites at which only one single highly conservative conversion has so far been found are probably mostly sites at which substitutions are greatly restricted. If we add to these sites the number of strictly invariant globin sites, we find that at about 31 globin sites, i.e., at 21% of the total number of sites, possible substitutions, if any occur, may be restricted, in each case, to one most conservative one. Thus, although the number of absolutely invariant sites is very small, one-fifth of the globin molecule will tolerate substitutions, if any, of maximum conservatism only.

In the present treatment we do not examine primarily substitutions at particular molecular sites. Rather, by tabulating the evidence for all individual globin sites we attempt to diagnose some general features of amino acid conversions and of properties of residues.

In contrast to the stable molecular sites, the most variable sites are F3, with 8 different residues recorded to date, and B4, E13, and G14, with 7 different residues at each site. At bends and in interhelical regions the variability is about the same as elsewhere in the molecule. For the 28 interhelical sites found in myoglobin as mentioned (the list of these sites may not be exactly coincident with the one applicable to hemoglobins), the mean number of different residues found at a site is 3.0, identical with the mean that holds for the whole molecule.

The number of different residues that may replace a given residue is very large, if we consider conversions in general rather than conversions at any particular site. At lysine, histidine, alanine, leucine, serine, and threonine sites all amino acids have already been found in globins, or the few that are missing occur in such small numbers in the molecule that their nonparticipation in certain conversions is at the moment nonsignificant. If we consider only conversions whose absence is of possible general significance because of the relatively frequent occurrence of the residues in the molecule, the only conversions not so far found in globins are the following: Neither aspartic nor glutamic acid has been replaced by phenylalanine. Proline has not been replaced by the large apolar or related amino acids valine, leucine, phenylalanine, or methionine. Phenylalanine has been replaced neither, as mentioned, by proline, aspartic, or glutamic acid, nor by arginine or glycine. Glycine has not been replaced by arginine or phenylalanine. None of these conversions is allowed to proceed in one mutational step according to Eck's proposal for a genetic code (16), except the conversion glycine–arginine. None of them is allowed according to the set of coding triplets of Wahba et al. (cf. Jukes, 37). Perhaps the reason why none of these conversions occurs evolutionarily resides in the requirement of intermediate mutational steps, although two-step conversions might be circumvented if the two residues are arrived at through single steps from a common ancestral residue. More probably the causal relationship is in the opposite direction: Conversions that most of the time are nonfunctional may have become two- or three-step conversions by virtue of a natural selection that modified the genetic code before it became fixed.

We shall examine conversions between amino acids in relation to

TABLE I

RESIDUE SITES AND THEIR CONVERSION CHARACTERISTICS IN GLOBINS

| Residue site | Number of residue sites | Number of different substituents found (maximum = 19) | Substituents occurring at above 20% of sites (in parentheses, percentage substituent sites in relation to total number of sites) | Average number of substituents per site | Number and, in parentheses, percentage of residue sites with only zero or one substituent. Nature of unique substituents. |
|---|---|---|---|---|---|
| asp | 32 | 14 | glu(47), ala(44), gly(34), asn(22), lys(28), ser(25), his(22), | 2.9 | 7 (22) *glu*, lys, his, gly, ser, pro |
| glu | 34 | 15 | asp(44), lys(41), ala(50), gly(38), pro(24) | 3.1 | 1 (3) ala |
| lys | 39 | 19 | glu(31), asp(28), gly(23), ala(23), arg(21), ser(21), leu(21) | 2.7 | 7 (18) *asp, arg*, leu |
| arg | 12 | 12 | lys(58), his(50), ser(25) | 2.3 | 3 (25) *lys* |
| his | 27 | 18 | lys(30), asp(26), leu(26), ser(22), thr(22) | 2.8 | 4 (15) leu, asp |
| pro | 14 | 10 | glu(57), asp(43), ala(50), gly(43), lys(21) | 2.6 | 4 (29) asp, ala, (thr?) |
| gly | 32 + 1[a] | 14 | ala(51), ser(36), asp(33), glu(30), lys(27) | 2.7 | 5 (15) *ala*, asp, ser |
| ala | 51 | 19 | gly(33), ser(31), glu(31), asp(28) | 2.7 | 8 (16) *gly, leu*, val, glu, ser, pro |

[a] Because of an uncertainty concerning homology relations, N-terminal residues are not included in the evaluation of conversion characteristics.

TABLE I (*Continued*)

| Residue site | Number of residue sites | Number of different substituents found (maximum = 19) | Substituents occurring at above 20% of sites (in parentheses, percentage substituent sites in relation to total number of sites) | Average number of substituents per site | Number and, in parentheses, percentage of residue sites with only zero or one substituent. Nature of unique substituents. |
|---|---|---|---|---|---|
| val | 28 + 1[a] | 17 | leu(43), ala(36), ilu(21), lys(21) | 2.4 | 9 (31) *leu, phe, thr,* ilu, gly, ala |
| leu | 40 | 18 | val(30), phe(28), ilu(23), lys(23), ala(21) | 2.1 | 15 (40) *phe, val, met,* ilu, lys |
| ilu | 13 | 13 | leu(58), val(46), ala(39) | 2.5 | 4 (33) *leu,* val, (pro?) |
| phe | 18 | 11 | leu(61), his(22) | 1.7 | 11 (61) *leu,* val, his, try |
| met | 9 + 1[a] | 10 | leu(89), val(45), ilu(22), phe(22), ala(22) | 2.6 | 2 (22) *leu* |
| ser | 33 | 16 | ala(49), thr(40), gly(36), lys(24), asp(24), glu(24), gly(24), lys(24) | 2.8 | 5 (15) thr, asn, gly, ala, leu |
| thr | 25 | 17 | ser(52), ala(32), glu(28), gly(24), lys(24) | 2.9 | 3 (12) ser, val |
| asn | 15 | 14 | asp(47), lys(33), his(33), ala(33), ser(33), thr(33) | 3.3 | 1? (7?) (tyr?) |
| glm | 10 | 12 | lys(70), asp(56), his(40), glu(30) | 3.1 | 1 (10) asp |
| tyr | 6 | 10 | phe(50), his(33) | 2.1 | 2 (30) asn |
| try | 5 | 9 | phe(60), leu(40), ala(40) | 2.8 | 1 (20) phe |
| cys | 3 | 8 | | | |

general functional types of residues before considering individual kinds of residues.

The types of residues that appear at the largest number of globin sites when the evidence from the different known globin chains is pooled (cf. Table I) are the charged residues except arginine, the smallest, functionally most neutral residues glycyl and alanyl, the bulky apolar

TABLE II

SUBSTITUTION FREQUENCIES IN GLOBINS[a]

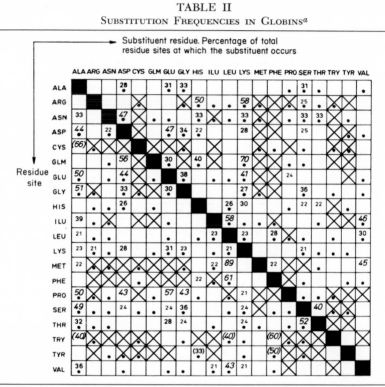

Substituent residue. Percentage of total residue sites at which the substituent occurs

| Residue site | ALA | ARG | ASN | ASP | CYS | GLM | GLU | GLY | HIS | ILU | LEU | LYS | MET | PHE | PRO | SER | THR | TRY | TYR | VAL |
|---|---|---|---|---|---|---|---|---|---|---|---|---|---|---|---|---|---|---|---|---|
| ALA | ■ | | 28 | | | 31 | 33 | | | | | | | | | 31 | • | • | | • |
| ARG | | ■ | | ✕ | ✕ | ✕ | 50 | • | • | | 58 | ✕ | ✕ | ✕ | | 25 | • | • | ✕ | • |
| ASN | 33 | | ■ | 47 | ✕ | • | • | 33 | ✕ | | 33 | ✕ | | | | 33 | 33 | ✕ | • | |
| ASP | 44 | 22 | | ■ | ✕ | 47 | 34 | 22 | | | 28 | | ✕ | | | 25 | | ✕ | • | • |
| CYS | (66) | ✕ | ✕ | ✕ | ■ | ✕ | ✕ | ✕ | | ✕ | | ✕ | • | ✕ | | • | | ✕ | ✕ | ✕ |
| GLM | | • | 56 | ✕ | | ■ | 30 | ✕ | 40 | ✕ | 70 | ✕ | | • | • | | | | | |
| GLU | 50 | | 44 | ✕ | • | • | ■ | 38 | | • | 41 | • | 24 | | | | | ✕ | | • |
| GLY | 51 | ✕ | 33 | ✕ | ✕ | 30 | | ■ | | | 27 | ✕ | | | | 36 | | • | • | • |
| HIS | | • | 26 | | • | | | | ■ | 26 | 30 | | | • | | 22 | 22 | ✕ | • | |
| ILU | 39 | • | ✕ | | ✕ | ✕ | • | | | ■ | 58 | • | • | ✕ | | • | | ✕ | ✕ | 46 |
| LEU | 21 | • | • | | | • | | • | 23 | | 23 | 28 | ✕ | • | | | • | | | 30 |
| LYS | 23 | 21 | • | 28 | | • | 31 | 23 | | • | 21 | ■ | | 21 | • | • | • | | | |
| MET | 22 | ✕ | ✕ | ✕ | ✕ | ✕ | ✕ | | 22 | 89 | ✕ | | 22 | ✕ | ✕ | | • | | | 45 |
| PHE | | ✕ | ✕ | | • | ✕ | | 22 | ✕ | 61 | | | | ■ | | • | | • | • | ✕ |
| PRO | 50 | ✕ | ✕ | 43 | | • | 57 | 43 | • | | ✕ | 21 | ✕ | ✕ | ■ | • | • | ✕ | ✕ | |
| SER | 49 | • | • | 24 | • | • | 24 | 36 | | • | 24 | ✕ | • | • | 40 | ■ | ✕ | ✕ | ✕ | |
| THR | 32 | • | • | | | 28 | 24 | | • | • | 24 | • | • | 52 | | ■ | ✕ | ✕ | | |
| TRY | (40) | ✕ | ✕ | ✕ | ✕ | ✕ | • | ✕ | (40) | | (60) | ✕ | ✕ | | ✕ | | ■ | ✕ | ✕ | |
| TYR | | ✕ | • | ✕ | ✕ | ✕ | (33) | ✕ | | | (50) | ✕ | ✕ | | | | ■ | | | |
| VAL | 36 | | | • | | | • | • | | 21 | 43 | 21 | | • | ✕ | ✕ | | ✕ | | ■ |

[a] Along the column dimension, the alphabetical list of amino acids represents residue sites. Figures at intersections between rows and columns represent percentages of these residue sites at which a given substituent has been found. (Example: glutamyl occurs at 47% of aspartyl sites.)

Large figures in italics: "very conservative" substitutions (see Table V), at or above 40%. Medium-sized figures: "fairly conservative" substitutions (see Table VI), above 25%. Small figures: substitutions that occur at 21 to 25% of any given residue site. Frequencies of rarer substitutions are not listed. Blank spaces therefore represent substitutions that so far have been found to occur rarely or very rarely in globins. Spaces occupied by a cross indicate substitutions so far not found at all. In parentheses, figures of particularly low level of significance on account of the small number of residue sites involved. Solid dots: one-step conversions allowed according to Eck's (16) genetic code.

residue leucyl, and the small hydrogen-bond-forming residue seryl. If we group related residues, we find that several major categories of residues occur at one-third to one-half of the globin sites (Table III). On the other hand, at one time or another, nearly all molecular sites have been uncharged. The number of sites at which only one or the other of these types of residues occur is restricted: alanyl plus glycyl alone occur at only 3 sites; acidic residues alone at 2 sites; basic residues alone at 7 sites; charged residues alone at 15 sites; seryl, threonyl plus the amides,

TABLE III

NUMBER OF RESIDUE SITES OF DIFFERENT TYPES IN GLOBIN CHAINS
PRESENTLY AVAILABLE FOR COMPARISON

| Type of sites | Number of sites | Per cent of total sites |
|---|---|---|
| Total | 148 | |
| Charged | 90–91 | 61 |
| Acidic | 51–52 | 35 |
| Basic | 57 | 39 |
| Hydrogen-bond-forming | | |
| (ser + thr + asn + glm) | 61 | 41 |
| ser + thr alone | 45 | 30 |
| ala + gly | 67 | 46 |
| Apolar with bulky side chains | | |
| (val, leu, ilu, phe) + met | 66 | 45 |
| Uncharged | 133 | 90 |

alone, at 3 sites. On the other hand the apolar bulky residues, valyl, leucyl, isoleucyl, phenylalanyl plus methionyl, occur to the exclusion of any other residue at 26 sites. These figures give an indication of the surprising frequency of conversions between residues with different chemical properties. They also show that there are more sites that seem to specialize in carrying residues fit for apolar bonding than any other sites at which the residues found are limited to one given chemical category. Apolar bonding may be the most specifically determined business of molecular sites in globular proteins.

The correctness of this last statement in relation to globins is confirmed by the figures that represent the average number of different substituents found for any particular amino acid residue (Table I). For most amino acids one finds an average number of substituents per site that is close to 3. Exceptions are valine, leucine, and foremost phenylalanine, the latter with 1.7 substituents per site on the average. The number of sites with no substituents or with only one substituent is highest for leucine and phenylalanine, the two apolar amino acids with the bulkiest side chains.

It may turn out that the larger the side chains in aliphatic residues, the smaller, in general, is the number of substituents that occur. At the moment this correlation is upset by the case of isoleucine (Table I), although the relative smallness of the sample of isoleucine sites that are so far known in globins prevents one from attributing significance to this finding.

Table IV and Fig. 1 show that the proportion of different types of substituents generally decreases as the hydrophobic side chains increase in bulk. If we draw the best straight line through the points on Fig. 1, the

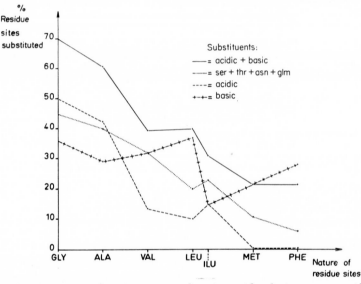

Fɪɢ. 1.  Frequency of various types of amino acid substituents at residue sites for hydrophobic side chains of increasing bulk. Values from Table IV.

line relative to all charged substituents considered together has a slope not unlike that of the line relative to the hydrogen-bond-forming residues serine, threonine, asparagine, and glutamine considered together, although the latter are less frequent substituents. When we consider acidic and basic substituents separately, an interesting difference between these two categories appears, however. The slope for the acidic substituents is the greatest, whereas that for the basic substituents is the smallest and is, on the average, not far from zero. This observation means that as the side chains of hydrophobic residues increase in length or bulk the sites for such residues become rapidly intolerant to acidic residues, whereas, as far as can be judged from available data, their tolerance to basic residues does not vary significantly. This observation

## TABLE IV

### Conversion Frequencies at Globin Sites in Relation to Substituents Grouped According to Functional Characteristics[a]

| Vector of structural properties | Residue sites | Acidic + basic substituents | Ser + thr | Ser + thr + asn + glm | Acidic substituents | Basic substituents | Ratio of basic over acidic substituents |
|---|---|---|---|---|---|---|---|
| ⟶ | gly | 67(22/33) | 39(13/33) | 45(15/33) | 49(16/33) | 36(12/33) | 0.7 |
| | ala | 61(31/51) | 37(19/51) | 41(21/51) | 43(22/51) | 29(15/51) | 0.7 |
| | val | 39(11/28) | 29( 8/28) | 32( 9/28) | 14( 4/28) | 32( 9/28) | 2.3 |
| | leu | 40(16 or 17/40) | 12( 5/40) | 20( 8/40) | 10( 4/40) | 38(15/40) | 3.7 |
| | ilu | 31( 4/13) | 23( 3/13) | 23( 3/13) | 15( 2/13) | 15( 2/13) | 1.0 |
| | met | 22( 2/9 ) | 11( 1/9 ) | 11( 1/9 ) | 0( 0/9 ) | 22( 2/9 ) | 2/0 |
| | phe | 22( 5/18) | 6( 1/18) | 6( 1/18) | 0( 0/18) | 28( 5/18) | 5/0 |
| ⟶ | asp | | 31(10/32) | 53(17/32) | | | |
| ⟶ | glu | | 32(11/34) | 47(16/34) | | | |
| ⟶ | lys | | 26(10/39) | 44(17/39) | | | |
| | arg | | 42( 5/12) | 62( 7/12) | | | |
| | his | | 33( 9/27) | 56(15/27) | | | |
| ⟶ | ser | 58(19/33) | | | 36(12/33) | 42(14/33) | 1.2 |
| | thr | 52(13/25) | | | 48(12/25) | 52(13/25) | 1.1 |
| | asn | 73(11/15) | | | 53( 8/15) | 80(12/15) | 1.5 |
| | glm | 100(10/10) | | | 70( 7/10) | 90( 9/10) | 1.3 |
| | pro | 79(11/14) | 14( 2/14) | 14( 2/14) | 79(11/14) | 21( 3/14) | 0.3 |

[a] The first figure gives the percentage of the residue sites inved. In parentheses, the actual figures of the ratio are given.

is, of course, reflected in the ratio of basic to acidic substituents. At the sites for the smallest residues of the series, glycine and alanine, the acidic substituents predominate. The trend is reversed for the residues with larger apolar side chains. The fact that the larger the apolar side chains the larger, in general, is the proportion of basic to acidic substituents may be related to the difference in size between the acidic and the basic amino acid residues. The basic amino acid residues that occur in proteins are larger than the acidic residues. The large basic residues may have a function beside those linked to their charge and to their capacity to form hydrogen bonds, namely one connected with their capacity to form hydrophobic bonds. A globular protein may be able to tolerate a charged amino acid residue at its inside if, along with the charge, this residue offers a sufficient opportunity for hydrophobic interaction.

The behavior of proline is exceptional. Although this residue is bulky and apolar, the number of sites with acidic substituents is definitely higher than the number of sites with basic substituents. The case of substituents at proline sites is examined more closely in separate papers (72, 73).

Charged residues of either sign occur at one time or another at 90 or 91 different molecular sites, i.e., at over 60% of the sites. The distribution of these sites is such that they cannot be all at the outside of the molecule. Since, however, in any one "edition" of the globin chain the great majority of the charged sites, along with other polar sites, may be expected to be at the outside of the molecule, in conformity with Kendrew's finding on myoglobin (38), and since charged sites and other polar sites are more variable, on the average, than apolar sites (with the exception of glycine, alanine, and proline, Table I), we may venture the generalization that the outside of the globin molecule, and perhaps of globular proteins in general, is more variable than the inside. (Glycine and alanine residues are not confined to the interior of the myoglobin molecule; 38.) It is plausible that this should be so, since it is at the inside of protein subunits that the requirement for steric fit between residues should be the most generalized.

The transition between glutamyl and aspartyl has been previously found to be a frequent one in evolution (71). It now appears that the transition between glutamyl and lysyl is equally frequent (Tables I and II). This shows, interestingly, that at many charged globin sites (i.e., at sites where charged residues occur in at least one known globin chain) the sign of the charge is of little consequence. Of equally little consequence is the question whether, at many of the charged sites, there is any charge at all in any particular case. Indeed, alanine and glycine are other very frequent substituents at charged sites, especially at acidic sites. Perhaps this bias in favor of the acidic sites is due to the fact that the basic side chains are larger than the acidic ones and may therefore be replaced with more difficulty by the very small residues alanine and glycine.

What counts primarily may be the distribution of the charges over the surface of the molecule, not their presence at any particular site. The function of alanyl and glycyl seems to be purely negative. The presence of these residues means "no charge at this site," "no obstacle to bend" (72), or "no obstacle to close contact between different parts of the polypeptide chain." More often than not, glycyl or alanyl seem to be no more than molecular spacers along the polypeptide chains. Evolutionarily, only one glycine in globins seems to be absolutely stable and, hence, absolutely required, at 1 out of 33 glycine sites (B6, see above). The situation, from this point of view as from others, is greatly different in cytochrome $c$; 10 out of the 12 glycines of yeast cytochrome $c$ seem to have remained stable since the time of the common ancestor of yeast and man. A possible reason for the stability of glycine residues, beside their importance in providing opportunities for short contacts and for sharp bends, has been suggested earlier (Section II.1).

At present, no sequence of more than 3 consecutive molecular sites is left at which no charged amino acid has been found in globin molecules. Five such sequences of 3 are present. Two uninterrupted series of seven "charged sites" are found (E20-EF6, G17-GH4). Except for site D5 all sites of helix D are sometimes charged. Helical and interhelical regions alike show great concentrations of "charged sites."

Of the 57 (or 58) sites at which no charged amino acid has so far been found, 29 sites, one-half of the number, display only the bulky nonpolar side chains of valine, leucine, isoleucine, or phenylalanine. Only once are 2 such sites found consecutively, at G7 and G8, where only leucine and phenylalanine occur. Five times such sites are found 4 residues apart in helical regions (A8, A12; B10, B14; E11, E15; G12, G16; H7, H11). There are 6 further sites at which only bulky apolar side chains or alanine are found. Evolutionarily effective conversions leading to charged amino acids are unlikely at sites at which so far only bulky apolar side chains have been found and somewhat more probable at sites where also alanine has been found. One may estimate that the total proportion of sites with charged amino acids tends toward a maximun of about two-thirds of the globin molecule.

Conversions between uncharged polar hydrogen-bond-forming residues and charged residues are very frequent (Table IV). At 52% of the sites where a charged residue has been found, an uncharged hydrogen-bond-forming residue has also been found. It can be seen by reference to Table IV that there is no significant variation in the ability of the different charged amino acids to be substituted by a member of the group of hydrogen-bond-forming amino acids. On the other hand, there is a variation in the readiness of different types of hydrogen-bond-forming residues to be substituted by charged residues. This readiness increases with the size of the hydrogen-bond-forming side chains. This observation suggests that, for conversions between polar residues, the bulk of the side chain is more important than the presence or the absence of a charge.

Substitution patterns at some individual residue sites may now be briefly discussed. The usual indifference to the sign of the charge at charged sites is well borne out by the fact that basic residues occur at about one-half the aspartyl and the glutamyl sites (Table I). Conversely, acidic residues occur to the same extent at lysyl sites. Acidic residues occur at only one-third of the histidyl sites, and this smaller proportion probably expresses the fact that the basic character of histidyl represents only one of several equally important functions of this residue. Arginyl, on the other hand, a much rarer residue in globins than either of the two other basic residues, is replaced by acidic residues only at 2 out of 12 arginine sites. Its most frequent substituents are either of the two other basic residues. As to histidyl, it is substituted with an approximately equal frequency by either lysyl, aspartyl, or leucyl. The fact that leucyl occurs at 26% of the histidyl sites suggests that histidyl, besides acting by virtue of a charge, is functioning by its bulk through hydrophobic bonding. When histidyl interacts with another ring, $\pi$-bonding may be important. A further character of functional importance of histidyl may reside in the polar, uncharged part of the molecule, since seryl and threonyl also occur with a significant frequency at histidyl sites. By the multiplicity of its substituents that occur each with a frequency between 20 and 30% (Table I), none being recorded with a higher frequency, histidine appears to be the amino acid in which the most diverse chemical properties play an equally important role in relation to function in globins and perhaps proteins in general. If histidine shares each of its major properties with some other residue, it should be possible for a protein to dispense with histidine at most sites, without any radical change in functional properties. In fact histidine sites are no more stable than other residue sites (Tables I, II, and IV). Only at 15% of the histidine sites is the number of substituents limited to 0 or 1 (Table I). This number is smaller, or not larger, than at the sites of most other residues that occur frequently in globins (Table I).

Besides histidine, asparagine displays a series of substituents that occur with equal frequency: Lysine, histidine, serine, threonine, and alanine are all found at one-third of the asparagine sites. Only aspartic acid is a more frequent substituent, namely at one-half of the asparagine sites. Although asparaginyl is no more versatile in its substitution properties than other residues, its functional affinities with a number of other residues are more nearly equal than is usually found.

It is no surprise that leucine should be the most frequent substituent of phenylalanine, because of the apolar and bulky characters of both residues. It is of interest, however, that, next in line among the frequent substituents of phenylalanine, although at a percentage value far below leucine, one finds histidine. One might have thought of tyrosine as the likely next most frequent substituent. And, indeed, phenylalanine is the most frequent substituent at tyrosine sites. But tyrosine appears at only about 10% of the phenylalanine sites, although the conversion apparently can occur in a single mutational step (Table II). The relative frequency of histidine at phenylalanine sites is paralleled by its relative frequency at tyrosine sites. Apparently the ring character of the histidine residue is in many cases more prominent than the charge of the imidazole group. This is the more plausible, as numerous imidazole groups, in hemoglobins and myoglobins, are inaccessible to titration (e.g., 65). Because of their relatively low pK, the imidazoles in globins are at any rate expected to be only partly ionized. Charge may be entirely suppressed in some histidine residues, notably when the ionizable nitrogen is surrounded by apolar residues.

Because of the smallness of the sample of tryptophan sites in the globin chains whose amino acid sequence is available to us (5 sites, plus 1 in myoglobin, whose exact position, from the point of view of homologies, is not certain), it is difficult to deduce from the nature of the most frequent substituents the type of properties of the tryptophan residues that is mostly made use of in the protein. It appears, however, that at some residues, at least, the action of tryptophan is likely to be linked to apolar bond formation and bulkiness, or to ring character (cf. 50, p. 44ff). This seems to be the case at residues A12, CD4, and H7. On the other hand, at residues C3 and E6, charged or hydrogen-bond-forming substituents are recorded in certain chains in lieu of tryptophan.

For serine and threonine the most frequent substituents are the other partner in this couple, plus alanine and glycine, as one might expect. Yet charged substituents, either acidic or basic, also occur with significant frequency (Table I). This fact may be associated with the hydrogen-bond-forming capacity of charged residues, whereas the substituents alanine and glycine may be selected for because of their small bulk, reminiscent of the bulk of serine and threonine.

To conclude this section, let us briefly consider alanine sites and glycine sites. We count at present 33 glycine sites, although the content of glycine per hemoglobin or myoglobin polypeptide chain, as far as is known at present, varies between 5 (human α chain) and 15 (horse β chain). The figure of 33 glycine sites can be interpreted to mean that nearly one-fourth of the globin sites, and perhaps an even larger proportion, can accommodate at one time or another during evolution a residue whose role can only be not to interact or not to prevent some other interaction. About one-half (18 out of 33) glycine sites are in interhelical regions or at or near the end of a helix, as judged from the distribution of helical regions in myoglobin. Only a few of the glycine sites that are found inside helices can have the function of allowing short contacts between helices, since many occur at positions where no such contacts take place. Among the frequent substituents of glycine, the unexpected ones are aspartic acid, glutamic acid, and lysine (Tables I and II). With the exception of three sites (B5, E6, H13), glycine sites with bulky substituents are in interhelical regions or near the end of helices. It may be that bulky substituents for glycine are predominantly concerned with the stabilization of bends. In particular, lysine seems to occur at glycine sites only in interhelical regions or at the end of helices. In this connection, one may point out that lysine and glycine are among the more frequent substituents of proline.

Of alanine sites we count at present 51. Over one-third of the globin chains is made of alanine sites, and this figure may of course increase further. Sometimes alanine sites are found in a row. Thus, between B2 and B9 nearly every site is an alanine site, and likewise between H1 and H6, and between H15 and H20. The same applies to glycine sites: between B3 and B7 every site is a glycine site. At other times, in helical regions, both alanine and glycine sites are 4 residues removed from one of the preceding sites and point therefore in nearly the same direction. There are also significant stretches with hardly any alanine or glycine sites, notably the interhelical region FG and the first half of the following helix G.

Alanine sites are the most frequent of all residue sites. Next in line are leucine and lysine sites. It is interesting that next to one of the functionally least prominent residues, alanine, the residues occurring at the greatest numbers of sites are one of the largest apolar ones and one of the largest charged ones. This tends to indicate that the principle functions in the globin molecule are "no function," hydrophobic bonding, and charge. Residues whose main function probably resides in hydrogen bonding come next in importance. In their "no-function" function alanine and glycine seem, in part, simply to act as spacers along the linear dimension of the primary structure. In such positions, wherever alanine or glycine are found there is room for future functional differentiation of the protein molecule.

The present analysis leads to a few generalizations. We note that the substitutions that occur frequently are mostly those that lead to a change in some of the properties of the residue, while other properties of the residue are being preserved. This may be an important rule, to which conform the great majority of amino acid substitutions that are retained by natural selection. It appears that the basis for extensive changes in amino acid sequence without any radical change in tertiary structure and protein function is furnished by the fact that each amino acid residue has several important functional properties, and that the set of amino acids that are coded for is chosen so that changes in one or more of these properties can occur while one or more other properties are maintained constant. By a propitious choice of the properties to be maintained constant, in the case of each particular residue, the amino acid sequence of the polypeptide chain can be transformed, and yet its basic pattern of intramolecular and intermolecular interactions remain the same.

When a given residue is found at contiguous sites in different globin chains, as occurs not only in the case of glycine and alanine but also in the cases of valine (e.g., region G11–G18), leucine (e.g., region G12–G19), serine (e.g., region H12–H21), lysine (e.g., region F2–F6) (there are at present a few interruptions in the regions quoted), histidine (G17–G19), etc., the suggestion is that the residue in question is required to occur not at any one particular site, but at some site or sites in the region. This leads to the concept of regional functional differentiation in polypeptide chains, which has also been established by Margoliash and Smith (this volume) in relation to hydrophobic segments and to basic segments in cytochrome *c*. The evolving functional unit often is not a single amino acid residue, but a small region of the molecule. Nonhelical, bent regions of the polypeptide chains are a case in point. The analysis of proline sites and of their environment (72, 73), indicates that the stabilization of interhelical regions is founded on the collaborative action of several amino acid residues. This is also emphasized by Dr. L. Stryer (personal communication). Quite generally, several contiguous residues may collaborate in carrying out a regional function in the protein molecule. Within the section devoted to this function, the "division of labor" that seems to exist between different amino acid residues may be redistributed a number of times during evolution, as is the function of different ministers in a typical French government. Within the limits of a given protein function, "evolution" may consist more often in such a reshuffling than in significant functional change. This is not to say that in the case of any particular version of the globin chain the exact position of a certain residue is sometimes indifferent. Whether such an indifference is possible we do not know. The reshuffling in question does not demonstrate it, since its modality and extent may be strictly dependent on changes in other parts of the polypeptide chain.

The distribution of clusters of certain types of residue sites suggests that certain functions are of particular importance for certain regions of the globin molecule. Thus, from the data described above, it is evident that large apolar side chains have a particular role to play in the second part of helix G, and hydrogen-bond-forming residues in the second part of helix H. Helices G and H are the two that have been implicated in the interaction between like chains in tetrahemic hemoglobin molecules (Cullis et al., 13).

### 3. Conservatism and Radicalism of Amino Acid Substitutions

The treatment of this subject is already implicit in the preceding section. The notions of conservatism and radicalism of substitutions are here relative to protein function.

The best criterion for the conservatism of a substitution is the high frequency with which it is found to occur during protein evolution. As emphasized by Professor J. Lederberg (personal communication), the evolutionary change of any given species of protein is marked by the conservation of the basic functional properties of the protein. Therefore the substitutions most frequently adopted by natural selection must be the most conservative ones, whereas rarely occurring substitutions will be relatively radical—only relatively, since it will never be so radical as to interfere with the basic function of the protein. Such an interference can be detected only in abnormal mutants of a given protein, and most of these "radical" mutants may escape observation, because the criteria whereby the protein is normally recognized may not apply any longer in most cases of radical substitutions.

The average degree of conservatism of a given substitution can be considered to be represented numerically by the frequency with which this substitution is found. Although such figures cannot be blindly applied to any particular site—there are indeed sites at which a conversion that is usually very conservative is very radical—these figures will give an estimate of a priori likelihood of conservatism of an observed conversion and will, on the other hand, attract attention to the rare substitutions that are likely to introduce a significant functional change into the molecule. In the present article no differentiated scale of conservatism and radicalism of conversions is as yet proposed. Meanwhile, and in relation to globin sites, we distinguish between only three sets of conversions, with arbitrarily chosen limits for the frequencies of occurrence, namely "very conservative" conversions (Table V), "fairly conservative" conversions (Table VI), and nonconservative conversions (cf. Table II).

TABLE V

VERY CONSERVATIVE SUBSTITUTIONS IN GLOBINS[a]

| | | | |
|---|---|---|---|
| ala–ser | asp–asn | glu–lys | gly–ala |
| ala–thr | asp–glm | glu–pro | |
| ala–asp | asp–glu | | |
| ala–glu | asp–pro | | |
| ala–pro | | | |

| | | | | |
|---|---|---|---|---|
| his–arg | leu–ilu | lys–glm | ser–thr | val–leu |
| | leu–phe | lys–arg | | val–ilu |
| | leu–met | | | val–met |

[a] Conversions occurring at 40% or more of the residue sites of at least one of the members of a couple of residues. The rarely occurring residues tyr, try, cys not included. The least bulky residue is in general listed first.

TABLE VI

FAIRLY CONSERVATIVE SUBSTITUTIONS IN GLOBINS[a]

| | | | | | |
|---|---|---|---|---|---|
| ala–val | asn–lys | asp–lys | glm–his | glu–glm | gly–ser |
| ala–asn | asn–his | asp–his | | | gly–asp |
| ala–ilu | | | | | gly–glu |
| | | | | | gly–lys |
| | | | | | gly–pro |

| | | | | | |
|---|---|---|---|---|---|
| leu–his | lys–his | phe–tyr | ser–asn | thr–asn | tyr–his |
| | | phe–try | | | |

[a] Conversions occurring at more than 25% of the residue sites of at least one of the members of a couple of residues. The least bulky residue is in general listed first.

The "very conservative" conversions are defined as those that occur at 40% or more of the sites of at least one of the members of any couple. Most of the rarely occurring residues are not included. In Tables V and VI the smaller residue in any couple is quoted first. We count 22 different "very conservative" transitions in globin chains. A number of these transitions would not, so far, have been considered a priori as conservative, notably ala–thr, ala–glu, ala–pro, asp–pro, glu–pro, glu–lys, glm–lys. The inadequacy of a priori views on conservatism and nonconservatism is patent. Apparently chemists and protein molecules do not share the same opinions regarding the definition of the most prominent properties of a residue.

To the 22 types of "very conservative" transitions we may add 21 "fairly conservative" ones, that occur at more than 25% of the sites of at least one member in each couple (Table VI). Here we find surprising transitions such as ala–ilu, gly–glu, gly–lys, gly–pro. Whereas only one histidine transition is "very conservative" (his–arg), four more histidine transitions are "fairly conservative" (his–lys, his–asp, his–leu, his–tyr). It has been contended that any substitution of histidine must be a "radical" substitution. In fact, however, some of the histidine substitutions appear, like the average American radical, astonishingly conservative (cf. Section II.2).

Among the reputedly radical substitutions that turn out to be conservative are those of proline by some other residues. According to presently available data on globins, glutamic acid occurs at 57% of the proline sites, and some charged amino acid (negatively or positively charged) occurs at 79% of the proline sites. If any substitution is conservative, it must be that of a charged residue for proline. It is clear that glutamic acid has properties different from those of proline. One prolyl residue will break an α helix; one glutamyl residue cannot, by itself, achieve this. In fact, however, as already mentioned, neither proline nor glutamic acid works alone in the stabilization of the conformation of a nonhelical, bent region of the polypeptide chain. Either is able, apparently, to contribute effectively to the collaborative work among several residues that results in such stabilization.

The intuition of the chemist, based on what appear to him prominent properties of amino acid residues, is correct with respect to what he thinks should be conservative conversions. It is in relation to nonconservatism that he may go astray. Take the case of substitutions for lysine. The conversion between lysine and arginine was considered as conservative. This is indeed so. The conversion occurs at 21% of the lysine sites and at 58% of the arginine sites (Tables I and II). On the other hand, although Šorm (64), for one, has included the conversion lysine–glutamic acid in his list of "standard interchangeable amino acids," it seemed legitimate, up to the present time, to consider the conversion lysine–glutamic acid as mainly nonconservative. Although both residues are charged, weight is given a priori to the opposite sign of the charges. It turns out that this weight is light, from the point of view of the protein, and that the transition lys–glu is, like the transition lys–arg, a very conservative one. It occurs at 31% of the lysyl sites and at 41% of the glutamyl sites. Finally, few transitions would appear a priori less conservative than the transition lysine–leucine. Yet leucine occurs at 21% of the lysine sites, and lysine at 23% of the leucine sites. A substitution that is found at one-fifth of the sites of a frequently occurring residue (there are 39 lysine sites and 40 leucine sites) is not an exceptional, but a systematic occurrence. Therefore it cannot be a very radical substitution, within the framework of observed protein evolution, which is, as mentioned, one of preservation of protein function.

Of course, any substitution by a different residue excludes absolute conservatism. And the survival of a given type of protein excludes absolute radicalism. Examples of nonconservative substitutions, which have been found either rarely or not at all in globins, may be read off Table II. The status of shifts toward rarely occurring residues such as tryptophan and cysteine cannot be evaluated a priori. Some types of conversions may occur only rarely, not because they are radical, but because they have only rarely the opportunity to be conservative. This may apply in particular to tryptophan, a residue that seems to be able to take the place of phenylalanine in a conservative fashion, but only rarely so.

The conversion glutamic acid–valine is fairly radical. It occurs at 2 out of 34 glutamyl sites and at 2 out of 28 valyl sites. The example of this conversion allows one to show how the "radicalism" of a substitution can vary according to the environment of the molecular site involved. At site E9 the lamprey chain has glutamyl, and the sperm whale myoglobin chain valyl. At site G3 the human α chain has valyl, and the human β chain glutamyl. The conversion therefore can occur in normal globin chains, although it occurs very rarely. A considerable interference with hemoglobin function appears in the shift glutamyl–valyl at position A3 that characterizes sickle cell hemoglobin (31, 28). A still more radical interference is observed for the reverse transition, valyl–glutamyl, at E11, which was found in an abnormal human β chain and defines Hb M$_{Milwaukee}$. In this modified chain the capacity of reversible combination with oxygen is lost, the iron of the heme being oxidized to the trivalent state (20).

It is striking that most of the other structurally known abnormal human hemoglobins are characterized by conservative substitutions. Of a total of 22 substitutions in abnormal human α and β chains (Table VII), 8 are "very conservative," 11 "fairly conservative," and 3 "radical." The third radical substitution is that found in the α chain of Hb Shimonoseki, where an arginine allegedly replaces a glutamine (21). Several causes may be responsible for the predominance of conservative substitutions in abnormal human hemoglobins: Firstly, nonconservative substitutions may lead to hemoglobin chains that cease to be recognizable as such. Secondly, most abnormal hemoglobins are detected on account of a change in electrostatic charge, and we saw that at charged sites changes to uncharged residues or oppositely charged residues are frequent and therefore "conservative." Finally, the genetic code may well favor, for one-step transitions, the conservative over the nonconservative transitions.

There is at present a tendency among some workers interested in the evolution of proteins to propose that a "very conservative" substitution such as that of a glycine for an alanine may often be strictly neutral in relation to natural selection. It is to be noted that, judged from the evolutionary frequency of the conversion, the glycine–alanine conversion is not expected to be more closely neutral in its functional effects than, say, the shift between lysine and glutamic acid, or between glutamic acid and histidine. Glycine occurs in place of alanine, lysine instead

TABLE VII

DEGREE OF CONSERVATISM OF THE SUBSTITUTIONS IN ABNORMAL HUMAN
HEMOGLOBIN CHAINS[a]

| Conversion | Number of occurrences | Degree of conservatism[b] |
|---|---|---|
| ala↔glu | 2 | v.c. |
| asn→lys | 1 | f.c. |
| asp←lys | 1 | f.c. |
| glm→arg | 1 | rad. |
| glu↔glm | 3 | f.c. |
| glu→lys | 5 | v.c. |
| glu↔val | 2 | rad. |
| gly→asp | 2 | f.c. |
| gly←glu | 1 | f.c. |
| his→arg | 1 | v.c. |
| his→tyr | 3 | f.c. |

[a] The table includes Hbs C, S, $G_{San Jose}$, E, $M_{Emory}$, $M_{Milwaukee}$, $D_{Punjab}$, $O_{Arabia}$, $C_{Georgetown}$, Zurich, $G_{Baltimore}$, Coushatta, Seattle, I, $G_{Honolulu}$, Norfolk, $M_{Boston}$, $G_{Philadelphia}$, Shimonoseki, $O_{Indonesia}$, Mexico, $M_{Kankakee}$ (refs. 4–9, 20, 21, 25, 28–31, 35, 44, 45, 51, 56, 66).

[b] v.c = very conservative; f.c. = fairly conservative; rad. = radical (cf. Tables II, V, VI).

of histidine, and glutamic acid instead of lysine at one-third of the corresponding sites. No one has as yet claimed that a substitution such as that of lysine by glutamic acid or of histidine by lysine is not likely to be acted upon by natural selection. On the basis of the frequency data, the glycine–alanine conversion should not be judged differently.

It is of interest to see how the notion of conservative and nonconservative substitutions, as derived for the globins on the basis of frequency data, fares when applied to the cytochromes. If we exclude yeast and tuna fish cytochromes $c$ from the comparison and consider only the cytochromes $c$ from the more closely related forms—man, monkey, dog, horse, pig, cow, rabbit, and chicken (41)—we find, by considering all possible conversions at sites with multiple substitutions, that there are 31 possible conversions. Of these, 8 are nonconservative by exclusion from the lists of very conservative and fairly conservative substitutions as established for the globins (Tables V and VI). Let us briefly examine the "nonconservative" substitutions in this group. At site 12, the conversion glm–met has not been found in globins, but since there are only 10 met sites and 9 glm sites so far known, this conversion may yet be discovered in globins and not be as radical as it appears at present from its apparent zero frequency in globins. At site 25, the conversion pro–lys occurs at 21% of the proline sites. It is at present below the limit arbitrarily chosen as that of "fairly conservative" substitutions, yet it is not a very radical substitution, and we may discount it as such. At site 58 the conversion thr–ilu is fairly radical in terms of globin. It appears in globin only at $2/13 = 15\%$ of the ilu sites. At site 82 the conversion phe–ilu is not on the lists of conservative ones. This circumstance is likely to be an accident attributable to the small number of known ilu sites in globins, on account of the fact that leu, a residue closely related to ilu, is a very conservative substituent of phe. It is thus likely that, in the future, the conversion phe–ilu will have to be added to the list at least of the fairly conservative substitutions, and we may not count this shift here as clearly radical. At site 88, the conversion thr–lys has been found at 24% of the threonine sites and is therefore, at this point, just below the arbitrary limit of conservative substitutions. It may be discounted as radical. At site 89, the shift ser–asp, one of the possible substitutions, does not have to be postulated, since the observed change may have occurred over another channel. Besides, this shift occurs in globins at 24% of the serine sites. Again, we may not count it among the established radical substitutions in the cytochromes $c$ under consideration. At site 92 the shift glu–val occurs in globins at only 7% of the val sites and at 6% of the glu sites. We have referred to it earlier. It is a radical substitution, but its occurrence does not have to be postulated here, since it is possible to account for the observed situation by proposing that alanine found at this site in several of the cytochromes $c$ has been an intermediary substituent between valine and glutamic acid. We are thus left with only two substitutions, at sites 12 and 58, that are at present legitimately to be considered as radical, in terms of substitutions in globin chains. This figure represents 6% of the possible conversions that can be envisaged in this group of cytochromes. In both cases the Primate chains are implicated in carrying the exceptional evolutionarily effective mutation. Since conservatism is what one should expect, we may conclude that the notion of conservatism as defined in relation to the globins seems to be applicable also to cytochrome $c$, and may be applicable to globular proteins in general.

Let us emphasize the following general conclusion: The properties of charge, hydrogen-bond-forming capacity, apolarity, and bulk, and perhaps others, are distributed over various amino acid residues in various combinations. Therefore conversions within a large number of couples of amino acid residues will be conservative with respect to one or more of these traits, and nonconservative with respect to others. The fact that the set of amino acid residues that are coded for by the genetic code forms a network of overlapping properties is probably the basis for the extensive change in amino acid sequence that may occur without a change in the fundamental traits of tertiary structure and protein function. A certain new function—say, associated with charge—may be introduced while the former function—say, apolar interaction—is maintained. This simultaneity of conservatism and nonconservatism may well also be one of the basic conditions of protein evolution and organic evolution in general. There might indeed not be sufficient opportunities for the invention of new functions of polypeptides if the chemical relationship between the different amino acid residues were not such that a number of sequence patterns are compatible with one given polypeptide function. The possibility of extensive variations of the primary structure within the limits of a given function probably provides the richness in combinatory resources that is necessary for making mutations with radical structural effects sometimes successful in relation to a novel function.

### 4. Conservative Amino Acid Substitutions and the Genetic Code

The possibility was referred to that, when living matter first evolved toward its present form, the genetic code itself went through a phase of evolution during which those transitions between amino acid residues in polypeptides that are most frequently retained by natural selection were made to correspond to relations between codons such that the transitions could be accomplished in single mutational steps.

It is probable, at any rate, that the most frequently observed substitutions do occur in one mutational step. The only data on amino acid substitutions in metazoa that have so far been used for establishing relationships between codons are those bearing on mutants abnormal in relation to the "wild type." When normal chains from different animals are compared, even when their homology is duplication-independent (for the definition of this term see Section III), and unless the number of differences between the chains is limited to one or a few, the probability that any particular observed conversion has occurred in more than one step is indeed not negligible. On the other hand, when all molecular sites of different homologous chains are examined, as we have done, it is unlikely that conversions that are found with particular frequency require more than one mutational step.

If we consider conversions that occur evolutionarily at 30% or more of the sites of at least one of the amino acid residues in the couple, 38 conversions, defined in the matrix of Table II, require probably no more than one mutational step according to the frequency data. As many as 10 of these conversions require a minimum of two mutational steps according to Eck's proposal for a complete genetic code (16). Of these 10, 5 appear, however, as allowed one-step conversions in the set of code triplets of Wahba *et al.* (see Jukes, 37, Table I), namely his–lys (conversion frequency = c.f. = 30% at his sites), ilu–ala (c.f. = 39% at ilu sites), met–leu (c.f. = 89% at met sites), asn–ala (c.f. = 33% at asn sites), and glm–asp (c.f. = 56% at glm sites). Not allowed by either code as one-step conversions are try–phe (c.f. = 60%, nonsignificant because of there being so far only a few tryptophan sites known in globins) and met–val (c.f. = 45%). The most remarkable discrepancy with both systems of code triplets occurs for proline conversions. The conversion frequency at prolyl sites is 57% for pro–glu, 43% for pro–asp, and 43% for pro–gly. All three conversions require a minimum of two mutational steps according to either the experimental results of Wahba *et al.* or the systematization and extrapolation of Eck. It is not unlikely that, with respect to these proline conversions, the genetic code will have to be revised. The code under its present form is compatible with the conversions observed at proline sites, if it is postulated that alanine is consistently the ancestral residue. From alanine it is possible to reach proline as well as most other proline substituents in one mutational step, according to available lists of code words. The likelihood of the generality of this relationship decreases, however, with an increasing number of times it has to be postulated.

As shown in Table II, of the 190 conversions that are possible, regardless of their direction, among 20 different amino acids, 89, nearly one-half, occur relatively rarely or very rarely (conversions that occur with a significant relative frequency in one direction but not in the other are not counted), and 52, i.e. 27%, have so far not been found at all. Thus, at least in globins, roughly one-quarter of the possible types of substitutions do not occur. It is interesting to compare these figures with the minimum numbers of mutational steps as defined by Eck's code. We are indebted to Professor J. Lederberg for a table prepared by him, with the help of an IBM 7090 computer, and used in our Table II. According to Professor Lederberg's matrix, there are, in Eck's code, 83 allowed one-step mutational conversions, which corresponds to 44% of the possible pairs of amino acids. There are 97 pairs separated by at least two mutational steps, and 10 pairs (5% of the total number of pairs) separated by at least three mutational steps. Since Eck's code is the most degenerate among those proposed on the basis of the experimental and observational data, the 107 conversions between amino acid residues that require more than one mutational step may be considered a minimum number, and the 83 allowed one-step conversions a maximal number. Only about one-half this latter number have been classified here as conservative. This suggests that there are a number of one-step conversions allowed by the genetic code that are only rarely compatible with the preservation of a given molecular function.

Indeed, a number of one-step conversions have so far not been found in globins and are therefore radical. There are 18 of these, according to a count of the squares in Table II that contain both a dot and a cross. 29 further one-step conversions have been found with a frequency below 20% in both directions of the conversion. If the genetic code perhaps favors conservative substitutions by allowing them to proceed in one step, it does not on the other hand avoid all conversions that are radical in globins. Because of the provisional character of Eck's code these indications are tentative. It is of interest to ascertain which types of conversion, although presumably of easy access mutationally, are not retained by evolution.

Some of the conversions that require more than one mutational step may be achieved by isosemantic substitution (75), which Sonneborn (this volume) calls effects of synonymy. In such cases two successive single base substitutions occur in a codon, but only the second base substitution leads to an amino acid substitution. Selective value of isosemantic base substitutions might be associated with a change in the quantitative regulation and timing of polypeptide synthesis.

The comparison between homologous "normal" polypeptide chains, rather than between mutants and wild-type, can contribute to the elucidation or to the confirmation of the genetic code, not only, as mentioned, because the most frequently observed substitutions are most likely to occur through a single mutational step, but also because substitutions may be examined at sites that are almost, but not quite, invariant. The more seldom a given site is found to vary, the greater the chances that a rare substituent be introduced via a single mutational step.

Freese (19) has defined transitions as substitutions, in codons, of a purine by a purine, or of a pyrimidine by a pyrimidine, and transversions as substitutions of a purine by a pyrimidine or the opposite. If we consider the most frequently occurring substitutions listed in Table V, which are most likely to be accomplished in single mutational steps, we find that the substitutions most frequently retained by evolution comprise 60% or 63% of transversions, according to whether one uses the list of code words of Wahba *et al.* (cf. Jukes) or Eck's system. If we count only the substitutions that represent either a transition or a transversion to the exclusion of the other term, we find, according to Eck's code, 4 transitions and 8 transversions (67% transversions), and, according to Wahba *et al.*, 5 transitions and 9 transversions (64% transversions). Thus, in the case of vertebrate globins both transitions and transversions are frequently retained by evolution, transversions perhaps somewhat more frequently, although the bias cannot at this point be considered as significant.

## III. The Time Dependence of Evolutionary Transformations at the Level of Informational Macromolecules

### 1. The Issue

At this meeting, as well as at a preceding one on the evolution of proteins that took place in Bruges earlier this year (71), objections have been raised to the ambition to express evolutionary transformations of informational macromolecules as a simple function of time. We shall propose one such formulation presently. Professor Ernst Mayr expressed the view here that evolution is too complex and too variable a process, connected with too many factors, for the time dependence of the evolutionary process at the molecular level to be a simple function. The measure of wisdom of the opposite assumption depends on its measure of success. So far, the refutations of the time function have been weaker than its formulations. For instance, to ridicule the contention that the number of differences between two homologous polypeptide chains is roughly proportional to the phyletic distance of the forms in which these chains are found, it was pointed out at this meeting that the number of differences between cytochromes *c* are 12 in the man–horse comparison and only 8 in the man–kangaroo comparison. Hence, the speaker concluded, the kangaroo, on the basis of molecular evidence, would appear to be more closely related to man than the horse, in flagrant contradiction to solid knowledge. The speaker's conclusion was, however, unwarranted, since the probable fluctuation in every comparison may be evaluated a priori as equal at least to plus or minus the square root of the number of differences. On this basis the observed ratio 12/8 for the relative distance of horse and kangaroo from man might as well be taken to be 9/11. It would be unreasonable to require that any such single measure be accurate in terms of phyletic distance. An accurate measure should be approached as an increasing number of different types of polypeptide chains from two organisms are being analyzed. Counting numbers of differences in amino acid sequence is only one stage of the analysis, and recording the nature of the differences is a necessary further step in the establishment of a molecular phylogeny. When both operations are combined, chemical paleogenetics, in its aptitude to determine phylogenetic relationships, should not be fundamentally different from the immunological method; it is only potentially less equivocal, more accurate, suited for absolute instead of only relative evaluations, and able to extrapolate from the present to the past. Anyone who recognizes the value of the immunological approach for estimating phyletic distance within certain limits should find it impossible to deny that the comparison of amino acid sequences is potentially an even better tool.

In this connection one may also recall the following comment of Simpson (60) about there having been found only one difference in amino acid sequence between the human and the gorilla hemoglobin β chains. This number, he says, "has nothing to tell us about affinities or indeed tells us a lie." To be sure, the difference in question tells us little about the affinities of man and gorilla—it tells us only that they are very closely related. But it does not tell us a lie. The sensitivity of any polypeptide chain as a measuring rod for phyletic distance will increase with its length, with the magnitude of the phyletic distance measured (up to a point), and with the rate of evolutionarily effective amino acid substitutions, a rate that is expected to differ for different polypeptide chains. As to accuracy, it cannot be expected to be satisfactory, except by coincidence, on the basis of one single type of polypeptide chain. Obviously, the fact that one single, rather slowly evolving type of polypeptide chain does not tell us much about the phyletic distance of two closely related organisms does not demonstrate a disadvantage of the molecular approach to phylogeny.

Ernst Mayr recalled at this meeting that there are two distinct aspects to phylogeny: the splitting of lines, and what happens to the lines subsequently by divergence. He emphasized that, after splitting, the resulting lines may evolve at very different rates, and, in particular, along different lines different individual systems—say, the central nervous system along one given line—may be modified at a relatively fast rate, so that proteins involved in the function of that system may change considerably, while other types of proteins remain nearly unchanged. How can one then expect a given type of protein to display constant rates of evolutionary modification along different lines of descent?

One of us (71) has recently drawn a generalization that, if valid,

should, in principle, vindicate Professor Mayr's misgivings. We are referring to the following postulate: A contemporary organism that morphologically closely resembles an ancestor of another contemporary
organism also closely resembles that ancestor with respect to the amino
acid sequence of most of its polypeptide chains. If no considerable morphological difference between two organisms is observed, whatever their
relationship in time, no considerable change in the majority of their
polypeptide chains is expected. The consequences that result from
this postulate do not appear to be borne out by most of what is now
becoming apparent about evolutionarily effective rates of amino acid substitutions in hemoglobin chains. The evidence is so far not extensive
enough for a final conclusion to be reached, nor is it altogether unequivocal. We find it worth while to discuss the issues involved.

To this effect, a system of nomenclature of hemoglobin chains that
is appropriate for the study of their evolution must first be adopted.

## 2. A System of Nomenclature of Polypeptide Chains in Relation to Gene Duplication during Evolution

The different human hemoglobin chains have originally been defined
by their N-terminal sequence (57). This sequence may change partially
or totally during evolution, and yet the structural genes that control a
changed and an unchanged chain of a given type may still be homologous.
We need to be able to refer to homologous structural genes and to the
corresponding polypeptide chains irrespective of the actual sequences
involved. We shall therefore redefine operationally the human hemoglobin chains and the corresponding genes in terms of a particular gene
lineage rather than in terms of a particular amino acid sequence. The
common ancestor of two or more of the human hemoglobin genes is
designated by juxtaposition of the symbols that relate to the genes derived by the postulated duplication. Thus the common ancestor of the
β chain gene and the δ chain gene will be called the β–δ gene, the
common ancestor of the β, δ, and γ genes, the β–γ–δ gene, and so forth.

The different α chains found in higher Primates have presumably
arisen not by gene duplication but by simple filiation from a single gene,
and similarly for the different β chains, and so on. They thus possess
another degree of homology than the α chain and the β chain, which have
presumably become distinct through the duplication of an ancestral
gene. Thus it is useful to distinguish duplication-dependent homology
from duplication-independent homology. Genes related by duplication-
dependent homology occupy nonhomologous chromosomal loci; i.e., they
are nonallelic or at most pseudoallelic (very closely linked). Genes
related by duplication-independent homology may or may not occupy

homologous chromosomal loci, since they may or may not have changed place by translocation in the course of time. In fairly closely related forms, however, it is probable that no evolutionarily effective translocation of a given gene has occurred since the time of their common ancestor.

The homology of chromosomal loci could so far be demonstrated only in organisms that give rise to viable crosses, i.e., in closely related forms. Hoyer, McCarthy, and Bolton (26) have now developed a method whereby the degree of homology of stretches of DNA from any source can be tested *in vitro*. This method seems promising in this connection and in others. When the common ancestor of two contemporary forms is too remote, such a thorough reshuffling of the hereditary material may have occurred that the notion of homologous genic loci has become meaningless. Duplication-independence of homology can in such cases be deduced only through the examination of relatively unmodified descendants of forms that were intermediate between the very distant ancestor and his very modified descendants. The validity of such a procedure will rest on the validity of the above-mentioned postulate, according to which a near-constancy in the morphological traits of a type of organism is accompanied by a high average stability of its genome.

Thus, in our studies, hemoglobin structural genes or polypeptide chains, as designated by Greek letters or groups of Greek letters, are defined by their participation in a pedigree in which the original ancestor directly results from the last gene duplication that one must assume to have occurred in the ascendancy of the genes and polypeptide chains. For instance, when we say that two hemoglobin polypeptide chains are both β chains, they are so called, not on account of an identity of their N-terminal amino acid sequence, nor because they both function as the adult major-component non-α chain and are thus under the same type of control as the human β chain as to period and amount of synthesis, but because between the common chain ancestor and the two descendent chains no evolutionarily effective gene duplication presumably occurred.

On this basis, the adult major-component non-α chain of, say, horse should not be called a β chain, since the duplication of the β–δ gene, to yield the β gene and the δ gene, has presumably occurred in the line of descent of the Primates *after* the time of the common ancestor of the Primates and the Ungulata (see Section III.6). Let us call any adult major-component non-α chain a "β" chain (in quotation marks). The horse "β" chain may be a β–δ chain, but this is not necessarily so. Between the gene duplication that gave rise to the β–δ gene and the γ gene, and the later duplication of the β–δ gene that gave rise to the β gene and the δ gene, one or more further gene duplications may conceivably have occurred, and the horse "β" chain may be related by duplication-independent homology to one of the daughter genes resulting from these latter duplications. How shall we confer on the nomenclature the flexibility that will allow one to insert gene duplications, as they are discovered, at places where the accepted lettering leaves no room for them? We shall refer to genes resulting from such duplications by the Greek letters, with the index "prime," "second," etc., that pertain to the genes resulting from the oldest previously known duplication. This procedure is illustrated on Fig. 2, where dotted lines represent a hypothet-

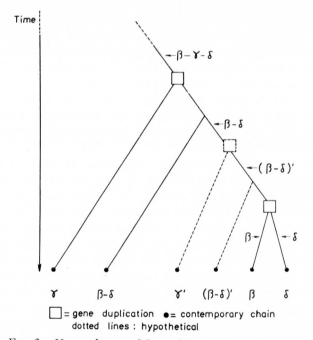

Fig. 2.   Nomenclature of hemoglobin polypeptide chains.

ical gene duplication, considered for the purpose of explaining the nomenclature. This nomenclature is imperfect because the topological relationship of a gene with the index prime, second, etc., cannot be deduced from the nomenclature, but must be read off a graphically presented tree. The present system of nomenclature is therefore provisional.

Further specification will be provided by the subscripts E, F, and A for early embryonic, later fetal, and adult hemoglobin chains, and by the subscripts M and m, for major and minor components in relation to their proportions found.

Since, according to present usage, adult non-α chains are frequently called β chains, and fetal non-α chains, γ chains, we shall, when referring to this type of nomenclature, put the Greek letters between quotation marks. For instance a chain or gene designated as $(\beta-\delta)_{FM}$ is a "γ" chain or gene.

### 3. A Priori Considerations on the Rate of Change of Primary Structure in Proteins

We shall now return to the issue of the time-dependence of evolutionarily effective mutations. The postulate relative to the correlation between morphological stability and stability of the base sequence in structural genes appears to imply that the rate of evolutionarily effective substitutions in homologous polypeptide chains will in general be very unequal along two lines of descent, one characterized by a great evolutionary stability of the organism as a whole, the other by a relatively high rate of evolutionary change of the organism as a whole.

What is meant in this connection by "organisms as a whole" remains, however, undefined. It is possible that striking evolutionary changes may be correlated with changes in genes that represent only a very small to moderate fraction of the genome. If this is so, there is only a very slight to moderate increase in probability that any given type of gene will be substantially changed along lines of descent characterized by a rapid evolutionary rate. Thus, if we compare hemoglobins or cytochromes $c$ from organisms whose ancestors we have reason to believe to have evolved at very different rates, the rates of change in the hemoglobins or cytochromes may not share in this difference. This may explain the apparent approximate constancy of the rate of evolution of the "mammalian type" of cytochrome $c$ over very long evolutionary times (41). Complete data about hemoglobins and related globins in relation to a lapse of evolutionary time of comparable magnitude are not yet available. One may expect a priori that the rate of evolution of hemoglobin will have varied more frequently than the rate of evolution of cytochrome $c$. The functional requirements to be met by cytochrome $c$ are probably constant over a wider variety of organisms and of ecological niches than the functional requirements to be met by hemoglobin. However, even in the case of the hemoglobins, the expectancy of a relative constancy of rate of change during evolution may be justified on the basis of some considerations to be developed below.

To play it as safe as possible when we want to postulate comparable rates of evolution of a given type of polypeptide chains along different lines of descent, we ought preferably to compare homologous polypeptide chains, either as found in organisms whose ancestors are known to have evolved at comparable rates ( or, better, in organisms in which the function the polypeptide is participating in, say the respiratory function, has evolved at comparable rates—if rates are definable in such terms), or as found within the same organism. The latter type of comparison, say between the human α and β hemoglobin chains, or between the human α and γ hemoglobin chains, may be the safest one to be used for an evaluation of an absolute time of common molecular ancestry. Indeed, in that case, there is no difference in rate of change between two organisms to be taken into account. Although it is by no means thereby implied that the past rates of evolution of the two chains that are being compared have been constant, at least the chances seem best that the factors that influence the rate of evolution will have influenced the evolution of the two chains similarly.

Further potential factors of inequality of rates of polypeptide evolution are in the difference between major and minor components of a given type of polypeptide chain—this applies to the comparison between the human hemoglobin β and δ chains—and the Ingram effect, namely a probable difference in rates of evolution between, on the one hand, polypeptide subunits that form components of several versions of a protein with a given quaternary structure and, on the other hand, polypeptide subunits that participate in only one such version. The latter, indeed, have to be adapted to but one different type of partner chain, whereas the former have to sterically fit several different types of partner chain. The magnitude of the Ingram effect may, however, be expected to be small. It will increase with the proportion of amino acid residues that are involved in the interaction between unlike chains in the quaternary structure, but this proportion will usually not be considerable. Moreover, if we take hemoglobin as an example, the relative expected invariance of the α chain will in turn decrease the variability, along the surfaces of contact, of all the non-α chains. Like chains will also interact over certain surfaces, and so the more significant generalization may be that polypeptide chains of a given type should in general evolve more rapidly when they exist as monomers than when they exist in association. This would make it difficult, for instance, to evaluate the time of the common molecular ancestor of a human hemoglobin chain and human myoglobin. This comparison may be further compromised by the possible significance in relation to evolutionary rates of the fact that the functions of hemoglobin and myoglobin are slightly different and that the two types of molecules carry out their function in different tissues. We must be aware of the factors that may influence the rate of evolutionarily effective amino acid substitution, although all these effects may turn out to fall within the limits of the statistical fluctuations. For instance, the comparison of the amino acid sequences of the human (23) and sperm whale (58) myoglobin chains does *not* suggest that the myoglobins have evolved faster than the hemoglobins.

## 4. The Pattern Presented by the Number of Differences between Various Hemoglobin Polypeptide Chains

In spite of the objections against using numbers of differences between polypeptide chains for evaluations of the absolute time at which their common chain ancestor presumably existed, available data show an encouraging measure of consistency. This applies to the cytochrome *c* data discussed by Margoliash and Smith (this volume), and it applies to the hemoglobin data presented in Table VIII. In this matrix the numbers of differences between various mammalian hemoglobin chains are recorded. (Deletions or insertions are not counted, and where a "hole" is observed in one chain residues that fill the hole in other chains are disregarded.) Many figures are only approximate, because the analysis of a given polypeptide chain has not yet been completed, or because amino acid sequence was not established directly but deduced mostly, with good probability, from the amino acid composition of tryptic peptides, by reference to a homologous tryptic peptide of known sequence.

Although an approximate constancy in rate of evolution of different hemoglobin chains is not borne out by all the data in this matrix, it is strongly supported by the majority of them. The agreement between the numbers of differences that distinguish all α chains from all non-α chains is surprisingly good. This seems to imply that the fetal non-α chains have evolved at an average rate that is not significantly different from the average rate of evolution of the adult non-α chains. More generally, it also seems to imply that, since the rather remote time of their common ancestry—several hundred million years (see Section III.6)—all α chains and non-α chains recorded in the table evolved at similar average rates.

Some of the values relative to the cattle "β" and "γ" chains will be discussed in Section IV. The most aberrant value recorded in the table, which is far outside the expected range of statistical fluctuations, is the number of differences between the horse and cattle α chains. There may be something peculiar about the evolutionary history of the cattle α chain.

Aberrant values are expected and are not very disturbing, as long as they appear occasionally rather than generally, as seems to be the case on the basis of our rather small sample of data. The difficulty lies, however, in the interpretation of such inconsistencies. The most striking inconsistency that has so far turned up in the hemoglobin field involves

TABLE VIII

Number of Differences Between Some Mammalian Hemoglobin Chains[a]

| | α man | α horse | α cattle | β man | "β" horse | "β" cattle[b] | γ man | "γ" cattle |
|---|---|---|---|---|---|---|---|---|
| α man | 0 | 17 | ~27 | 74 | 81 | ≈75 | 79 | 82 |
| α horse | 17 | 0 | ~38 | 77 | 75 | ≈77 | 77 | 77 |
| α cattle | ~27 | ~38 | 0 | ~81 | ~83 | ~83 | ~81 | ~88 |
| β man | 74 | 77 | ~81 | 0 | 26 | ≈27 | 39 | 32 |
| "β" horse | 81 | 75 | ~83 | 26 | 0 | ≈35 | 43 | 33 |
| "β" cattle[b] | ≈75 | ≈77 | ≈83 | ≈27 | ≈35 | 0 | ≈45 | ≈28 |
| γ man | 79 | 77 | ~81 | 39 | 43 | ≈45 | 0 | ~40 |
| "γ" cattle | 82 | 77 | ~88 | 32 | 33 | ≈28 | ~40 | 0 |

[a] Differences due to deletions are not counted.

[b] Estimated on the basis of 65% of the cattle β chain (composition of tryptic peptides).

the adult non-α chains of primitive Primates, analyzed by Hill and the Buettner-Janusches (24). They find, for instance, 6 differences between the α chain of *Lemur fulvus* and the human α chain, and 27 differences between the corresponding β chains. It is significant that the observed number of differences between the α chains is in line with other data. We do not believe that the Ingram effect can account for the unexpectedly high number of differences between the β chains. From the small sample of data presented in Table IX it appears that the Ingram

TABLE IX

MINIMUM NUMBER OF AMINO ACID SUBSTITUTIONS IN ANIMAL HEMOGLOBIN CHAINS AS COMPARED TO THE CORRESPONDING HUMAN HEMOGLOBIN CHAINS[a]

| Species | α chain | β chain | Reference |
|---|---|---|---|
| Horse | 17 | 26 | (12, 62) |
| Pig | ≈18[b] | ≈14[b] | (10) |
| Cattle | ≈27 | ≈27 | (53) |
| Rabbit | ~27 | | (14) |

[a] Mean number of differences for the pooled α chains and β chains: 22. Approximate time for common ancestor of man, horse, pig, cattle, and rabbit: 80 million years. Mean period of time between evolutionarily effective amino acid substitutions: $7 \times 10^6$ years according to this sample of data.

[b] Computed from peptide composition studies relative to 72% of α chain and 81% of β chain.

effect, if present at all, may be blurred by other factors and may be disregarded at least in certain groups. Table IX also presents a re-evaluation, which is provisional, like our first evaluation of this type (74), of the mean length of time that elapses during two successive evolutionarily effective amino acid substitutions in hemoglobin chains. The order of magnitude has remained the same.

The main alternative in interpreting the large difference between the *Lemur* "β" chain and the human β chain appears to be as follows. Either the number of evolutionarily effective amino acid substitutions is not even roughly proportional to time in the case of a comparison between lower Primates and man, or the *Lemur* "β" chain and the human β chain are not related by duplication-independent homology.

One may accept very large fluctuations in the rate of evolutionarily effective amino acid substitutions and reconcile them with the consistency of the cytochrome *c* results and with that of the comparisons between the hemoglobin α chains and non-α chains on the basis of the proposal of Margoliash and Smith (41) that over long stretches of evolutionary time fluctuations in the rate of structural change of polypeptide chains will tend to cancel out. If, however, some especially potent selective pressure caused the major adult hemoglobin component of the ancestors of *Lemur* to evolve at an especially rapid rate, why did the α chain in these ancestors not also evolve more rapidly than expected? In view of the interactions between the two types of chains, such a discrepancy in evolutionary behavior would be puzzling.

On the other hand, the postulate according to which the *Lemur* adult non-α chain is controlled by a structural gene that resulted from a gene duplication other than the one that gave rise to the human β gene is, at the moment, illegitimate, although perhaps correct, because this type of postulate may be used to explain away any uncomfortable discrepancy. It is perhaps significant that the N-terminal amino acid in the adult non-α chain of *Lemur fulvus* is threonine (23). N-Terminals in vertebrate hemoglobins are stable, and threonine had so far not been found in that position. Perhaps the *Lemur* and human "β" chains are related by a duplication-dependent homology. A reasonable explanation of the observations is that the *Lemur* "β" chain is in fact a γ chain.

## 5. Interpretation of the Apparent Constant Rate of Evolutionary Change in Most Polypeptide Chains

If we provisionally accept the conclusion to be drawn from the data recorded in Table VIII—namely that the mean rates of evolutionarily effective amino acid substitutions are usually comparable, not only along different lines of descent, but also for different hemoglobin polypeptide chains—we must explain why this is so, in spite of reasons to expect the opposite. Several tentative explanations may be proposed.

It may be that differences between organisms in terms of amino acid sequence of polypeptides are more nearly a simple function of time than are differences due to changes in the control of rate and period of synthetic activity of structural genes. Some of the especially rapid evolutions, say along the hominid line, may be due to a significant extent to changes in the control of gene activity (69, 70) and not be reflected in significant changes in the rate of evolution of most polypeptide chains.

It may also be, as mentioned by Prof. Mayr, that during phases of exceptionally rapid evolution only certain systems and, hence, probably only certain types of polypeptide chains are structurally more affected than would be expected from their normal rate of change. The great majority of the genes may continue to change at a rather slow and perhaps relatively regular rate. A small sample of proteins may, by accident, show that evolution has been exceptionally fast along a given line of descent, but a larger sample of proteins may establish the basic stability of the organism in spite of the important phenotypic variation that is observed. A vastly predominant number of unmodified or nearly unmodified genes may participate in the formation of an organ that appears significantly changed with respect to relative dimensions and other properties. At the level of the structural genes the constancies may far exceed the changes when, as judged from the "looks" of two organisms, the changes seem to exceed the constancies. Independently of the question concerning the relative contributions of structural genes and controller genes (which are distinct at least in their action, if not otherwise), it is therefore likely that the ratio of differences to similarities can be determined at the polypeptide level with a type of significance that does not obtain elsewhere and cannot be matched at the level of the phenotype as seen by the organismal biologist.

Perhaps the most important consideration is the following. There is no reason to expect that the extent of functional change in a polypeptide chain is proportional to the number of amino acid substitutions in the chain. Many such substitutions may lead to relatively little functional change, whereas at other times the replacement of one single amino acid residue by another may lead to a radical functional change. That this is so is at present amply documented (cf. Section II). Therefore an abnormally rapid change in phenotype along a given evolutionary line need not imply an abnormally high rate of evolutionarily effective amino acid substitutions even in those proteins that are most directly involved in the evolutionary change. It is the type rather than the number of amino acid substitutions that is decisive. Of course the two aspects are not unrelated, since the functional effect of a given single substitution will frequently depend on the presence or absence of a number of other substitutions. But if, for bringing about significant functional changes, the emphasis is on type rather than on number of amino acid substitutions, periods of rapid evolutionary change need not be expressed by a substantial increase in rate of amino acid substitution at the polypeptide level.

If this view is correct, it leads to an interesting consequence. It would then appear that the changes in amino acid sequence that are observed to be approximately proportional in number to evolutionary time should not be ascribed to vital necessities of adaptive change. On the contrary, the changes that occur at a fairly regular over-all rate would be expected to be those that change the functional properties of the molecule relatively little—namely the so-called isogenetic or conservative substitutions (see Section II). As we saw, this point of view is confirmed—and was independently suggested—by the great majority of substitutions that we actually observe in the comparison of hemoglobin polypeptide chains whose presumed common molecular ancestor is not excessively remote in evolutionary time.

*There may thus exist a molecular evolutionary clock.* The basic rate of evolutionarily effective substitutions may express the degree of plasticity or of looseness in the relationship between a given rather narrowly defined molecular function and amino acid sequence. If this plasticity is great, the observed rate of evolutionarily effective change will be high, because a relatively large proportion of the amino acid substitutions that occur by chance mutation will be slightly advantageous. If the plasticity of the amino acid sequence in relation to molecular function is very restricted, if only a few substitutions will change molecular function slightly rather than radically, only a smaller proportion of the mutations will be advantageous, and the average time elapsing between two evolutionarily effective substitutions will be larger. *Superimposed* on this basic rate of molecular change are then the functionally highly significant changes. Since the latter changes are relatively rare, the rates of evolutionarily effective amino acid substitutions during periods of rapid evolution may not substantially differ from the rates that obtain during periods of slow evolution. The molecular evolutionary clock would work through a shuttle motion at a certain number of molecular sites from one to the other among a small number of amino acid residues whereof, according to circumstances, the ones or the others are slightly more advantageous for the organism. Hence there arise the multiple molecular coincidence or "convergence" effects that are observed (see Section V). The basic rate of evolutionary molecular change would in a sense be comparable to moderate thermal motion, in that the molecule is reversibly altered structurally without loss of function and at a constant average rate. Each type of polypeptide chain would, in this sense, have its specific evolutionary "temperature."

What is the relationship between this theory and the above-mentioned postulate according to which most polypeptide chains in morphologically stable organisms have stable amino acid sequences? These two tentative generalizations are compatible only if the postulate is amended in the following way: Along lines of descent marked by high evolutionary stability, the shuttle motion between functionally similar amino acid residues will also occur. The changes in amino acid sequence will, however, be limited almost exclusively to the functionally nearly neutral changes. The rate of the functionally nearly neutral evolutionarily effective amino acid substitutions may be lower in organisms that live in a very stable environment than in organisms that live in a more variable environment, because in the very stable environment only few nearly neutral substitutions may be slightly advantageous and thereby spread in the population. In organisms exposed to a more variable environment, a larger proportion of nearly neutral amino acid substitutions may turn out to be slightly advantageous at one time or another, even during periods marked by a relative over-all evolutionary stability.

Which of the two ideas, if any, applies to a greater extent—the idea of an over-all stability of the amino acid sequence of polypeptide chains along lines of descent where little change in "organismal" phenotype occurs, or the idea of a molecular evolutionary clock in which all organisms participate, irrespective of the rate of evolutionary change of the phenotype? The verdict of the facts will be looked forward to.

### 6. *Quantitative Relationship between Number of Observed Differences in Homologous Polypeptide Chains and the Time of Their Common Ancestry*

On the basis of the postulate encouraged by observation, that the rate of evolutionarily effective amino acid substitutions in hemoglobin chains is comparable along different lines of descent, the relation between the number of observed differences between two homologous polypeptide chains and the time of their common ancestry may be formulated as follows.

Let the chance of a mutation's affecting one amino acid site of a polypeptide chain in time $t$ be $\alpha t$. For $N$ sites, the total number of mutations is about $N\alpha t$.

Let us consider the time, $t$, at which $N\alpha t$ mutations have occurred. We assume equal probability for all sites. The probability that the first site is unchanged after the first mutation is

$$P_1 = \frac{N-1}{N} = 1 - \frac{1}{N}$$

and after $N\alpha t$ mutations is

$$P_{Nat} = P_1{}^{Nat} = \left(1 - \frac{1}{N}\right)^{Nat}$$

At the limit, as $N$ increases to infinity,

$$\lim_{N \longrightarrow \infty} \left(1 - \frac{1}{N}\right)^{N} = \frac{1}{e}$$

Hence[2]

$$P_{Nat} \cong \left(\frac{1}{e}\right)^{at} = e^{-at} = A^t$$

where $A = e^{-a}$.

Let us use the expression $P(t)$ as the average probability for any given site to be unchanged at time $t$. Let $\tau$ be a unit lapse of time. Then

$$P(n\tau) = P^n$$

---

[2] This equation is an application of well-known probability theory. An equivalent equation is used by Margoliash and Smith (this volume).

In the present treatment back mutations are ignored because of uncertainty of their probability and because accuracy of experimental points does not justify a refinement of the theory.

Consider a type of protein such as the globins with practically all sites changeable. Table IX shows that the mean difference between some mammalian hemoglobin chains and the corresponding human

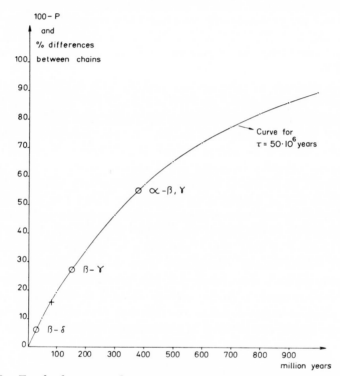

FIG. 3. Epoch of common chain ancestors as a function of the proportion of differences between polypeptide chains. + = point for difference between human and some other mammalian hemoglobin α and β chains (cf. table IX), with common ancestry assumed at −80 million years. O = observed per cent differences between hemoglobin chains, inserted on curve as defined in part by the above assumption.

chains is 22. This figure represents 15% of the hemoglobin chains, in relation to the mean length of the α and β chains (143.5 residues). We assume the mean epoch of separation of man and that of each of the mammals listed in Table IX to be at −80 million years. Thereby τ is defined as on Fig. 3. It is approximately equal to 50 million years. The average α–β and α–γ change is 55%. On the curve of Fig. 3 this gives the α–β,γ separation at −375 million years. This figure is one-third lower than the one obtained by a previous preliminary evaluation (74). The epoch of separation of other chains is also indicated on Fig. 3. The more remote the epoch of the common molecular ancestor, the larger is the error due to ignoring back mutations.

The cytochrome *c* data will fit this curve and lead to a reasonably remote epoch for the common ancestor of yeast and man only on the basis of the assumption that a large proportion of the molecular sites in cytochrome *c* are evolutionarily invariant for a reason other than that of statistical accident. The necessity of this assumption in relation to the calculation constitutes an argument in favor of the assumption (cf. Section II.1).

It is appropriate to compare one protein with another by reference to the rate of evolutionarily effective mutations *per amino acid residue*. The observed rate (the probability) of amino acid substitutions is to be divided by the number of residues in the polypeptide chain. In hemoglobin chains, if we accept the provisional figure (Table IX) of one evolutionarily effective mutation per 7 million years, we find that the chance for any given site to undergo an evolutionarily effective mutation along a given line of descent is on the average about 1 in 1 billion years. One may refer the rate of evolutionarily effective amino acid substitution to the number of evolutionarily changeable residue sites, rather than to the total number of sites. Since, according to present counts, there are about 117 evolutionarily changeable sites in hemoglobins (including the lamprey chain), the chance for any given changeable site to be changed evolutionarily is on the average about 1 in 800 million years. In fact, the chances vary, of course, for different sites of the molecule, but the average figures can be used in comparisons between proteins.

## IV. GENE DUPLICATION IN GLOBINS

Gene duplication may be associated with the following distinct processes: (a) duplication of the whole genome during cell division; (b) intralocus multiplication of some or all genes in the course of cell differentiation; (c) interlocus duplication of individual genes or duplication of whole individual chromosomes in the course of evolution.

The three types of processes differ, in part, by the order of magnitude of the time during which the duplicate genes are maintained in a given type of cell.

We need not comment on the first process and shall refer only briefly to the second hypothetical process.

Itano, Neel, and Wells (cf. 33) evaluated the proportions of different hemoglobin components in members of families that included heter-

ozygotes for normal adult hemoglobin, HbA, and an abnormal hemoglobin, namely HbS or HbC. The HbA components found in different
families appeared to be structurally identical as far as could be determined by the available criteria, yet the proportions of the normal and
the abnormal hemoglobins in heterozygotes was found to be different.
As heritable characteristics, these different proportions were assumed
to be under genetic control. It was further suggested that the proportions of hemoglobin components as found in the red cells of the
peripheral circulation reflect relative rates of synthesis of these components. The apparently identical alleles that differed by the rate of their
synthetic activity were called "isoalleles." In a seminar given at the
California Institute of Technology in 1961, one of us (E.Z.) had noted,
on the basis of the available family studies, that the ratios of hemoglobin
components found in the offspring are in accordance with expectation, if
one assumes that the relative amounts of chain synthesis in the parents
represent small heritable integral multiples of a basic polypeptide
production unit. This way of "quantizing" the results of Itano and his
collaborators introduced the question of a fit between the situation
found in the parents and that found in the offspring without reference
to the "modifying genes" considered by Neel et al. (47). The presentation
of the data pointed to the possibility, also considered by Nance (46),
that several contiguous duplicates of the same gene are usually active
in hemoglobin synthesis. We shall go neither into the examination of
the data nor into the reasons to doubt that the gene duplication hypothesis, as developed in detail by Nance, offers the correct explanation of
the facts. What we want to point out is the following: If the apparent
ratios of integers, whose possible existence is suggested by the data of
Itano et al., should turn out not to be due to coincidence, then they
might be attributed tentatively not only to genic multiplication resulting
in the creation of new loci on the chromosome, but at least equally well to
intralocus genic multiplication. This process is conceived as a somatic
occurrence during development, which is directed differentially and
heritably for different genes and in different tissues and represents a
means of control of rate of protein synthesis. Some genes may be
thought to display intralocus multiplication in one tissue, and other
genes in other tissues. Possibly the giant chromosomes in salivary glands
of Diptera represent the extreme case in which all loci undergo a high
order of intralocus multiplication, although it is also possible that this
phenomenon is qualitatively different from the one envisaged here.
Support for the idea of intralocus genic multiplication may be derived
from the observation of DNA "puffs" in certain regions of polythene
chromosomes of cells engaged in active protein synthesis (17, 67). A

slight structural alteration of the gene, as occurs in most abnormal hemoglobin genes, might reduce intralocus genic multiplication to a smaller order. Isoalleles might be alleles that are structurally identical but differ in their degree of intralocus multiplication. This degree would be a heritable property of the locus and at the same time a function of cellular conditions. It is plausible that simple ratios between orders of intralocus multiplication could be maintained. Certainly it is also possible that cryptic substitutions in the gene, either expressed in an undetected change in the amino acid sequence of the corresponding peptide, or isosemantic (75) and not expressed in this sequence, might affect the order of intralocus multiplication.

Less doubtful, although not directly demonstrated, but almost unavoidable, is the postulate of interlocus gene duplication or chromosome duplication as the basis for the existence of isogenes—i.e., nonallelic, structurally different, yet homologous structural genes. The detailed application of this postulate to the evolution of the hemoglobin chain genes was probably first made in a lecture given by one of us (E.Z.) at Dalhousie University (Halifax) in 1960 (unpublished). At about the same time Ingram (32) independently arrived at the same conclusion. Some further consequences of the existence of isogenes were examined later (74, 69).

The frequency of gene duplications, and that of evolutionarily effective gene duplications, namely of those that are retained by natural selection in a given line of descent, are unknown. In the latter connection we may examine some evidence in favor of a further gene duplication in mammals, beyond those that have already been presumed to have occurred during mammalian evolution. This evidence rests on data kindly made available to us, prior to publication, by Drs. Donald Babin and Walter A. Schroeder of the California Institute of Technology.

The tabulation of the number of differences in amino acid sequence between several mammalian hemoglobin polypeptide chains as given in Table VIII contains suggestive evidence to the effect that the fetal chain of cattle separated from the β chain at a later date than the fetal chain of man. The cattle γ chain does not appear to be a true γ chain, nor the cattle β–δ chain a true β–δ chain. The two chains probably arose through a duplication of the β–δ chain gene, distinct from the one that, in the line of descent of the Primates, gave rise to the β gene and to the δ gene. According to the system of nomenclature described in Section III of this article, the cattle "γ" chain will be called a γ' chain, and the cattle β–δ chain, a (β–δ)' chain.

Schroeder *et al.* (59) have shown that there are 39 differences in sequence between the human β chain and γ chain. We would expect to find between the cattle β–δ chain (that we may call "β" chain) and the cattle γ chain a difference of 39, plus or minus the square root of 39, i.e., between 33 and 45 differences. Instead we find only roughly 28 differences. This is roughly the same number of differences as that between the β chain of man and the "β" chain of cattle, and also between the β chain of man and the "β" chain of horse. Thus, from the point of view of the number of differences in primary structure, the fetal chain of cattle behaves like a β chain in relation to other mammalian β chains. It also behaves like a β chain in relation to the γ chain of man. Indeed, there are about 40 differences in sequence between the cattle fetal and the human γ chains, i.e., the same number of differences as between the human β and the human γ chains (Table VIII).

The tentative conclusion about the evolutionary relationships of the cattle fetal non-α chain that we draw from the data in Table VIII is confirmed by some specific structural features. Drs. Babin and Schroeder found methionine at the N-terminus of both the fetal and the adult non-α chain in cattle, a character that had before been encountered only in the "β" chains of the related sheep and goat. Cattle has preserved the habitual valine at the N-terminus of its α chain. Horse α and "β" chains have valine at their N-terminus, as do all other mammalian α and "β" chains, except cattle "β," sheep "β," and goat "β." The introduction of methionine at the N-terminus hence seems to have occurred in the immediate ancestry of the Artiodactyla. The finding that methionine is present at the N-terminus of the cattle fetal non-α chain furnishes an important character shared by the cattle adult and fetal non-α chains, and an important distinction between the human and cattle fetal non-α chains.

Furthermore the cattle adult and fetal non-α chains both lack one residue in their N-terminal tryptic peptide (a peptide split off by the action of trypsin) in comparison with all other known "β" chains and with the only other γ chain whose primary structure has been established, the human γ chain. The lack of this globin site is an α chain character that is found in all structurally known α chains. It does not follow that the cattle non-α chains are phyletically close to the α chains. There is convincing evidence to the contrary. We do believe it to be significant, however, that, in a character as important from the evolutionary point of view as a deletion, the cattle fetal non-α chain is identical with a cattle adult non-α chain and different from the human fetal non-α chain.

A number of characters of sequence are common to the cattle adult and fetal non-α chains while different from the human γ chain, for instance at sites E15 (phe–leu), H7 (phe–try), and H10 (val–met); however, a few other characters of sequence are common to the human and cattle fetal non-α chains, and differ in the cattle adult non-α chain. Therefore the situation, from this point of view is not entirely unambiguous. However, methionine and tryptophan are rare residues in hemoglobins, and their presence in the human γ chain and absence from the other non-α chains under consideration is more meaningful than any of the other pertinent relationships that are observed.

On the basis of the evidence, we propose the relationship between chains shown in Fig. 4. In this figure, the vertical dimension is propor-

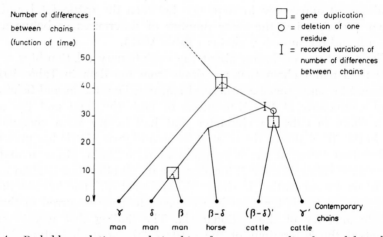

Fɪɢ. 4.   Probable evolutionary relationship of some mammalian hemoglobin chains.

tional to the number of differences between chains as given in Table VIII. An ancestral gene has duplicated to yield two daughter genes, one of which has become the human γ gene, and the other the horse β–δ gene and the β–δ gene present in the descent of the Primates prior to the appearance of the β and δ genes. Not a great many million years before the "Artiodactyl duplication," the ancestor of the cattle non-α chains lost a residue at or next to the N-terminus (which term of this alternative obtains cannot at present be ascertained) and adopted methionine as its N-terminus. The "Artiodactyl duplication" then yielded two daughter genes, one of which continued to be used as an adult major-component non-α chain in cattle, whereas the other was adopted for use as the fetal non-α chain in cattle. Figure 4 suggests that man and horse are slightly more closely related than man and oxen, but this piece of molecular evidence cannot be taken seriously as long as it remains single.

As mentioned, the absence of one residue at or next to the N-terminus of non-α chains seems to be limited to a relatively small group of mammals. We may therefore assume that we are dealing with a deletion of the residue in this small group, rather than with the addition of a residue in all other known non-α chains.

On the other hand, an *addition* of a residue at this molecular site may actually have taken place in a molecular ancestor of the β chain. This ancestor should be remote, but more recent than the gene duplication that led to the differentiation between α chains and non-α chains. Indeed, the very ancient lamprey hemoglobin chain (whose partial sequence was recently made public by Dr. Rudloff from Prof. Braunitzer's laboratory, 52), according to the most probable homology relations with other hemoglobin chains, displays at globin sites 1β, 2β, and 3β the sequence valine–leucine–serine, identical with the N-terminal sequence of the human α chain, although in the lamprey chain the first of these globin sites is preceded by nine others that had not so far been found elsewhere. Hence it seems that, some time after the duplication that led to the α gene on the one hand and to the β–γ–δ gene on the other, the addition of one residue in position 2β, namely histidine, occurred in the β–γ–δ line of descent. Later on, after the β–δ line had separated by a new gene duplication from the γ line, and the bovine β–δ line had separated, without gene duplication, from other mammalian β–δ lines, this added residue was again lost. The identity with respect to the absence of this residue of the α chains and the cattle non-α chains is the first example of a probable evolutionary convergence or coincidence at the molecular level that involves a deletion or an addition. It also illustrates a point that is a priori probable, namely that evolutionary changes at any given site of an informational macromolecule are potentially reversible. The rule of Dollo relative to the irreversibility of evolution is indeed not expected to apply at this level.

We noted earlier (Section II.2) that the lamprey chain differs from the other structurally known globin chains at very invariant sites at which all other known hemoglobin and myoglobin chains are identical. This, in conjunction with the presence of a unique N-terminal "tail," suggests the possibility that the common ancestor of the lamprey chain and mammalian hemoglobin chains may be even more remote than the very ancient common ancestor of mammalian hemoglobin and myoglobin chains. On the basis of apparent evolutionary rates of hemoglobins, it would not be surprising if the common molecular ancestor of mammalian and lamprey hemoglobin chains had existed at a time more remote than the Silurian, the geological era from which the oldest known remains of vertebrates have come down to us. This would mean either that the vertebrates are actually an older phylum than one thinks on the basis of present geological evidence, or that the common molecular ancestor under consideration existed in a prevertebrate. In the latter case the descent of the vertebrates would not be monophyletic, and the Cyclostomes would descend from a prevertebrate independently of the mammals.

One may presume that the contemporary lamprey hemoglobin chains have arisen by one or more evolutionarily effective gene duplications in the direct ancestry of the lamprey. Three is the probable minimum number, in view of the likelihood that the four distinct lamprey chains are controlled by nonallelic genes (1, 2). In fact, six structurally distinct components have recently been identified in *Petromyzon marinus* (40).

The recent discovery by Huehns *et al.* (27) of the human ε chain added a fifth unit to the group of nonallelic human hemoglobin genes. The lack of allelism between the ε gene and any other human globin gene can be inferred, with some probability, from the fact that the ε chain differs from other chains by more than one character of sequence, and more safely from its unique behavior with respect to its period of synthetic activity. Thus, a further evolutionarily effective gene duplication (or chromosome duplication) must be postulated to account for the existence of the ε gene.

The total number of probable evolutionarily effective gene duplications of globin genes, on the basis of the data available at this writing, is about 10, and it is 6 in the human line of descent if we include the common ancestor of man and lamprey.

Suppose that the time at which the β–δ gene duplicated is close to that of the most recent evolutionarily effective globin gene duplication in the human line of descent, and suppose that this length of time is not very far from a mean figure for evolutionarily effective duplications of globin genes per unit time; we may then evaluate the order of magnitude of the number of evolutionarily effective gene duplications as 10 in 400 million years (cf. 74) per line of descent, i.e., since the approximate time of the rise of the Vertebrates. The figure checks quite well with the number of presumed gene duplications in the human line of descent since the common ancestor of man and lamprey—a number that will no doubt be increased by at least several units as more information about hemoglobin sequences and nonallelism of genes becomes available. In facts, the true number of evolutionarily effective duplications of globin genes may be significantly larger, since neither of the two estimates given above takes into account the disappearance of globin genes, either by bodily elimination, or by their conversion into dormant genes (74), or by their transformation into a gene so different that its polypeptide product is not recognizable as a globin, although selected for because fit to carry out a novel, useful function.

If we assume that the evolution of man has started with a single gene 2 billion years ago, and if we assume that man has a complement of about 100,000 different genes as estimated by one of us (L.P.), and, furthermore, that gene duplication accounts for most of the growth of the genetic material, neglecting chromosome multiplication, then 17 generations of duplicating genes are required, each of the daughter genes duplicating again at each generation. The mean lapse of time, over the whole period of evolution, per generation of a duplicating set, would be roughly 120 million years. This figure, which would apply to any single gene with average behavior, turns out to be of the same order of magnitude as the two independent estimates given above. This rough agreement supports the idea that gene duplication has played a major role in the increase of the genetic material per cell in the course of evolution toward higher forms.

## V. Evolutionary Convergence and Coincidence in Protein Molecules

Evolutionary convergence is the movement that goes from different ancestral structures to similar descendent structures with similar functions. When descendent residues at homologous sites of polypeptide chains differ from the ancestral residue, they may either differ among themselves, or be identical. If we examine evolutionary periods over which a two-step mutation in any single line of descent is unlikely to occur, then the number of different descendent residues will be limited to a maximum equal to the number of one-step conversions between amino acid residues that are allowed by the genetic code. If more than that number, $p$, of independently evolving polypeptide chains are compared, namely $p + n$, it is evident that identical residues will be found at the molecular site under consideration in at least $n$ descendent polypeptide chains. On the other hand, the nature of the residues retained by evolution is believed not to be determined by the chance effect of mutations. Over reasonably long periods of evolutionary time, most or all allowed one-step transitions will have had an opportunity to occur, as can be shown by a rough calculation. The residue actually found will be the one that is functionally the most favorable among those proposed to natural selection. When the residues present at a given molecular site in the two lines of molecular descent are identical, but differ from the presumed ancestral residue, this identity is therefore probably established for functional reasons.

The observed identities of this type are not necessarily to be called evolutionary convergence effects. Indeed, different functional reasons may lead to the selection of the same residue, especially when the number of allowed one-step transitions is smaller than the number of observed independently evolving homologous polypeptide chains. Not only does the function of a residue depend on its environment in the molecule; moreover, the distribution of functional properties over the twenty amino acids provided for by the genetic code is such that, on the one hand, as we saw (Section II), different residues may carry out the same function, but also, on the other hand, the same residue different functions. In the absence of evidence to the effect that the function and selective advantage of a given residue are the same in two chains, the term convergence is biased and should be replaced by coincidence (see also ref. 69).

It appears a priori probable that a certain fraction of the coincidence effects will be convergence effects. Indeed, the homologous polypeptide chains that are being compared are too similar in structure and function for identical residues at corresponding sites not to have sometimes identical functions. In this sense one may say that the frequency of coincidence effects establishes the existence, although not the extent, of convergence in protein molecules.

Coincident amino acid conversions are very frequent indeed in the course of the evolution of globin chains. One of us has previously discussed some examples of this effect (71). In fact, coincidence effects offer an alternative of three rather than of two terms. Besides selection of the same residue for identical functional reasons (convergence) and selection of the residue for different functional reasons, there may be coincidence effects in the absence of any selection by genetic drift.

Some abnormal human hemoglobins are characterized by substituent residues that also occur as normal residues in some animal hemoglobins. There can be, in such cases, no question of convergence as long as we do not assume that the rare human mutant has been selected for. Aspartic acid instead of glycine at site E6 characterizes the abnormal human hemoglobin Norfolk and probably an orangutan hemoglobin chain (5, 6, 36). Lysine instead of asparagine at position E17 in the α chain is a character of HbG Philadelphia as well as probably of pig hemoglobin (7, 10). Aspartic acid instead of glycine is found at position A13 in the β chain of HbJ Baltimore and of the horse (9, 62). Such occurrences will allow one to study the physicochemical effects of single substitutions that occur in combination with other substitutions in other hemoglobins.

As we saw, alanine occurs at at least 51 out of 148 sites of globin chains (Table I). Conversions to proline have been found at only 9 of these sites. The conversion alanine–proline is one of the 7 allowed one-step conversions from alanine, according to Eck's code. The chances are that mutations to proline will at some time have occurred at most of the 51 alanine sites. Most of these mutations have been eliminated by natural selection and, in the case of alanine sites that are inside α helices, the reason is obvious. The disrupting effect of prolyl residues on α helices presumably is also the reason why proline has been selected for at some alanine sites in interhelical sections of the polypeptide chain. Thus, when the conversion from an ancestral alanine to a descendent proline has occurred twice or more times independently, as may well obtain at globin site 4α ($=$ A2) (71), proline should be present in the descendent chains for very similar if not strictly identical reasons. Such are cases of convergence.

Whether we witness convergence or coincidences without convergence, the frequency of such effects in globin chains is high. Nevertheless we may, in most cases, be assured that these effects do not lead to the establishment of false homology relations. The progressively increasing number of differences between globin chains as one compares forms further removed from each other on the evolutionary scale sets limits to the amount of changes per unit evolutionary time, and thereby to the amount of similarity between chains that can be generated by coincidence and convergence. Moreover, differences also may be generated by chance and compensate for coincidences.

What may be obscured by secondarily generated identities, at any molecular site, is the correct branching of the phylogenetic tree established for that single site, when one attempts to determine the branching independently from knowledge derived from classical taxonomy. This only means, however, that on account of coincidences with or without convergence, one cannot expect to safely establish phylogenetic relationships from similarities and differences that are observed at a single molecular site. When the information contained in the phylogenetic trees for all molecular sites of a given polypeptide chain is combined, one may expect that the resulting measurement of phyletic distance between the chains will approach reality; the more so, the longer the chain. It is intended to carry out such measurements and to compare the results with those of organismal biology.

When the organismal biologist speaks of convergence—a phenomenon that has been disturbing to taxonomists—he refers to structures of independent phylogenetic origin that have become apparently identical or strikingly similar. To inquire whether a molecular equivalent of this phenomenon exists in informational macromolecules, we may ask the question in the following way: If we consider two polypeptide chains with random amino acid sequences, is there enough evolutionary time available for the chance to be significant that a succession of evolutionarily effective mutations generates significant similarities between the two chains so that the chains appear to be homologous?

By far the largest proportion of evolutionarily effective mutations will be those that change the polypeptide within the limits of its established function and tertiary structure. Only a small, and probably very small, proportion of evolutionarily effective mutations will be of the kind that alter radically the function and tertiary structure of the polypeptide.

Of these presumably only a small or very small proportion will lead to types of proteins that duplicate in tertiary structure and function already existing types of proteins.

Although countless pathways exist for the transformation of one polypeptide chain into another by point mutations, deletions, additions, intracistronic partial duplications, and recombinations, the assumption that a channel can be found during evolutionary time, such that each step in the pathway is functionally useful and selected for, appears to be a daring one.

The difficulty is not to imagine that the product at each step of transfunctional transformation of a polypeptide chain has some kind of enzymatic activity. Interestingly, Professor Sidney Fox (18) has detected some weak enzymatic activities in his synthetic proteinoids. It seems significant, however, that these activities are weak.

It may be a fallacy to think that, when a polypeptide chain displays a weak enzymatic activity of a given kind, this can be turned into a strong enzymatic activity of the same kind by a succession of evolutionarily effective mutations. In other words, it may be a fallacy to think that weak enzymes are the evolutionary antecedents of strong enzymes with the same type of activity.

It may well be that all polypeptide chains are endowed with weak enzymatic activities of some kind, especially in the presence of trace metals. For natural selection to retain a polypeptide, a weak enzymatic activity may be sufficient only in the beginning phases of evolution. In organisms that are already established, it is probable that a weak enzymatic activity will be selected for only rarely. For most weak activities developed, there will already be a stronger activity available, and therefore the "new" enzyme will not be retained. Moreover a weak enzymatic action of a novel kind may not suffice to encourage the evolvement of a novel function within organisms already endowed with intense metabolic activities.

A strong enzymatic activity is likely to require a much higher degree of specificity, notably in tertiary structure, than a corresponding weak enzymatic activity. From an enzyme with a weak activity to an enzyme with a strong activity of the *same* kind, the evolutionary pathway, in terms of transformations of primary, tertiary, and quaternary structure, may be most of the time as involved as the pathway between two specified functionally *different* types of proteins.

One may thus deem it likely that a new enzyme that is retained by natural selection arises with a tertiary structure not remote from that which is finally evolved. The evolution of a functionally important new polypeptide chain may well be a saltatory phenomenon and not a progressive one. Once a rare random mutational event leads to a privileged tertiary structure combined with features of primary structure that are, together, associated in determining some intense enzymatic activity, this polypeptide, if retained by natural selection, will undergo, in the early stages of its history, a limited amount of "perfecting" steps to further the function that was attained at once (cf. Section II.1). Thereafter most of the evolutionary history of the polypeptide will be marked by variations on a functional theme rather than by the perfecting of a function.

Synthetic proteinoids seem to be of great interest mainly in relation to very early stages of evolution. A chemical model of an evolutionary process as it occurs in any of the presently existing phyla should allow the production in a test tube of polypeptides with strong enzymatic activities. The chances for this to occur by copolymerization are probably small. It would not be surprising that a template mechanism for polypeptide production is a necessary requirement for strong, specific enzymatic activities to arise, because the rare polypeptide endowed with these properties can hardly be produced reproducibly in sufficient amounts except through a template mechanism of molecular multiplication. In copolymerization experiments, such a rare polypeptide, with a rare tertiary structure, is likely to be only a "contaminant," and the observed enzymatic activity will be weak.

To achieve a pseudo-homology between two polypeptide chains of independent evolutionary origin, it would be necessary, according to the above discussion, that there exist a pathway of functional transformations such that mutations can lead the polypeptide chain in saltatory fashion from one type of strong enzymatic activity to another type of strong enzymatic activity. For this to happen it would be necessary that the number of required functional transformations between, say, a random polypeptide chain and a hemoglobin chain be very small indeed. There is no reason to assume that such is the case.

Whereas one cannot say that pseudo-homologies between polypeptide chains never arise in evolution, it seems very unlikely that such a process has occurred in the case of any particular polypeptide chain one is considering. It is thus likely that proteins as different in amino acid sequence as mammalian hemoglobins and myoglobins indeed derive from a common molecular ancestor, not because of the characters of amino acid sequence they have in common, but because of the common characters of primary structure, tertiary structure, and function taken together. The ease with which variations of a given type of protein can be produced through duplication and mutation of a gene should be so much greater than the ease of convergent evolution from independent starting points that on the basis of this consideration alone any variants within a given type of tertiary structure and function seem to have a much greater chance to be phyletically related than unrelated.

## Acknowledgment

The authors thank Mr. Jean-Pierre Salleï for his help in preparing the tables. This work was supported in part by N.I.H. award # GM 11272-01A1.

## References

1. Allison, A. C., Cecil, R., Charlwood, P. A., Gratzer, W. B., Jacobs, S., and Snow, N. S., *Biochim. Biophys. Acta*, **42**, 43 (1960).
2. Allison, A. C., personal communication.
3. Babin, D., and Schroeder, W. A., personal communication.
4. Baglioni, C., *Biochim. Biophys. Acta*, **59**, 437 (1962).
5. Baglioni, C., *J. Biol. Chem.*, **237**, 69 (1962).
6. Baglioni, C., personal communication.
7. Baglioni, C., and Ingram, V. M., *Biochim. Biophys. Acta*, **48**, 253 (1961).
8. Baglioni, C., and Lehmann, H., *Nature*, **196**, 229 (1962).
9. Baglioni, C., and Weatherall, D. J., *Biochim. Biophys. Acta*, **78**, 637 (1963).
10. Braunitzer, G., communicated at Conference on Hemoglobin, November 5-7, 1962, Arden House, Harriman, New York.
11. Braunitzer, G., and Hilse, K., *Z. Physiol. Chem.*, **330**, 234 (1963).
12. Braunitzer, G., and Matsuda, G., *J. Biochem.*, **53**, 262 (1963).
13. Cullis, A. F., Muirhead, H., Perutz, M. F., and Rossmann, M. G., *Proc. Roy. Soc.*, **A265**, 161 (1961).
14. Diamond, M., and Braunitzer, G., *Nature*, **194**, 1287 (1962).
15. Dobzhansky, Th., personal communication (1964).
16. Eck, R. V., *Science*, **140**, 477 (1963).
17. Ficq, A., and Pavan, C., *Nature*, **180**, 983 (1957).
18. Fox, S. W., this volume.
19. Freese, E., *Proc. Natl. Acad. Sci. U.S.*, **45**, 622 (1959).
20. Gerald, P. S., and Efron, M. L., *Proc. Natl. Acad. Sci. U.S.*, **47**, 1758 (1961).
21. Hanada, M., and Rucknagel, D. L., *Biochem. Biophys. Res. Commun.*, **11**, 229 (1963).
22. Hill, R. J., and Kraus, A. P., *Federation Proc.*, **22**, 597 (1963).
23. Hill, R. L., personal communication.
24. Hill, R. L., Buettner-Janusch, J., and Buettner-Janusch, V., *Proc. Natl. Acad. Sci. U.S.*, **50**, 885 (1963).
25. Hill, R. L., Swenson, R. T., and Schwartz, H. C., *J. Biol. Chem.*, **235**, 3182 (1960).
26. Hoyer, B. H., McCarthy, B. J., and Bolton, E. T., *Science*, **140**, 1408 (1963).
27. Huehns, E. R., Dance, N., Beaven, G. H., Keil, D. V., Hecht, F., and Motulsky, A. G., *Nature*, **201**, 1095 (1964).
28. Hunt, J. A., and Ingram, V. M., *Nature*, **184**, 640 (1959).

29. HUNT, J. A., AND INGRAM, V. M., *Biochim. Biophys. Acta*, **42**, 409 (1960).
30. HUNT, J. A., AND INGRAM, V. M., *Biochem. Biophys. Acta*, **49**, 520 (1961).
31. INGRAM, V. M., *Nature*, **180**, 326 (1957).
32. INGRAM, V. M., *Nature*, **189**, 704 (1961).
33. ITANO, H. A., *Advan. Protein Chem.*, **12**, 215 (1957).
34. ITANO, H. A., Symposium on Abnormal Hemoglobins, Ibadan, 1963. Blackwell, Oxford.
35. JONES, R. T., personal communication.
36. JONES, R. T., AND ZUCKERKANDL, E., unpublished results.
37. JUKES, T. H., *in* "The Origins of Prebiological Systems," (S.W. Fox, ed.), p. 407, Academic Press, New York, 1965.
38. KENDREW, J. C., *Brookhaven Symp. Biol.*, **15**, 216 (1962).
39. LANNI, F., *Proc. Natl. Acad. Sci. U.S.*, **47**, 261 (1961).
40. LOVE, W. E., *Federation Proc.*, **22**, 597 (1963).
40a. MARGOLIASH, E., *Brookhaven Symp. Biol.*, **15**, 266 (1962).
41. MARGOLIASH, E., AND SMITH, E. L., this volume.
42. MONOD, J., CHANGEUX, J. P., AND JACOB, F., *J. Mol. Biol.*, **6**, 306 (1963).
43. MUIRHEAD, H., AND PERUTZ, M. F., *Cold Spring Harbor Symp. Quant. Biol.*, **28**, 451 (1963).
44. MULLER, C. J., AND KINGMA, S., *Biochim. Biophys. Acta*, **50**, 595 (1961).
45. MURYAMA, M., *Federation Proc.*, **19**, 78 (1960).
46. NANCE, W. E., *Science*, **141**, 123 (1963).
47. NEEL, J. V., WELLS, I. C., AND ITANO, H. A., *J. Clin. Invest.*, **30**, 1120 (1951).
48. PATTEE, H. H., *Biophys. J.*, **1**, 683 (1960).
49. PAULING, L., AND ZUCKERKANDL, E., *Acta Chem. Scand.*, **17**, 9 (1963).
50. PERUTZ, M. F., "Proteins and Nucleic Acids," Elsevier, Amsterdam, 1962.
51. PIERCE, L. E., *New Engl. J. Med.*, **268**, 862 (1963).
52. RUDLOFF, V., communicated at the 6th Intern. Congr. Biochem., New York, 1964.
53. SATAKE, K., AND SASAWAKA, S., *J. Biochem. (Tokyo)*, **52**, 232 (1962).
54. SCHACHMAN, H. K., *Cold Spring Harbor Symp. Quant. Biol.*, **28**, 409 (1963).
55. SCHELLMAN, J. A., AND SCHELLMAN, Ch., *in* "The Proteins," (H. Neurath, ed.), Vol. II, p. 1, Academic Press, New York, 1964.
56. SCHNEIDER, R. G., HAGGARD, M. E., MCNUTT, C. W., JOHNSON, J. E., BOWMAN, B. H., AND BARNETT, D. R., *Science*, **143**, 697 (1964).
57. SCHROEDER, W. A., *Fortschr. Chem. Org. Naturstoffe*, **17**, 322 (1959).
58. SCHROEDER, W. A., *Ann. Rev. Biochem.*, **32**, 301 (1963).
59. SCHROEDER, W. A., SHELTON, J. R., SHELTON, J. B., CORMICK, J., AND HONES, R. T., *Biochemistry*, **2**, 992 (1963).
60. SIMPSON, G. G., *Science*, **146**, 1535 (1964).
61. SIMPSON, G. G., *Science*, **143**, 769 (1964).
62. SMITH, D. B., *Can. J. Biochem.*, **42**, 755 (1963).
63. SMITH, E. L., personal communication.
64. ŠORM, F., *Collection Czech. Chem. Commun.*, **27**, 994 (1962).
65. STEINHARDT, J., AND BEYCHOK, S., *in* "The Proteins" (H. Neurath, ed.), Vol. II, p. 140, Academic Press, New York, 1964.
66. SWENSON, R. T., HILL, R. L., LEHMANN, H., AND JIM, R. T. S., *J. Biol. Chem.*, **237**, 1517 (1962).
67. SWIFT, H., *in* "The Molecular Control of Cellular Activity" (J. M. Allen, ed.), p. 73, McGraw-Hill, New York, 1962.

68. VOGEL, H. J., BRYSON, V., AND LAMPEN, J. O., eds., "Informational Macromolecules," Academic Press, New York, 1963.
69. ZUCKERKANDL, E., in "Classification and Human Evolution" (S. L. Washburn, ed.), p. 243, Aldine Publishing Co., Chicago, 1963.
70. ZUCKERKANDL, E., J. Mol. Biol., 8, 128 (1964).
71. ZUCKERKANDL, E., in "Protides of Biological Fluids," Proceedings of the 12th Colloquium (H. Peeters, ed.), p. 102, Bruges, 1964.
72. ZUCKERKANDL, E., Abstr. 6th Intern. Congr. Biochem., New York, Vol. III, p. 210 (1964).
73. ZUCKERKANDL, E., in preparation.
74. ZUCKERKANDL, E., AND PAULING, L., in "Horizons in Biochemistry," (M. Kasha and B. Pullman, eds.), p. 189, Academic Press, New York, 1962.
75. ZUCKERKANDL, E., AND PAULING, L., in "Problems of Evolutionary and Industrial Biochemistry," p. 54, Science Press, Academy of Sciences, USSR, 1964, and J. Theoret. Biol., 8, 357 (1965).
76. ZUCKERKANDL, E., AND SCHROEDER, W. A., Nature, 192, 984 (1961).
77. ZUCKERKANDL, E., AND SCHROEDER, W. A., unpublished observations.

# Evolution of Hemoglobin in Primates[1]

JOHN BUETTNER-JANUSCH[2] AND ROBERT L. HILL

*Department of Anthropology, Yale University, New Haven, Connecticut, and
Department of Biochemistry, Duke University, Durham, North Carolina*

## INTRODUCTION

The invariant replication of the genetic material (DNA) and the invariant translation of the genetic information into protein structure are conceived as the molecular basis for the maintenance of a species and its distinctness from other species. The extinction of a species or the transformation of a species into one or more descendant species may be thought of as the result of specific chemical changes in the genetic material. But specific chemical changes, mutations, in the genetic material do not produce a species transformation, let alone a generic, familial, or subordinal one, until sufficient changes have accumulated within a population so that it is genetically isolated from all others. Selection on the *population* of organisms within which these mutational alterations occur preserves some and eliminates others. And this is a continuous process (25, 35, 36). In this paper we discuss the interplay between molecular and organismal aspects of these evolutionary events through study of the hemoglobin of man and his primate relatives.

Organisms, populations of them, evolve. And molecules evolve with them. The evolution of proteins, as we have spoken of it in the past, must be understood in an organismal framework, in our case that of the Primates. Paleontologists insist that we are playing with metaphors when we speak of molecules evolving and that we are constructing taxonomies of molecules, not phylogenies of organisms. Such discussions have a way of becoming academic arguments over semantic niceties (33, 36).

The correct phylogeny of the Order Primates is, for an egocentric species such as our own, a matter of overwhelming fascination. It is unfortunate that investigation of such an inherently interesting problem has not yet produced an acceptable, systematic classification of the Primates based on phylogeny (3, 32). A relatively sound and generally acceptable phylogeny of the higher categories—infraorders and super-

---

[1] The work reported here was supported in part by research grants from the National Institutes of Health, U.S. Public Health Service.

[2] Research Career Development awardee of the U.S. Public Health Service.

families—exists. A systematic account of the species and genera, extant and extinct, is still not available.

There are two major methodological approaches to the problem of the phylogeny of the Primates: paleontological, the study of fossils, and neontological, the comparative study of living forms. It is unwise to immerse oneself in one method without cognizance of the other (29). One paleontologist says, "Phylogeny of the Primates based on analysis of modern forms alone is at best metaphorical and at worse irrelevant" (30). The neontological approach has been devoted, primarily, to comparative osteology and anatomy. There have been attempts at phylogenetic investigation of other traits of the living forms, but, until recently, the results have not been well integrated with other aspects of primate neontology.

If we are to study the phylogeny of molecules, an obvious question must be asked. Do molecules evolve? The obvious answer is yes, for the organisms chosen have evolved. But some molecules are not good subjects for phylogenetic studies, for they vary little among organisms. Before we can pick a protein with which to study evolution, we must have some inkling that it varies in structure among living organisms which became phylogenetically distinct at succeeding time periods.

Hemoglobin has been modified structurally in the course of evolution. The evidence for this modification has been summarized concisely by Ingram (22). The hemoglobins of the Primates were chosen for study for several reasons. The hemoglobin of one of the Primates, *Homo sapiens*, has been the subject of extensive research (26, 27). The body of data available provides an excellent perspective on the differentiation and the variation of the hemoglobin molecule within a single species. We have shown that the normal hemoglobins of various species of Primates are not identical (2, 4-6, 16, 17). Hemoglobin is an ideal protein for studies of molecular evolution. The living primates are one of the orders of Mammalia that promise most as a subject for the study of organismal evolution. The study of the hemoglobins of the Primates should be an unbeatable combination for evolutionary studies. We have been investigating the differences that exist in the primary structures of the hemoglobins among the Primates. We have, thus, been able to *begin* a molecular study of primate evolution and an organismal study of hemoglobin evolution (2, 5, 16, 17).

## PRIMATE PHYLOGENY

Before we discuss the hemoglobins of primates in some detail, we believe a few words about the molecular approach to phylogeny are needed. This approach has been pursued with enthusiasm by many (11, 14, 15, 17, 19, 38, 39). Such enthusiasm has not always been moderated by a discriminating appreciation of modern evolutionary theory. Torn out of context, the logical and substantive statements may appear reckless and absurd, though within the specific context of comparisons among molecules they are not. Nevertheless, the pitfalls into which one may tumble are demonstrated when the protein is assumed to be definitive in determining phylogenetic relationships and taxonomic issues. For example, the close similarity in the structure of the hemoglobins of man and gorilla (38, 40) is an important datum; it is simply not a datum that is conclusive in systematics.

The immunochemical similarities between the serum proteins of the African apes and man have been used as an argument to remove the great apes from the Pongidae and to place them in the Hominidae (14, 15). But Hominidae is a taxon whose distinctions from Pongidae are determined by the total adaptive complexes and relationships of each. This total adaptive relationship may be determined by serum proteins, as well as by more classical morphological and ecological analyses, but serum proteins are not the sufficient or the necessary criteria for distinction.

Accusations of circular reasoning are sometimes difficult to refute. If phylogeny is inferred from molecular data, and molecular evolution from the phylogeny, then circular reasoning is evident (36). Some investigators choose protein molecules for study on the basis of an accepted phylogeny of the animals from which the proteins are taken. When interpretation of their data agrees with the phylogeny, then added weight is given the molecular approach. When the phylogeny does not conform to the interpretation of the molecular data, the phylogeny is revised. Since these are phylogenies of organisms, not molecules, the validity of such reasoning is suspect. It *is* possible to construct taxonomies of molecules and even phylogenies of molecules, but they have *no phylogenetic significance* apart from the phylogenies of the organisms from which they were taken.

The particular primate phylogeny that is the basis of our work is presented in Table I. If we consider only the living members, the Order Primates consists of eight taxa, monophyletic in origin, which are assigned to various levels of the Linnaean hierarchy. There are various ways in which the phylogeny of the Primates is interpreted (3, 18, 33). The one used here is generally accepted, and it is derived from Simpson's now classic work on mammalian classification (32).

The Tupaiiformes, the tree shrews of southeast Asia, are living representatives of an ancient mammalian stock, which, if it were alive today, would be placed with the Insectivora. But the living Tupaiiformes, as LeGros Clark showed, are best placed with the Primates (7, 8). They *represent* the first major adaptive radiation of the Primates which occurred in the early Paleocene. They are often considered a kind of intermediate group between Insectivora and Primates.

The Lorisiformes and Lemuriformes probably represent the next major adaptive radiation which occurred in the late Paleocene or early Eocene. These two groups are the galagos (bush babies), lorises, and pottos of Africa and Asia and the lemurs of Madagascar.

The Tarsiiformes are clearly prosimians, though one prominent monographer of the Primates wishes to place them in the same major group as the monkeys, apes, and man (18). They differentiated in late Paleocene or early Eocene times.

TABLE I

CLASSIFICATION OF THE PRIMATES SHOWING THE EIGHT MAJOR TAXA

| | |
|---|---|
| Order: | Primates |
| Suborder: | Prosimii |
| Infraorder: | Tupaiiformes (I) |
| | Tarsiiformes (II) |
| | Lorisiformes (III) |
| | Lemuriformes (IV) |
| Suborder: | Anthropoidea |
| Superfamily: | Ceboidea (V) |
| | Cercopithecoidea (VI) |
| | Hominoidea |
| Family: | Pongidae (VII) |
| | Hominidae (VIII) |

The Cercopithecoidea are representatives of another major adaptive radiation. Though they are usually assumed to be intermediate between prosimians and anthropoids, it is not unlikely that most modern cercopithecines are part of a relatively recent adaptive radiation. Some Cercopithecoidea had differentiated in the Oligocene.

The Pongidae are the apes—*Pan* (gorilla and chimpanzee), *Pongo* (orangutan), and *Hylobates* (gibbon) (34). This group was distinct by the late Oligocene.

The Ceboidea, the New World primates, are, in a sense a side issue and an evolutionary experiment. They developed in isolation in the New World with many adaptive and structural parallels to the primates of the Old World. Like the Malagasy lemurs, they show the extent to which a primate stock may radiate and differentiate if left in isolation. They appear as a distinct group, fully differentiated, in Miocene deposits in South America.

The Hominidae, with a single living member—*Homo*—became a distinct evolutionary lineage sometime in the Miocene (31). The adaptive radiation, based upon erect posture and bipedal locomotion, was fully underway in the early Pleistocene when the genus *Homo* became distinct.

The living primates have long been recognized as constituting a series of successively more advanced forms (20). They have been called a living family tree in miniature. Therein lies their value for students of mammalian evolution. As LeGros Clark stated (9), ". . . the trees of African and Asiatic forests still retain . . . a stratified population of Primates which represents the successive grades of the evolutionary tree of this order." This evolutionary stratification of the living members of our own mammalian order, based principally upon interpretations of comparative anatomy and fossil records, is the foundation for our study of hemoglobin. We selected hemoglobin from those members of the Order which represent stages in development from the most primitive—tree shrews, lemurs—to the more advanced—baboons, apes—to the most advanced form—man.

But first a word of caution. Implicit in our work is the assumption that the hemoglobin of *Tupaia glis* is a more primitive hemoglobin than that of *Lemur fulvus,* and that of *Lemur fulvus* more primitive than that of *Hylobates lar.* Tree shrews, galagos, pottos, tarsiers, lemurs, monkeys, apes, and men may be taken to represent Paleocene, Eocene, Oligocene, Miocene, Pliocene, and Pleistocene developments within the Order (Table II). But we are not investigating Paleocene, Eocene, Oligocene, Miocene, Pliocene, or Pleistocene hemoglobins. We are investigating hemoglobins of living primates who themselves are the products of change and development since their differentiation during various epochs from a common stock or population.

## HEMOGLOBINS AND EVOLUTION

Human hemoglobin is the base line against which the other hemoglobins are compared. The $\alpha$, $\beta$, and $\gamma$ chains of *Homo sapiens* are the referents when we speak of substitutions and relative similarities and differences (23, 24, 28). Amino acid sequences of primate peptides presented here were deduced from comparisons with sequences of homologous peptides from human hemoglobins. The methods used for these studies have been described elsewhere (2, 5, 6, 16, 17, 37).

There are some trends or similarities throughout the Order Primates which are significant. The $\alpha$ chain, or $\alpha$-like chain, seems to be relatively constant throughout the Order. Few replacements have been found when the $\alpha$ chain of human hemoglobin is compared with the $\alpha$ chains of primate hemoglobins (Table III). Considerable additional data from peptide fingerprint patterns support this finding (17). There is one apparent exception; the baboon, *Papio*, has an α-like chain that is somewhat different from that of other primates.

The non-α or β-like chains of primate hemoglobins are quite variable when compared with the β chain or the γ chain of human hemoglobin (Tables IV and V). The sequence of most of the non-α chain of *Lemur fulvus* has been demonstrated. When we compare this sequence with the

TABLE II

PRIMATES USED IN CURRENT STUDIES OF HEMOGLOBIN[a]

| Epoch | Taxon | Genera | |
| | | Genus | Common name |
|---|---|---|---|
| Pleistocene | Hominidae | *Homo* | Man |
| Pliocene | Hominidae | — | |
| Miocene | Ceboidea | *Saimiri* | Squirrel monkey |
| | | *Cacajao* | Uakari |
| Oligocene | Pongidae | *Pongo* | Orangutan |
| | | *Hylobates* | Gibbon |
| | Cercopithecoidea | *Papio* | Baboon |
| | | *Cercopithecus* | Guenon |
| Eocene | Lemuriformes | *Lemur* | Lemur |
| | | *Propithecus* | Sifaka |
| | Lorisiformes | *Galago* | Bush baby |
| | | *Perodicticus* | Potto |
| | Tarsiiformes | — | |
| Paleocene | Tupaiiformes | *Tupaia* | Tree shrew |

[a] The genera chosen are representatives of most of the major taxa of the Order Primates. They are also representatives of the major geological time periods in which each major taxon differentiated.

TABLE III

AMINO ACID REPLACEMENTS—COMPARISON OF α CHAINS OF NONHUMAN PRIMATES WITH α CHAIN OF HUMAN HEMOGLOBIN[a]

| Primate | Number of peptides examined | Number of amino acids | Probable number of replacements |
|---|---|---|---|
| *Hylobates* | 5 | 53 | 0 |
| *Perodicticus* | 3 | 37 | 0 |
| *Galago* | 2 | 33 | 1 |
| *Lemur fulvus* | 10 | 101 | 6 |
| *L. catta* | 2 | 33 | 0 |
| *L. variegatus* | 4 | 24 | 3 |
| *Propithecus* | 4 | 21 | 4 |

[a] Data taken from earlier publications (16, 17).

β and γ chain sequences of human hemoglobin, we see that there is an homology among the three. Those positions in the sequence at which human β and γ chains differ correspond to segments of the *L. fulvus* non-α chain at which there are replacements (Table VI). If we compare *L. fulvus* non-α chain with human β chain there are 6 replacements that are homologous with human γ chain out of a total of 23 replacements.

TABLE IV

AMINO ACID REPLACEMENTS—COMPARISON OF β- OR γ-LIKE CHAINS OF NONHUMAN PRIMATES WITH β CHAIN OF HUMAN HEMOGLOBIN[a]

| Primate | Number of peptides examined | Number of amino acids | Probable number of replacements |
|---|---|---|---|
| Hylobates | 7 | 65 | 0 |
| Papio | 6 | 64 | 3 |
| Perodicticus | 5 | 49 | 8 |
| Galago | 10 | 87 | 9 |
| Lemur fulvus | 12 | 134 | 23 |
| L. variegatus | 11 | 96 | 23 |
| Propithecus | 3 | 30 | 4 |

[a] Data taken from earlier publications (16, 17).

TABLE V

AMINO ACID REPLACEMENTS—COMPARISON OF β- OR γ-LIKE CHAINS OF NONHUMAN PRIMATES WITH γ CHAIN OF HUMAN HEMOGLOBIN[a]

| Primate | Number of peptides examined | Number of amino acids | Probable number of replacements |
|---|---|---|---|
| Hylobates | 7 | 65 | 18 |
| Papio | 6 | 64 | 18 |
| Perodicticus | 5 | 49 | 9 |
| Galago | 10 | 87 | 21 |
| Lemur fulvus | 12 | 134 | 36 |
| L. variegatus | 11 | 96 | 25 |
| Propithecus | 3 | 30 | 10 |

[a] Data taken from earlier publications (16, 17).

Comparison of *L. fulvus* non-α chain with human γ chain shows 19 replacements that are homologous with β chain out of a total of 36 replacements. Seventeen replacements are unlike the amino acids at those positions in either β or γ chain. One of the most noteworthy differences between the non-α chain of *L. fulvus* and human β and γ chains is the presence of threonine as the NH₂-terminal amino acid. Threonine is also present in the NH₂-terminal position of the non-α chain of the hemoglobin of *Propithecus, Lemur catta,* and *Lemur variegatus* (2).

TABLE VI

Partial Sequences of β-Like Chain of Hemoglobin of *Lemur fulvus* and β and γ Chains of Human Hemoglobin[a]

Homo β  Val-His-Leu-Thr-Pro-Glu-Glu-Lys-Ser-Ala-Val-Thr-Ala-Leu-Try-Gly-Lys-Val-Asn-Val-Asp-Glu-
Lemur   *Thr-Leu-Ser-Ala-Glu-Glu-Ala-His-Val-*Thr-Ser-Leu-Try-Gly-Lys-Val-Asn-Val-*Glu-Lys-*
Homo γ  Gly-His-Phe-Thr-Glu-Glu-Asp-Lys-Ala-Thr-Ileu-Thr-Ser-Leu-Try-Gly-Lys-Val-Asn-Val-Glu-Asp-

Homo β  Val-Gly-Gly-Ala-Leu-Gly-Arg-Leu-Leu-Val-Val-Tyr-Pro-Try-Thr-Gln-Arg-Phe-Phe-Glu-Ser-
Lemur   *Val-*Gly-Glu-*Ala-*Leu-Gly-*Ala-*Leu-Gly-Arg-Leu-Leu-Val-Val(Tyr,Pro,Try,Thr,Gln,Arg,Phe,Phe,*Glu,*Ser,
Homo γ  Ala-Gly-Gly-Glu-Thr-Leu-Gly-Arg-Leu-Leu-Val-Val-Tyr-Pro-Try-Thr-Gln-Arg-Phe-Phe-Asp-Ser-

Homo β  Phe-Gly-Asp-Leu-Ser-Thr-Pro-Asp-Ala-Val-Met-Gly-Asn-Pro-Lys-Val-Lys-Ala-His-Gly-Lys-Lys-
Lemur   Phe,Gly,Asp)(Leu,*Ser,Ser,Pro,Ser,*Ala,*Val,*Met,Gly,Asn,Pro,Lys,Val,Lys,Ala,His,Gly,Lys,Lys,
Homo γ  Phe-Gly-Asn-Leu-Ser-Ser-Ala-Ileu-Met-Gly-Asn-Pro-Lys-Val-Lys-Ala-His-Gly-Lys-Lys-

Homo β  Val-Leu-Gly-Ala-Phe-Ser-Asp-Gly-Leu-Ala-His-Leu-Asp-Asn-Leu-Lys-Gly-Thr-Phe-Ala-Thr-Leu-
Lemur   Val,Leu,*Ser,Ala,*Phe,Ser,*Glu,Gly)(Leu,*His,His,Leu,Asp,*Asp,Leu,Lys,Gly,Thr,Phe,Ala,*Ala,*Leu,
Homo γ  Val-Leu-Thr-Ser-Leu-Gly-Asp-Ala-Ileu-Lys-His-Leu-Asp-Asp-Leu-Lys-Gly-Thr-Phe-Ala-Gln-Leu-

Homo β  Ser-Glu-Leu-His-Cys-Asp-Lys-Leu-His-Val-Asp-Pro-Glu-Asn-Phe-Arg-Leu-Leu-Gly-Asn-Val-Leu-
Lemur   Ser,Gln,Leu,His,Cys,*Val,Ala,*Leu,His,Val,Asp,Pro,Glu,*Asp,Phe,*Lys,Leu,Leu,Gly,*Asp,*Ser,Leu,
Homo γ  Ser-Glu-Leu-His-Cys-Asp-Lys-Leu-His-Val-Asp-Pro-Glu-Asn-Phe-Lys-Leu-Leu-Gly-Asn-Val-Leu-

Homo β  Val-Cys-Val-Leu-Ala-His-His-Phe-Gly-Lys-...
Lemur   *Ser,Asp,*Val,Leu,Ala,*Asp,His,Phe,Gly,Lys)...
Homo γ  Val-Thr-Val-Leu-Ala-Ileu-His-Phe-Gly-Lys-...

Homo β  Val-Val-Ala-Gly-Val-Ala-Asn-Ala-Leu-Ala-His-Lys-Tyr-His
Lemur   Val-Val-*Ala-*Gly-Val-*Ala-Gly-Val(*Ala,*Asp)Ala-Leu-*Ala-*His-*Lys-Tyr-His
Homo γ  Met-Val-Thr-Gly-Val-Ala-Ser-Ala-Leu-Ser-Ser-Arg-Tyr-His

Position markers: 1, 10, 20, 30, 40, 50, 60, 70, 80, 90, 100, 110, 120, 133, 140

[a] Residues italicized in *Lemur* sequences differ from analogous residues in β or γ chains.

The comparison of adult *Lemur* hemoglobin chains with human fetal chains was suggested by our earlier observation that adult prosimian hemoglobin was resistant to alkaline denaturation, as is human fetal hemoglobin (6). Recently we examined hemoglobin from a premature stillborn lemur and a newborn galago by means of starch-gel electrophoresis and alkaline denaturation. No differences between the fetal hemoglobin and the adult hemoglobin from each of these two species were demonstrated.

At this stage in our work certain interpretations of these data are possible. The α-like chains of primate hemoglobins are apparently subject to some kind of constraint, for they are much less variable than the non-α chains. A functional hemoglobin probably requires that one of the two chains remains stable. We know that human α chains form functional hemoglobins with β, γ, and δ chains (22). Now we also know that many other sequences are presented by the β-like chains of nonhuman primates for combination with α chains. Since the genes controlling synthesis of the α, β, γ, and δ chains of human hemoglobin are nonallelic, we assume that the genes for synthesis of α and non-α chains in other primates are also nonallelic. The data presented here suggest that mutations in one locus put a constraint on mutations in the other locus.

TABLE VII

PROBABLE INVARIANT SEQUENCES OF AMINO ACIDS IN α CHAINS
OF PRIMATE HEMOGLOBINS[a]

| Tryptic peptide[b] | Primates in which compositions are identical |
|---|---|
| αT-1 | *Homo, Hylobates, Perodicticus, Lemur fulvus, L. variegatus* |
| αT-2 | *Homo, Hylobates, Perodicticus, Lemur fulvus, L. catta* |
| αT-5 | *Homo, Propithecus, Lemur fulvus* |
| αT-6 | *Homo, Hylobates, Lemur fulvus* |
| αT-7 | *Homo, Hylobates* |
| αT-9 | *Homo, Hylobates, Galago, Perodicticus, Lemur catta* |

[a] Data taken from earlier publications (16, 17) and unpublished observations.

[b] Peptides numbered according to the nomenclature proposed by Gerald and Ingram (13).

Certain segments of the hemoglobin molecule appear to be invariant throughout the Order—this suggests that the function of the molecule or its synthesis is disrupted by alterations in this area (Tables VII and VIII). Mutations which produce substitutions here are quickly lost if they are not lethal. But there are a large number of differences, nonetheless, among the various hemoglobins, most of them in the non-α chains (Tables III, IV, V). Each species which we have examined has a unique hemoglobin, unique in at least one amino acid (16). The meaning of this is obvious: there are a large number of distinct primate hemoglobins, and the many alterations in sequence of amino acids apparently do not alter the function, and the efficient function, of the molecule.

Now we must consider some of the more general implications of these data. First, we shall consider the question of calculating rates of effective mutation using the hemoglobin of *L. fulvus* as our example.

There are 6 replacements in the partial sequence of the α chain of *Lemur fulvus*, when this sequence is compared with the analogous sequence of human hemoglobin (Table IX). *Lemur* has been phylogenetically separate from man for a maximum of $55 \times 10^6$ years. Thus the average number of years for a single mutation to be fixed in the α chain of the hemoglobin of a population of lemurs is $9.1 \times 10^6$ years. But the

TABLE VIII

PROBABLE INVARIANT SEQUENCES OF AMINO ACIDS IN β CHAINS
OF PRIMATE HEMOGLOBINS[a]

| Tryptic peptide[b] | Primates in which compositions are identical |
|---|---|
| βT-1 | *Homo, Hylobates* |
| βT-2 | *Homo, Hylobates* |
| βT-3 | *Homo, Hylobates, Papio, Perodicticus* |
| βT-4 | *Homo, Homo* γT-4, *Hylobates, Papio, Galago, Perodicticus, Propithecus, Lemur fulvus, L. variegatus, L. catta* |
| βT-5 | *Homo, Hylobates* |
| βT-6 | *Homo, Homo* γT-6, *Hylobates, Papio, Galago, Perodicticus, Propithecus, Lemur fulvus, L. variegatus, L. catta* |
| βT-7 | *Homo, Homo* γT-7, *Hylobates, Papio, Galago, Propithecus, Lemur fulvus, L. variegatus, L. catta* |
| βT-14 | *Homo, Galago, Lemur fulvus* |
| βT-15 | *Homo, Homo* γT-15, *Galago, Lemur fulvus, L. variegatus* |

[a] Data taken from earlier publication (16, 17).

[b] Peptides numbered according to the nomenclature proposed by Gerald and Ingram (13).

rate is quite different if we compare β-like chains of *Lemur fulvus* with human β and γ chains. There are 23 replacements in *L. fulvus* β-like chain when it is compared with β chain of man. The average number of years for a single mutation to be fixed in the β-like chain of the hemoglobin of a population of lemurs is $2.4 \times 10^6$ years. If we use human γ chain for comparison, the average number of years is $1.5 \times 10^6$. Thus if we make the assumption that *Lemur fulvus* α chains and β-like chains are derived from a common ancestor with human chains, then the rate at which effective mutations occur is neither constant nor linear. At least for lemur hemoglobins.

Second, we must consider the problem of the meaning of the large

TABLE IX

Composition of α Chain of Hemoglobin of *Lemur fulvus* and α Chain of Human Hemoglobin[a]

*Homo*   [1] Val-Leu-Ser-Pro-Ala-Asp-Lys-Thr-Asn-Val-Lys-Ala-Ala-Try-Gly-Lys-Val-Gly-Ala-His-Ala-Gly-[20]
*Lemur*   (Val,Leu,Ser,Pro,Ala,Asp,Lys)(Thr,Asn,Val,Lys)(Ala,Ala,Try,Gly,Asp,Val,Gly,Ala,His,Ala,Gly,

*Homo*   Glu-Tyr-Gly-Ala-Glu-Ala-Leu-Glu-Arg-Met-Phe-Leu-Ser-Phe-Pro-Thr-Thr-Lys-Thr-Tyr-Phe-Pro-[40]
*Lemur*   Glu,*Thr*,Gly,Ala,Glu,Glu,Leu,Glu,Arg)(Met,Phe,Leu,Ser,Phe,Pro,Thr,Thr,Lys)(Thr,Tyr,Phe,Pro,

*Homo*   His-Phe-Asp-Leu-Ser-His-Gly-Ser-Ala-Gln-Val-Lys-Gly-His-Gly-Lys-Lys-Val-Ala-Asp-Ala-Leu-[60]
*Lemur*   His,Phe,Asp,Leu,Ser,His,Gly,Ser,*Gly*,Gly,Val,Lys)(*Ala*,His,Gly,Lys)(Lys)(Val,Ala,Asp,Ala,Leu,

*Homo*   Thr-Asn-Ala-Val-Ala-His-Val-Asp-Asp-Met-Pro-Asn-Ala-Leu-Ser-Ala-Leu-Ser-Asp-Leu-His-Ala-[80]
*Lemur*   Thr,Asp,Ala,Val,Ala,His,*Leu*,Asp,Asp,Met,Pro,Asn,Ala,Leu,Ser,Ala,Leu,Ser,Asp,Leu,His,Ala,

*Homo*   [90] His-Lys-Leu-Arg-Val-Asp-Pro-Val-Asn-Phe-Lys-[99] . . . Tyr-Arg [140]
*Lemur*   His,Lys)(Leu,Arg)(Val,Asp,Pro,Val,Asp,Phe,Lys) . . . (Tyr,Arg)

[a] Residues italicized in *Lemur* sequences differ from analogous residues in *Homo*.

number of amino acid substitutions found among various primate hemo-globins. When we use the α, β, and γ chains of human hemoglobin as the referents, we find a relatively large number of amino acid substi-tutions in the hemoglobins of the Primates during their long evolutionary history. This implies a large number of point mutations. The amino acid substitutions at many positions in the sequences are considered chem-ically equivalent by protein chemists. That is, the substitution of an aspartyl for a glutamyl residue, or of leucyl, isoleucyl, or valyl for each other, is not expected to have any great effect on the activity. It is also known that, in some proteins, certain residues can be extensively altered or eliminated with no significant loss of activity (1, 10). Does this suggest that there are neutral traits and, hence, neutral genes? The evidence that highly modified amino acids can be incorporated into proteins without altering their activity or function is taken from *in vitro* experiments. There is no evidence yet, from complex organisms such as the Primates, that such "neutrally altered" proteins would function and would persist in a population of organisms.

If these replacements are *biologically* equivalent, then we have neu-tral traits. But what is the evidence that these traits are neutral? The fact that they may seem to have an equivalent role in the molecule does not answer the question. The question really is, how does an effective mutation, which is a relatively rare event, become common or fixed in a population? At present the only mechanism we know by which this occurs is natural selection. The animals that carry the mutation must have a reproductive advantage over others in the population that do not carry it. Unless this is the case, the trait is likely to disappear through accidents of sampling, sometimes called genetic drift, or to remain at a very low frequency. If the known substitutions in lemur hemoglobins are selectively neutral, then it seems we must postulate synchronous muta-tions throughout the population or species. And this is highly improbable.

We are confronted by a difficulty, for we cannot at the moment demonstrate increased biological advantage for any of these substitutions. On the evidence we have, however, we can reason that neutral substi-tutions probably do not occur. First, there appears to be an invariant segment of the hemoglobin molecule (Tables VII and VIII). If neutral substitutions are possible, i.e., functionally equivalent amino acid resi-dues, why not here? Second, there is a lesson in the variable hemoglobins of one primate, *Homo sapiens*. At least one case is known in this species where a single substitution has profound physiological effects—the case of hemoglobin S (21). And the only sound explanation for the relative frequency of hemoglobin S in certain populations is positive selection on the heterozygotes, that is, positive differential fertility of the AS heterozygote individuals over AA and SS homozygotes (12). This is quite independent of whether or not it is indeed *Plasmodium falciparum* which is the *agent* of selection.

Finally, we must consider hemoglobin data in the context of primate phylogeny and systematics. There are some general trends worth pointing out and some things to be said about the use of such data in analyzing primate systematics.

The hemoglobins of the Anthropoidea and the Prosimii differ from each other more than the hemoglobins of primates within each group differ from each other (17). On the basis of our evidence from fingerprints, electrophoresis, and some peptide compositions, the hemoglobins of the Anthropoidea are very similar to those of man. Hemoglobins of the Prosimii vary among themselves much more than do hemoglobins of the Anthropoidea.

One interesting exception to the general rule is the hemoglobin of the baboon, *Papio*. Clearly, this hemoglobin appears to differ a great deal more from human hemoglobin than does that of all the other Anthropoidea examined so far. Fingerprint patterns alone of *Papio* hemoglobin show as many differences from human hemoglobin fingerprint patterns as do those of some prosimian hemoglobins. Nevertheless it is unlikely that we shall wish to switch the phylogenetic position of the baboon solely on the basis of this evidence.

Phylogenetic distance between two taxa is a confusingly applied concept. As Mayr has clearly shown, two things make up phylogenetic relationships. One is the fact that phyletic branching has occurred. The other consists of all the genetic, ecological, and selective events that occurred after branching (25).

The hemoglobin of *Tupaia*, judging from fingerprints alone, differs considerably from human hemoglobin, more than the hemoglobin of most of the other primates studied. But probably no more so than does hemoglobin from some Lemuriformes. It is worth noting here that *Tupaia* hemoglobin differs considerably from hemoglobins of certain Insectivora, namely the Macroscelididae, elephant shrews of East Africa.

The hemoglobins of the Lemuriformes resemble each other more than they resemble human hemoglobin or hemoglobin from most of the other primates. There appear to be many more similarities between hemoglobins of Lemuriformes and Lorisiformes than there are between the hemoglobins of either and those of the other primates. Amino acid composition, end group analysis, and grosser methods such as starch-gel electrophoresis and peptide mapping confirm this (2, 5, 16, 17).

The hemoglobins of the Ceboidea are apparently similar to human hemoglobin. The Ceboidea are most interesting in this respect, for they are not closely related to man. They are descended from an ancient stock which must have been phylogenetically distinct from other primates well before their first appearance in Miocene deposits of South America. Dentition separates them from all other living primates, and the only presently known fossil group to whom they relate are the Omomyidae, Eocene prosimian fossils found in many parts of the world, but not in South America. The hemoglobin data, based solely on peptide patterns and starch gels, suggest that their hemoglobin has become quite similar to that of *Homo sapiens* (5, 17).

We have relatively little information about the hemoglobins of the Cercopithecoidea. What we have suggests that they are quite similar to human hemoglobin. There is, of course, the one exception, *Papio*.

Pongid hemoglobin is very much like that of man. The information available indicates that several pongid hemoglobins, if the source were not known, might easily be lost among the many variant human hemoglobins (5, 17, 38, 40).

Our notions of primate classification will not be changed by the hemoglobin data we have presented. The differences and similarities among primate hemoglobins reflect, to a large extent, present classifications and notions of phylogeny. The exceptions present us with further research problems, not new classifications.

In this paper we have tried to show how to synthesize an approach to molecular-organismal evolution. We have tried to show where this synthesis should begin, what organisms to use as substrates, what proteins to use as enzymes, and how much classical evolutionary biology to stir in as inhibitors. After a few more years of effort we hope to have an elegant and useful product.

## SUMMARY

Hemoglobins from several primates, representative of the various taxa within the Order, have been examined. Determination of partial sequences and peptide patterns indicated that the α chains are conservative, differing relatively little among the various species. The β (or β-like) chains vary considerably. The implications of these data for calculation of effective mutation rates, for molecular evolution, and for phylogeny were discussed.

## REFERENCES

1. ANFINSEN, C. B., "The Molecular Basis of Evolution," Wiley, New York, 1959.
2. BRADSHAW, R. A., ROGERS, L. A., BUETTNER-JANUSCH, J., AND HILL, R. L., *Arch. Biochem. Biophys.*, in press (1965).
3. BUETTNER-JANUSCH, J., *in* "Evolutionary and Genetic Biology of Primates" (J. Buettner-Janusch, ed.), Vol. I, p. 1, Academic Press, New York, 1963.
4. BUETTNER-JANUSCH, J., AND BUETTNER-JANUSCH, V., *Nature,* **197**, 1018 (1963).
5. BUETTNER-JANUSCH, J., AND BUETTNER-JANUSCH, V., *in* "Evolutionary and Ge-

netic Biology of Primates" (J. Buettner-Janusch, ed.), Vol. II, p. 75, Academic Press, New York, 1964.

6. BUETTNER-JANUSCH, J., AND TWICHELL, J. B., *Nature*, **192**, 669 (1961).
7. CLARK, W. E. LeGROS, *Proc. Zool. Soc. London*, **1**, 461 (1924).
8. CLARK, W. E. LeGROS, *Proc. Zool. Soc. London*, **2**, 1053 (1924).
9. CLARK, W. E. LeGROS, "The Antecedents of Man," Quadrangle Press, Chicago, 1960.
10. COWIE, D. B., AND COHEN, G. N., *Biochim. Biophys. Acta*, **26**, 252 (1957).
11. DOOLITTLE, R. F., AND BLOMBÄCK, B., *Nature*, **202**, 147 (1964).
12. FIRSCHEIN, I. L., *Am. J. Human Genet.*, **13**, 233 (1961).
13. GERALD, P. S., AND INGRAM, V. M., *J. Biol. Chem.*, **236**, 2155 (1961).
14. GOODMAN, M., *Human Biol.*, **33**, 131 (1961).
15. GOODMAN, M., *in* "Classification and Human Evolution" (S. L. Washburn, ed.), p. 204, Aldine, Chicago, 1963.
16. HILL, R. L., AND BUETTNER-JANUSCH, J., *Federation Proc.*, **23**, 1236 (1964).
17. HILL, R. L., BUETTNER-JANUSCH, J., AND BUETTNER-JANUSCH, V., *Proc. Natl. Acad. Sci., U.S.*, **50**, 885 (1963).
18. HILL, W. C. O., "Primates," Vol. I, Interscience, New York, 1953.
19. HOYER, B. H., MCCARTHY, B. J., AND BOLTON, E. T., *Science*, **144**, 959 (1964).
20. HUXLEY, T. H., "Man's Place in Nature," Appleton, New York, 1876.
21. INGRAM, V. M., *Nature*, **180**, 326 (1957).
22. INGRAM, V. M., "The Hemoglobins in Genetics and Evolution," Columbia Univ. Press, New York, 1963.
23. KONIGSBERG, W., GOLDSTEIN, J., AND HILL, R. J., *J. Biol. Chem.*, **238**, 2028 (1963).
24. KONIGSBERG, W., AND HILL, R. J., *J. Biol. Chem.*, **237**, 2547 (1962).
25. MAYR, E., "Animal Species and Evolution," Belknap Press, Harvard University, Cambridge, 1963.
26. RUCKNAGEL, D. L., AND NEEL, J. V., *in* "Progress in Medical Genetics" (A. G. Steinberg, ed.), Vol. I, p. 158, Grune & Stratton, New York, 1961.
27. SCHROEDER, W. A., *Ann. Rev. Biochem.*, **32**, 301 (1963).
28. SCHROEDER, W. A., SHELTON, J. R., SHELTON, J. B., CORMICK, J., AND JONES, R. T., *Biochemistry*, **2**, 992 (1963).
29. SIMONS, E. L., *Ann. N.Y. Acad. Sci.*, **102**, 282 (1962).
30. SIMONS, E. L., *in* "Evolutionary and Genetic Biology of Primates" (J. Buettner-Janusch, ed.), Vol. I, p. 65, Academic Press, New York, 1963.
31. SIMONS, E. L., *Proc. Natl. Acad. Sci., U.S.*, **51**, 528 (1964).
32. SIMPSON, G. G., *Bull. Am. Museum Nat. Hist.*, **85**, 1 (1945).
33. SIMPSON, G. G., *Ann. N.Y. Acad. Sci.*, **102**, 497 (1962).
34. SIMPSON, G. G., *in* "Classification and Human Evolution" (S. L. Washburn, ed.), p. 1, Aldine, Chicago, 1963.
35. SIMPSON, G. G., "This View of Life," Harcourt, Brace and World, New York, 1964.
36. SIMPSON, G. G., *Science*, **146**, 1535 (1964).
37. SINGER, K., CHERNOFF, A. I., AND SINGER, L., *Blood*, **6**, 413 (1951).
38. ZUCKERKANDL, E., *in* "Classification and Human Evolution" (S. L. Washburn, ed.), p. 243, Aldine, Chicago, 1963.
39. ZUCKERKANDL, E., JONES, R. T., AND PAULING, L., *Proc. Natl. Acad. Sci., U.S.*, **46**, 1349 (1960).
40. ZUCKERKANDL, E., AND SCHROEDER, W. A., *Nature*, **192**, 984 (1961).

# Constancy and Variability of Protein Structure in Respiratory and Viral Proteins

G. Braunitzer

with V. Braun, K. Hilse, G. Hobom, V. Rudloff, and G. v. Wettstein

*Max-Planck-Institut für Biochemie, Munich*

The chemical investigations of the hemoglobins have provided a large number of interesting results, which cannot be discussed in detail here (9). We are concentrating our effort on the phylogeny of the molecule, but even these studies have many facets. Accordingly, I shall confine myself to only one aspect, the so-called "sequence gaps," which we first identified in hemoglobin (8, 12).

The examination of these gaps or, better described, holes represents, without doubt, the most difficult part of the chemical work. On the other hand, this problem provides some particularly intriguing chemical challenges.

With respect to the chemical results, we therefore are interested in the homology (9, 12) of the peptide chains, as demonstrated by the studies of Rudloff (13) and Hilschmann (6, 7), which also provided final confirmation of the phylogenic theory of the peptide chains (8, 23, 25, 30). We could show that the homology of the α and β chains of hemoglobin is sometimes interrupted (9); that is, some amino acids of the α chain have no corresponding partner in the β chain, and vice versa (12). The accompanying diagram shows that residues 19 and 20 in the α chain

| | | | | | | | | |
|---|---|---|---|---|---|---|---|---|
| α-Human | Lys 16 | Val 17 | Gly 18 | Ala 19 | His 20 | Ala 21 | Gly 22 | Glu 23 |
| β-Human | Lys 17 | Val 18 | Asp 19 | | | Val 20 | Asp 21 | Glu 22 |
| Myoglobin | Lys | Val | Glu | Ala | Asp | Val | Ala | Gly |

have no partners in the β chain. Glycine β46 has no partner in the α chain.

| | | | | | |
|---|---|---|---|---|---|
| α-Human | His 45 | Phe 46 | | Asp 47 | Leu 48 |
| β-Human | Ser 44 | Phe 45 | Gly 46 | Asp 47 | Leu 48 |
| Myoglobin | Arg | Phe | Lys | His | Leu |

183

Residues β51 to 55 have no corresponding partners in the α chain.

| α-Human | Leu 48 | Ser 49 | His 50 | | | | | | Gly 51 | Ser 52 | Ala 53 |
|---|---|---|---|---|---|---|---|---|---|---|---|
| β-Human | Leu 48 | Ser 49 | Thr 50 | Pro 51 | Asp 52 | Ala 53 | Val 54 | Met 55 | Gly 56 | Asp 57 | Pro 58 |
| Myoglobin | Leu | Lys | Thr | Glu | Ala | Glu | Met | Lys | Ala | Ser | Glu |

The same is true for histidine β2.

| α-Human | Val 1 | | Leu 2 | Ser 3 |
|---|---|---|---|---|
| β-Human | Val 1 | His 2 | Leu 3 | Thr 4 |
| Myoglobin | Val 1 | | Leu 2 | Ser 3 |

The C-terminal end of sperm whale myoglobin contains a "tail" of six amino acids which are not found in human hemoglobin (5, 16, 28).

| α-Human | Thr 137 | Ser 138 | Lys 139 | Tyr 140 | Arg 141 | | | | | |
|---|---|---|---|---|---|---|---|---|---|---|
| β-Human | Ala 142 | His 143 | Lys 144 | Tyr 145 | His 146 | | | | | |
| Myoglobin | Ala | Ala | Lys | Tyr | Lys | Glu | Leu | Gly | Tyr | Glu, Gly |

Rudloff recently demonstrated such a "tail" of eight amino acids at the N-terminal end, representing eight additional residues for the hemoglobin of a primitive vertebrate, the lamprey, *Lampetra fluviatilis* (26).

| α-Human | | | | | | | | | Val | | Leu | Ser | Pro | Ala | Asp | Lys |
|---|---|---|---|---|---|---|---|---|---|---|---|---|---|---|---|---|
| β-Human | | | | | | | | | Val | His | Leu | Thr | Pro | Glu | Glu | Lys |
| Myoglobin | | | | | | | | | | | Val | Ala | Gly | Glu | Try | |
| Lamprey | Pro | Ileu | Val | Asp | Ser | Gly | Ser | Ala, Pro | Val | | Leu | Ser | Ala | Ala | Glu | Lys |

Hilse could further show that one of the sequence gaps is closed in carp hemoglobin (4). (See Diagram A on Page 185.)

The hemoglobin of the lamprey consists of only one peptide chain, similar to myoglobin. By comparison with other hemoglobins we have found no sequence gaps in this hemoglobin. (See Diagram B on Page 185.)

**DIAGRAM A**

| Protein | Sequence (residue numbers in parentheses) |
|---|---|
| α-Human | Thr · Tyr · Phe · Pro · His(45) · Phe · Asp · Leu · Ser · His(50) · Gly · — · — · Ser · Ala · Glu · Val(55) · Lys · Gly · His · Gly · Lys(60) · Lys |
| β-Human | Arg(40) · Phe · Phe · Glu · Ser · Phe(45) · Gly · Asp · Leu · Ser · Thr(50) · Pro · Asp · Ala · Val · Met(55) · Gly · Asp · Pro · Lys · Val(60) · Lys · Ala · His · Gly · Lys(65) · Lys |
| Myoglobin | Glu · Lys · Phe · Asp · Arg(45) · Phe · Lys · His · Leu · Lys(50) · Thr · Glu · Ala · Glu · Met · Lys(55) · Ala · Ser · Glu(60) · Asp · Leu · Lys · Lys · His(65) · Gly · Ileu · Gly · Glu |
| α-Carp | Thr · Phe · Ala · His · Ala · Try · Asp · Leu · Ser · Gly, Pro · — · — · Ser · Pro, Gly · Val · Lys |

**DIAGRAM B**

*Upper section*

|  |  |
|---|---|
| Lamprey | Try, Asp, Ser, Ser, Pro, Ala, Ala, Val, Tyr, Tyr, Asp, Thr, Ser, Glu, Gly, Val, Val, Ileu, Leu, Lys · Phe · Ala · Gly · Tyr · Gly · Ala · Glu · Ala · Leu · Glu · Arg · Met · Phe · Leu · Ser · Phe · Pro · Thr · Thr · Lys · Thr · Glu · Glu |
| α-Human | Ala · Ala · Try · Gly · Lys · Val · Gly · Ala · His · Ala · Gly · Glu · Tyr · Gly · Ala · Glu · Ala · Leu · Glu · Arg · Met · Phe · Leu · Ser · Phe · Pro · Thr · Thr · Lys · Thr |
| β-Human | Ala · Leu · Try · Gly · Lys · Val · Val · Asp · Glu · Val · Gly · Gly · Glu · Ala · Leu · Gly · Arg · Leu · Leu · Val · Val · Tyr · Pro · Try · Thr · Pro · Try · Thr · Arg |
| Myoglobin | His · Val · Try · Ala · Lys · Val · Glu · Ala · Asp · Ileu · Ala · Gly · His · Gly · Glu · Asp · Ileu · Leu · Ileu · Arg · Leu · Phe · Lys · Ser · His · Pro · Glu · Thr · Leu · Glu |

*Lower section*

|  |  |
|---|---|
| Lamprey | Phe · Phe · Pro · Lys · Phe · Lys · Gly · Met · Thr · Ser · Ala · Asp · Glu · Leu · Lys · Lys · Ser · Ala · Asp · Val · Arg · Try · His · Ala · Glu · Arg · Ileu |
| α-Human | Tyr · Phe · Pro · His · Phe · Asp · Leu · Ser · His · Gly · Ser · Ala · Glu · Val · Lys · Gly · His · Gly · Lys · Lys · Val · Gly · His · Val · Val |
| β-Human | Phe · Phe · Glu · Ser · Phe · Gly · Asp · Leu · Ser · Thr · Pro · Asp · Ala · Val · Met · Gly · Ala · Lys · Lys · Ala · His · Gly · Lys · Lys · Val · Gly · Thr · Val |
| Myoglobin | Lys · Phe · Asp · Arg · Phe · Lys · His · Leu · Lys · Thr · Glu · Ala · Glu · Met · Lys · Ala · Ser · Glu · Asp · Leu · Lys · Lys · His · Gly · Val · Thr · Val |

Table I lists the length of the peptide chains of a number of hemo-globins which we think are derived from one common phylogenetic ancestor. Thus we find not only exchanges of amino acids but also changes in the length of the peptide chains. We were much surprised by the

TABLE I

COMPARISON OF THE LENGTH OF THE PEPTIDE CHAINS OF VARIOUS HEME PROTEINS WHICH ARE THOUGHT TO BE DERIVED FROM A COMMON ANCESTOR

| Source of heme protein | Number of amino acid residues |
|---|---|
| *Chironomus thummi* | ~125 |
| Lamprey | ~160 |
| Myoglobin | 153 |
| β-Human, horse | 146 |
| β-Bovine | 145 |
| α-Carp | 142 |
| α-Human, horse | 141 |

TABLE II

AMINO ACID ANALYSES OF THE α AND β CHAINS OF COMPONENT I OF *Chironomus thummi* HEMOGLOBIN

| Amino acid | α chain | β chain |
|---|---|---|
| Lys | 9 | 8 |
| His | 3 | 3 |
| Arg | 3 | 3 |
| Asp | 13 | 13 |
| Thr | 8 | 6–7 |
| Ser | 8–9 | 12 |
| Glu | 8 | 10 |
| Pro | 5 | 4 |
| Gly | 10 | 8 |
| Ala | 15 | 15 |
| Cys | — | 1 |
| Val | 8 | 7 |
| Met | 4 | 6 |
| Ileu | 8 | 6 |
| Leu | 6 | 10 |
| Tyr | 2 | 3 |
| Phe | 13 | 8 |
| Total | 123–124 | 123–124 |

results of our preliminary studies on an insect hemoglobin (3). The length of all the peptide chains is about 125 residues (Tables I and II). The purification of the hemoglobin involved a final step of DEAE column chromatography.

We isolated three different hemoglobins from *Chironomus thummi;* all have a molecular weight of 31,500 (27). These investigations were made difficult by our initial problems with the purification of the globins by countercurrent distribution (19). Finally, we were able to demonstrate (for all hemoglobins) two different peptide chains which we designate as $\alpha_I\beta_I$, $\alpha_{II}\beta_{II}$, and $\alpha_{III}\beta_{III}$. The amino acid analyses of the peptide chains as well as the investigation of the tryptic peptides show that the chains consist of about 125 amino acids, which is considerably shorter than the vertebrate chain length.

The low cysteine and histidine content as well as the high phenyl-alanine content of the insect hemoglobins are striking. I might remark that the *Chironomus* hemoglobins have the greatest affinity for oxygen of all the respiratory proteins (1). Figure 1 shows the fingerprint patterns of the *Chironomus* α and β chains.

It is thought today that the peptide chains of the hemoglobins and the myoglobins originate from a common phylogenetic ancestor, and that they have been developed through duplication of the genes coding for hemoglobins (1, 8, 23, 25). The strong differences in protein chain length make one suppose that the genes have either grown through insertions or been reduced by the deletion of nucleotide triplets. The findings with carp and lamprey hemoglobins by Drs. Hilse and Rudloff at our Institute make us suppose that, at least in these cases, triplets of the original common ancestor were lost through deletion.

Sequence gaps as yet cannot be unequivocally explained; the mechanism of their production is even more mysterious, since deletions in protein sequence and in nucleic acid sequence have not yet been correlated. We are, therefore, concerned with the question of these gaps in the nucleic acid and by what substances they might be induced.[1]

Crick (14, 15) and co-workers have published some genetic results on this subject; they feel that proflavine induces a special type of insertion or deletion mutation which is not revertible by base analogs but is revertible by proflavine itself. Ingram later mentioned a similar, very plausible model (24).

Dr. G. Hobom in our Institute has attempted to carry out such experiments, in combination with an analysis of the corresponding protein. Our system consists of the phage fd (21, 22) (isolated by Hoffmann-Berling in Heidelberg) which contains single-stranded DNA. The molecular weight of the phage particle is $1.1 \times 10^7$. The subunit of the coat protein is very small, however. We were surprised by the amino acid analyses of purified preparations (Table III), which yielded a value

---

[1] The sequence gaps can also be considered as resulting from cross-over events in genes corresponding to the peptide chains of hemoglobin.

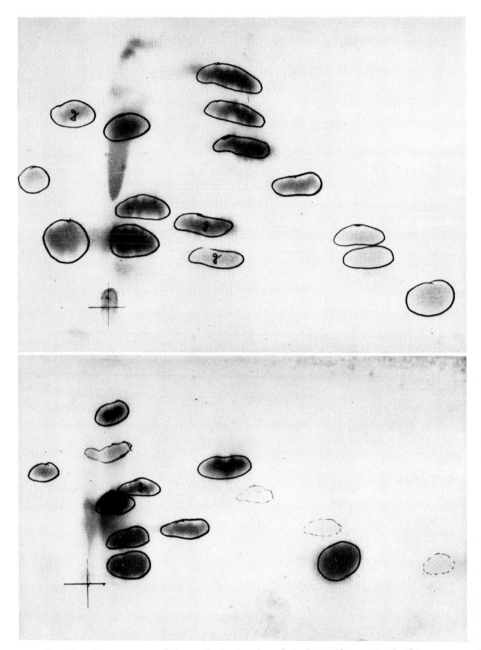

Fig. 1.   Fingerprints of the α chain (*top*) and β chain (*bottom*) of *Chironomus thummi* hemoglobin following countercurrent distribution.

of 85 amino acids for a single chain (29). This result could be verified by fingerprint analysis. The purity of the protein is evident from electrophoretic mobility studies in the continuous-flow apparatus developed by Hannig (18). The wild-type infectivity band is narrow, and small neighboring bands are only $10^{-6}$ as infectious (2, 10, 11).

TABLE III
AMINO ACID ANALYSIS OF THE SINGLE PEPTIDE CHAIN
OF PHAGE FD COAT PROTEIN

| Amino acid[a] | Number of residues |
|---|---|
| Lys | 8.12 |
| Asp | 5.98 |
| Thr | 6.05 |
| Ser | 7.90 |
| Glu | 5.90 |
| Pro | 2.04 |
| Gly | 8.10 |
| Ala | 16.85 |
| Val | 4.68 |
| Met | 0.96 |
| Ileu | 5.90 |
| Leu | 4.09 |
| Tyr | 3.00 |
| Phe | 5.41 |
| Total | ~85 |

[a] Ammonia, 13.75.

We have treated phage fd with either of the two mutagens, proflavine and 2,7-diaminofluorene. Figures 2, 3, and 4 illustrate the electrophoretic

Proflavine

2, 7-Diaminofluorene

mobilities of the phage grown in the presence and in the absence of these compounds. As can be seen, fractions 29 through 32 clearly contain phage peaks not seen in the control. With proflavine, the effect was obtained only in the light; diaminofluorene was active in the dark as well. The action of both chemicals thus produced altered phage coat proteins which we could detect in the continuous-flow electrophoresis apparatus.

We obtained pure phage mutant strains by single-plaque isolation. That the strains were indeed mutant was proved by amino acid analyses

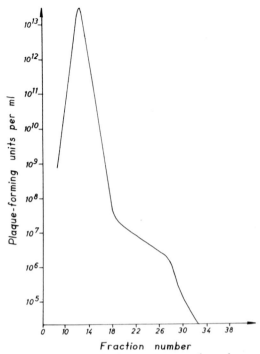

FIG. 2. Mobility of wild-type fd phage in carrier-free electrophoresis. 0.025 *M* Na acetate buffer, pH 5.3, 1500 volts, 125 ma.

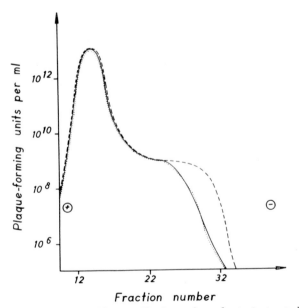

FIG. 3. Electrophoresis of wild-type fd phage from bacteria treated with pro-flavine. Conditions as in Fig. 2. Dashed line, proflavine incubation in the light; dotted line, proflavine incubation in the dark; solid line, no proflavine treatment.

which showed differences between these true-breeding strains and the wild type; even a new amino acid such as histidine, which is not found in the wild type, is found in some mutants (20). Thus, there is no doubt that proflavine and diaminofluorene can cause mutational alterations which are reflected in protein structure.

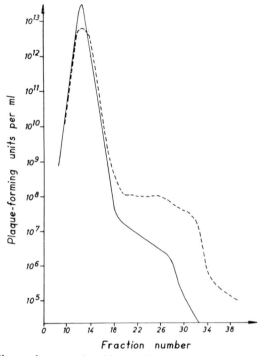

Fig. 4. Electrophoresis of wild-type fd phage from bacteria treated with diaminofluorene (dashed line). Conditions as in Fig. 3. The solid line refers to untreated phage.

It remains for the protein sequence analysis to determine exactly the changes in the mutant proteins. We hope that these analyses not only will shed light on the mechanism of action of these chemicals and the hypothesis of Crick, Lerman, and others, but also will help answer the question of the different chain lengths of the hemoglobins.

### ACKNOWLEDGMENTS

The authors wish to thank Professor A. Butenandt, Director of the Institute, for his generous support of this work. The investigations have been aided by a grant of the Deutsche Forschungsgemeinschaft. We wish to thank Miss B. Schrank and Mrs. Steinhoff for assistance.

## REFERENCES

1. ALLISON, A. C., AND GRATZER, W. B., *Biol. Rev.*, **35**, 459 (1960).
2. BRAUNITZER, G., *Z. Physik. Chem.*, **68**, 733 (1964).
3. BRAUNITZER, G., AND BRAUN, V., *Z. Physiol. Chem.*, **340**, 88 (1965).
4. BRAUNITZER, G., AND HILSE, K., *Z. Physiol. Chem.*, **330**, 234 (1963.
5. BRAUNITZER, G., GEHRING-MÜLLER, R., HILSCHMANN, N., HILSE, K., HOBOM, G., RUDLOFF, V., AND WITTMANN-LIEBOLD, B., *Z. Physiol. Chem.*, **325**, 283 (1961).
6. BRAUNITZER, G., HILSCHMANN, N., HILSE, K., LIEBOLD, B., AND MÜLLER, R., *Z. Physiol. Chem.*, **322**, 96 (1960).
7. BRAUNITZER, G., HILSCHMANN, N., AND LIEBOLD-WITTMANN, B., *Z. Physiol. Chem.*, **325**, 96 (1961).
8. BRAUNITZER, G., HILSCHMANN, N., RUDLOFF, V., HILSE, K., LIEBOLD, B., AND MÜLLER, R., *Nature*, **190**, 480 (1961).
9. BRAUNITZER, G., HILSE, K., RUDLOFF, V., AND HILSCHMANN, N., *Advan. Protein Chem.*, **19**, 1 (1964).
10. BRAUNITZER, G., HOBOM, G., AND HANNIG, K., *Z. Physiol. Chem.*, **338**, 276 (1963).
11. BRAUNITZER, G., HOBOM, G., AND HANNIG, K., *Z. Physiol. Chem.*, **338**, 278 (1963).
12. BRAUNITZER, G., LIEBOLD, B., MÜLLER, R., AND RUDLOFF, V., *Z. Physiol. Chem.*, **320**, 170 (1960).
13. BRAUNITZER, G., RUDLOFF, V., HILSE, K., LIEBOLD, B., AND MÜLLER, R., *Z. Physiol. Chem.*, **320**, 283 (1960).
14. BRENNER, S., BARNETT, L., CRICK, F. H. C., AND ORGEL, A., *J. Mol. Biol.*, **3**, 121 (1961).
15. CRICK, F. H. C., BARNETT, L., BRENNER, S., AND WATT-TOBIN, R. J., *Nature*, **192**, 1227 (1961).
16. EDMUNDSON, A. B., AND HIRS, C. H. W., *Nature*, **190**, 663 (1961).
17. FORMANEK, H., HUBER, R., BRAUN, V., BRAUNITZER, G., AND HOPPE, W., *Z. Physik. Chem.*, **68**, 818 (1964).
18. HANNIG, K., *Z. Anal. Chem.*, **181**, 244 (1960).
19. HILL, R. J., AND CRAIG, L. C., *J. Am. Chem. Soc.*, **81**, 2272 (1959).
20. HOBOM, G., Thesis, University of Munich, 1964.
21. HOFFMANN-BERLING, H., DÜBWALD, H., AND BEULKE, I., *Z. Naturforsch*, **18b**, 893 (1963).
22. HOFFMANN-BERLING, H., MARVIN, D. A., AND DÜRWALD, H., *Z. Naturforsch.*, **18b**, 876 (1963).
23. INGRAM, V. M., *Nature*, **189**, 704 (1961).
24. INGRAM, V. M., "The Hemoglobins in Evolution and Genetics in Evolution;" Columbia Univ. Press, New York and London, 1963.
25. ITANO, H., *Advan. Protein Chem.*, **12**, 215 (1957).
26. RUDLOFF, V., AND BRAUNITZER, G., unpublished results.
27. SVEDBERG, T., AND PETERSEN, K. O., "The Ultrazentrifuge," Verlag Steinkopff, 1940.
28. WATSON, H. C., AND KENDREW, J. C. *Nature*, **190**, 670 (1961).
29. WETTSTEIN, G. V., AND BRAUNITZER, G., unpublished results.
30. ZUCKERKANDL, E., AND PAULING, L., *in* "Horizons in Biochemistry" (M. Kasha and B. Pullman, eds.), Academic Press, New York, 1962.

# Discussion of Part III

S. Spiegelman, G. Braunitzer, E. Freese, N. H. Horowitz, J. Buettner-Janusch, N. O. Kaplan, E. Zuckerkandl, E. L. Smith, R. L. Hill, C. A. Williams, A. Cronquist, C. B. Anfinsen, E. Mayr, E. Margoliash, T. H. Jukes

Dr. Spiegelman: I would like to get clarification, Dr. Braunitzer. I was not clear on whether you were analyzing mutants or cultures grown in the presence of mutagen.

Dr. Braunitzer: Cultures were grown in the presence of mutagen, and alterations in the electrophoretic mobility of the phage were observed. Phage mutants with particular changes in amino acid composition and mobility could be isolated.

Dr. Freese: The initially isolated phages with altered electrophoretic mobility could have arisen by a phenotypic change of the phage protein alone, somehow caused by the presence of the mutagen in the growth medium. The contention that these altered phages are actually mutated in their nucleic acid is only proved by the observation that their altered electrophoretic mobility as well as their altered amino acid composition bred true in subsequent passages through bacteria grown in the absence of the mutagens.

Dr. Spiegelman: It is surprising to have a mass change in the population, as a result of exposure to a mutagen unless it selects.

Dr. Horowitz: I would like to ask Dr. Buettner-Janusch a question. It seemed to me that he proved to his own satisfaction that neither mutations nor selection were involved in the establishment of various human hemoglobins. I would like to know just what mechanism he is proposing.

Dr. Buettner-Janusch: I stated quite clearly that it is obvious that selection has operated to increase the relative frequency of hemoglobin S in certain populations. But the mechanism by which selection operates has never been demonstrated to my satisfaction or to that of a number of other people.

Dr. Horowitz: Since I come from a place that does not have this point of view on sickle cell hemoglobin, I would like to know what your objections are to the existing evidence on the selective forces.

Dr. Buettner-Janusch: The only evidence that shows there is a selective advantage for the heterozygote is from Central America, where among the black Caribs there is a positive differential fertility for females of the AS genotype.

The statistical associations are interesting, but they don't demonstrate any functional relationship between falciparum malaria and sickle cell.

In some of our data from Madagascar and Kenya on human groups indigenous to those countries, there have been very high levels of hemoglobin S, but no *Plasmodium falciparum*.

DR. HOROWITZ: What about the famous experiment of Allison that is always quoted in this connection?

DR. BUETTNER-JANUSCH: It is an interesting experiment, but not conclusive.

DR. HOROWITZ: Say more. As I remember, he inoculated 15 controls.

DR. BUETTNER-JANUSCH: A malariologist pointed out to me that the greatest frequency of the parasites in the peripheral blood occurs not during acute phases of the disease, but during quiescent periods. Thus, the technique that Allison used appears to be related not to the acute phase but to the least acute phase of the disease. Clinical malariologists in Africa told me they feel that his experiment demonstrates the exact opposite of his conclusion.

DR. HOROWITZ: Thank you.

DR. KAPLAN: You say there is no functional difference in the various primate hemoglobins. Have detailed studies been done on the Bohr effect as well as on other properties?

DR. BUETTNER-JANUSCH: I never said there are no functional differences. We just know of none.

DR. KAPLAN: Has the Bohr effect been carefully studied?

DR. BUETTNER-JANUSCH: We have been very much occupied with merely working out sequences and demonstrating differences in peptides, and so forth. We hope someday someone will look at some of these functional things. At the moment we are busy with structural studies.

DR. ZUCKERKANDL: Dr. Buettner-Janusch, you said that molecular data are just a further interesting contribution to taxonomy, but the impression gained from what you said is that you believe they have no privileged position in this respect. You also said that you thought that the fact that there is one difference between human and gorilla hemoglobin chains is not significant from the taxonomic point of view.

As you probably know, I don't think as you do on that score because I feel that informational macromolecules, as distinct from any other type, do contain the greatest amount of information that is available in an organism.

Obviously, if you take one polypeptide change, that will not give you a correct assessment of phyletic distance, but ideally these types of characters seem to me to be the most promising and most fundamental taxonomic characters of all.

DR. BUETTNER-JANUSCH: If I may make one comment, I would like to support the point that the closer we get to the genetic material, the better. But, of course, I have been brainwashed by classical taxonomists, and it is very difficult for me to see that gorilla and *Homo* are particularly close phylogenetically. This may simply be my personal revulsion against the idea. This has played a great role in primate taxonomy. I am only considering primate taxonomy. The point I want to make is that hemoglobin is a single trait. I could pick out lots of other macromolecules from the gorilla, which show many, many differences from human macromolecules. Hemoglobin is a nice one to work with, nevertheless, but I would like to examine 30 proteins before I made a taxonomic decision.

Dr. SMITH: I am not sure which protein chemist Dr. Buettner-Janusch is libeling by saying we believe isoleucine, leucine, methionine, etc. play the same role in proteins.

I think most of us would vigorously deny this, particularly since we don't know what half the amino acid residues do in proteins in the first place. I don't know of any definitive evidence which indicates why we should have arginine in some positions and lysine in others in some homologous proteins, when in various other positions they are completely interchangeable. It is clear that in some spots in a protein molecule you cannot replace arginine or you cannot replace lysine.

When we talk about conservative substitutions, and Dr. Margoliash will have more to say about this, I think we have to interpret such substitutions very strictly in terms of the position of that particular residue in a given protein molecule. There are situations when clearly isoleucine and valine are replaceable or interchangeable with each other without any detectable effect on function. In other situations, however, this may represent a very drastic change, because we find other substitutions where isoleucine and threonine are interchangeable, the only two amino acids where there is a second asymmetric center.

In another situation we find threonine and serine interchangeable, but no other residues. I don't think we can make any generalization at the moment about the exact role of any single side chain except in the particular context of a given protein.

Dr. BUETTNER-JANUSCH: That is very welcome news indeed, but I will allow the protein chemist who has had most influence on me to comment on this point.

Dr. HILL: I hope I didn't influence you quite the way you mentioned. Dr. Smith has stated the problem very exactly and I would agree with him. However, the point we wanted to make was as follows. At certain positions in the sequences of the hemoglobin chains, a number of amino acids often appear to be interchangeable; for example, valine, isoleucine, and leucine occur at the same position in β chains of hemoglobins from

different species. Each of these amino acids has a hydrophobic side chain
and it is difficult to judge why one may possess a different structural role
than another. In this respect they possess, perhaps, almost equivalent side
chains. On the other hand, each type of residue appeared as the result
of a mutation. It is thought that since the mutation survived, it must have
been selected throughout evolution. This is another way of saying that
each mutant gene is not neutral. From our knowledge of protein structure
we should be able to gain an explanation for this lack of neutrality. But
on the basis of knowledge of the structural requirements of hemoglobin,
it is not at all evident why residues with essentially equivalent side chains
would be selected. Perhaps all mutants are not neutral with respect to
selection, although we must, I realize, evaluate this problem at a
molecular level in the context of a particular protein.

DR. WILLIAMS: I don't know whether I am going to be able to make
these differences among us any clearer or not. But at the risk of con-
founding it more, I would like to point out that I also came into the
study of phylogeny by the biological route, with a profound respect for
taxonomy, but this has not permitted me to lump together taxonomy
and phylogeny.

When we are speaking of evidence concerning the genome and if we
are convinced also that protein structure, particularly primary structure,
is direct evidence of the nature of the genome, then we are talking more
of phylogeny—that is, relationship through genetic descent. We are
not talking about systematic schemes by which organisms are classified.

I think also that there is only one biochemist or immunochemist that
I know of who is willing to change the taxonomic scheme.

I feel it has been very fortunate and much to the credit of the
taxonomists that, insofar as our immunochemical and biochemical data
are concerned, these data and the notions of phylogeny and taxonomy
in the mammals, particularly in the primates, appear to coincide rather
nicely, with a few exceptions which are inevitable when one is speaking
of variations that can occur in any portion of a genome.

However, I don't think we have to worry about taxonomy changing
because taxonomists are among the most conservative organisms I know.
But notions of phylogeny can certainly be altered on the basis of accumulated information of the molecular structures.

DR. BUETTNER-JANUSCH: I happen to agree, more or less, with the
point of view that Dr. Williams takes, but I am kind of an optimist. I
think that the best taxonomy, for the time being, that we can attempt
to achieve for the order Primates is one that is based on phylogenetic
principles. For that reason I would caution against the over-enthusiastic

switching of animals from one taxon to another on the basis of one molecule or another.

Nevertheless, I can't really disagree too violently with the general theory upon which Dr. Williams operates.

DR. CRONQUIST: I am from the New York Botanical Garden. I am primarily a taxonomist, not a biochemist. Maybe I am a conservative organism, but I wouldn't be here if I didn't think that biochemical data had taxonomic significance.

I do wish to point out, however, that one of the most fundamental taxonomic principles which taxonomists have learned over many generations, and which we have to have drummed into us each generation anew, is that a character is only as important as it proves to be in delimiting a group that we recognize on the basis of all of the information we can get about it. The proof of the pudding is in the eating.

If we start out with an *a priori* assumption that a certain character, because of something about it, is more important than other characters, we are just asking for trouble. This has been done repeatedly, and it always does lead us into trouble.

Some characters that seem on *a priori* grounds not to be very important turn out to be very useful. I'll mention a chemical character. There are different carotenoids in the various groups of algae. They differ in relatively small features, and if I understand correctly, the chemical change from one to another of these carotenoid pigments is a relatively simple and easy change, and it wouldn't seem that this could be very important. Yet it turns out that they are very strongly correlated with the groups of algae which we recognize on the basis of all of our information. And so we come out and say the carotenoid type is a very important and useful character. This is an *a posteriori* judgment, not an *a priori* judgment.

The same will have to be said for any character, chemical or other. We may suspect that it will be likely to be of more importance if many genes are concerned with it, instead of a few. The probability is we will be right in suspecting it in such cases, but it is only a probability.

What we are trying to do is group things on the basis of their totality of characteristics, insofar as we can determine. Dr. Mayr likes to talk in terms of predictive values, and it is a good term. On that basis, the differences in hemoglobin, for example, are interesting. They are potentially useful, but neither they nor any of the other characters can properly be taken as of overriding importance.

CHAIRMAN ANFINSEN: Dr. Mayr may want to talk about it.

DR. MAYR: I think we actually are much closer together than we appear to be. Everybody agrees when you get down to the gene level and deal with components of the genotype, you are obviously better off than with purely phenotypical characters, where you go by inference.

On the other hand, a higher organism, a primate, has about five million cistrons. When you deal with only a single one of these five million cistrons, you cannot say too much about the classification of primates; the taxonomist, however, who deals with the phenotypic reflections of these five million cistrons, quite often, to the surprise of the biochemist, comes awfully close to a rather acceptable classification. The danger of basing a classification on single cistrons, no matter how important they are, is quite nicely illustrated by the hemoglobins of the primates. The baboon, which is a cercopithecoid very close to the macaques, has a remarkably different hemoglobin pattern, while the South American ceboids, which—according to the paleontologists—did not evolve out of the cercopithecoid group, but independently from the prosimians, nevertheless have a hemoglobin pattern awfully similar to that of the cercopithecoid monkeys.

Here is quite clearly a case where we would come up with a rather misleading classification, if we relied entirely on these molecular characters.

There is one last thing I would like to mention. The term "phyletic distance" is thrown around a great deal. The whole concept of phylogeny in the literature is rather confused. Phylogeny always includes two phenomena: the splitting of lines and what happens to the lines subsequently. The lines leading to *Homo sapiens* and to the African apes (*Pan*) have split rather recently, perhaps in the Pliocene. There is now almost universal agreement about this. Some of their biochemical constituents are still quite similar. On the other hand, what happened after the branching point is that the *Homo sapiens* line came under an enormous selection pressure. The resulting rate of change in certain characters is almost unprecedented, according to Haldane, in the total history of evolution. If you would draw a phylogenetic tree on the blackboard, the human line would shoot off in a totally different new direction almost parallel to the base line. The resulting new taxon is something quite novel in the history of the organic world.

Therefore, even though this splitting happened quite recently, the total phylogenetic picture, which is composed of the two elements—splitting and divergence—puts man into a taxon that is very different from that of the African apes.

DR. MARGOLIASH: If I may say so, I agree entirely with Dr. Mayr. There is really no fundamental discrepancy between the point of view expressed in our presentation, with regard to cytochrome *c* primary structures, as they may or may not relate to the evolution of species, and the position of accepted evolutionary theory, as succinctly stated by Dr. Mayr.

One point should, however, be added, because it may be contributing to an erroneous impression of an opposition between the cytochrome *c* data and ordinary evolutionary thought. This idea has been beautifully expressed by Dr. G. G. Simpson [*Science*, **146**, 1535 (1964)] and simply states that the further one is from the genetic machinery, the nearer one is to the site of selective action. The length and complexity of the functional chain leading from the gene to the phenotypic character upon which selection can act may be such that we are unable to follow it intelligibly. Classically, evolutionists have dealt with complex polygenic morphological characters, which sample a much larger proportion of the genome than does a single polypeptide chain and often are the actual locus at which selection can act, and thus may be importantly significant to an over-all understanding of the evolution of species. In our case, we are dealing with a gene that merely determines the amino acid sequence of one small representative of the immense group of proteins, while the site of selection at the mitochondrial functional level probably includes a whole complex of numerous proteins, cofactors, and subcellular structures. Is it therefore surprising that we have difficulties in relating primary-structure variations in cytochrome *c* to mechanisms of selection, or that it appears that changes in amino acid sequence may, in the majority of cases, have become fixed in populations through the relatively rare mechanisms that do not directly involve natural selection? The apparent disagreement is thus no more than a difference in emphasis.

DR. JUKES: The polypeptide chains of the hemoglobins and myoglobins are generally considered to have originated from the protein coded by an archetypal gene which has undergone four duplications that gave rise to separate genes for myoglobin, α, β, γ, and δ hemoglobins in human beings, and the counterparts of some of these proteins in other vertebrates. The duplication of the genes allowed for their independent evolution and differentiation as mirrored in comparisons of sequences of amino acids in the respective polypeptide chains of myoglobin and the four hemoglobins in human beings. Additional changes, due to the sequestration of various species, are revealed by comparing the homologous globins of one species with another. Such comparisons show, for example, that the myoglobins of human beings and of the sperm whale resemble each other closely, as do human and horse α hemoglobins. In contrast, human myoglobin differs widely from human α hemoglobin in primary structure, even though the secondary and tertiary structures resemble each other closely.

It is possible to place the amino acid sequences of the various proteins in this series side by side so that homologous sites may be compared. This was done for whale myoglobin and human α, β, and γ hemoglobins [B. Keil, *Ann. Rev. Biochem.*, **31**, 139 (1962)]. Much more information is now available and the number of comparisons may be considerably increased. We have done this with information summarized in articles and reviews [G. Braunitzer, K. Hilse, V. Rudloff, and N. Hilschmann, *Adv. Protein Chem.*, **19**, 1 (1964); B. Keil, *Ann. Rev. Biochem.*, **31**, 139 (1962); W. A. Schroeder, *Ann. Rev. Biochem.*, **32**, 301 (1963); R. L. Hill, J. Buettner-Janusch, and V. Buettner-Janusch, *Proc. Natl. Acad. Sci. U.S.*, **50**, 885 (1963)] for amino acid sequences in human and whale myoglobins, in the hemoglobins of human beings, or of various monkeys, the horse, cow, sheep, pig, llama, carp, and a lamprey, and in human variant (mutant) hemoglobins. The number of different amino acids that occupy each site were summarized and compared with the Poisson distribution, with the results shown in the accompanying table.

| (1) Number of amino acids | (2) Number of sites occupied by (1) | Number of changes | Poisson distribution (m = 2.1) |
|---|---|---|---|
| 1 | 12 | 0 | 18 |
| 2 | 41 | 1 | 38 |
| 3 | 55 | 2 | 40 |
| 4 | 25 | 3 | 28 |
| 5 | 11 | 4 | 15 |
| 6 | 4 | 5 | 6 |
| > 6 | 0 | > 5 | 1 |

A larger sample of different globins might bring the values even closer to the Poisson distribution, it being likely that sites occupied by 4, 5, or 6 different amino acids would tend to increase at the expense of sites where only two or three different amino acids have so far been observed due to the small size of the sample.

The necessity for a definite and restricted tertiary structure in the globins arises from their specialized function in the transport of heme [J. C. Kendrew, *Brookhaven Symp. Biol.*, **15**, 216 (1962)]. In turn, the tertiary structure depends on their secondary and primary structure. The latter is referable to the sequence of bases in the globin genes, this being subject to evolutionary changes whose perpetuation depends on the rigors of natural selection. The selective process will obviously be influenced by the suitability of the protein for its needed task. In view of these restrictions, it is somewhat surprising to see an indication of even a partial degree of randomness in the variations that take place within the polypeptide chains as hinted by the comparison with the Poisson distribution. Undoubtedly large numbers of unacceptable variations that occur due to mutations are discarded. Nevertheless, the degree of evolutionary flexibility displayed by the globin molecules is a tribute to the suitability of amino acids for their function as versatile units that can adapt the processes of life to its mutational pressures.

PART IV

# EVOLUTION OF PROTEINS II

# Chairman's Remarks

EMIL L. SMITH

*Department of Biological Chemistry,*
*University of California,*
*School of Medicine,*
*Los Angeles, California*

Could I have your attention please? I think we should start the last session for today. I'm not sure why I was asked to introduce the next speaker. Probably it would be more necessary to introduce myself than to introduce Dr. Handler to this audience.

# Comparative Aspects of the Structure and Function of Phosphoglucomutase

J. G. Joshi, T. Hashimoto, K. Hanabusa,
H. W. Dougherty, and P. Handler

*Department of Biochemistry,*
*Duke University Medical Center,*
*Durham, North Carolina*

Total amino acid sequence analysis has proved to be a powerful tool for the study of evolution and phylogenetic comparison of proteins. At this writing, the most extensive studies have been conducted with hemoglobin and cytochrome *c*. Unfortunately, however, hemoglobin, with a few exceptions, is confined to the vertebrates, and no bacterial cytochrome, from its properties, would suggest itself as genetically homologous to the cytochrome *c* of yeast and higher plant or animal forms. Criteria other than sequence analysis have been applied in phylogenetic characterization of aldolase, triose phosphate dehydrogenase, and lactic dehydrogenase from diverse sources. These studies are reported elsewhere in this volume.

The present studies, initiated two years ago, were undertaken largely in the hope of identifying a protein which, in all living forms, is the expression of a homologous gene, thereby presumably bespeaking the common ancestry of life on this planet. Phosphoglucomutase (PGM) seemed to offer several advantages for such a study. The reaction which it catalyzes,

$$\text{Glucose 1-phosphate} \longleftrightarrow \text{glucose 6-phosphate}$$

was presumed to be biologically ubiquitous, as it is preliminary to the formation, from glucose, of such compounds as UDP-glucose. The reaction therefore must occur in virtually all living forms, and, since it represents a major metabolic activity, the responsible enzyme should be relatively abundant. As obtained from rabbit muscle, the enzyme exhibited a relatively low molecular weight (67,000), and, of particular interest, the catalytic process had been shown (6) to consist of the reaction

$$\text{Enzyme-OH} + \text{glucose 1,6-diphosphate} \longleftrightarrow \text{Enzyme-O-phosphate}$$
$$+ \text{glucose (1- or 6-) phosphate}$$

207

The phosphate attached to the enzyme had been found to be esterified to a seryl residue, and the pentapeptide sequence in which the serine is lodged had been established by Milstein and Sanger (5), thereby providing, as a marker, a portion of the peptide sequence at the "active site" of the enzyme. Phosphoglucomutase had also been isolated from yeast by McCoy and Najjar (3) and found, in a general way, to resemble that from rabbit muscle. In the present study, this series has been extended to include highly purified PGM from flounder muscle, *Escherichia coli*, *Micrococcus lysodeikticus*, and *Bacillus cereus*. This group was chosen because they are nonpathogenic, relatively readily cultured in quantity, and the GC contents of the bacterial DNA's are, respectively, 52%, 72%, and 34%, presumably representing extremes of evolutionary pressure. These studies are incomplete, and this note must be taken as an interim progress report.

## EXPERIMENTAL PROCEDURE AND RESULTS

### Preparation of Phosphoglucomutases

The details of the preparative procedures which were developed for these enzymes are irrelevant to this Symposium. It must suffice to state that each proved to be a rather difficult problem, and the procedures which were developed proved to be dramatically different for each

TABLE I
PURIFICATION OF PHOSPHOGLUCOMUTASES

| Species | Convenient starting amount (grams) | Yield Amount (mg) | Yield Per cent | Fold purification | Specific activity at optimal pH |
|---|---|---|---|---|---|
| Rabbit | 900 | 40 | 10 | 52 | 830 |
| Flounder | 1000 | 48 | 16 | 84 | 2900 |
| E. coli | 300 | 125 | 32 | 52 | 200 |
| M. lysodeikticus | 400 | 38 | 30 | 248 | 870 |
| B. cereus | 150 | 1 | 15 | 250 | 250 |
| Yeast | 400 (dry) | 87 | 24 | 115 | 294 |

species investigated. It is noteworthy that the length and complexity of the procedure were minimal for flounder, somewhat greater with *E. coli*, and greatest with the other two microorganisms, for which entirely satisfactory procedures have not yet been developed. The first two routinely yield crystals readily; microcrystalline preparations have been obtained from *M. lysodeikticus* and *B. cereus*, but even these were not homogeneous proteins. An over-all summary is provided in Table I. How-

ever, the data for *M. lysodeikticus* and *B. cereus* are somewhat misleading. Although these were isolated as materials which were homogeneous
in the ultracentrifuge and by several chromatographic procedures, they
were not homogeneous on electrophoresis. The final specific activity
shown is an estimate based on the degree of contamination observed
electrophoretically.

The enzymes from all sources were found to be free of hexokinase,
glucose 1-phosphate kinase, glucose 1-phosphatase, glucose 6-phosphatase,
fructose 1,6-diphosphatase, glucose 6-phosphate dehydrogenase, mannose
6-phosphate isomerase, glucose 1-phosphate transphosphorylase, and acid
and alkaline phosphomonoesterase. The bacterial enzymes were all free
of glucose 1,6-diphosphatase activity. The flounder enzyme, which was
devoid of aldolase, enolase, and phosphoenolpyruvate kinase, contained
somewhat less than 0.1% of lactic dehydrogenase and a trace of
phosphofructose isomerase. The latter activity was also detected in the
*M. lysodeikticus* preparations.

## Enzymatic Properties of Phosphoglucomutases

Some relevant properties of these enzymes will be found in Table II.

TABLE II
SOME PROPERTIES OF PHOSPHOGLUCOMUTASES[a]

| Species | Molecular weight | P/mole (as isolated) | Stimula- tion by imidazole | Reactive —SH per mole | Turnover number (moles of substrate) | Optimal pH |
|---|---|---|---|---|---|---|
| Rabbit | 62,000 | 1.0 | 3–5 × | 2–3 | 10,000 | 7.4 |
| Flounder | 63,000 | 0.5 | 1.5 × | 4 | 36,500 | 8.0 |
| Yeast | | | + | | | 7.4 |
| E. coli | 62,000 | 0 | — | 2 | 2,500 | 8.8 |
| M. lysodeikticus | 58,000 | 0 | — | 2 | 10,500 | 8.5 |
| B. cereus | 63,000 | 0 | — | < 0.5 | 3,200 | 8.3 |

[a] Blank spaces = information unavailable.

Most significant, perhaps, from the possibility of their genetic relationship
is the fact that, within the limits of error of such procedures, all exhibited
substantially the same molecular weights. Both rabbit and flounder
enzymes, which are isolated in the phospho- form, exhibit weak activity
in the absence of added glucose 1,6-diphosphate; the three bacterial
enzymes exhibit an absolute dependence on glucose 1,6-diphosphate.
All catalyze the reaction at about 10% of maximal velocity in the absence
of added $Mg^{++}$, and all are inhibited by an excess of this ion. Since
excess of both glucose 1-phosphate and glucose 1,6-diphosphate is

inhibitory with all enzymes in the group, determination of $K_m$ values is difficult, and a statement of $K_m$ lacks some of the significance attributed to this parameter with simpler enzymes; nevertheless, it can be stated that these values are of the same order among the group—about $10^{-7}$ $M$ for glucose diphosphate and $10^{-5}$ to $10^{-4}$ $M$ for glucose 1-phosphate. In all cases, inhibition at high glucose 1-phosphate concentration is alleviated by an increase in glucose diphosphate concentration, and vice versa. Not shown in the table is the fact that all enzymes in the series are competitively inhibited by urea; $K_i = 0.8$ $M$. The equilibrium position of the over-all reaction, obtained with each enzyme independently, proved to be essentially identical. And for those for which such studies have been conducted (rabbit, flounder, yeast, *M. lysodeikticus*) it was shown that, as the equilibrium state is attained, all forms of phosphate in the system come to the same specific activity, regardless of which member of the system was introduced in the $P^{32}$-labeled form.

The first parameter to show a seemingly significant difference among the series was the pH optimum. Although the flounder enzyme markedly resembles that from rabbit, it showed a somewhat alkaline pH optimum, whereas all three bacterial enzymes showed a strikingly high pH optimum. Indeed, at pH 7.2 the bacterial enzymes exhibit less than 25% of their optimal activity, and at pH 6.5 they are essentially inert.

## Sulfhydryl Groups

The behavior of this group of enzymes with respect to sulfhydryl reagents was surprisingly diverse.

1. The rabbit enzyme is unaffected by cysteine if the medium contains histidine or imidazole. In the absence of the latter, cysteine enhances activity markedly. Most but not all of this effect appears to reflect binding of traces of heavy metals. The enzyme reacts rapidly with 2 moles of PCMB per mole of enzyme, and a third group appears to react in 75 to 90 minutes. At completion of this reaction the enzyme is 30% inhibited.

2. The flounder enzyme also appears to utilize either histidine or cysteine as an activator. Thus at pH 7.4 in Tris buffer the enzyme inhibits only 8 to 10% of the activity manifest when either histidine or cysteine is present. The enzyme titrates 4 moles of PCMB per mole within 10 minutes. Surprisingly, when only one —SH group has reacted, the enzyme shows an increase of 130% in activity; after a second group has reacted, activity returns to the original level, and reaction of the final two groups is without effect. (See Fig. 1.)

3. In contrast to the vertebrate enzymes, *E. coli* PGM was in no

way affected by histidine. In Tris, this enzyme exhibited only 15% of the activity shown when cysteine was present. However, to achieve half-maximal activity, $2 \times 10^{-3}$ $M$ cysteine was required, and maximal activity was not evident until $10^{-2}$ $M$ and was maintained at yet higher concentrations. This enzyme possesses two reactive sulfhydryl groups; reaction of the first with PCMB results in 60% loss of activity, and reaction of the second occasions complete loss of activity, which is restored to normal by addition of cysteine.

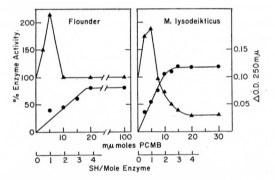

Fig. 1.    Reaction of phosphoglucomutases of flounder muscle and *M. lysodeikticus* with PCMB. Flounder muscle, 0.32 mg in histidine buffer, was incubated with PCMB at pH 7.4 for 10 minutes and then assayed. The *M. lysodeikticus* enzyme, 0.6 mg, in this case of specific activity 570, hence of 65% purity, was incubated for 1 hour in 0.05 $M$ phosphate, pH 7, and the cysteine-independent activity then assayed. The value of sulfhydryls per mole is based on the corrected value, allowing for the known purity of the preparation.

4. *Micrococcus lysodeikticus* PGM also exhibited about 20% of full activity in the absence of cysteine; maximal activity was seen at $10^{-2}$ $M$, but further increase in cysteine concentration reduced activity so that, at $4 \times 10^{-2}$ $M$, activity was 40% of maximal. Again the enzyme appears to contain two reactive —SH groups per mole. But reaction of the first of these, with PCMB, as in the case of flounder enzyme, resulted in an 85% increase in observable catalytic activity. Reaction of the second reduced activity to 30% of the original value, and only extremely high concentrations of the reagent ($8 \times 10^{-4}$ $M$) induced complete inhibition.

5. The enzyme from *B. cereus* behaved in yet another manner. Unlike the enzymes from *E. coli* and *M. lysodeikticus*, in this instance there was no apparent requirement for or stimulation by cysteine. Indeed 0.01 $M$ cysteine resulted in 10 to 15% inhibition. Titration with PCMB yielded data of equivocal nature. After addition of 2 moles of PCMB, the increase in absorbancy suggested 0.4 to 0.5 mole of sulfhydryl per mole

of enzyme but did not affect activity. Further addition of an 8-fold molar excess elicited no increase in absorbancy but resulted in 40% inhibition of activity. Surprisingly, "neutralization" with cysteine or addition of the mercaptide of cysteine and PCMB in 7-fold molar excess resulted in 70% inhibition. In any case, although the titration was not performed in the presence of urea, it does not appear that this enzyme bears a reactive sulfhydryl group.

Thus, although all members of the series have reactive sulfhydryl groups, this small series includes enzymes which are unaffected, inhibited, or extremely dependent upon an external sulfhydryl source (cysteine) and also includes examples which are inhibited, stimulated, or virtually unaffected by PCMB.

## Activation by Histidine

Najjar and his colleagues (6) found that rabbit PGM, which requires histidine or cysteine in the medium for catalysis, increases about 5-fold in activity if preincubated for several minutes with histidine and $Mg^{++}$ or imidazole and $Mg^{++}$. The mechanism of this effect remains obscure. The isolated enzyme contains one phosphate per mole which can be transferred to G 1-P if incubated with an excess of the latter. The dephosphoenzyme so prepared, when assayed in the usual medium, displays an activity equal to that of the histidine-preactivated phospho-enzyme. As isolated, flounder enzyme is a variable mixture of phos-pho- and dephospho- forms (30 to 60% phosphoenzyme). In keeping with this fact, flounder enzyme preparations show an increase in activity of 50 to 150% when preincubated with histidine. The bacterial enzymes, all of which are isolated free of phosphate, show no effect when pre-incubated with histidine, but there is no reason to expect that necessarily they would do so.

## $P^{32}$-Labeling of Phosphoglucomutases

The reaction mechanism described above, first proposed by Najjar, was based on demonstration of incorporation, from G 1,6-diP$^{32}$ or from G 1-P$^{32}$ in the presence of a catalytic amount of unlabeled G 1,6-diP, of P$^{32}$ into PGM. As noted earlier, this phosphate was shown to be ester-ified to a seryl residue. As a prelude to isolation and comparison of "active-site peptides" in this series, it was necessary first to study this incorporation of P$^{32}$.

1. *Flounder.* Only preliminary studies have been made with this enzyme. The system always contains G 1-P$^{32}$, a trace of G 1,6-diP, and cysteine. Labeling is maximal in a few minutes and then declines. This

is the consequence of the presence of glucose 1,6-diphosphatase activity in these preparations. Since the protein is estimated to be about 98% pure, this could well reflect a contaminant enzyme. However, if so, it is a highly specific glucose 1,6-diphosphatase, since none of a series of other mono- and diphosphates were hydrolyzed by the preparation. No equivalent activity has been observed with PGM from other species.

In any case, by using techniques similar to those previously described, $P^{32}$-labeled flounder PGM was isolated repeatedly. The apparent equilibrium constant for the half-reaction,

$$G \ 1,6\text{-diP} + E \longleftrightarrow G \ 6\text{-P} + E\text{-P}$$

was found to be 4.3, quite close to that of the rabbit (6) and yeast (3) enzymes. Until the preparation has been purified further, amino acid assays will not be attempted. Meanwhile, a study of the active-site peptide has been initiated.

2. *Escherichia coli.* When *E. coli* PGM (dephospho- form, as isolated) was incubated with G 1-$P^{32}$ in the presence of a catalytic amount of G 1,6-diP, the enzyme was successfully labeled. Excess substrate was removed by exhaustive dialysis, leaving a protein containing 0.4 to 1.05 moles of P per mole of enzyme. No variations in procedure succeeded in assuring maximal labeling. Partial acid hydrolysis followed by electrophoresis revealed $P_i$, a trace of serine phosphate, a glucose monophosphate (see below), and a major ninhydrin-positive spot. Purification of the latter by chromatography and electrophoresis was followed by a second partial hydrolysis to yield six new peptides. These were separated and analyzed, yielding the sequence

$$-\text{Thr}-\text{Ala}-\text{Ser}-\text{P}-\text{His}-\text{Asp}(\text{NH}_2)-$$

Particularly noteworthy is the fact that these materials accounted for all the $P^{32}$ of the protein. Najjar and Harshman had proposed a different sequence for the active-site peptide (7) of rabbit muscle PGM and most recently have found that, in that protein, the most probable sequence is

$$-\text{Thr}-\text{Ala}-\text{SerP}-\text{His}-\text{Asp}(\text{NH}_2)-\text{Gly}-\text{Glu}-\text{SerP}-\text{Ala}-\text{Gly}-\text{Val}-$$

This is attractive, as it offers the possibility of a single site of G 1,6-diP attachment with a seryl acceptor for each end of the molecule. If, indeed, this is the case, there is no evidence for the second portion of this sequence in the *E. coli* enzyme, but it is most striking that the pentapeptide of *E. coli* is identical with one portion of the rabbit sequence. Indeed, the presence of this sequence at the active site of two proteins of identical function and molecular weight, even though they are from species as remote from each other as *E. coli* and a rabbit, strongly tempts one to conclude that they bespeak a homologous genetic basis. However, as the amino acid analysis in Table III and the fingerprints in Fig. 2 indicate, these proteins are, otherwise, dramatically different.

TABLE III

TOTAL AMINO ACID COMPOSITION OF PHOSPHOGLUCOMUTASES
FROM RABBIT MUSCLE AND *E. coli*

| Residue | Residues per mole | |
|---|---|---|
| | *E. coli* | Rabbit muscle[a] |
| Aspartic acid | 37 | 59 |
| Threonine | 23 | 29 |
| Serine | 18 | 24 |
| Glutamic acid | 69 | 43 |
| Proline | 26 | 29 |
| Glycine | 56 | 49 |
| Alanine | 65 | 49 |
| 0.5 Cystine | 2[b] | 10 |
| Valine | 42 | 39 |
| Methionine | 11 | 10 |
| Isoleucine | 40 | 48 |
| Leucine | 44 | 43 |
| Tyrosine | 13 | 15 |
| Phenylalanine | 24 | 31 |
| Lysine | 36 | 46 |
| Histidine | 11 | 12 |
| Arginine | 25 | 27 |

[a] Original values (8) here recalculated for a molecular weight of 62,000 (2).

[b] Estimated as cysteic acid.

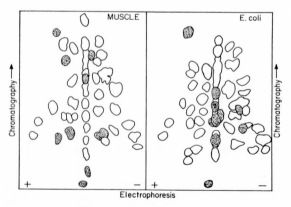

FIG. 2. Fingerprints of rabbit muscle and *E. coli* phosphoglucomutases, obtained after tryptic digestion.

*Substrate Binding to Phosphoglucomutases*

Two observations suggested the following experiments: (a) It was noted above that acid hydrolysis of $P^{32}$-labeled PGM from *E. coli* yielded a small amount of a glucose monophosphate—an observation made much earlier by Milstein (4) with rabbit muscle PGM. (b) Najjar (6) had reported that addition of substrate to rabbit PGM during the course of preincubation with imidazole $+$ $Mg^{++}$ interrupted the activation; i.e., 100 units of enzyme require 5 minutes of preincubation to develop 500 units of activity; addition of substrate at 2 minutes stops activity at the 200-unit level. The latter observation suggested the possibility of firm substrate binding to the enzyme under these conditions. To test this, PGM from *E. coli*, flounder, and rabbit has been incubated with G 1-$P^{32}$ in parallel with $C^{14}$-G 1-P, and the influence of histidine examined only in the case of the rabbit muscle. This type of experiment has been done by a variety of procedures. In general, the incubation mixture contains enzyme, a 50-fold molar excess of G 1-P, a 10-fold molar excess of G 1,6-diP, and cysteine. With *E. coli* and rabbit enzyme, excess substrate has been removed by prolonged and extensive dialysis, followed by ammonium sulfate precipitation, repeated five times, and two precipitations by acetone. When comparing flounder and rabbit enzymes, the protein has not been exhaustively dialyzed, owing to the lability of the flounder enzyme. Instead, the reaction mixture has been poured over a Dowex–Cl column, the effluent collected, and the protein precipitated twice by ammonium sulfate and once by trichloroacetic acid.

The striking observation in all these experiments is that, within the experimental error, the molar binding of glucose is equivalent to the molar binding of phosphate. Some typical data are presented in Tables IV and V. The significance of these findings is uncertain, but they suggest strongly that the simple mechanism described earlier is insufficient as a description of the modus operandi of this enzyme but that the enzymes from *E. coli*, flounder, and rabbit do share a common mechanism. The kinetic experiments of Ray (9) indicated that, when a G 1,6-diP molecule binds to the rabbit enzyme, it must be used at least twenty times before it comes away. Accordingly, it would follow that most of the enzyme molecules in an operating system have bound glucose at any given time. But the present data appear to indicate that it is a glucose monophosphate which is on the enzyme and, further, that the binding is surprisingly tight.

It should be remarked that neither heat- nor acid-inactivated enzyme binds either the carbon chain or the phosphate moiety under these circumstances and, further, that the isolated, doubly labeled protein loses both labels almost instantly when exposed to an excess of nonlabeled G 1-P.

Finally, in this regard, it may be noted, but with reservation, that in two experiments in which rabbit muscle PGM was preincubated with

### TABLE IV
#### LABELING OF RABBIT MUSCLE PHOSPHOGLUCOMUTASE[a]

| Preincubation with histidine | Moles P / mole enzyme | Moles glucose equivalent / mole enzyme |
|---|---|---|
| — | 0.81 | 0.67 |
| + | 0.96 | 1.42 |
| — | 0.68 | 0.68 |
| + | 1.68 | 1.82 |
| — | 0.74 | — |
| + | 1.65 | — |

[a] For each experiment 10 mg of enzyme in cysteine, phosphate buffer, pH 7.2, and a 2-fold molar excess of G 1,6diP were placed in a small dialysis sac. Labeled substrate, G 1-P$^{32}$ or $^{14}$C-G 1-P, in 100-fold molar excess was dialyzed in for several hours, and the contents of the dialysis bag was dialyzed exhaustively against repeated changes of phosphate buffer.

### TABLE V
#### LABELING OF FLOUNDER PHOSPHOGLUCOMUTASE[a]

| Incubation time (min) | Cpm μmole P GDP (× 10⁻⁴) | Cpm μmole enzyme (× 10⁻⁴) | Moles P / mole enzyme | Cpm μmole G GDP (× 10⁻⁴) | Cpm μmole enzyme (× 10⁻⁴) | Moles G / mole enzyme |
|---|---|---|---|---|---|---|
| 10 | 66.5 | 26.0 | 0.39 | 3.4 | 1.15 | 0.34 |
| 30 | 93 | 41.6 | 0.43 | 5.8 | 2.27 | 0.39 |
| 60 | 111 | 39.9 | 0.36 | 7.9 | 2.48 | 0.32 |

[a] The enzyme (2.3 mg, 0.0365 μmole) was incubated with 1.96 μmole of G 1-P$^{32}$ (115 × 10⁴ cpm/μmole), 0.37 μmole of $^{14}$C-G 1-P (8.73 × 10⁴ cpm/μmole), 0.2 μmole of GDP, 2 μmole of Mg$^{++}$, and 10 μmole of cysteine, pH 7.6, at 30° in total volume of 0.5 ml. At times shown, reaction mixture was poured over a Dowex–Cl column (0.8 × 1.5 cm). The glucose phosphates were eluted and separated, and their specific activity was estimated. The calculation of moles of phosphate or glucose bound is based on the specific activity of the GDP in the sample. Owing to the GDPase activity of the enzyme, the absolute amount of GDP declined to about 20% of the original level during 60 minutes. At that time, the GDP exhibited about 90% of the specific activity of the original G 1-P.

histidine before labeled substrate was introduced, labeling by both C$^{14}$ and P$^{32}$ somewhat more than doubled. Indeed, these represent the only instances in which, apparently, 2 moles of glucose and of phosphate were bound per mole of enzyme.

*Attempts to Label PGM from M. lysodeikticus and B. cereus*

In view of the foregoing observations, it has come as a surprise that, despite repeated trials and variations in procedure, attempts to label PGM from *M. lysodeikticus* have been uniformly unsuccessful. Enzyme has been incubated for 2 to 60 minutes with G 1-P$^{32}$ (5- to 200-fold molar excess) and with G 1,6-diP (1- to 20-fold molar excess) in various combinations and at pH from 7 to 9. The protein has been isolated by simple dialysis, ammonium sulfate precipitation, and TCA precipitation. The radioactivity observed thereafter has never exceeded that suggesting 0.05 mole of P per mole of enzyme and was usually less. Essentially similar results were obtained in a few experiments employing a carbon label.

Closely analogous findings were made with PGM from *B. cereus*. However, when *B. cereus* enzyme was briefly incubated with labeled substrate, separated by passage over Dowex-1–Cl, and precipitated with trichloroacetic acid, the precipitated protein contained 0.65 to 1.0 mole of P per mole of enzyme which moved with the enzyme during electrophoresis. When, however, this protein was hydrolyzed in 12 $N$ HCl, the radioactive material so formed proved to be glucose 6-phosphate plus some P$_i$, and no serine phosphate was discernible. It was clear then that, although this enzyme rather tightly binds its substrate, there is no evidence for phosphoenzyme formation during the catalytic process.

Although these enzymes were, admittedly, somewhat impure, the impurity could not conceivably have exceeded 50% and was, more probably, considerably less than 10%. Hence, the failure to achieve labeling must be accepted as a real distinction between the properties of these two enzymes and the other members of the series. Accordingly, it seemed worth while to attempt other approaches to the study of these enzymes.

The failure to label, i.e., the failure to transfer phosphate from G 1,6-diP to enzyme, was confirmed by direct examination of such a system, in which the product, G 6-P, was sought by G 6-P dehydrogenase activity. Whereas by this procedure, with reagent amounts of the rabbit enzyme, stoichiometric reaction was readily demonstrated, no glucose 6-phosphate was found when the *M. lysodeikticus* enzyme was incubated with glucose diphosphate.

Since, however, the over-all reaction is the same as in those instances where labeling is feasible, and since these two bacterial enzymes do require glucose diphosphate and rapidly equilibrate label among G 1-P, G 6-P, and both phosphates of G 1,6-diP, it appeared that this pair of enzymes must catalyze a metathetical reaction between the glucose mono- and diphosphates. This distinction should be observable kinetically. Cleland (1) has described a kinetic approach which distinguishes between a "ping-pong" mechanism:

$$\text{Enzyme} + \text{AX} \longleftrightarrow \text{Enzyme X} + \text{A} \qquad (1)$$
$$\text{Enzyme X} + \text{B} \longleftrightarrow \text{Enzyme} + \text{BX} \qquad (2)$$

and a metathetical reaction on the enzyme surface:

$$\text{AX} + \text{B} \xleftrightarrow{\text{E}} \text{BX} + \text{A}$$

The latter may be ordered, i.e., a compulsory order of substrate binding in each direction, or unordered.

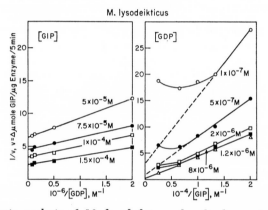

FIG. 3.   Kinetic analysis of *M. lysodeikticus* phosphoglucomutase. The data in each form of the plot are from the same experiment. Normal assay conditions were employed. If the data are then replotted, $1/V_{max}$ vs. $1/G$ 1-P, a value for the "true" $K_m$ of G 1-P is obtained of $1.3 \times 10^{-3}$ $M$.

The data obtained for the *M. lysodeikticus* enzyme are shown in Fig. 3. There is a clear slope effect with each substrate; the lines in the plots are not parallel, and the data conform to those expected for a sequentially ordered metathetical reaction on the enzyme surface. In contrast, flounder muscle enzyme behaved as shown in Fig. 4. Both sets of lines are truly parallel, and this enzyme, therefore, must catalyze a "ping-pong" type of reaction involving a transient, essentially stable enzyme-bound intermediate which reacts with the second type of substrate molecule, as Ray (9) has recently found with the rabbit muscle enzyme.

## SUMMARY

Patently, this study is incomplete. But the data thus far obtained indicate a similarity in mechanism among the phosphoglucomutases from rabbit, flounder, yeast, and *E. coli* and a decidedly different mechanism for the enzymes from *M. lysodeikticus* and *B. cereus*. Although the *E. coli* enzyme can be labeled with substrate-derived phosphate and then shown to possess a seryl phosphate embedded in the same pentapeptide as muscle enzyme, there are gross differences between them, including absence of a second reactive seryl residue in the *E. coli* enzyme. At this writing, there seems no reason to suppose that the phosphoglucomutases of *M. lysodeikticus* and *B. cereus* are genetically homologous

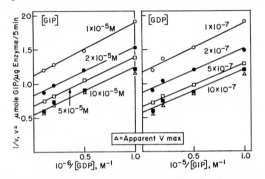

Fig. 4.   Kinetic analysis of flounder muscle phosphoglucomutase. The data in each form of the plot are from the same experiment. If higher concentrations of substrates are employed, both are inhibitory. $K_i$ (GDP) $= 7 \times 10^{-4}$ M; $K_i$ (G 1-P) $= 1 \times 10^{-3}$ M.

with the other members of the series. But the preliminary data reported here concerning binding of the glucose as well as the phosphate moiety of the substrates suggests that such a conclusion be held with reservation, as these data hold out the possibility that the two unlabelable enzymes may have lost the capacity to bind substrate covalently but, still capable of efficiently making Michaelis complexes with substrate, and still possessing the additional functional groups operative in the catalytic mechanism (histidine, aspartate, sulfhydryl, etc.), might continue to serve as an efficient phosphoglucomutase.

## References

1.   Cleland, W. W., *Biochim. Biophys. Acta,* **67**, 104, 173, 188 (1963).
2.   Filmer, D. L., and Koshland, D. E., *Biochem. Biophys. Acta,* **77**, 34 (1963).
3.   McCoy, E. E., and Najjar, V. A., *J. Biol. Chem.,* **234**, 3017 (1959).
4.   Milstein, C., *Biochem. J.,* **79**, 574, 584, 591 (1961).
5.   Milstein, C., and Sanger, F., *Biochem. J.,* **79**, 456 (1961).
6.   Najjar, V. A., *in* "The Enzymes" (P. D. Boyer, H. Lardy, and K. Myrbäck, eds.), 2nd ed., Vol. 6, p. 161, Academic Press, New York, 1961.
7.   Najjar, V. A., and Harshman, S., *Abstr. 6th Intern. Congr., Biochem., New York, 1964.*
8.   Ray, W. J., and Koshland, D. E., *J. Biol. Chem.* **237**, 2493 (1962).
9.   Ray, W. J., Jr., and Roscelli, G. A., *J. Biol. Chem.,* **239**, 1228 (1964).

# Structural and Functional Aspects of Cytochrome $c$ in Relation to Evolution

E. Margoliash

*Abbott Laboratories, North Chicago, Illinois*

AND

Emil L. Smith

*University of California, Los Angeles, California*

## Introduction

Two circumstances make possible the study outlined in the present paper. The first is the availability of a protein, namely cytochrome $c$, from species covering the widest possible expanse of the taxonomic scale, these molecules constituting a set of evolutionarily homologous structures. The other depends on the mechanism of protein biosynthesis which automatically translates the structure of parts of the genetic material into an amino acid sequence.

First observed by MacMunn (23-26) in the last decades of the nineteenth century, rediscovered by Keilin (18) in 1925, and partially purified by Dixon *et al.* (6) in 1931, cytochrome $c$ is the only common component of the terminal respiratory chain of aerobic organisms which can easily be obtained in a soluble form. In recent years it has been purified and in numerous cases crystallized from a very wide variety of organisms, including a large selection of vertebrates, some invertebrates, and even fewer plants or microorganisms (see Margoliash, 28; Yamanaka and Okunuki, 61). The proteins from all these species have common fundamental characteristics, including a single heme per molecule, a molecular weight near 12,500, an isoelectric point in the basic pH range, an oxidation-reduction potential very near $+250$ mv, and, most important, the ability to react readily with cytochrome oxidase preparations from mammalian sources. This last characteristic has prompted the grouping of all these proteins into one class, named the "mammalian type" of cytochrome $c$ (28, 33), to contrast with the cytochromes of the C group which can be obtained from a variety of microorganisms, have physicochemical properties which usually differ considerably from those of the mammalian type of cytochrome *c*, and react with oxidase preparations from these microorganisms but are largely unaffected by mammalian cytochrome oxidase. That such relationships are not strictly all or none but only approximate has been recently demonstrated by Yamanaka and Okunuki (61). Nevertheless, the fact that "mammalian-type" cytochromes *c* can to a large extent substitute one for another in complete mitochondrial oxidation chain systems (Jacobs and Sanadi, 17; Estabrook and Margoliash, 9), at least insofar as electron transport is concerned, makes it certain that they constitute a homologous set of proteins *from the functional point of view*. The studies to be discussed below have demonstrated that they also possess homologous structures in terms of their amino acid sequences and consequently also *from the evolutionary point of view*.

With the exception of many microorganisms, the mammalian type of cytochrome *c* is practically universally present in species for which oxygen serves as the terminal oxidant of metabolism. This class of protein was presumably utilized ever since the beginning of aerobic life on earth. Its phylogenetic antiquity thus assured, cytochrome *c* appears to be a particularly suitable object for the study of the relationships, if any, between the evolution of species and that of a particular protein. In this connection it is interesting to note that thermodynamic considerations have recently led George (10) to suggest that the entire respiratory chain is of greater antiquity than cytochrome oxidase, being presumably earlier utilized with a chemically simpler terminal oxidant than gaseous oxygen.

Ever since, some years ago, it was learned that the amino acid sequence of protein polypeptide chains was a direct translation of portions of the genetic material according to a definite code, it became obvious that the primary structure of proteins would contain a rich record of past evolutionary history. An obvious attraction, therefore, to the study of the molecular taxonomy of proteins has been the possibility, however remote, to reconstitute today long-past evolutionary transitions of species and analyze them in terms of unit molecular mutational events. This goal is still out of sight, and the analysis is yet at its very crudest stage. Nevertheless, first results accruing from the knowledge of the complete amino acid sequences of the cytochromes *c* from fourteen different species appear to warrant presentation and may serve, if nothing else, to pinpoint those areas of ignorance which have to be eliminated before significant advances can be expected. The ideas developed with regard to the evolutionary significance of the primary structure variations in cytochrome *c* should be viewed in relation to similar considerations of other proteins and peptides, such as hemoglobin (Ingram, 16; Zuckerkandl and Pauling, 64; Zuckerkandl, 63; Pauling and Zuckerkandl, 48; Hill *et al.*, 15), the hormonal pituitary peptides, insulin, and fibrinopeptides derived from fibrinogen. Many of these topics are reviewed in the proceedings of a recent conference (Peeters, 49).

The cytochromes *c* of known primary structure, in the historical order in which their amino acid sequences became known, come from the following species: horse (35, 21, 38, 32, 36, 27, 60), man (39), pig (34, 57), chicken (5, 34, 3), baker's yeast (41, 42), cow (62), sheep (4), the tuna fish (20), a rhesus monkey (50), the domestic rabbit (43), an insect (3), the dog (40), a marsupial (44), and the rattlesnake (2). From the strictly evolutionary point of view, this study should, in addition to cytochrome *c*, also encompass two other types of protein. The first would include the products of the gene which may have preceded the cytochrome *c* gene, which directed the synthesis of another protein and whose descendants may still be present in extant organisms. The second would be represented by the products of genes which may on occasion have evolved from the cytochrome *c* gene, following duplication and translocation, to a point where they yield non-cytochrome *c* proteins. However, since there is as yet no practical way of identifying such proteins, our study is necessarily limited to those proteins in which variations of amino acid sequence have not so fundamentally affected the character of the protein that it would no longer be recognizable as a cytochrome *c* of the "mammalian type."

Several reports of the evolutionary connotations of the sum of information represented by the known primary structures of cytochrome *c* from various species have already appeared (34, 56, 29, 30, 55, 37). This paper will consider, *first*, the features of cytochrome *c* that remain constant in evolution and their use in inferring the evolutionary homology of these proteins, *second*, the variable features of cytochrome *c* and certain apparently quantitative aspects of phylogeny exhibited by this protein, and *last*, some evolutionary aspects of structure-function relations in cytochrome *c*.

### Constant Features of Cytochrome *c* Structure—Evolutionary Homology

The "mammalian type" of cytochrome *c* affords, on a molecular basis, an excellent illustration of the Darwinian concept of organismal evolution as "descent with modification." From the constancy of some amino acid residues one infers descent, while the variable features represent modifications, the mode of development of which will be discussed below.

## Identical Residues in Identical Positions

Cytochrome $c$ does in fact exhibit evolutionary constancy at three different levels. The first type of constancy is illustrated in Fig. 1. It is simply the occurrence of identical residues in identical positions. Approximately 50% of the molecule remains strictly invariant in the proteins from the wide taxonomic range of species so far examined. If convergent evolution were to underlie this extensive degree of identity, one would

Gly – – – – Gly – – – Phe – – – CyS – – CyS·His·Thr·
                 10             └—Heme—┘

Val·Glu – Gly·Gly – His·Lys – Gly· Pro· AspNH$_2$·Leu – Gly – – Gly·
20                               30

Arg – – Gly· GluNH$_2$·Ala – Gly – – Tyr – – Ala·AspNH$_2$ – – Lys
    40                          50

– – – Try – – – – – – Glu· Tyr·Leu – AspNH$_2$· Pro·Lys·Lys· Tyr·
     60                      70

Ileu· Pro· Gly· Thr· Lys· Met – – – Gly – – Lys – – – Arg –
             80                    90

                     D        D
Asp·Leu – – Tyr·Leu – Lys – – – –
                  100

FIG. 1. Invariant residues in "mammalian-type" cytochromes $c$. In those positions in which the same residue occurs in all the fourteen cytochromes $c$ under consideration (see text), the amino acid is given, while the dashes represent positions in which more than one amino acid has been observed. The "D" above residues 99 and 103 indicates that the amino acids occupying these positions are absent in one or more of the cytochromes $c$.

have to accept that, on the average, every second residue is an absolutely immutable structural requirement. This is a very unlikely situation. Indeed, the active site of proteins is composed of only a very few residues, while the rest of the molecule is required only to take a particular conformation, presumably that tertiary structure which is the hallmark of the protein in question. This latter requirement is known to be compatible with a variety of primary structures, as exemplified by the myoglobins (19, 53). One must, therefore, conclude that the cytochromes $c$ of the mammalian type all derive from a common primordial form, thus demonstrating evolutionary homology, and, as far as the authors are aware, for the first time the actual survival of a distinct recognizable gene for some 2 billion years, a remarkable feat of genetic conservatism. Very recent analyses of the cytochromes *c* obtained from a higher plant, wheat germ (12), and from a mold, *Neurospora* (14), leave no doubt that these also fall into the same evolutionary group of proteins. If one excludes the large group of bacteria, it thus appears probable that all biological species, both extant and extinct, plant and animal, had at one time a common living ancestor, clearly implying that there was only one effective emergence of life on Earth, a conclusion often reached on a variety of less direct grounds (45).

Among the residues which are strictly conserved, one finds three of the four prolyl residues (at positions 30, 71, and 76) and eleven glycines (positions 1, 6, 23, 24, 29, 34, 37, 41, 45, 77, and 84). These residues may play a role in permitting a particular conformation of the polypeptide chains, the prolines as helix breakers and the glycines as locations in which peptide chains may approach one another closely without interference by residue side chains.

Similarly, two histidines (positions 18 and 26) and two cysteines (positions 14 and 17) are maintained throughout. The two histidines have been assumed to proffer the two requisite cytochrome *c* hemochrome-forming imidazole groups (for a discussion see Margoliash, 28; also 58, 8, 46, 31, 13). Atomic model studies have shown that a spacing of two residues between the cysteines permits the correct spatial arrangement for the binding of the polypeptide chain to the heme, through addition of the sulfhydryl groups across the double bonds of the vinyl side chains (8, 31). This conclusion has been fully verified by the condensation of protoporphyrinogen with the synthetic peptide CySH·Gly·Gly·CySH (52), as well as by the recombination of the reduced porphyrin with cytochrome *c* apoprotein (51).

The amino-terminal residue in all the vertebrate cytochromes *c* is N-acetylated, while the yeast and moth proteins, probably exhibiting a more primitive structure at this point, carry, instead of the acetyl, five and four extra amino acid residues, respectively. This might simply mean that a free amino group at residue 1 would interfere with the proper structural stability of the protein, for example, by competing with one of the correct hemochrome-forming groups for the heme iron. The primitive solution to this structural problem was simply a longer peptide chain, while vertebrates have apparently learned to use a shorter peptide chain by acetylating it.

Thus, in these and other cases, reasonable assumptions appear to provide links between features of the primary structure that are conserved in evolution and structural or functional requirements of proteins in general or cytochrome *c* in particular. It should, however, be strongly emphasized that, except for the positional requirements of the two heme-bonded cysteines, the other explanations offered are no more than un-proved hypotheses. Furthermore, there are many residues, conserved in evolution just as strictly as those mentioned above (see Fig. 1), for which there appears to be, at present, no obvious structural or functional role. Among the latter may be mentioned the tryptophan at position 59, the two arginines at positions 38 and 91, the methionine at position 80, and the threonines at positions 19, 49, and 78. The threonine at position 19 immediately follows the first histidyl residue which itself is immediately adjacent to the second heme-peptide bond. (It is remarkable that the same sequence, CySH–His–Thr, is observed not only in mammalian-type cytochromes $c$ but also in cytochromes functionally entirely different from the mammalian-type protein, such as the cytochrome $c_2$ from *Rhodospirillum rubrum* (47) and the variant heme protein from *Chromatium* (7).) The most outstanding conserved area is the remarkably constant sequence of eleven amino acids extending from residue 70 to residue 80, which will be discussed below.

## Conservative Substitutions

Another type of constancy involves not particular residues, but classes of residues which are mutually interchangeable, in the sense that their chemical structures are similar to the extent that one may assume them to be capable of the same structural or functional role. These are the so-called "conservative substitutions" previously defined (55, 56) and exemplified in the constant presence of either lysine or arginine in position 13, or the invariable occurrence of either phenylalanine or tyrosine and serine or threonine in positions 46 and 47, respectively. Figure 2 lists the conservative substitutions occurring in the cytochromes $c$ under consideration.

## Constancy of Hydrophobic and Basic Segments

The third type of constancy, and possibly that of greatest significance with regard to the formation and maintenance of the tertiary structure specific to cytochrome $c$, is one which conserves the over-all physico-chemical character of certain segments of the amino acid sequence. Thus the presence of eight regions having a highly hydrophobic character was noted in the horse heart protein (27), the first for which the amino acid sequence was determined. In all the cytochromes $c$ so far examined, the hydrophobicity of these eight areas has been very strictly maintained. They cover residues 9 to 12, 32 to 36, 46 to 48, 57 to 59, 64 to 68, 74 to 75, 80 to 85, and 94 to 98, and contain from 23 to 27 of the 26

```
                                              Lys
        Asp      Ala Lys              Thr  Thr Met          Ala                Lys
  Gly Val Pro    Ser      Val Ala Lys     Ala Thr Leu  Val Thr     Arg Ser Leu           Ala
  – Glu·Phe·Lys – – AspNH₂·Ileu·Glu·AspNH₂ – Lys·Lys·Ileu – Ileu·GluNH₂·Lys – Glu·GluNH₂ – – – – – AspNH₂
  -5            1                          10                        20


                                              Pro
              Try    Phe                      Val                    Ala
    Pro   Thr    His    Leu Tyr    His Ser    Glu    Phe Ser   Ser Asp
  – – Lys – – Val – – – – AspNH₂ – Ileu·Phe – – Lys·Thr – – – GluNH₂ – Tyr·Thr – Thr·AspNH₂
              30                   40                          50


      Lys                 Thr  Lys
      Ala                 Val  Gly   Glu   Glu                 Ser
    Lys Ser      Gly      Val Leu  Asp   Asp   Asp   Thr   Leu Phe      Thr
  – – Ileu·AspNH₂ – AspNH₂ Ileu·Ileu – AspNH₂·AspNH₂·AspNH₂·AspNH₂·Met·Met – – – Glu – – – – – – –
                          60                                 70


                              Lys
                              Thr              Val
                              Ser              Thr
                  Val         Thr Gly          Ala                         Ser CySH Lys    Lys
          Ala         Thr     Ala Glu          Glu                         Ala Thr  Thr    Ala
          Val Phe Ala    Leu Ser  Glu Asp      Glu  GluNH₂     Val Thr     Glu Ser  Ala    Ser
  – – – – Ileu·Ileu·Gly – Ileu·Lys – Lys·AspNH₂·Asp – AspNH₂ – – Ileu·Ala – – Lys – Asp·Ala· AspNH₂·Glu
          80                           90                      100               104
```

FIG. 2. Radical and conservative amino acid substitutions in "mammalian-type" cytochromes *c*. The amino acid sequences of the fourteen cytochromes *c* considered (see text) have been aligned as in Fig. 3. Invariant residues are represented by dashes. In positions in which only conservative substitutions have been observed the residues are in **bold-face** type, where both conservative and radical substitutions occur ordinary characters are used, and where only radical substitutions have been found the residues are in *italics*. It should be noted that this classification is only tentative, since the decision as to whether a particular substitution at a particular locus is conservative or radical will depend to a large extent on the interpretation of the function of the residues involved (see text).

to 29 hydrophobic residues. The amino acids usually considered to belong to this group are leucine, isoleucine, valine, phenylalanine, tyrosine, tryptophan, and methionine (see Fig. 3 and Table I). In most cases in which there have been substitutions of such residues they are replaced by other hydrophobic residues. Whenever hydrophobic have replaced nonhydrophobic amino acids, the added hydrophobic residues

*Val* Val *Leu* Val
– – *Phe* – – – – *Ileu* – – – – – – Ileu·**Phe**·Ileu·Met – – – *Leu* – – – **Val**
-5 1 10 20

**Phe**
**Leu Tyr**
– – – – – – – – Val – – – **Leu**·*Try* – **Ileu**·**Phe** – – – – – – – – Val –
30 40

*Leu*
**Tyr** **Val** *Val* **Met Phe**
**Phe** – **Tyr** – – – – *Ileu* – – – **Ileu**·Ileu·**Try** – – – – **Leu**·**Met** – **Tyr**·**Leu** – –
50 60 70

Val **Leu** **Val**
– – – **Tyr**·**Ileu** – – – – **Met**·Ileu·**Phe**·Val – **Ileu** – – – – – – – – – **Leu**·**Ileu**
80 90

– **Tyr**·**Leu** – – – – – –
100 104

FIG. 3. Composite distribution of hydrophobic residues in "mammalian-type" cytochromes *c*. The amino acid sequences of the fourteen cytochromes *c* considered (see text) have been aligned by superimposing the two cysteinyl residues (positions 14 and 17 in the vertebrate proteins) binding the heme to the polypeptide chain. The moth and yeast proteins having longer sequences on the amino-terminal side of the heme binding site, the extra residues have been numbered —1 to —4 and —1 to —5 for these two cytochromes *c*, respectively. The residues in *italics* occur in the protein of only one species, those in ordinary characters in more than one protein, while in positions which contain only hydrophobic residues all are marked in **boldface** type.

merely serve to complete internally or extend peripherally one of the eight clusters noted above. Thus, *the entities conserved in evolution are the clusters of hydrophobicity,* rather than individual residues.

A very similar situation occurs with respect to the basic residues lysine, arginine, and histidine. These also tend to occur in groups that are conserved during the evolution of species. However, conservatism of clusters of basicity in terms of their exact position along the polypeptide chain does not appear to be quite as rigid as in the case of the hydrophobic segments (see Fig. 4 and Table I).

The question as to whether this remarkable stability of hydrophobic and basic regions represents only an effect of natural selection based

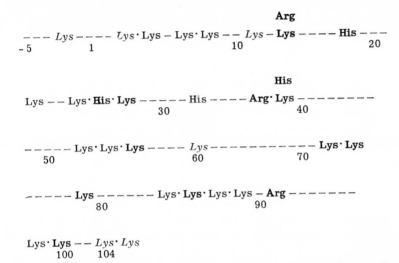

FIG. 4. Composite distribution of basic residues in "mammalian-type" cytochromes *c*. The amino acid sequences of the fourteen cytochromes *c* considered (see text) have been aligned as in Fig. 3. The residues in *italics* occur in the protein of only one species, those in ordinary characters in more than one protein, while in positions which contain only basic amino acids all residues are marked in **bold-face** type.

solely on structural-functional requirements of cytochrome *c*, or may in part express a phase of the genetic mechanism of protein variability, has previously been raised and discussed (29).

## Minimal Primary Structure Requirements

An important question yet to be fully explored is what are the minimal requirements of primary structure for a protein to be a cytochrome *c*, in terms of the three types of constant features delineated above. In the present series approximately 50% of the residues are unchanged, conservative variations account for a proportion of the substitutions observed, and the basic or hydrophobic characters of certain regions are largely immutable. Because of the relatively small number of cytochromes *c* for which complete amino acid sequences have so far been worked out, it is highly unlikely that every one of these unaltered features plays a vital part in the final elaboration of the functionally competent protein. In this context one must also consider cooperative effects between residues. It is entirely conceivable that a particular variation at one point of the amino acid sequence may, under certain conditions, become structurally unacceptable or functionally deleterious, unless "compensated" for by one or more other changes at different residues. There is, however, no reason to doubt that eventually it will be possible to define rather closely the common traits of cytochrome $c$ primary structures, as

TABLE I

GROUPINGS OF BASIC AND HYDROPHOBIC RESIDUES IN CYTOCHROME $c^a$

| Species | Basic residues | | Hydrophobic residues | |
|---|---|---|---|---|
| | Total | Excluded from groups | Total | Excluded from groups |
| Man | 23 | 4 | 29 | 2 |
| Monkey | 23 | 4 | 28 | 2 |
| Pig, cow, sheep | 23 | 4 | 26 | 2 |
| Horse | 24 | 5 | 26 | 2 |
| Rabbit | 23 | 4 | 27 | 2 |
| Dog | 23 | 4 | 26 | 2 |
| Kangaroo | 22 | 3 | 27 | 2 |
| Chicken | 23 | 4 | 27 | 2 |
| Rattlesnake | 23 | 4 | 28 | 2 |
| Tuna | 20 | 4 | 28 | 3 |
| Moth | 20 | 4 | 27 | 3 |
| Yeast | 23 | 5 | 27 | 4 |

$a$ Under the headings "Excluded from groups" is given the total number of basic and hydrophobic residues outside the seven basic and eight hydrophobic clusters of amino acid residues characteristic of cytochrome $c$.

found in nature. Whether these properties will in fact be strictly the minimal requirements of a protein able to function as a cytochrome $c$ will depend on whether evolutionary stability is or is not strictly synonymous with functional necessity. This problem is discussed below.

## VARIABLE FEATURES OF CYTOCHROME $c$ STRUCTURE—PHYLOGENETIC RELATIONSHIPS

Just as the stable characters of the amino acid sequences of various cytochromes $c$ may serve as indicators of structural-functional requirements, the variable features must represent a partial record of the interplay of genetic variability and natural selection on the structural gene of the protein, during the evolutionary history of the species containing these proteins.

## Quantitative Relationships

Qualitatively, as has been reported before (34, 29, 30), there appears to be a connection between the taxonomic kinship of species and the number of residue differences in the amino acid sequences of their cytochromes *c*. The proteins of closely related species show few or no differences, while those of species, the lines of descent of which diverged further back in evolutionary history, exhibit relatively large degrees of dissimilarity (see 34, 29, 30, 37, 55). Thus, for example, the proteins from man and *Macacus mulatta* differ by a single residue, the cytochromes *c* of the horse and the tuna fish show twenty variant residues, while those

TABLE II

NUMBER OF VARIANT RESIDUES AMONG CYTOCHROMES *c* OF DIFFERENT CLASSES AND PHYLA OF ORGANISMS[a]

| Proteins from | compared to | Proteins from | Number of variant residues | |
|---|---|---|---|---|
| | | | Span | Average |
| Mammals | | Mammals | 0–12 | |
| Mammals | | Chicken | 10–15 | 12.4 |
| Mammals and chicken | | Tuna fish | 18–21 | 20.2 |
| Vertebrates | | Moth | 28–33 | 30.0 |
| Vertebrates and moth | | Baker's yeast | 43–49 | 45.7 |

[a] The cytochromes *c* compared include the proteins from nine mammals, the chicken, the tuna fish, a moth (*S. cynthia*), and baker's yeast (see text).

of the horse and baker's yeast have as many as forty-five amino acid differences. What is remarkable is that these relations exhibit a definite quantitative aspect when one compares the cytochromes *c* of species in different zoological classes or higher categories of systematic classification (Margoliash, 29). Table II shows that the primary structures of the proteins from seven mammals differ from that of the chicken by a relatively constant number of residues (ten to fifteen), which the mammalian proteins vary among themselves by as little as none to as many as twelve residues. It should also be noted that in no case is the difference between the mammalian proteins significantly greater than that between the mammalian and bird proteins. This sort of relation appears to hold true for all major points of evolutionary divergence. The line of evolution which later gave rise to both mammals and birds having diverged from that which led to present-day fish at an earlier date than the divergence of the mammalian and avian lines, the cytochromes *c* of various mammals and the chicken are all roughly equally different from the tuna protein. Similar relations are evident for the comparison of all vertebrate cytochromes *c* with the protein from an invertebrate, the moth *Samia cynthia*, as well as for the comparison of the vertebrate and moth proteins with baker's yeast cytochrome c.

Recent evidence with regard to the cytochromes c of five species of birds from different orders shows that the relations described above are in fact maintained in this case (3). If these observations are validated with proteins from several species of each class, it would appear to imply that elapsed time as such is an important parameter in determining the number of effective mutations accumulated by the cytochrome c structural gene along any line of evolutionary descent. This should not be taken to indicate that mutant genes are retained, diluted out into the available gene pool, or eliminated, by means other than those well recognized, such as the operation of natural selection, genetic drift, genetic linkage, or accidental occurrence together with characters of selective importance. Rather, it would simply mean that in the case of cytochrome c, over relatively long stretches of evolutionary history—some 200 million years appears to be the minimal required period—other factors affecting the rate of accumulation of primary structure changes having canceled each other out or averaged themselves out, elapsed time remains the variable most obviously related to the extent of amino acid variations. Thus the calculation of an average period required for a single residue difference to occur in two diverging lines of evolution, or *unit evolutionary period* (29, 37), is valid only insofar as the unit time obtained is considered a result of many influences acting over a prolonged period of evolutionary history (see Fig. 5).

It should not be overlooked that for the purposes of this discussion all amino acid residue changes are equated to single mutational events. This may be relatively correct when few mutable sites have changed. However, it becomes less and less accurate and eventually grossly wrong as one approaches the limit represented by changes at all mutable sites, several mutational events per site becoming the rule rather than the exception. This difficulty may be partially overcome when the nucleic acid base sequences coding for amino acid residues in polypeptide chains will have been fully determined. This code will indeed provide a means of estimating the minimal number of single mutational events and the most probable genetic pathway from one residue in the cytochrome c of one species to another in the corresponding position in the protein of another species (see 34).

Another, though less satisfactory, approach to the estimation of corrections for the cumulative effect of changes at many variable sites on the observability of subsequent changes is illustrated in Table III and Fig. 5. Simple statistical calculations can be used to approximate the number of mutational events from the number of variant amino acid residues, if one assumes a definite maximal number of changeable positions and considers that every such amino acid is equally subject to mutational effects. If one accepts that there is a simple proportional relationship between the number of amino acid residue differences between two cytochromes *c* and the time elapsed since the lines of evolution which

TABLE III

CALCULATION OF THE STATISTICALLY PROBABLE NUMBER OF UNIT MUTATIONAL EVENTS REQUIRED TO YIELD THE OBSERVED NUMBER OF VARIANT RESIDUES AS A FUNCTION OF THE TOTAL NUMBER OF VARIABLE RESIDUES[a]

| Observed number of variant residues ($\lambda$) | Assumed number of variable residues ($n$) | Probable number of mutational events ($r$) |
| --- | --- | --- |
| 12.40 | 50 | 14 |
| | 60 | 13 |
| | 70 | 13 |
| | 80 | 13 |
| | 90 | 13 |
| | 100 | 13 |
| 20.25 | 50 | 25 |
| | 60 | 24 |
| | 70 | 23 |
| | 80 | 23 |
| | 90 | 22 |
| | 100 | 22 |
| 30.00 | 50 | 45 |
| | 60 | 41 |
| | 70 | 39 |
| | 80 | 37 |
| | 90 | 36 |
| | 100 | 35 |
| 45.70 | 50 | 122 |
| | 60 | 86 |
| | 70 | 74 |
| | 80 | 67 |
| | 90 | 63 |
| | 100 | 61 |

[a] Calculated according to the formula (Feller, 9a):

$$r = n \ln \frac{n}{\lambda}$$

eventually led to the two species carrying these proteins diverged, then one should be able to estimate such times of divergence from the amino acid sequences of the cytochromes *c*. In Fig. 5 the primary standard used is a paleontologically estimated period of 280 million years for the time elapsed since the divergence of the mammalian and avian evolutionary lines (55). This yields a *unit evolutionary period* of 22.6 million years. Linear extrapolation of the relation thus defined gives a time of divergence of about 460 million years for the lines of descent leading to mammals and birds on the one hand and to the tuna fish on the other, a period of 680 million years for the divergence of the vertebrate and invertebrates line of descent, and somewhat over 1000 million years for the time elapsed since the divergence of the lines leading to baker's yeast on the one

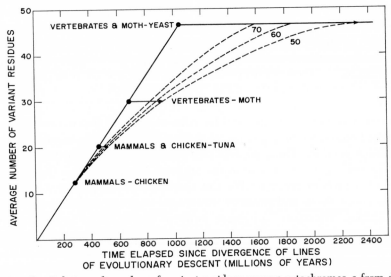

FIG. 5. Relation of number of variant residues among cytochromes *c* from different classes and phyla of organisms to the time elapsed since the divergence of the corresponding lines of evolutionary descent. The straight line in the figure was calculated on the basis of a value of 280 million years for the time elapsed since the divergence of the mammalian and avian lines of descent, corresponding to a *unit evolutionary period* of 22.6 million years (see text). The curved lines are drawn through points representing values corrected for the statistically probable number of mutational events required to yield the observed number of variant residues, assuming the occurrence of a total of 50, 60, and 70 variable positions in the protein, respectively, as noted in the figure (see also Table III). The arrows indicate the corresponding corrected times of divergence for the main taxonomic groups considered.

hand and all the other species examined on the other (see Fig. 5). Statistical estimates of the actual number of mutational events which have probably led to the observed spans of amino acid residue differences yield the three curved lines in Fig. 5. These have been calculated by assuming 50, 60, and 70 as the maximal number of changeable residues, respectively (see Table III), and in all probability encompass a closer approximation to reality than the simple proportional relationship given by the straight line.

*Degrees of Freedom in Amino Acid Variability*

In the present context it must not be forgotten that the limits of this study specify that mutable positions in cytochrome *c* are to be interpreted as all those in which amino acid residues can vary without so fundamentally affecting the character of the protein that it would no longer be recognizable as a cytochrome *c* of the mammalian type, as defined above. However, even within these limits, the above all-or-none definition of mutable residues in cytochrome *c* is obviously a gross simplification of the true situation. The latitude of variation available to residues in different positions will vary from none at all, for those residues that are specifically required in certain positions, to complete latitude of residue substitution, for those positions for which there are no restrictions whatsoever. More importantly, there are intermediate steps leading to a stratification of degrees of variability. These are exemplified by so-called "conservative substitutions" and by conservatism of the over-all physicochemical character of segments of the peptide chain, as discussed in the preceding section. Thus, an accurate statement of the variability of the cytochrome *c* gene, even within the limits of its definition as the structural gene of a protein recognizable functionally as cytochrome *c*, must take into account these and possibly other, still undetected, different degrees of freedom. Therefore, an exact study of quantitative aspects of cytochrome *c* evolution in relation to the evolution of species will be possible only if and when appreciably accurate knowledge will become available of the structural-functional role of each amino acid residue, alone and in conjunction with others.

A previous attempt to relate quantitatively the number of amino acid residue differences between cytochromes *c* of various species and the time of divergence of the appropriate lines of evolutionary descent (29) suffered from the error that the standard chosen was obtained from a comparison of two species in the same taxonomic class, whereas the constancies observed were in comparisons of species in different major taxonomic groups. This is obviated in the above calculations (Fig. 5), which appear to yield somewhat more satisfactory results and which have in fact made it possible to predict, within narrow limits, the number of variant residues in the cytochromes *c* of two species, before the amino acid sequences had actually been determined chemically.

### EVOLUTIONARY ASPECTS OF STRUCTURE-FUNCTION RELATIONS IN CYTOCHROME *c*

When confronted with a large set of homologous amino acid sequences, the homology being both functional and evolutionary, as in the case of cytochrome $c$, one is tempted to conclude that areas which vary extensively have few if any structural requirements for function, whereas residues and areas which remain stubbornly unchanged, in proteins from species at all levels of the phylogenetic scale, must be of great functional importance and have highly specific requirements in terms of the particular amino acid residues in them.

The proposition that variable areas have functions compatible with a variety of sequences must be correct, since the resultant proteins are functionally satisfactory. But as these proteins derive from a common ancestral form, it is difficult to see how such areas could vary, when neutral mutations cannot be preserved by natural selection. A mutant gene lacking any selective effect whatsoever would dilute itself into the total available gene pool and have a negligible chance of expressing itself as the common structural gene for a protein in a species. Thus if the function of a particular area is equally well subserved by a variety of amino acid sequences, why should evolution have conserved any mutation in this area? On the contrary, one might expect such areas to be essentially invariant in a homologous set of proteins.

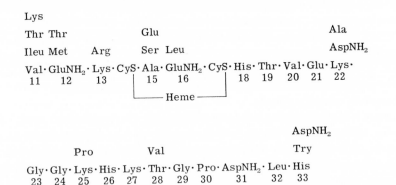

FIG. 6. Amino acid substitutions in the area concerned with hemochrome formation. The amino acid sequence given in the bottom line is common to six of the fourteen cytochromes $c$ considered (see text). The residues placed above it are those that have been observed, in the positions indicated, in one or more of the other cytochromes $c$.

The proposition that the constant parts of a protein in an evolutionary series are functionally the most significant has been defended and documented by Anfinsen (1).

The known primary structures of cytochromes $c$ from different species appear to afford examples that it may be useful to discuss in relation to the above considerations.

*Hemochrome Area of Cytochrome c*

An example of an area importantly involved in function is the hemochrome area extending from residue 11 to residue 33 (see Fig. 6). This is where the prosthetic group is covalently bonded to the peptide chain through thioether links formally made by the addition of the sulfhydryl groups of the cysteinyl residues in positions 14 and 17 across the double bonds of the vinyl side chains of protoheme. This area also contains one, and possibly both, of the hemochrome-forming side chains (see Margoliash, 28, for a discussion), which coordinate with the heme iron, perpendicularly from above and below the planar heme molecule (coordination positions 5 and 6), to give the characteristic cytochrome *c* spectrum. This area also has the single lysyl residue with an unreactive ε-amino group (22, 28), and probably forms part of the "crevice" (11) in which the heme is buried. Clearly, here also must be at least part of the area through which electrons are taken up from, and transferred to, the appropriate members of the terminal oxidation chain. In short, as far as is known, this is the most highly sensitive and functionally important portion of the protein. Nevertheless, of the twenty-three residues considered, nine have shown variations. In four of these, two different amino acids have been observed so far; in four, three different residues; and in one, four different amino acids. The longest invariant sequence is only five residues long.

It is important to point out that such a degree of variability in an area having all the hallmarks of a so-called "active site" is to be considered reasonable. There appears to be no difficulty in accepting most of the constant features as functionally necessary or structurally essential, while the variable residues indicate less specific or no requirements. It can confidently be expected that, if enough cytochromes *c* are examined, the minimal structural requirements of this area will become obvious.

*Invariant Area (Residues 70 to 80)*

In sharp contrast, the utter immutability of the eleven amino acid sequence extending from residue 70 to residue 80 is, within the admittedly narrow limits of our present understanding, quite unexpected (see Fig. 1). Considering that the cytochromes *c* so far examined are the products of several mammals, a bird, a reptile, a teleost, an invertebrate, and baker's yeast, the likelihood that this constancy is purely coincidental is vanishingly small. One is therefore faced with the question as to whether the structural-functional requirements of this area are so rigid that no substitutions whatsoever are permissible. It would appear to be unlikely that there could be any tertiary structure that would require, strictly and only, a particular eleven amino acid sequence. Similarly, if this area represents a surface at which cytochrome c reacts with other members of the terminal respiratory chain, also proteins and also subject to evolutionary variation, greater constancy than over other parts of the protein might be expected, but not absolute invariance. The abnormal stability of the section of the cytochrome c gene corresponding to residues 70 to 80, over a time lapse of presumably 1 to 2 billion years, is clearly brought out by comparison with the reasonable degree of variation observed in an area known to be part of the active site of the protein, namely, the hemochrome region considered above. The only biological molecules, structurally stable on an evolutionary time scale, that might be invoked here, are the cofactors, such as heme, or those involved in energy conservation, such as ATP or ADP. Conceivably, the stable sequence might be involved in interaction with a molecule of this class, either intra- or intermolecularly. Nevertheless, however unlikely it appears, the possibility that stability in this case is an expression of a complete lack of any structural-functional requirements, other than those of a peptide chain of α-amino acids, cannot as yet be entirely ignored. Molecules carrying appropriate chemical substitutions in this area should make it possible to distinguish between the two extreme possibilities— strict, precise requirements, or complete lack of requirements.

## Carboxyl-Terminal Sequence of Cytochrome c

At the opposite extreme of evolutionary behavior from the unexplainably invariant area, the carboxyl-terminal sequence of cytochrome c shows an extraordinary degree of variation (see Fig. 7). Three of the cytochromes c show single residue deletions in two different positions. At each of residues 101, 102, 103, and 104, four different amino acids have been found. These substitutions run practically the whole gamut of possible side chains, with the single exception of hydrophobic residues, uniformly absent. Clearly, therefore, the function, if any, of the carboxyl-terminal hexapeptide of cytochrome c can be met by a wide variety of amino acid sequences. In this connection it should not be forgotten that all the cytochromes under consideration can effectively substitute one for another in the terminal oxidation chain. For example, in terms of the efficiency of electron transport in the succinate oxidase system, mitochondria depleted of their own cytochrome c can react with foreign cytochromes c either better or worse than their original protein, the range of activities being approximately tenfold (9).

To compound the confusion it has been well authenticated that removal of the last four residues of the protein by digestion with carboxypeptidase A does not affect the reaction rate with enzyme systems derived from the terminal oxidation chain (59).

When all these facts are taken into account, it becomes difficult to maintain, at one and the same time, that the function of the carboxyl-terminal sequence of cytochrome *c*, if any, is compatible with an impressive array of radically different amino acids and that only those mutations which have a definite selective advantage will be conserved.

$$
\begin{array}{cccc}
 & & \text{D} & \\
\text{Glu} & \text{CySH} & \text{Ala} & \text{Ala} \\
\text{Ser} & \text{Ser} & \text{Thr} & \text{Ser} \\
\text{Asp} & \text{Ala} & \text{Lys} & \text{Lys}
\end{array}
$$

$$
\overset{\text{D}}{\text{Lys}} \cdot \text{Lys} \cdot \text{Ala} \cdot \text{Thr} \cdot \text{AspNH}_2 \cdot \text{GluCOOH}
$$

$$
99 \quad 100 \quad 101 \quad 102 \quad\quad 103 \quad\quad 104
$$

Fig. 7. Amino acid substitutions in the carboxyl-terminal sequence of cytochrome *c*. The amino acid sequence given on the bottom line is common to seven of the fourteen cytochromes *c* considered (see text). The residues placed above it are those that have been observed, in the positions indicated, in one or more of the other proteins. "D" indicates the position of single residue deletions.

## Conclusions

To summarize, questions have been raised both in regard to the apparently quantitative constancy of an evolutionary molecular time scale for cytochrome *c* and in regard to the apparently contradictory relations observed in this protein between structural-functional parameters and evolutionary variations.

The facile answer to these questions is that our bewilderment is purely an expression of the paucity of our knowledge of structure-function relations in cytochrome *c*. One might easily maintain that if we truly understood these relations, not only in simple enzymic and tertiary structure terms, but also in the possibly more complex *in vivo* situation, of which the mitochondrion is only a partial reflection, it would then become clear that the rules and regulations that have been worked out for the evolution of species equally apply to the evolution of a single protein. The alternative, that the rules and regulations of evolution of complex organismal characters resulting from the interaction of numerous genetic influences are not completely identical in emphasis and mechanism to those that apply on some molecular levels, is yet to be ruled out. The primary structure of a protein representing a simple automatic translation of a minute portion of the genetic material, even though it might well decide the tertiary structure and therefore the functional activity of the protein, can scarcely be considered to be under the same selective stress as morphological or functional variations directly related to the survival of the organism. This is particularly so if more or less features of the primary structure appear to be largely unrelated to functional activity, as in the case of cytochrome c. (For a general discussion of the evolution of molecules as compared to the evolution of organisms, see Simpson, 54.)

In conclusion, a far greater emphasis on function is necessary if we are to interpret the evolutionary changes observed in the cytochromes c of various species. Clearly, in this case, the accumulation of structural data presents no particular difficulty, whereas our understanding of functional relationships is still quite elementary when viewed from the broad biological aspects, now necessary. Nevertheless, only a thorough-going knowledge of function in the context of the complete biological unit can make out of the molecular evolution of proteins a respectable branch of science.

## Acknowledgment

The authors are grateful to Mr. P. G. Sanders, Abbott Laboratories, for the calculations given in Table III.

## References

1. Anfinsen, C. B., "Molecular Basis of Evolution," Wiley, New York, 1959.
2. Bahl, O. P., and Smith, E. L., unpublished results.
3. Chan, S. K., and Margoliash, E., unpublished results.
4. Chan, S. K., Needleman, S. B., Stewart, J. W., and Margoliash, E., unpublished results.
5. Chan, S. K. Needleman, S. B., Stewart, J. W., Walasek, O. F., and Margoliash, E., Federation Proc., 22, 658 (1963).
6. Dixon, M., Hill, R., and Keilin, D., Proc. Soc. 109B, 29 (1931).
7. Dus, K., Bartsch, R. G., and Kamen, M., J. Biol. Chem., 237, 3083 (1962).
8. Ehrenberg, A., and Theorell, H., Acta Chem. Scand., 9, 1193 (1955).
9. Estabrook, R. W., and Margoliash, E., unpublished observations.
9a. Feller, W., "Probability Theory and Its Applications, 1st ed., Vol. I, p. 71, Wiley, New York, 1950.
10. George, P., Symposium on Oxidases and Related Oxidation–Reduction Systems, Amherst, Massachusetts, 1964, in press.
11. George, P., and Lyster, R. L. J., Proc. Natl. Acad. Sci. U.S., 44, 1013 (1958).
12. Glazer, A. N., and Smith, E. L., unpublished results.
13. Harbury, H. A., and Loach, P. A., Proc. Natl. Acad. Sci. U.S., 45, 1344 (1959).
14. Heller, J., and Smith, E. L., unpublished results.
15. Hill, R. L., Buettner-Janusch, J., and Buettner-Janusch, V., Proc. Natl. Acad. Sci. U.S., 50, 885 (1963).
16. Ingram, V. M., Nature, 189, 704 (1961).
17. Jacobs, E. E., and Sanadi, D. R., J. Biol. Chem., 235, 531 (1960).
18. Keilin, D., Proc. Roy. Soc., 98B, 312 (1925).
19. Kendrew, J. C., Brookhaven Symp. Biol., 15, 216 (1962).
20. Kreil, G., Z. Physiol. Chem., 334, 154 (1963).
21. Kreil, G., and Tuppy, H., Nature, 192, 1123 (1961).

22. LUSTGARTEN, J., AND MARGOLIASH, E., *Proc. Can. Federation Biol. Soc.*, **5**, 47 (1962).
23. MacMUNN, C. A., *Phil. Trans. Roy. Soc. London*, **177**, 267 (1886).
24. MacMUNN, C. A., *J. Physiol. (London)*, **8**, 57 (1887).
25. MacMUNN, C. A., *Z. Physiol. Chem.*, **13**, 497 (1889).
26. MacMUNN, C. A., *Z. Physiol. Chem.* **14**, 328 (1890).
27. MARGOLIASH, E., *J. Biol. Chem.*, **237**, 2161 (1962).
28. MARGOLIASH, E., *Brookhaven Symp. Biol.* **15**, 266 (1962).
29. MARGOLIASH, E., *Proc. Natl. Acad. Sci. U.S.*, **50**, 672 (1963).
30. MARGOLIASH, E., *Can. J. Biochem.*, **42**, 745 (1964).
31. MARGOLIASH, E., FROHWIRT, N., AND WIENER, E., *Biochem. J.*, **71**, 559 (1959).
32. MARGOLIASH, E., KIMMEL, J. R., HILL, R. L., AND SCHMIDT, W. R., *J. Biol. Chem.*, **237**, 2148 (1962).
33. MARGOLIASH, E., AND LUSTGARTEN, J., *Ann. N.Y. Acad. Sci.*, **94**, 731 (1961).
34. MARGOLIASH, E., NEEDLEMAN, S. B., AND STEWART, J. W., *Acta Chem. Scand.*, **17**, S250 (1963).
35. MARGOLIASH, E., AND SMITH, E. L., *Nature*, **192**, 1121 (1961).
36. MARGOLIASH, E., AND SMITH, E. L., *J. Biol. Chem.*, **237**, 2151 (1962).
37. MARGOLIASH, E., AND SMITH, E. L., *Abstr. 6th Intern. Congr. Biochem.*, New York, Vol. III, p. 206 (1964).
38. MARGOLIASH, E., SMITH, E. L., KREIL, G., AND TUPPY, H., *Nature*, **192**, 1125 (1961).
39. MATSUBARA, H., AND SMITH, E. L., *J. Biol. Chem.*, **238**, 2732 (1963).
40. McDOWALL, M., AND SMITH, E. L., unpublished results.
41. NARITA, K., TITANI, K., YAOI, Y., MURAKAMI, H., KIMURA, M., AND VANĚČEK, J., *Biochim. Biophys. Acta*, **73**, 670 (1963).
42. NARITA, K., TITANI, K., YAOI, Y., AND MURAKAMI, H., *Biochim. Biophys. Acta*, **77**, 688 (1963).
43. NEEDLEMAN, S. B., AND MARGOLIASH, E., unpublished results.
44. NOLAN, C., AND MARGOLIASH, E., unpublished results.
45. OPARIN, A. I., "The Origin of Life," 3rd ed., Academic Press, New York, 1957.
46. PALÉUS, S., EHRENBERG, A., AND TUPPY, H., *Acta Chem. Scand.*, **9**, 365 (1955).
47. PALÉUS, S., AND TUPPY, H., *Acta Chem. Scand.*, **13**, 641 (1959).
48. PAULING, L., AND ZUCKERKANDL, E., *Acta Chem. Scand.*, **17**, S9 (1963).
49. PEETERS, H. (ed.), *XII Colloquium, Protides of the Biological Fluids, Bruges, 1964*, Elsevier Publishing Co., Amsterdam, 1965.
50. ROTHFUS, J. A., AND SMITH, E. L., unpublished results.
51. SANO, S., AND TANAKA, K., *J. Biol. Chem.*, **239**, PC3109 (1964).
52. SANO, S., IKEDA, K., AND SAKAKIBARA, S., *Biochem. Biophys. Res. Commun.*, **15**, 284 (1964).
53. SCOULOUDI, H., *Proc. Roy. Soc.*, **258A**, 181 (1960).
54. SIMPSON, G. G., *XII Colloquium, Protides of the Biological Fluids, Bruges, 1964*, p. 29, Elsevier Publishing Co., Amsterdam, 1965.
55. SMITH, E. L., AND MARGOLIASH, E., *Federation Proc.*, **23**, 1243 (1964).
56. SMITH, E. L., MATSUBARA, H., McDOWALL, M., AND ROTHFUS, J. A., *Science*, **140**, 385 (1963).
57. STEWART, J. W., AND MARGOLIASH, E., *Canad. J. Biochem.*, in press.
58. THEORELL, H., AND ÅKESSON, Å., *J. Am. Chem. Soc.*, **63**, 1812, 1818, 1820, (1941).
59. TITANI, K., ISHIKURA, H., AND MINAKAMI, S., *J. Biochem. (Tokyo)*, **46**, 151 (1959).

60. TUPPY, H., AND KREIL, G., *Monatsh. Chem.*, **92**, 780 (1962).
61. YAMANAKA, T., AND OKUNUKI, K., *J. Biol. Chem.*, **239**, 1813 (1964).
62. YASUNOBO, K. T., NAKASHIMA, T., HIGA, H., MATSUBARA, H., AND BENSON, A., *Biochim. Biophys. Acta*, **78**, 791 (1963).
63. ZUCKERKANDL, E., *in* "Classification and Human Evolution" (S. L. Washburn, ed.), p. 243, Wenner-Gren Foundation, New York, 1963.
64. ZUCKERKANDL, E., AND PAULING, L., *in* "Horizons in Biochemistry" (M. Kasha and B. Pullman, ed.), p. 189, Academic Press, New York, 1962.

# Evolution of Dehydrogenases[1]

Nathan O. Kaplan

*Graduate Department of Biochemistry,*
*Brandeis University, Waltham, Massachusetts*

In recent years studies have clearly shown that enzymes from different species, which catalyze the same reaction, differ in their catalytic, physical, and immunological properties as well as in their amino acid compositions. Margoliash and Smith have elucidated differences in amino acid sequences for cytochrome *c*, which have been summarized in the present Symposium. Comparative enzymological investigations have led to the suggestion that the evolution of enzymes may be related to morphological evolution and of considerable significance in natural selection. Furthermore, the comparative enzymological approach has added a new parameter to studies in systematics and phylogeny. It is the purpose of this paper to describe methods whereby the relationship among the same enzymes from different organisms can be compared; in addition, the significance of changes in enzyme structure during evolution is discussed. The present review deals largely with the DPN-linked dehydrogenases.

## Coenzyme–Enzyme Relationships

Comparative biochemical studies have demonstrated that the coenzymes are ubiquitous in all living systems, and that there has been little or no evolutionary change in the structure of coenzymes. The proteins appear to have been evolving, and not the small molecules. It is worth while to consider briefly the implications of such observations. We have found that a number of pyridine bases can be incorporated into the DPN instead of nicotinamide to form analogs of the coenzyme (20). One such base is 3-acetylpyridine (3-AcPy) (18, 19); the structure of this compound is given in Fig. 1. The question may be asked why 3-AcPy cannot replace nicotinamide as a growth factor. Table I shows the relative rate of the 3-AcPy analog of DPN with a number of dehydrogenases obtained from the rabbit. An enzyme such as liver alcohol dehydrogenase has a higher turnover rate with the DPN analog than with the natural coenzyme. If it is assumed that an increased $V_{max}$ with an enzyme is

---

[1] Publication No. 329.

beneficial to the organism, then 3-AcPy would be more valuable to the rabbit as a vitamin than nicotinamide, particularly with respect to ethanol oxidation. The dinucleotide analog can also effectively replace DPN in liver glutamic dehydrogenase and in mitochondrial malic dehydrogenases. However, enzymes such as the β-hydroxybutyrate dehydrogenase and the α-glycerophosphate dehydrogenase show little or no

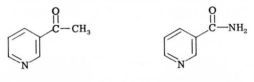

3-Acetylpyridine                          Nicotinamide

Fig. 1.   Structure of 3-acetylpyridine and nicotinamide.

activity with the analog. There may be more than several hundred different pyridine nucleotide-linked enzymes in one organism. Hence, if there was a change in the nature of the pyridine base during evolution, a change in many proteins would consequently have been required to accommodate the modified coenzyme resulting from the alteration in the structure of the vitamin. Such changes might have no effect on some dehydrogenases, as indicated in Table I, but the chances that the modified coenzyme could replace DPN in all DPN-linked proteins are very slim.

TABLE I

RATES OF REACTION OF THE 3-ACETYLPYRIDINE ANALOG OF DPN WITH
DIFFERENT RABBIT DEHYDROGENASES

| Dehydrogenase | Rate of AcPyDPN compared to DPN (%) |
|---|---|
| Liver alcohol | 450 |
| Liver glutamic | 150 |
| Heart mitochondrial malic | 125 |
| Muscle lactic | 22 |
| Muscle triosephosphate | 10 |
| Heart lactic | 4 |
| Liver β-hydroxybutyrate | < 1 |
| Muscle α-glycerophosphate | 0 |

Therefore, it seems reasonable to predict that a change in DPN structure would not occur, because of the large number of enzymes that would be affected. One might expect the chances for evolutionary change in vitamins to be related to the number of different types of enzymes of which the particular vitamin is a constituent.

In contrast to DPN, the structure of vitamin $B_{12}$ has undergone changes without significant effect on the organism (4). This may have been due to the fact that the $B_{12}$ coenzyme is a cofactor for only a few enzymes. Minor alterations of carotene or ubiquinone structures may also have been possible, because these cofactors are associated with only a relatively small number of proteins. This is evident in the existence of both vitamin $A_1$ and vitamin $A_2$. Evolution of enzymes requiring particular coenzymes, therefore, must be restricted to the extent that the enzyme can interact with the cofactor. In view of the above facts, one must conclude that enzymes have undergone changes in structure as a result of primary sequence changes, whereas the various vitamins and coenzymes have experienced little evolution.

There are two types of pyridine nucleotides—DPN and TPN—that occur in nature. The two coenzymes are ubiquitously distributed. They also appear to have different functions. Reduced DPN seems primarily to be used as a potential source of high-energy phosphate in the form of ATP after oxidation. Reduced TPN, on the other hand, appears to have a primary role as a reducing agent. Aspects of the functional roles of the two nicotinamides containing coenzymes have been recently considered elsewhere (25) and will not be discussed in detail here.

A large number of enzymes are known that are either DPN- or TPN-linked. TPN-specific dehydrogenases are usually very specific and will not react with DPN. Some of the DPN-linked dehydrogenases show slight activity with TPN.

It is interesting that a large number of enzymes can react with a specific coenzyme such as DPN. This would imply that there might be common structural features of the various DPN dehydrogenases that are essential for the binding of the pyridine coenzyme. At present a number of DPN-linked dehydrogenases have been purified and their properties studied in some detail. These investigations permit at least a preliminary approach to comparative studies. Knowledge of the properties of TPN-specific enzymes is relatively limited, and little information is now available from which a comparison of properties of the TPN- and DPN-linked dehydrogenases can be made. In this paper, only the DPN-linked proteins are considered.

## SIZE OF THE DEHYDROGENASES

During the past several years, we have crystallized a large number of DPN-linked specific lactic dehydrogenases (LDH's) and have studied their properties in some detail. In most animals there are essentially two *main* types of LDH. One type we have referred to as the H form, since it is found largely in heart muscle; and the second type we have termed the M type, because it is usually present in skeletal muscle. The M-type

LDH and the H-type LDH appear to be under the control of separate genes; each has quite different physical, catalytic, and immunological properties. Differences in amino acid compositions of the two types are easily detectable, as illustrated in Table II, for the chicken and for the beef enzymes. The chicken M catalyst has an unusually high number of histidine residues. This high histidine content is characteristic of avian M-type LDH's (Table III). Tables III and IV, which have selec-

TABLE II

AMINO ACID COMPOSITIONS OF HEART- AND MUSCLE-TYPE LACTIC DEHYDROGENASES FROM CHICKEN AND BEEF[a]

| Amino acid | Chicken | | Beef | |
|---|---|---|---|---|
| | $H_4$ | $M_4$ | $H_4$ | $M_4$ |
| Lys | 99 | 112 | 96 | 103 |
| His | 30 | 63 | 26 | 33 |
| Arg | 35 | 35 | 34 | 42 |
| Asp | 129 | 125 | 132 | 127 |
| Thr | 75 | 51 | 56 | 48 |
| Ser | 107 | 110 | 97 | 87 |
| Glu | 122 | 102 | 129 | 121 |
| Pro | 38 | 44 | 46 | 51 |
| Gly | 96 | 104 | 98 | 100 |
| Ala | 88 | 81 | 80 | 78 |
| Val | 125 | 121 | 138 | 115 |
| Met | 25 | 31 | 36 | 32 |
| Ileu | 66 | 85 | 85 | 91 |
| Leu | 149 | 121 | 143 | 136 |
| Tyr | 31 | 19 | 29 | 29 |
| Phe | 19 | 27 | 21 | 29 |
| Try | 22 | 24 | 22 | 24 |
| Cys | 26 | 26 | 17 | 26 |

[a] From Pesce *et al.* (32).

tive lists only for a number of vertebrate H LDH's and M LDH's and a few selected amino acids, show that closely related species appear to have relatively similar amino acid compositions. Certain amino acids appear to be more variable than others. For example, in the M type, the number of histidine units appears to have changed considerably during evolution, whereas the phenylalanine content seems to have varied little. Some changes can be detected in arginine and isoleucine residues of the H type, whereas the values for lysine appear to be quite constant.

Examination of the tryptic fingerprint patterns of the chicken H LDH and M LDH indicated that approximately one-half of the peptides was different (Table V) (15). A comparison of the patterns of the chicken M and dogfish M enzymes revealed considerable differences in the primary structures of these two related LDH's; H LDH's from different species were also different. As indicated in the table, less tryptic peptides were found when equal mixtures of chicken H and turkey H LDH were chomatographed than when equal mixtures of chicken H and beef H were run together. These results indicate that there are less differences between the chicken and the turkey enzyme than between the chicken

### TABLE III
AMINO ACID COMPOSITION OF $H_4$ LACTIC DEHYDROGENASE[a]

| Species | Arginine | Isoleucine | Lysine |
|---|---|---|---|
| | (residues/mole) | | |
| Chicken | 35 | 66 | 99 |
| Pheasant | 38 | 67 | 97 |
| Turkey | 34 | 69 | 87 |
| Cow | 34 | 85 | 96 |
| Rabbit | 33 | 84 | 97 |
| Man | 30 | 88 | 96 |
| Frog | 21 | 65 | 95 |

[a] Data from Pesce (31).

### TABLE IV
AMINO ACID COMPOSITION OF $M_4$ LACTIC DEHYDROGENASE[a]

| Species | Histidine | Phenylalanine |
|---|---|---|
| | (residues/mole) | |
| Chicken | 63 | 27 |
| Pheasant | 61 | 29 |
| Turkey | 73 | 24 |
| Duck | 57 | 27 |
| Caiman | 46 | 26 |
| Cow | 33 | 29 |
| Rabbit | 41 | 26 |
| Leopard frog | 26 | 28 |
| Bullfrog | 29 | 26 |
| Halibut | 49 | 29 |
| Dogfish | 42 | 26 |
| Lamprey | 41 | 24 |

[a] Data from Pesce (31).

H LDH and the beef H LDH. This is what would be expected. Differences in M-type LDH's are also shown by this method of "fingerprint" comparison. It seems that one can make a preliminary index of differences between two enzymes by fingerprinting the enzymes together and then counting the number of peptides. The increase in number of peptides when the enzymes are fingerprinted together over the quantity observed when they are fingerprinted separately gives this index of difference.

From the analysis of fingerprint patterns it is evident that there has been considerable change in the primary structures of the LDH's during evolution.

Although the LDH's vary considerably in many of their properties, they all appear to have about the same molecular weight (Table VI).

TABLE V

FINGERPRINT PATTERNS OF H-TYPE LACTIC DEHYDROGENASE
AND M-TYPE LACTIC DEHYDROGENASE[a]

| Lactic dehydrogenase | Number of ninhydrin-positive spots |
|---|---|
| Chicken | 34–38 |
| Chicken M | 35–38 |
| Turkey H | 33–35 |
| Beef H | 33–35 |
| Turkey M | 34–37 |
| Dogfish M | 34–37 |
| Chicken H + chicken M | 50–53 |
| Chicken H + turkey H | 35–40 |
| Chicken H + beef H | 45–47 |
| Chicken M + dogfish M | 52–56 |
| Chicken M + turkey M | 36–38 |

[a] Data largely from Dr. T. P. Fondy.

TABLE VI

MOLECULAR WEIGHTS OF VARIOUS LACTIC DEHYDROGENASES[a]

| Species | $H_4$ | $M_4$ |
|---|---|---|
| Beef | 131 | 153 |
| Man | 146 | — |
| Rabbit | — | 149 |
| Chicken | 151 | 140 |
| Turkey | 147 | 144 |
| Pheasant | — | 148 |
| Bullfrog | | 154 |
| Dogfish | — | 141 |
| Halibut | — | 148 |
| Lobster | | 152 |
| Lactobacillus arabinosus | 153 | |

[a] Data (in thousands) were obtained by the Ehrenberg method of approach to sedimentation equilibria, mainly by Dr. A. Pesce and Mr. J. Everse of our laboratory.

The L-specific LDH from *Lactobacillus arabinosus* is approximately the same size as the animal enzymes. A preliminary estimate, by Miss E. Tarmy of our laboratory, of the molecular weight of *Escherichia coli* L-specific LDH gave a weight about the same as that of the *Lactobacillus* enzyme. In contrast, the D-specific LDH's from *Leuconostoc mesenteroides* and *Lactobacillus arabinosus* have somewhat lower molecular weights than the L-specific dehydrogenases, with values of about 85,000. The L-specific LDH's all appear to have the same shape, as indicated by their similar sedimentation constants (Table VII).

TABLE VII

SEDIMENTATION CONSTANTS FOR $H_4$ AND $M_4$ LACTIC DEHYDROGENASES AND
FOR LACTIC DEHYDROGENASE FROM *Lactobacillus arabinosus* (31)

| Species | $S_{20.w}$ | |
| | $H_4$ | $M_4$ |
|---|---|---|
| Beef | 7.45 | 7.32 |
| Man | 7.46 | — |
| Chicken | 7.31 | 7.33 |
| Turkey | 7.49 | 7.52 |
| Bullfrog | | 7.56 |
| Dogfish | | 7.56 |
| Lobster | | 7.40 |
| *Lactobacillus arabinosus* | 7.50 | |

TABLE VIII

MOLECULAR WEIGHT AND NUMBER OF SUBUNITS OF
DIFFERENT DEHYDROGENASES

| Dehydrogenase | Molecular weight | Number of subunits |
|---|---|---|
| Lactic | 145,000 | 4 |
| Triosephosphate | 150,000 | 4 |
| Yeast alcohol | 140,000 | 4 |
| Liver alcohol | 68,000 | 2 |
| Malic | 67,000 | 2 |
| Glutamic | 1,000,000 | 30[a] |

[a] Approximate.

The L-specific LDH's consist of four subunits of identical weights of about 35,000. In the pure H or M enzymes, the four subunits are identical. However, in cells that synthesize both types of LDH polypeptides, hybrids containing units of the M form and the H form can be detected.

Most DPN-linked dehydrogenases apparently consist of subunits (Table VIII); the mannitol-1-phosphate dehydrogenase of *Aerobacter aerogenes* is an exception that appears to consist of a single polypeptide chain. As indicated in Table VIII, the size of the subunits of the various dehydrogenases is approximately the same. These data suggest the possibility that all DPN-linked dehydrogenases arose from a common ancestral dehydrogenase, and that the size of the genes responsible for synthesis of subunits of dehydrogenases has not been altered appreciably during duplication and evolution.

In general we, as well as other investigators, have found that the molecular weights of like enzymes from different species are quite similar. Recently we have used Sephadex columns to estimate molecular weights. We have found an unusually good correlation between values obtained by sedimentation methods as compared to the molecular weights determined by the Sephadex procedure. Mr. B. Kitto and Mr. J. Everse of our laboratory have recently surveyed the weights of malic dehydrogenases from many sources. Several crystalline malic dehydrogenases have been found by the Ehrenberg method (12) to be 67,000 (16, 36): an almost identical value was obtained by the use of a Sephadex G-100 column. The malic dehydrogenases in crude extracts can be eluted from the Sephadex column in the identical way that they can with the purified proteins. With the Sephadex column it is possible to estimate the molecular weights of the malic dehydrogenases directly in crude extracts without purification. As shown in Tables IX and IXA, nearly all malic dehydrogenases examined gave values of 67,000. Only a few of the *Bacillus* species (those principally related to *B. subtilis*) had the higher value of 97,000. The higher molecular weight obtained for the *B. subtilis* enzyme is easily reproducible on the Sephadex column. The value obtained for the *Bacillus* malic dehydrogenase does not appear to be due to an artifact. Dr. W. Murphey of our laboratory has recently obtained the *B. subtilis* malic dehydrogenase in pure form; this enzyme retained the molecular weight of 97,000 on the Sephadex G-100 column. A molecular weight of 110,000 was obtained by the Ehrenberg ultracentrifugal method; there seems to be no doubt that the molecular weight of the *subtilis* malic dehydrogenase is larger than that found in most organisms. It will be worth while to determine whether the difference in size observed with the *subtilis* enzyme is due to the fact that this enzyme contains three subunits instead of the usual two.

## ACTIVE SITE OF DEHYDROGENASES

Most DPN-linked dehydrogenases seem to contain essential sulfhydryl (—SH) groups that can react with alkylating agents or with mercurials. These essential groups appear to be involved largely in the coenzyme binding site. Figure 2 shows the inactivation produced by iodoacetate with crystalline horse liver alcohol dehydrogenase (HL-ADH). Ethanol exerts some protection against this inactivation; the reduced DPN, however, gives complete protection. It has been the usual observation that the substrate offers little protection against —SH reagents. Lactate and pyruvate are ineffective with LDH (11). The protection of ethanol, however, on the HL-ADH is reproducible.

It has been found that p-mercuribenzoate can inactivate chicken H and beef H LDH. The extent of inactivation of these enzymes de-

TABLE IX

Malic Dehydrogenases: Molecular Weight Determination by Sephadex Gel Filtration[a]

Crystalline Enzymes
  Chick heart (mitochondrial)
  Pig heart (mitochondrial)
  Ostrich heart (supernatant)
  *Propionibacterium shermanii*
Purified Enzymes and Crude Extracts
  Pig heart (supernatant)
  Chick heart
  Beef liver
  Bullfrog heart (*Rana catesbiana*)
  Garter snake heart (*Thamnophis sirtalis sirtalis*)
  Tuna heart
  Dogfish heart
  Horseshoe crab heart (*Limulus*)
  Oak silkworm (*Antheraea perneyi*)
  Potato
  Slime mold (*Polysphondylium pallidum*)
  *Neurospora crassa*
  *Euglena gracilis*
Bacterial Extracts

| | |
|---|---|
| Pseudomonadaceae: | *Rhodopseudomonas palustris* |
| | *Xanthomonas pruni* |
| | *Spirillum serpens* |
| Rhizobiaceae: | *Chromobacterium violaceum* |
| Achromobacteraceae: | *Alcaligenes faecalis* |
| | *Achromobacter parvulus* |
| Enterobacteriaceae: | *Escherichia coli* B |
| | *Citrobacter freundii* |
| | *Aerobacter aerogenes* |
| | *Erwinia carotovora* |
| | *Proteus vulgaris* |
| Micrococcaceae: | *Micrococcus lysodeikticus* |
| Actinomycetaceae: | *Streptomyces coelicolor* |

[a] The samples listed all have malic dehydrogenases of 67,000 molecular weight by gel filtration. All the crude extracts, except for the bacterial, were examined by starch gel electrophoresis and found to contain multiple forms of malic dehydrogenase.

pends on the number of moles of mercurial bound (11). For example, when one mole of mercurial is bound, approximately 25% of the enzymatic activity is lost. These titrations suggest that there is one active —SH group per subunit of the LDH. After p-mercuribenzoate binding,

## TABLE IXA
MALIC DEHYDROGENASES OF *Bacillus* SPECIES: MOLECULAR WEIGHT
DETERMINATION BY SEPHADEX GEL FILTRATION

|                            | Molecular weight 97,000 | Molecular weight 67,000 |
| -------------------------- | :---------------------: | :---------------------: |
| *B. subtilis* 168 W        | +                       |                         |
| *B. brevis*                | +                       |                         |
| *B. licheniformis*         | +                       |                         |
| *B. macerans*              | +                       |                         |
| *B. stearothermophilus*    | +                       |                         |
| *B. coagulans*             | +                       |                         |
| *B. megaterium*            | +                       |                         |
| *B. cereus*                | +                       |                         |
| *B. subtilis* var. *niger* | +                       |                         |
| *B. pasteurii*             |                         | +                       |
| *B. sphaericus*            |                         | +                       |
| *B. circulans*             |                         | +                       |
| *B. laterosporus*          |                         | +                       |
| *B. thuringiensis*         |                         | +                       |
| *B. lentus*                |                         | +                       |
| *B. natto*                 | +                       |                         |

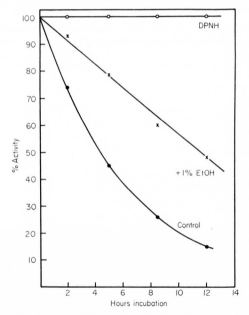

FIG. 2. Effects of addition of DPNH and ethanol on inactivation of HL-ADH by iodoacetate. Control contained only $10^{-4}$ $M$ iodoacetetate; DPNH added at $10^{-4}$ $M$.

the activity can be restored by the addition of cysteine. DPNH and AcPyDPNH can protect against the binding of the mercurial and thereby prevent inactivation; the oxidized coenzymes have somewhat less of a protective action (see Fig. 3). The rate of reaction of $p$-mercuribenzoate

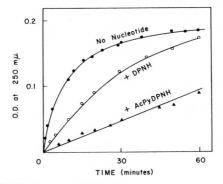

Fig. 3. Effect of DPNH + AcPyDPNH on $p$-mercuribenzoate binding of beef H LDH. From Di Sabato and Kaplan (11).

TABLE X

CYSTEINE SULFHYDRYL CONTENT OF DIFFERENT LACTIC DEHYDROGENASES[a]

| LDH | Number of cysteine —SH residues |
|---|---|
| Pheasant H | 26 |
| Chicken H | 25 |
| Beef H | 17 |
| Turkey M | 24 |
| Chicken M | 24 |
| Frog M | 6 |
| Beef M | 26 |
| Dogfish M | 24 |
| Halibut M | 14 |
| Lamprey M | 20 |
| Lobster M | 20 |
| Caiman | 30 |

[a] Data of Fondy and Everse (14).

with beef H LDH and chicken H LDH is quite slow. It should be pointed out that only slightly more than four —SH groups react per mole of enzyme. As indicated in Table X, the total —SH groups of different LDH's vary.

The unusually low number of only six cysteines in frog M LDH led us to investigate this enzyme in detail. The finding of only six cysteines is somewhat disturbing, since this would give one and one-half —SH groups per subunit. Eight cysteic acid residues, however, were found after performic acid oxidation of the frog M LDH. We believe that during the purification of the enzyme two of the —SH groups might have been oxidized. The stoichiometry of binding of p-mercuribenzoate to the loss of enzymatic activity of a number of LDH's is compared in Fig. 4. The

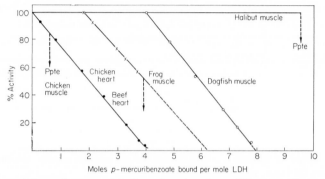

FIG. 4. p-Mercuribenzoate binding of active-site —SH groups in various LDH's. Data of Fondy and Everse.

frog M enzyme is quite different from the mammalian or avian LDH's in that only after two moles of p-mercuribenzoate are bound is any loss of catalytic properties observed. However, the additional four cysteines react to give a stoichiometry of inhibition identical to that described for beef H LDH and chicken H LDH. Dr. T. Fondy of our laboratory has found that the two fast-reacting —SH groups of the frog LDH will also react with iodoacetate. None of the —SH groups in the native avian and mammalian LDH's will react with the alkylating reagent. The first two —SH groups per *subunit* of dogfish M LDH appear not to be essential for enzymatic activity, whereas the third and slower reacting group (cysteine) is essential. In the halibut enzyme, there appear to be three —SH moieties per subunit, which react faster than the essential —SH groups. It should be emphasized that reduced DPN and its analogs interfere with the binding of p-mercuribenzoate to only the essential —SH groups and not to the nonessential —SH's.

Dr. Fondy has been able to obtain a peptide from the frog M LDH that contains the apparent essential —SH group involved in the binding of the pyridine coenzyme. This was achieved by reacting the native enzyme with "cold" iodoacetate, then removing the excess of the reagent by dialysis. Only the two nonessential —SH groups of the frog dehydrogenase were alkylated. The four essential —SH's were alkylated by the use of $C^{14}$-iodoacetate in 6 $M$ urea. After tryptic digestion, the peptides were fingerprinted by high-voltage electrophoresis, and all the radioactivity was found essentially in one peptide. This peptide was extensively purified, and its composition determined. Since the position after migration of the peptide was known, treatment of five other LDH's with $C^{14}$-iodoacetate in urea led to the finding that the same peptide is present in LDH's other than the frog M enzyme. These results therefore suggest that an active-site peptide containing an —SH group and involved in coenzyme binding is common to all LDH's. The peptide has been found both in the H type and M type of LDH of the same species.

The amino acid sequence of the "active site" has now almost unequivocally been established and is shown in Fig. 5. Also shown in the

LDH           :   - Val - Ileu - Ser - Gly - Gly, CMCys - Asn - Leu - Asp - Thr - Ala - Arg -

HL - ADH[a] :   - Val - Ala - Thr - Gly - Ileu - CMCys - Arg - Ser - Asp - Asp - His - Val -

Y - ADH[a]   :           - Tyr - Ser - Gly - Val - CMCys - His - Thr - Asp - Leu - His - Ala -

TPD[b]         :   - Val - Ser - Asn - Ala - Ser - CMCys - Thr - Thr - Asn - Cys - Leu - Ala -

FIG. 5.   Active-site peptides of various LDH's (a) From Harris (17). (b) From Perham and Harris (30).

figure are active-site peptides for triosephosphate dehydrogenase (TPD), obtained by Perham and Harris (30), as well as those for yeast alcohol dehydrogenase (Y-ADH) and HL-ADH recently reported by Harris (17). The sequence for the HL-ADH is relatively similar to that recently determined by Li and Vallee (28). With respect to TPD, the sequence is identical with both the yeast and the rabbit enzymes. Although there are some obvious differences, the similarities among the various dehydrogenases suggest that their sequences are related. Of particular interest are the close similarities between the two alcohol dehydrogenases, even though the two enzymes show great differences in their specificities as well as in other catalytic properties. The LDH sequence seems to be somewhat closer to the sequence of the two alcohol dehydrogenases than to that of the TPD peptide. We are at present attempting to elucidate the sequence of "active-site" peptides from glutamic and malic dehydrogenases.

## AMINO ACID COMPOSITIONS OF DEHYDROGENASES

The ideal method for elucidating evolutionary changes in enzymes would, of course, be to show the number of changes in the amino acid sequence. This approach has been carried out by Margoliash and Smith for cytochrome c. However, "sequencing" is such a time-consuming endeavor that it seems impractical to consider such an approach as a useful adjunct in evolutionary studies.

Some index of relationships can be determined by comparisons of the amino acid composition. As discussed above, with respect to the LDH's, enzymes from closely related species generally can be recognized by their amino acid compositions; the extent of changes in amino acid composition varies with different dehydrogenases. Table XI gives the amino acid

TABLE XI
AMINO ACID COMPOSITIONS OF ELEVEN TRIOSEPHOSPHATE DEHYDROGENASES[a]

| Amino acid | Rab-bit | Beef | Man | Chick-en | Tur-key | Pheas-ant | Hali-but | Stur-geon | Lob-ster | E. coli | Yeast |
|---|---|---|---|---|---|---|---|---|---|---|---|
| Lys | 90 | 90 | 84 | 84 | 87 | 87 | 87 | 97 | 94 | 87 | 91 |
| His | 34 | 34 | 31 | 30 | 31 | 32 | 42 | 20 | 15 | 19 | 27 |
| Arg | 34 | 35 | 31 | 34 | 35 | 36 | 35 | 37 | 28 | 36 | 36 |
| Asp | 131 | 131 | 139 | 138 | 137 | 134 | 110 | 130 | 118 | 148 | 130 |
| Thr | 70 | 71 | 70 | 68 | 68 | 66 | 59 | 68 | 65 | 92 | 77 |
| Ser | 58 | 57 | 68 | 61 | 62 | 59 | 72 | 58 | 76 | 50 | 88 |
| Glu | 71 | 74 | 74 | 64 | 63 | 62 | 77 | 65 | 84 | 76 | 72 |
| Pro | 43 | 43 | 42 | 42 | 42 | 42 | 41 | 42 | 38 | 31 | 41 |
| Gly | 113 | 112 | 117 | 115 | 115 | 112 | 94 | 97 | 108 | 106 | 90 |
| Ala | 114 | 111 | 108 | 121 | 120 | 117 | 106 | 111 | 114 | 124 | 108 |
| Val | 105 | 110 | 95 | 116 | 117 | 110 | 105 | 118 | 123 | 105 | 105 |
| Met | 31 | 30 | 31 | 30 | 31 | 31 | 28 | 29 | 34 | 24 | 21 |
| Ileu | 66 | 63 | 65 | 58 | 58 | 56 | 71 | 67 | 65 | 58 | 68 |
| Leu | 62 | 64 | 65 | 64 | 65 | 67 | 61 | 64 | 61 | 69 | 73 |
| Tyr | 30 | 31 | 31 | 31 | 31 | 31 | 32 | 39 | 30 | 28 | 38 |
| Phe | 48 | 48 | 46 | 44 | 45 | 46 | 50 | 46 | 50 | 37 | 35 |
| Try | 12 | 13 | 13 | 12 | 13 | 13 | 13 | 12 | 13 | 28 | 12 |
| Total | 1112 | 1117 | 1110 | 1112 | 1120 | 1098 | 1083 | 1110 | 1116 | 1118 | 1112 |

[a] From Allison and Kaplan (2).

compositions of eleven TPD's from different sources (2). Although there are some definite differences among them, the changes are not quite so dramatic as those observed with the LDH's. It is clearly indicated, however, that the TPD's isolated from closely related species have similarities in their patterns of amino acid distribution. Within the limitations of the method, the beef and rabbit enzymes appear to be identical in amino acid composition. The human TPD differs significantly, in some respects, from the beef and rabbit proteins; it has fewer residues of basic amino acids, a higher number of aspartic acids, a higher number of serine moieties, and fewer valine residues. It is noteworthy that catalytic differences also distinguish the human catalyst from the rabbit and beef dehydrogenases. The three galliform bird enzymes seem to have almost identical compositions. On the other hand, the compositions of the two bony fishes are somewhat different; these differences are also suggested by immunological experiments. When enzymes from taxonomically distinct sources are analyzed, considerable differences in certain amino acid residues are observed. For example, the lobster dehydrogenase has a considerably lower basic amino acid (histidine and arginine) content than do the vertebrate enzymes. The *coli* and yeast enzymes have a number of differences that distinguish them from each other as well as from the animal proteins. A feature that appears to be common to all the TPD's is the constantly high proportion of residues with aliphatic hydrocarbon side chains. A further feature is the relatively constant number of amino acid residues (1083 to 1117) in all the enzymes; this fact suggests that the size of the gene has not been appreciably altered during evolution.

## USE OF CATALYTIC CHARACTERIZATIONS IN EVOLUTIONARY STUDIES

Close analyses of the catalytic properties of the same enzyme from a variety of species have indicated that differences exist that may give valuable information for phylogenic and taxonomic studies. These differences are reflected by affinities for substrate or coenzyme, by relative rates of reaction with several different substrates or coenzyme analogs, as well

TABLE XII

COMPARISON OF RATES OF REACTION OF SOME ANALOGS OF DPN WITH YEAST ALCOHOL DEHYDROGENASE AND HORSE LIVER ALCOHOL DEHYDROGENASE[a,b]

| Coenzyme | Y-ADH | HL-ADH |
|---|---|---|
| DPN | 1 | 1 |
| Deamino DPN | 0.12 | 1.1 |
| 3-Acetylpyridine DPN | 0.05 | 6.0 |
| Pyridine-3-aldehyde DPN | < 0.02 | 0.95 |
| 3-Thionicotinamide DPN | 0.16 | 3.5 |
| 3-Benzolpyridine DPN | 0 | 0.31 |
| Propyl pyridyl ketone DPN | < 0.01 | 4.8 |
| Uracil DPN | 0.02 | 0.75 |

[a] From Kaplan and Ciotti (23).
[b] Ethanol (0.1 $M$) was used in all reaction mixtures.

as by the inhibition of excess substrate and various types of inhibitors. In our comparative studies, we have extensively used DPN and TPN analogs to show differences in pyridine nucleotide-requiring enzymes. Here we shall give only a few examples of this use.

Table XII shows the difference of DPN analogs with Y-ADH and HL-ADH (23). The Y-ADH is much more specific than the HL-ADH and reacts to only a slight extent with most of the coenzyme analogs. Several of the analogs give higher maximum rates of reaction with the HL-ADH than with the natural coenzyme.

A comparison of relative rates of reaction with several coenzyme analogs has been made for LDH for a large number of different animals. Table XIII summarizes this study briefly for both the H-type LDH and

TABLE XIII

CATALYTIC PROPERTIES OF VERTEBRATE LACTIC DEHYDROGENASES[a]

| Species | AcPyDPN/DPN | |
|---------|-----|-----|
| | $H_4$ | $M_4$ |
| Chicken | 0.15 | 1.1 |
| Turkey | 0.17 | 2.0 |
| Duck | 0.18 | 0.8 |
| Pigeon | 0.11 | — |
| Caiman | 0.07 | 0.7 |
| Turtle | — | 0.6 |
| Bullfrog | 0.18 | 0.3 |
| Sturgeon | 0.08 | 0.2 |
| Halibut | — | 1.0 |
| Mackerel | 0.12 | 0.7 |
| Dogfish | 0.26 | 0.9 |
| Lamprey | — | 0.2 |
| Cow | 0.06 | 0.3 |
| Man | 0.04 | 0.2 |
| Rabbit | 0.05 | — |

[a] Data from Wilson et al. (40).

the M-type LDH (40). By such a comparison the H LDH's and the M LDH's of a single species can easily be distinguished. As shown in the table, the H-type enzymes from different mammals are quite similar; the M enzyme shows somewhat more variation in the mammals. Differences in ratios among the various classes of vertebrates are also observed.

In our early studies with the coenzyme analogs, we were amazed by the differences found in the phylum Arthropoda (21). It was found that the crustacean muscle LDH could be characterized by a much higher reactivity with the AcPyDPN than with DPN itself (see Table XIV). In contrast, *Limulus* (horseshoe crab) possesses an enzyme that gives a higher rate of reaction with the natural coenzyme than with the analog. Furthermore, the thionicotinamide analog (TNDPN) reacted with the crustacean enzymes but not with the *Limulus* LDH. Other arachnids reacted similarly with the two DPN analogs, as did the *Limulus* LDH. From such catalytic data, it can easily be seen that the LDH's of the Arthropoda fall into two main groups and that the division of the LDH's is certainly in line with the known classification of this phylum. The insects, by the LDH criteria, appear to be more closely related to the crustaceans than to the arachnids. This agrees with the concensus of views on classification of the Arthropoda.

There appear to be two types of LDH in invertebrates as well as in vertebrates. However, differences in catalytic, chemical, and physical properties of LDH's make it almost impossible at present to ascertain whether there is an ancestral enzyme of either the vertebrate H or M in the invertebrates. It will be interesting to determine if such relation-

TABLE XIV

MUSCLE LACTIC DEHYDROGENASE OF THE PHYLUM ARTHROPODA[a]

| Subphylum | $\dfrac{\text{AcPyDPN}}{\text{DPN}}$ | Detectable reaction with TNDPN |
|---|---|---|
| Mandibulata | | |
| Hermit crab | 6 | + |
| Fiddler crab | 40 | + |
| Green crab | 18 | + |
| Edible crab | 22 | + |
| Crayfish | 15 | + |
| Lobster | 17 | + |
| Chelicerata | | |
| *Limulus* | 0.08 | − |
| Tarantula | 0.12 | − |
| Wolf spider | 0.06 | − |
| Scorpion | 0.16 | − |

[a] Data from Kaplan *et al.* (21).

ships exist or whether the gene duplication into H and M occurred as an independent evolutionary event in both invertebrates and vertebrates.

Table XV shows another example of the use of the catalytic method in studies of classification. It is well known, as illustrated in the table, that there is considerable variation in the per cent of $G + C$ content of DNA of members of the *Bacillus* group. The catalytic properties with the malic dehydrogenases from the various *Bacilli* correlate with the DNA composition of the enzymes. This correlation reaffirms that closely related species have like enzymes as indicated by their catalytic characteristics. Listed in Table XV is an organism ( *B. cereus megaterium* ), supposedly an intermediate between the two types of *Bacillus*, which appears to be very closely related to *B. cereus* and not to *B. megaterium*. The relationship among the *Bacilli* is not limited to the malic dehydrogenases, but the same relationships are shown in analog reactions rates with the mannitol-1-phosphate dehydrogenase (Table XV).

Relationships of enzymes also can be ascertained by the use of inhibitors. A number of years ago, we studied the inhibitory effect of

TABLE XV

Malic Dehydrogenase, Mannitol Phosphate Dehydrogenase, and DNA
Base Composition of Species in the Genus *Bacillus*[a]

| Species | Malic dehydrogenase[b] | Mannitol phosphate dehydrogenase[c] | G + C[d] (%) |
|---|---|---|---|
| B. subtilis | 16.0 | 0.70 | 43 |
| B. natto | 17.4 | 0.68 | 43 |
| B. subtilis var. aterrimus | 22.5 | 0.75 | 42.5 |
| B. subtilis var. niger | 17.9 | 0.75 | 43 |
| B. niger | 14.8 | 0.73 | 43 |
| B. polymyxa | 13.6 | 0.72 | 44 |
| B. licheniformis | 10.5 | 0.55 | 46 |
| B. pumilus | 6.4 | 0.56 | 39 |
| B. macerans | 0.8 | 0.53 | 50.5 |
| B. circulans | 0.6 | 0.31 | 35 |
| B. megaterium | 1.1 | 0.22 | 37 |
| B. cereus | > 100 | — | 33 |
| B. alvei | > 100 | — | 33 |
| B. cereus-megaterium | > 100 | | |

[a] From Wilson and Kaplan (39).

[b] Rate with DPN relative to rate with the ethyl pyridyl ketone analog; measurements made at 25°C in the presence of $5 \times 10^{-2}$ $M$ L-malate at pH 8.9.

[c] Rate with the 6-hydroxyethylamino purine analog relative to the rate with DPN.

[d] DNA from species above the dotted line can transform B. subtilis.

TABLE XVI

Effect of Isonicotinic Acid Hydrazide (INH) on the Diphosphopyridine
Nucleotidases of Various Animals[a]

| INH-"sensitive" | INH-"insensitive" |
|---|---|
| Goat | Pig |
| Beef | Horse |
| Lamb | Mouse |
| Deer | Guinea pig |
| Buffalo | Rat |
| | Rabbit |
| | Frog |
| | Man |

[a] The action of all the "sensitive" enzymes was inhibited to an extent greater than 65% by $7.5 \times 10^{-4}$ $M$ INH; the action of the "insensitive" enzymes was not significantly inhibited by $7.5 \times 10^{-4}$ $M$ INH.

a number of pyridine bases on the enzyme DPNase which cleaves DPN at the nicotinamide riboside bond (42). It was found, as shown in Table XVI, that isonicotinic acid hydrazide strongly inhibited the DPNase from a number of ruminants but not the enzyme from other animals (42). These results are particularly interesting, since they demonstrate that a particular characteristic (isonicotinic acid hydrazide sensitivity) is limited to one group of mammals, and that this particular characteristic is a feature of all ruminant DPNases. By such inhibition studies it may be possible to detect subtle evolutionary changes in a given enzyme.

Table XVII summarizes data on the inhibition of a number of TPD's

TABLE XVII

INHIBITION OF THE PURIFIED TRIOSEPHOSPHATE DEHYDROGENASES BY PYRIDINE-3-ALDEHYDE DIPHOSPHOPYRIDINE NUCLEOTIDE[a]

| Enzyme | Inhibition (%) at pyridine-3-aldehyde DPN concentration of: | | | | |
|---|---|---|---|---|---|
| | 1 µg | 2 µg | 5 µg | 10 µg | 100 µg |
| Rabbit | 3 | 13 | 25 | 38 | 80 |
| Beef | 4 | 16 | 25 | 37 | 79 |
| Human | 0 | 0 | 8 | 20 | 60 |
| Chicken | 12 | 14 | 26 | 47 | 83 |
| Turkey | 10 | 15 | 28 | 41 | 81 |
| Pheasant | 6 | 18 | 28 | 39 | 83 |
| Halibut | 8 | 18 | 31 | 41 | 75 |
| Sturgeon | 6 | 14 | 20 | 22 | 56 |
| Lobster | 7 | 12 | 34 | 65 | 89 |
| E. coli | 0 | 0 | 0 | 3 | 40 |
| Yeast | 39 | 54 | | 89 | 95 |

[a] From Allison and Kaplan (2).

by the pyridine-3-aldehyde analog of DPN (Py3AlDPN) and shows that differences among the various crystalline dehydrogenases can be detected. The human enzyme has a somewhat different inhibition pattern as compared to the beef and rabbit proteins. This difference is also reflected in some physical properties. Data such as are given in Table XVII are useful for showing relationships as well as for indicating subtle differences.

IMMUNOLOGICAL CHARACTERIZATIONS

Immunological methods have been used to show that similar proteins in different species vary in structure (27, 5), and it has been possible in this way to show the relationship of enzymes in various species (6, 7, 41, 1, 3, 40, 39).

In our immunological comparisons we have used primarily the micro complement (C') fixation method of Wasserman and Levine (37). For comparative purposes, only the enzyme to be used as the immunizing antigen must be pure. If the purity of the immunizing antigen is definitively established, then it is possible to carry out cross reactions with crude tissue extracts. It should be emphasized that this method gives the same fixation curves whether the antigen is in the pure form or whether it is present in crude extracts. The micro C′ fixation method is advantageous because the procedure requires less enzyme or antibody, by a factor of 100 to 1000, than is necessary for other quantitative immunological methods.

Another advantage of the micro C′ fixation method is that this method is considerably more sensitive to changes in structure than the quantitative precipitin or the usual micro C′ fixation method; this fact allows for the recognition of differences among homologous proteins of different species which is not possible by the other methods (see Table XVIII).

TABLE XVIII

COMPARISON OF SENSITIVITY OF IMMUNOLOGICAL METHODS[a]

| | | Cross reaction[b] | | |
| Antiserum | Heterologous antigen | Micro C′ fixation | Macro C′ fixation | Quantitative precipitin reaction |
| --- | --- | --- | --- | --- |
| Anti-human hemoglobin $A_1$ | Human hemoglobin S | 41 | 86 | 100 |
| Anti-human serum albumin | Chimpanzee serum albumin | 52 | 97 | 89 |
| Anti-chicken ovalbumin | Turkey ovalbumin | 3 | 89 | 96 |
| Anti-chicken $H_4$ LDH | Turkey $H_4$ LDH | 32 | 112 | 91 |

[a] From Wilson et al. (40).

[b] Heterologous reaction is expressed as a percentage of the homologous reaction.

The relatively large differences given by the homologous and the heterologous reactions with the diverse types of proteins strongly indicate that the micro C′ fixation procedure is a desirable method for taxonomic and evolutionary studies.

The micro C′ fixation method can detect differences in which a change of only one amino acid is involved, as indicated by a comparison of the reaction of human hemoglobins S and C with an antibody to hemoglobin A (see Table XIX) (33). The data in this table suggest a correlation between the number of sequence differences and the cross reaction by C′ fixation. This possibility is now under intensive study in our laboratory as well as in other laboratories.

The index of dissimilarity between the fixation reactions of a homologous and a heterologous antigen has been defined as the ratio of antiserum required to give 50% fixation with the homologous antigen, as compared to the amount of antiserum required to give 50% fixation

TABLE XIX

MICRO COMPLEMENT FIXATION BY ANTISERUM TO HEMOGLOBIN $A_1$[a]

| Hemoglobin | Number of amino acid substitutions | Antiserum concentration for 50% C fixation |
|---|---|---|
| $A_1$ | 0 | 1.0 |
| S | 1 | 1.3 |
| C | 1 | 1.3 |
| $A_2$ | 7–8 | 2.0 |
| F | 40 | > 5 |

[a] From Reichlin *et al.* (33).

TABLE XX

MICRO COMPLEMENT FIXATION WITH ANTISERA TO PURE CHICKEN PROTEINS[a]

| Species | \multicolumn{6}{c}{Antiserum concentration required for 50% C' fixation[b]} |
|---|---|---|---|---|---|---|

| Species | $H_4$ LDH | $M_4$ LDH | TPD[c] | GDH[d] | Aldolase | Hemo-globin |
|---|---|---|---|---|---|---|
| Chicken | 1.0 | 1.0 | 1.0 | 1.0 | 1.0 | 1.0 |
| Turkey | 1.4 | 1.2 | 1.0 | 1.0 | 1.0 | 1.0 |
| Duck | 1.5 | 4.3 | 1.2 | 1.2 | | 2.2 |
| Pigeon | 2.3 | 2.0 | 1.3 | 1.3 | | 3.6 |
| Ostrich | 1.9 | 3.1 | 1.3 | 1.4 | 5.0 | |
| Caiman | 3.3 | 4.2 | 3.8 | 4.0 | 6.5 | |
| Painted turtle | 4.0 | 5.2 | 4.2 | 4.0 | | 6.5 |
| Bullfrog | 14 | 40 | 30 | 19 | 18 | |
| Sturgeon | 80 | 20 | 12 | 25 | | |
| Halibut | e | >200 | >50 | | >100 | |
| Dogfish | >100 | >200 | >50 | | | |
| Lamprey | e | 30 | >50 | | | |
| Hagfish | >100 | >100 | | | | |

[a] From Wilson *et al.* (40).

[b] Data presented are based on the use of several anti-chicken $H_4$ LDH sera, two anti-chicken $M_4$ LDH sera, and one each of the other anti-chicken protein sera.

[c] Triosephosphate dehydrogenase.

[d] Glutamic dehydrogenase.

[e] Halibut and lamprey tissues contain no detectable $H_4$ LDH.

with the heterologous antigen. A value of 10 would mean that for a heterologous enzyme ten times as much antibody is required as for the homologous enzyme to give 50% C' fixation.

Table XX contains data showing the dissimilarity of several enzymes and hemoglobins from different species, as compared to the chicken. The turkey proteins are quite close to the chicken proteins; the two turkey LDH's can be distinguished from the corresponding enzymes in the chicken, whereas with the other proteins listed no differences can be detected by the C' fixation method. The indexes of dissimilarity increase from the turkey to fish in relatively the same way with each immune system in a manner that might be expected from the evolutionary positions of the various species. This fact suggests that parallel rates of change in enzymes might have occurred during evolution. The rates are by no means identical, but the order of magnitude is roughly the same.

Table XXI shows that changes in LDH and TPD have also occurred in fish. The indexes of dissimilarities are given for various fish, as compared to the halibut TPD and LDH. The fish are arranged in an approximate evolutionary series. Close relatives of the halibut are listed near the top; the most distant relatives are at the bottom of the table. It is noteworthy that closely related fish have relatively similar indexes of dissimilarities as compared to the halibut.

Table XXII presents data with an antibody to lobster TPD, with respect to indexes of dissimilarity to the dehydrogenase from other Arthropods. The evolutionary relationships are again quite apparent.

The use of the immunological structure of an enzyme as a means of determining taxonomic distance is shown for the Enterobacteriaceae in Table XXIII. An antibody to *Escherichia coli* phosphatase can react with the enzyme from *E. freundii* to the same extent as the homologous enzyme. However, the enzyme does not react as well with the *Aerobacter aerogenes* phosphatase, less so with *Serratia marcescens*, and very poorly with the *Proteus* species. The order of cross reaction correlates with the taxonomic relationship of the organism.

Dr. Allan Wilson has made a detailed comparison of the relationships of enzymes from halibut, chicken, and the sturgeon (Table XXIV). The table also includes some results with two other higher teleosts, the tuna and the mackerel. With the exception of the $H_4$, it is evident that the chicken enzymes are more closely related to the sturgeon proteins than to those of the higher teleosts. Conversely, it has been found that antibodies to halibut enzymes cross-react to a greater extent with the sturgeon enzymes than with the corresponding chicken catalysts. As might be expected, antibodies to sturgeon enzymes react comparatively well with both the chicken and higher teleost proteins. The evolutionary relationships between the sturgeon, chicken, and halibut are given in Fig. 6. The point of divergence of the fish line from the chicken line is some 400 million years. The data suggest that both the chicken and halibut enzymes have retained some of the characteristics of the primitive

TABLE XXI

Micro Complement Fixation by Antibodies to Halibut Enzymes[a]

| Species | Relative antibody concentration for 50% C' fixation at equivalence | |
| --- | --- | --- |
| | TPD | M₄LDH |

| Species | TPD | M$_4$LDH |
| --- | --- | --- |
| **Bony Fishes (Osteichthyes)** | | |
| *Teleostei* | | |
| Heterosomata | | |
| Pacific halibut, *Hippoglossus stenolepis* | 1.0 | 1.0 |
| Petrale sole, *Eopsetta jordani* | 1.3 | 1.1 |
| Commercial flounder (Boston) | 1.3 | 1.1 |
| Commercial sole (Boston) | 1.3 | 1.1 |
| Perciformes | | |
| Scorpion fish, *Scorpaenopsis gibbosa* | 2.0 | 1.2 |
| Mackerel, *Scomber scombrus* | 1.8 | 1.5 |
| Beryciformes | | |
| Squirrel fish, *Holocentrus ensifer* | 1.8 | 1.3 |
| Ostariophysi | | |
| Carp, *Cyprinus carpio* | 16 | 1.6 |
| Brown bullhead catfish, *Ictalurus nebulosus* | 18 | 1.7 |
| Apodes | | |
| Conger eel, *Conger marginatus* | 17 | 2.0 |
| Moray eel, *Gymnothorax hepaticus* | 20 | 4.0 |
| Moray eel, *Gymnothorax flavimarginatus* | 20 | 4.2 |
| Isospondyli | | |
| Brook trout, *Salvelinus fontinalis* | 6.0 | 1.6 |
| Commercial salmon (Boston) | 6.0 | 1.6 |
| Commercial smelt, *Osmerus mordax* | 4.1 | 3.2 |
| Chain pickerel, *Esox niger* | 11 | 6.0 |
| Atlantic herring, *Clupea herengus* | 13 | 35 |
| *Holostei* | | |
| Gar pike, *Lepisosteus spatula* | 17 | 20 |
| *Palaeoniscoidei* | | |
| Sturgeon, *Acipenser transmontanus* | 67 | 35 |
| *Dipnoi* | | |
| African lungfish, *Protopterus* sp. | NC[b] | 100 |
| **CARTILAGINOUS Fishes (Chondrichthyes)** | | |
| Spiny dogfish, *Squalus acanthias* | NC[b] | NC[b] |
| **Jawless Fishes (Agnatha)** | | |
| Lamprey, *Petromyzon marinus* | NC[b] | NC[b] |

[a] Data of A. C. Wilson and W. S. Allison.

[b] NC indicates that no cross reaction was detected at the highest antibody concentration tested.

sturgeon ancestor. The morphological characteristics of the sturgeon, based on fossil data, apparently have changed little. The enzyme data appear to substantiate this finding, since it seems reasonable to assume that the sturgeon enzymes as a whole have also undergone little change in structure. Further details of this study will be presented elsewhere.

The above examples certainly suggest that the immunological ap-

TABLE XXII

Cross Reactions of Various Arthropod Triosephosphate Dehydrogenases with Antibody to Lobster Triosephosphate Dehydrogenase[a]

| Arthropod | Relative antibody concentration for 50% C' fixation at equal enzyme concentration |
|---|---|
| Lobster | 1.0 |
| Crayfish | 1.1 |
| South African lobster | 1.3 |
| Centipede | 7.2 |
| Honey bee | 11.0 |
| Limulus | 30.0 |

[a] Data taken from Allison and Kaplan (1).

TABLE XXIII

Complement Fixation by Antiserum against Alkaline Phosphatase of *Escherichia coli* K12[a]

| Species | Strain and source | Antiserum amount[b] required for 50% C' fixation |
|---|---|---|
| *Escherichia coli* | K12 (C. Levinthal) | 1.0 |
| | T−A−U− (S. S. Cohen) | 1.0 |
| | C | 1.0 |
| | W | 1.0 |
| | I (S. Zamenhof) | 1.0 |
| | Crookes | 1.0 |
| *Escherichia freundii* | 17 (H. Blechman) | 1.0 |
| *Aerobacter aerogenes* | 1088 (Harvard Medical School) | 3.0 |
| *Serratia marcescens* | SR11 Parental (L. Baron) | 10 |
| *Proteus mirabilis* | 35 (H. Blechman) | ~70 |

[a] See Wilson and Kaplan (39).

[b] Relative units: One milliliter of an approximately 1–70,000 dilution of antiserum gave 50% C' fixation with the *Escherichia* enzymes. Micro C' fixation data from Drs. S. Cordes and L. Levine (unpublished) using a rabbit antiserum against pure alkaline phosphatase from *E. coli* K12. The enzyme was purified by Dr. C. Levinthal. The enzymes of other strains and species were studied in sonic extracts of cells grown in inducing medium.

proach can be a useful adjunct in taxonomic and evolutionary studies. It should be emphasized that, in order to elucidate relationships between closely related species, antibodies to enzymes of one of the members of the group must be obtained. For example, if one hopes to establish relationships within the reptilian class, it is preferable to use an antibody to a reptile rather than an antibody to a bird or amphibian enzyme.

TABLE XXIV

IMMUNOLOGICAL INDEX OF DISSIMILARITY OF SOME VERTEBRATES[a]

| Vertebrate | $H_4$ LDH | $M_4$ LDH | TPD | Aldolase | Mitochondrial MDH |
|---|---|---|---|---|---|
| Chicken | 1.0 | 1.0 | 1.0 | 1.0 | 1.0 |
| Sturgeon | 80 | 20 | 12 | 25 | 20 |
| Mackerel | — | 140 | — | — | — |
| Tuna | 80 | > 200 | — | > 100 | > 100 |
| Halibut | No $H_4$ | > 200 | > 50 | > 100 | — |

[a] Data of Dr. A. Wilson and Miss Natalie Grimes.

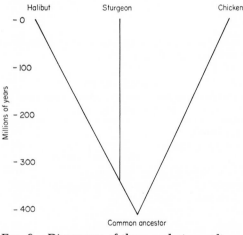

FIG. 6. Divergence of three evolutionary lines.

TEMPERATURE STABILITY AND ELECTROPHORESIS

Certain physical criteria, such as temperature stability and electrophoretic migration, can be used as parameters for showing relationships of enzymes from different species. An intensive study of the electrophoretic properties and stability of the $H_4$ LDH of vertebrates has been made in our laboratory and is summarized in Table XXV. These measurements can be made in crude extracts, if carefully controlled conditions are maintained.

TABLE XXV

TEMPERATURE STABILITY AND ELECTROPHORETIC MOBILITY OF $H_4$
LACTIC DEHYDROGENASE[a]

| Taxonomic group | Inactivation temperature[b] | Electrophoretic mobility[c] |
|---|---|---|
| Neognathous Birds[d] | | |
| Passeriformes (6/67) | 74 | 1.8 |
| Piciformes (3/7) | 79 | 2.8 |
| Coraciiformes (2/9) | 80 | 2.2 |
| Trogoniformes (1/1) | 68 | 0.2 |
| Apodiformes (1/3) | 77 | 2.2 |
| Caprimulgiformes (1/5) | > 63 | 0.2 |
| Strigiformes (1/2) | 68 | 2.1 |
| Cuculiformes (2/2) | 80 | 2.4 |
| Psittaciformes (1/1) | 67 | 2.9 |
| Columbiformes (2/2) | 76 | 2.2 |
| Charadriiformes (6/15) | 77 | 1.5 |
| Gruiformes (2/12) | 63 | 2.2 |
| Galliformes (1/3) | 77 | 2.8 |
| Falconiformes (3/5) | 78 | 2.1 |
| Anseriformes (1/2) | 76 | 2.1 |
| Ciconiiformes (1/7) | 79 | 2.1 |
| Pelecaniformes (3/5) | 80 | 1.7 |
| Procellariiformes (2/4) | 76 | 1.5 |
| Podicipediformes (1/1) | 79 | 1.5 |
| Gaviiformes (1/1) | 80 | 1.8 |
| Sphenisciformes (1/1) | 79 | 2.0 |
| Paleognathous Birds | | |
| Tinamiformes (1/1) | 80 | 6.6 |
| Rheiformes (1/1) (Rhea) | 79 | 6.8 |
| Struthioniformes (1/1) (ostrich) | 80 | 6.6 |
| Higher Reptiles | | |
| Caiman, *Caiman crocodilus* | 76 | 5.1 |
| Lizard, *Iguana iguana* | 82 | 5.6 |
| Lizard, *Varanus flavicens* | 85 | 2.5 |
| Snake, *Natrix* sp. | 80 | 6.3 |
| Snake, *Crotalus atrox* | 80 | 6.3 |
| Snake, *Constrictor constrictor* | 77 | 5.3 |
| Lower Reptiles | | |
| Snapping turtle, *Chelydra serpentis* | 58 | 6.1 |
| Painted turtle, *Chrysemys picta* | 52 | 5.7 |
| Cooter turtle, *Pseudemys scripta* | | 6.3 |
| Soft-shell turtle, *Trionyx ferox* | <60 | 5.2 |
| Mammals | | |
| Man | 65 | 15 |
| Domestic cow | 61 | 12 |
| Domestic pig | 61 | 16 |
| Laboratory rabbit | 65 | 12 |
| Laboratory mouse | 60 | 15 |

TABLE XXV (*continued*)

| Taxonomic group | Inactivation temperature[b] | Electrophoretic mobility[c] |
|---|---|---|
| Mammals (*continued*) | | |
| Laboratory rat | 60 | 15 |
| Squirrel, *Sciurus carolinensis* | 68 | 15 |
| European hedgehog, *Erinaceus europaeus* | 65 | 13 |
| Short-tail shrew, *Blarina brevicauda* | 66 | 7.7 |
| Opossum, *Didelphis virginiana* | 60 | 15 |
| Kangaroo, *Macropus robustus* | 69 | 15 |
| Amphibians | | |
| Bullfrog, *Rana catesbiana* | 52 | 10 |
| Leopard frog, *Rana pipiens* | 56 | 3.4 |
| Toad, *Bufo marinus* | 65 | 7.4 |
| Congo eel, *Amphiuma tridactylum* | 68 | 11 |
| Bony Fish | | |
| Sturgeon, *Acipenser transmontanus* | 62 | 6.9 |
| Haddock, *Melanogrammus aeglefinus* | 63 | 7.8 |
| Mackerel, *Scomber scrombrus* | 60 | 6.1 |
| Cartilaginous Fish | | |
| Seven-gill shark, *Notorhynchus maculatum* | 68 | 5.0 |
| Spiny dogfish, *Squalus acanthias* | 64 | 4.1 |
| Chimaera, *Hydrolagus collei* | < 65 | 7.0 |
| Cyclostomes | | |
| Lamprey, *Petromyzon marinus* | e | e |
| Hagfish, *Eptatretus stouti* | <65 | 4.8 |

[a] From Wilson *et al.* (40).

[b] Temperature (°C) required for 50% inactivation in 20 minutes.

[c] Distance (centimeters) moved during horizontal starch-gel electrophoresis at pH 7 for 16 hours at 10 volts/cm.

[d] So many birds have been studied that we have averaged the data for each order. The neognathous orders are arranged in a sequence, those near the bottom of the list being considered by ornithological authorities to be more primitive than those near the top of the list. In parentheses, we record the number of families examined as a fraction of the total number of families in the order.

[e] The lamprey has no $H_4$ LDH in the heart; all lamprey tissues examined contain only $M_4$ LDH, as judged by immunological, electrophoretic, and catalytic criteria.

In general, it has been found that the $H_4$ LDH of closely related species has similar migratory and thermal stability properties. Small but significant differences can be observed with some closely related species. In the bullfrog H, 50% of the enzymatic activity is lost after 20 minutes at 52°C; the temperature must be raised to 56°C to obtain the same degree of inactivation in 20 minutes for the leopard frog H LDH. These small differences are quite reproducible and represent subtle differences in the LDH structure. We have had adequate experience to state that these differences in heat lability can be used as an index of species relationships.

Table XXV indicates that a relatively large increase in the heat stability of the H-type LDH occurred at one point during vertebrate evolution. As the table shows, all the lower invertebrates examined, which include a diverse number of fish and amphibia, have a half-inactivation temperature of roughly 60°C. This is also true of the lower reptiles and the mammals. In contrast, the higher reptiles have temperatures of inactivation close to 80°C. Apparently this high-temperature stability occurred at a time when the higher reptiles were evolving from the lower reptiles. Birds generally have the high-temperature stable H LDH characteristic of the higher reptiles. There are some exceptions with regard to thermolability in a few higher birds; it is possible that those species with relatively unstable H-type LDH may have originated comparatively recently from the stable "primitive" higher reptile or bird enzyme. It is of interest that the thermal stability of the mammalian H type is similar to that of the lower invertebrate, indicating that at least with respect to this physical property the mammalian H LDH has undergone little change.

Closely related species usually have rather similar electrophoretic migrations for their H-type LDH's (8, 40) (see Table XXV). There are some closely related species, such as the bullfrog and leopard frog, which have significantly different mobilities: the mammals examined all have a very rapidly migrating H-type LDH (12 to 15 cm). Most fish, amphibia, and reptiles have enzymes that migrate considerably more slowly (5 to 10 cm). The bird H LDH's as a whole are exceptionally slow-moving. The paleagnathous birds (ostrich, rhea, and tinnamou), however, have somewhat faster migrating enzymes and are more like the higher reptiles in this respect. Among birds, on the basis of anatomical data, this group has long been considered to be primitive and appears to have evolved from reptiles before the modern birds had diversified. It is interesting that both the heat stability and electrophoretic properties of the primitive birds are similar to those of the higher reptiles. Figure 7 summarizes the evolutionary changes of LDH in vertebrates; these results show good agreement with what is known about the general direction of vertebrate evolution.

## Significance of Evolutionary Changes in Enzymes

The question can be posed as to whether change in enzyme structure during evolution has any functional or survival significance. At present, this is a difficult question to answer; however, our growing understanding of subtle differences in catalytic and physical properties of like enzymes from different species suggests that these changes may have been important in natural selection.

We have previously advanced the premise that the two types of LDH have functionally different roles (22, 24). This premise was based on observations that there was a marked difference in the degree of inhibition of the two types by excess pyruvate, as illustrated in Fig. 8 for the beef LDH's. The H type is maximally active at low levels of

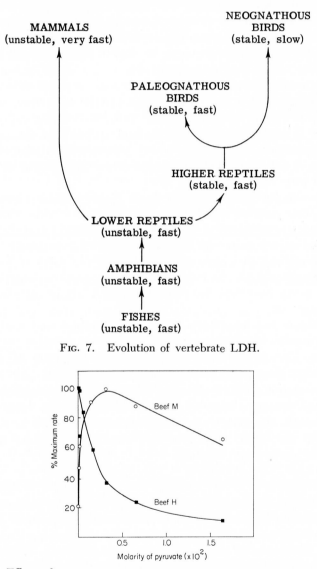

FIG. 7.   Evolution of vertebrate LDH.

FIG. 8.   Effect of pyruvate concentration on rate of beef M and chicken H LDH's (22).

pyruvate and is inhibited by higher concentrations of the keto acid. In contrast, the M type shows little substrate inhibition. These findings may be related to the metabolic differences of heart and skeletal muscles. In the heart a steady supply of energy is required and is maintained by a complete oxidation of pyruvate in the mitochondria; hence, inhibition of the LDH by excess pyruvate would favor the oxidation of the keto acid. In voluntary muscles, the need usually is for sudden energy and is associated with a rapid glycolytic formation of pyruvate. To maintain glycolysis it is essential continuously to oxidize the DPNH by LDH and pyruvate. Therefore, it appears reasonable that an M-type enzyme that can operate in the presence of temporarily high concentrations of pyruvate should be found in tissues that have a sudden demand for energy. The M-type enzyme appears to be geared for reduction of pyruvate, whereas the H-type LDH may be more directed toward lactate oxidation.

Investigations in our laboratory have supported the view of the different roles of the two types. In studies on various striated muscles it has consistently been found that those muscles that contract tonically or rhythmically have considerably more H subunits, as contrasted to muscles without contractions (26, 9, 38). A detailed examination of the breast muscle composition of a number of different birds showed that those birds that are sustained flyers have a large percentage of H subunits, whereas birds that have only a sudden need for use of their breast muscle have largely the M form. There is an excellent correlation between the flying habits of the birds and the LDH composition of the breast muscle (38).

Dr. Salthe of our laboratory has recently made a survey of the substrate (pyruvate) inhibition characteristics of a number of different amphibians. The terrestrial species have higher indexes of inhibition, as compared to the aquatic amphibians (see Table XXVI). There appears to be a correlation between the environmental oxygen tension and the LDH type. The more anaerobic the environment, as in the case of the aquatic animals, the greater is the relative amount of M-type LDH as indicated by the lower substrate inhibitor. Aquatic and terrestrial amphibians also have been found to differ in their hemoglobins (29); the aquatic animals have hemoglobins with considerably greater affinity for oxygen, as compared to the hemoglobins of the terrestrial amphibians. It is noteworthy that such relatively anaerobic vertebrates as the flat fish (halibut, flounder, sole) and the lamprey have only the M-type LDH in all their tissues.

Figure 9 shows that there have been evolutionary changes in the mammalian M-type LDH; this is indicated by the differences in sensitivity to high pyruvate concentration; there are other criteria for distinguishing the various mammalian LDH's. From the point of view of natural selection, the differences in the curves of Fig. 9 may be of some interest. The rabbit is an animal that produces a great deal of lactic acid during activity, and the evolution of a strongly anaerobic M-type LDH may have been advantageous to the survival of this mammal. In contrast, the human, whose dependence on sudden and extensive activity

TABLE XXVI

CORRELATION BETWEEN ENVIRONMENTAL OXYGEN AVAILABILITY AND SUBSTRATE INHIBITION OF LACTIC DEHYDROGENASE IN AMPHIBIAN HEARTS[a]

| Amphibian | $\dfrac{DPNH_L{}^b}{DPNH_H}$ |
|---|---|
| Terrestrial | |
| Spadefoot toad (*Scaphiopus*) | 2.54 |
| Spring peeper (*Hyla*) | 2.43 |
| Ant-eating toad (*Rhynophrynus*) | 2.32 |
| Spadefoot toad (*Pelobates*) | 2.31 |
| Green toad (*Bufo*) | 2.30 |
| American toad (*Bufo*) | 2.18 |
| Wood frog (*Rana*) | 2.08 |
| Marine toad (*Bufo*) | 2.01 |
| Pacific tree toad (*Hyla*) | 1.94 |
| Fire salamander (*Salamandra*) | 1.92 |
| European tree frog (*Hyla*) | 1.62 |
| Aquatic—cold, running water | |
| Pacific giant salamander larva (*Dicamptodon*) | 2.25 |
| Bell toad (*Ascaphus*) | 1.66 |
| Aquatic—standing water | |
| Painted frog (*Discoglossus*) | 1.70 |
| Fire-bellied toad (*Bombina*) | 1.66 |
| Axolotl (*Amblystoma*) | 1.64 |
| Surinam toad (*Pipa*) | 1.46 |
| Mudpuppy (*Necturus*) | 1.45 |
| Congo eel (*Amphiuma*) | 1.43 |
| Dwarf siren (*Pseudobranchus*) | 1.37 |
| African clawed water frog (*Xenopus*) | 1.32 |
| Greater siren (*Siren*) | 0.86 |
| Lesser siren (*Siren*) | 0.76 |

[a] From S. Salthe, in preparation.
[b] Indicates ratio of reaction of low to high pyruvate (see refs. 9, 38).

for survival is considerably less, has developed an enzyme that is somewhat more sensitive to high concentrations of pyruvate.

The LDH's also differ in their turnover numbers with respect to both pyruvate and lactate. Table XXVII lists some turnover numbers with pyruvate of several LDH's. The M-type LDH's have a higher turnover number than the H catalyst does; the fish M types have significantly higher turnover numbers than the corresponding enzymes in avian and mammalian species do. The *Lactobacillus* LDH appears to have a considerably lower turnover number than the animal enzymes studied. An *E. coli* enzyme, purified by Miss Tarmy, also appears to have a relatively low turnover number.

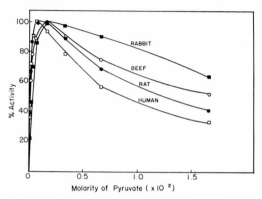

FIG. 9.   Substrate inhibition of various mammalian M LDH's (M. M. Ciotti and N. O. Kaplan, unpublished results).

TABLE XXVII

ANALOG RATIOS AND TURNOVER NUMBERS OF VARIOUS HEART- AND MUSCLE-TYPE LACTIC DEHYDROGENASES[a]

| Species | Turnover numbers[b] | |
|---|---|---|
| | $H_4$ | $M_4$ |
| Beef | 49,400 | 80,200 |
| Chicken | 45,500 | 93,400 |
| Frog | — | 86,000 |
| Dogfish | — | 109,000 |
| Rabbit | 41,500 | — |
| Haddock | | 146,000 |
| Tuna | | 165,000 |
| Halibut | | 153,000 |

[a] Data mainly from Pesce (31, 32).

[b] Values are given as moles of DPNH oxidized per mole of enzyme per minute at 25°C, pH 7.5, with pyruvate at $V_{max}$.

Similar enzymes operate under varying environmental conditions in different species. Organisms live in a manifold of temperatures, and hence one might expect that enzyme evolution has permitted adaptation to particular temperatures. Table XXVIII compares the rate of LDH activity at 45°C to that at 15°C with a low level of pyruvate. It is of interest that for the warm-blooded animals there is an increase in rate of reaction when the temperature is raised. However, the lobster and the halibut enzyme, whose habitat is a low-temperature one, show a decrease in activity as the temperature is increased. These data indicate that the affinity for low amounts of pyruvate in the warm-blooded animal increases with temperature and that for the LDH's of the cold-blooded animals generally decreases. We have found that the halibut M enzyme functions at temperatures of 8° to 10°C as the chicken M LDH does at 30°C. Apparently, cold-blooded animals have evolved enzymes with structures capable of functioning at low temperatures.

TABLE XXVIII

RATIO OF ACTIVITY OF 45°/15° OF DIFFERENT LACTIC DEHYDROGENASES AT LOW PYRUVATE CONCENTRATION $(2 \times 10^{-4} M)$[a]

| LDH | Ratio | LDH | Ratio |
|-----|-------|-----|-------|
| Chicken H | 4.6 | Frog M | 0.97 |
| Beef H | 3.8 | Sturgeon M | 1.10 |
| Chicken M | 1.7 | Dogfish M | 0.80 |
| Turkey M | 1.7 | Lamprey M | 0.80 |
| Duck M | 1.9 | Halibut M | 0.64 |
| Beef M | 2.0 | Lobster | 0.45 |

[a] N. O. Kaplan and S. White, unpublished experiments.

There are two types of malic dehydrogenases in animals. One usually is localized in the mitochondria; the second is found in the soluble part of the cell (10, 13, 34, 35). The mitochondrial enzyme appears to be geared toward malate oxidation, whereas the soluble malic dehydrogenase appears to function in the direction of reduction of oxaloacetate (10, 25).

The above examples certainly suggest that changes in enzyme structure may be important factors in natural selection. The rapid development of methodology for evaluating the chemical, catalytic, and physical properties of enzymes promises to add new understanding to the physiological significance of specific molecular changes in enzymes.

It should be emphasized that the use of the new biochemical procedures will not supersede the classical phylogenic and taxonomic studies but will add quantitative parameters for use together with the classical approach. Specific problems that the classical methods cannot resolve may be solved by the comparative enzyme techniques outlined in this paper. Perhaps, in years to come, investigators utilizing both classical and molecular biology approaches will be able to clarify the intimate mechanisms involved in evolutionary change and in the origin of new species.

## Acknowledgments

The author is grateful to Drs. A. C. Wilson, S. Salthe, T. P. Fondy, W. S. Allison, A. Pesce, Messrs. F. Stolzenbach, B. Kitto, J. Everse, and Miss N. Grimes for their contributions to various phases of this work. These investigations were supported, in part, by research grants from the National Aeronautics and Space Administration (NSG-375) and from the American Cancer Society (P-77G).

## References

1. ALLISON, W. S., AND KAPLAN, N. O., *in* "Taxonomic Biochemistry and Serology (C. A. Leone, ed.), p. 401, Ronald Press, New York, 1964.
2. ALLISON, W. S., AND KAPLAN, N. O., *J. Biol. Chem.*, **239**, 2140 (1964).
3. ALLISON, W. S., AND KAPLAN, N. O., *Biochemistry*, 3, 1792 (1964).
4. BARKER, H. A., *Federation Proc.*, **20**, 956 (1961).
5. BOYDEN, A., *in* "Serological and Biochemical Comparisons of Proteins (W. A. Cole, ed.), p. 3, Rutgers Univ. Press, New Brunswick, New Jersey, 1958.
6. BROWN, R. K., TACEY, B. C., AND ANFINSEN, C. B., *Biochim. Biophys. Acta*, 39, 528 (1960).
7. BUEDING, E., *Federation Proc.*, **21**, 1039 (1962).
8. CAHN, R. D., KAPLAN, N. O., LEVINE, L., AND ZWILLING, E., *Science*, 136, 962 (1962).
9. DAWSON, D. M., GOODFRIEND, T. L., AND KAPLAN, N. O., *Science*, 143, 929 (1964).
10. DELBRÜCK, A., SCHIMASSEK, H., BARTSCH, K., AND BÜCHER, T., *Biochem. Z.*, 331, 297 (1959).
11. DI SABATO, G., AND KAPLAN, N. O., *Biochemistry*, 2, 776 (1963).
12. EHRENBERG, A., *Acta Chem. Scand.*, 11, 1257 (1957).
13. ENGLARD, S., SIEGEL, L., AND BREIGER, H. H., *Biochem. Biophys. Res. Commun.*, 3, 323 (1960).
14. FONDY, T. P., AND EVERSE, J., *Federation Proc.*, **23**, 424 (1964).
15. FONDY, T. P., PESCE, A., FREEDBERG, I., STOLZENBACH, F., AND KAPLAN, N. O., *Biochemistry*, 3, 522 (1964).
16. GRIMM, F. C., AND DOHERTY, D. G., *J. Biol. Chem.*, **236**, 1980 (1961).
17. HARRIS, I., *Nature*, **203**, 31 (1964).
18. KAPLAN, N. O., AND CIOTTI, M. M., *J. Am. Chem. Soc.*, **76**, 1713 (1954).
19. KAPLAN, N. O., AND CIOTTI, M. M., *J. Biol. Chem.*, **221**, 823 (1956).
20. KAPLAN, N. O., *in* "The Enzymes" (P. D. Boyer, H. Lardy, and K. Myrback, eds.), 2nd ed., Vol. 3, p. 105, Academic Press, New York, 1960.
21. KAPLAN, N. O., CIOTTI, M. M., HAMOLSKY, M., AND BIEBER, R., *Science*, 131, 392 (1960).
22. KAPLAN, N. O., *in* "Mechanism of Action of Steroid Hormones," p. 247, Pergamon Press, Oxford, 1961.
23. KAPLAN, N. O., AND CIOTTI, M. M., *Ann. N. Y. Acad. Sci.*, **94**, 701 (1961).
24. KAPLAN, N. O., *Proc. 5th Intern. Congr. Biochem.*, Moscow, 1961, Vol. III, p. 97, Pergamon Press, Oxford, 1963.
25. KAPLAN, N. O., *Bacteriol. Revs.*, **27**, 155 (1963).
26. KAPLAN, N. O., AND CAHN, R. D., *Proc. Natl. Acad. Sci. U.S.* **48**, 2123 (1962).
27. LANDSTEINER, K., "The Specificity of Serological Reactions," Harvard Univ. Press, Cambridge, Massachusetts, 1945.
28. LI, T. K., AND VALLEE, B. L., *Biochemistry*, 3, 869 (1964).

29. McCUTCHEON, F. H., AND HALL, F. G., *J. Cellular Comp. Physiol.*, **9**, 191 (1937).
30. PERHAM, R. N., AND HARRIS, I., *J. Mol. Biol.*, **7**, 316 (1963).
31. PESCE, A., Ph.D. Dissertation, Brandeis University, 1964.
32. PESCE, A., McKAY, R. H., STOLZENBACH, F. E., CAHN, R. D., AND KAPLAN, N. O., *J. Biol. Chem.*, **239**, 1753 (1964).
33. REICHLIN, M., HAY, M., AND LEVINE, L., *Immunochemistry*, **1**, 21 (1964).
34. THORNE, C. J. R., *Biochim. Biophys. Acta*, **42**, 175 (1960).
35. THORNE, C. J. R., GROSSMAN, L. I., AND KAPLAN, N. O., *Biochim. Biophys. Acta*, **73**, 193 (1963).
36. THORNE, C. J. R., AND KAPLAN, N. O., *J. Biol. Chem.*, **238**, 1861 (1963).
37. WASSERMAN, E., AND LEVINE, L., *J. Immunol.* **87**, 290 (1961).
38. WILSON, A. C., CAHN, R. D., AND KAPLAN, N. O., *Nature*, **197**, 331 (1963).
39. WILSON, A. C., AND KAPLAN, N. O., *in* "Taxonomic Biochemistry and Serology (C. A. Leone, ed.), p. 321, Ronald Press, New York, 1964.
40. WILSON, A. C., KAPLAN, N. O., LEVINE, L., PESCE, A., REICHLIN, M., AND ALLISON, W. S., *Federation Proc.*, **23**, 1258 (1964).
41. YUNIS, A. A., AND KREBS, E. G., *J. Biol. Chem.*, **237**, 34 (1962).
42. ZATMAN, L. J., KAPLAN, N. O., COLOWICK, S. P., AND CIOTTI, M. M., *J. Biol. Chem.*, **290**, 453 (1954).

# Enzymatic Homology and Analogy in Phylogeny

W. J. RUTTER

*Division of Biochemistry, Department of Chemistry and Chemical Engineering, University of Illinois, Urbana, Illinois*

An analysis of the molecular features of functionally related proteins derived from various biological sources may provide interpretable evidence of basic evolutionary mechanisms and relationships. The determination of the primary structure is especially desirable, since the amino acid sequence reflects directly (excluding degeneracy) the degree of structural variance of some segments of the genome (51, 32) in phylogeny. On the other hand, less cumbersome comparisons of characteristic features of specific proteins such as molecular weight and subunit composition, and catalytic properties which reflect a specific though undefined amino acid sequence, may also be informative, especially in elucidating broad relationships of homology and analogy (42).

This paper summarizes a study (16, 42, 41) of the properties of fructose-1,6-diphosphate (FDP) aldolases obtained from phyletically divergent systems. The results indicate the presence in nature of two main aldolase classes. Because of their distinct molecular and catalytic properties and biological distribution, it is postulated that these classes have independent evolutionary origins and are *analogous* in that sense. Interspecies variants of each class have similar properties, suggesting a strong conservation of "critical" structure features in phylogeny. Intraorganismic redundancy of both analogous and homologous FDP aldolase variants has been detected in some systems. A preliminary survey of the basic properties of other enzymes catalyzing aldol-type reactions is also presented. With the exception of enzymes requiring biotin and pyridoxal phosphate, the properties of the enzymes appear to be similar to one or the other of the analogous FDP aldolases. These correlations allow the tentative suggestion that most enzymes facilitating aldolase-type reactions may contain "modulations" of either of two basic catalytically active sites. Thus, it is possible, though not proved, that this group of enzymes evolved from two primitive gene systems.

## Analogous FDP Aldolases

The properties and distribution of Class I and Class II aldolases are presented in Table I. The primary characteristics of Class I aldolases have been defined by the properties of the classical muscle enzyme, which are similar to those of the highly purified enzymes from the insect *Phormia* (28) and from the pea (*Pisum sativum*) (50, 16). Yeast (*Saccharomyces cerevisiae*) aldolase (36, 43) is the prototype of the Class II

TABLE I

ANALOGOUS FORMS OF FRUCTOSE DIPHOSPHATE ALDOLASE:
DISTRIBUTION AND MOLECULAR AND CATALYTIC PROPERTIES

| Class I | Class II |
|---|---|
| Animals, plants, protozoa, green algae, (*Euglena, Chlamydomonas*) | Bacteria, yeast, fungi, blue-green algae (*Euglena, Chlamydomonas*) |
| ~ 150,000  M.W. | ~ 70,000  M.W. |
| ~ 7.8 S | ~ 5.4 S |
| (3 subunits) | (2 subunits) |
| Probable Schiff base catalytic intermediate (lysine residue) | Divalent metal ion requirement |
| Functional carboxy-terminal residues (tyrosine) | K+ activation Functional SH groups |
| pH profile for exchange and over-all reactions broad and coincident | pH profile for exchange and over-all reactions sharp, displaced |

aldolases; its distinctive properties have been checked with those of highly purified preparations from *Clostridium perfringens* (16) and *Aspergillus niger* (24, 43). The specific characteristics of the prototype enzymes have then been compared with those crude preparations obtained for more than forty different species (16, 43). Much of the detailed experimental data have been discussed recently (42, 40) and therefore only will be summarized here. The molecular and catalytic characteristics of the two series of aldolases are strikingly different. The properties of interspecies variants of each aldolase show relatively minor deviations. Class I aldolases have molecular weights of approximately 150,000, as judged from the general similarity of the sedimentation constants among members of these series to that of muscle aldolase for which a molecular weight has been defined. (The possibility of fortuitous agreement of sedimentation constants of a number of proteins of differing molecular weight is considered small.) The bulk of the data at present available suggests that muscle aldolase is composed of three polypeptide chains (27, 11, 49, 41); presumably other members of this series also may have a similar subunit composition. Carboxy-terminal residues are important structural features of Class I aldolases, since carboxypeptidase specifically alters the catalytic activity and specificity of these enzymes (12). In the case of rabbit muscle aldolase, the change in catalytic activity caused by treatment with carboxypeptidase is co-incident with the loss of carboxy-terminal tyrosine residues. Class I aldolases appear to have a lysine at the active site and probably undergo Schiff base formation with the substrate. Horecker and associates (21) first demonstrated that treatment of muscle aldolase with sodium boro-hydride in the presence of dihydroxyacetone phosphate (DHAP) yields a stable, catalytically inactive product containing two β-glyceryl-lysine groups. This derivative corresponds to the product expected by reduction of the Schiff base formed from DHAP and a specific lysine at the active site of the enzyme. It has now been shown that all aldolases tested in this series show a specific loss of enzyme activity when treated with borohydride in the presence of their substrate (40, 44). This is presump-tive evidence for a similar catalytic intermediate probably involving lysine.

Class II aldolases have molecular weights of approximately 70,000 and, as judged from data recently available on yeast aldolase (43), may consist of two subunits. These enzymes are apparently metalloproteins, since purified enzymes contain either tightly bound metal ions (zinc) or require the addition of divalent metal ions ($Fe^{++}$ or $Co^{++}$) for activity. The activity of both purified and crude enzymes is inhibited by metal chelating agents (16, 42). Class II FDP aldolases are also specifically activated by monovalent cations, especially potassium, and require the presence of sulfhydryl compounds for maximum stability and catalytic activity (43). Attempts to form a stable enzyme–substrate compound by treatment of Class II aldolases with sodium borohydride in the presence of substrates have been unsuccessful (40, 41). In these enzymes, the divalent metal ion may be at the active site, since inhibition by metal chelating agents such as EDTA is competitive with the substrate FDP (16). The conclusion of distinct catalytic sites of Class I and Class II aldolases is also supported by the contrasting pH profile of the two enzymes classes. Whereas the pH profile of Class I aldolases for FDP cleavage and $H^3$ exchange into DHAP is maximal from pH 6.5 to 9.0, Class II aldolases exhibit sharp maxima of pH 7.5 for FDP cleavage reaction and pH 6.0 for the exchange reaction. Possible catalytic mech-anisms for Class I and II aldolases are presented in Fig. 1.

Members of each aldolase class exhibit a conformity of both specific molecular and catalytic characteristics. On the other hand, even though the same reaction is catalyzed, there is no evidence of similarity in the molecular or catalytic properties between the two enzyme classes. The possibility of interconversion from any recognizable relative of the two classes seems remote. It is thus presumed that the two aldolase classes arose during evolution by independent mechanisms.

Class I aldolases are found in plants, animals, protozoans, and green algae, whereas the Class II enzymes are present in bacteria, yeast, fungi, and the blue-green algae. This distribution is consistent with present

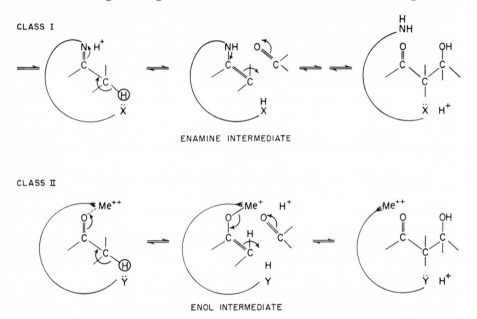

FIG. 1.   Possible mechanisms for aldolase-catalyzed reactions.

phylogenetic concepts in the sense that the occurrence of the two types of aldolase is restricted to related portions of the taxonomic system. Only two species thus far studied, *Euglena* and *Chlamydomonas,* contain both Class I and Class II aldolases (16, 40, 43). The presence of analogous FDP aldolases in these organisms is considered especially significant. Since the chloroplasts contain their own complement of DNA, it is possible that the aldolases are coded by independent genomes. The available evidence in *Euglena,* however, suggests that both forms of aldolase can be formed by transcription from the DNA of the nucleus, since all chloroplast-negative mutants tested still contain both aldolases (43). The proportion of aldolases synthesized depends strongly upon the growth conditions. When *Euglena* are grown under phototropic conditions, for example, they accumulate primarily the Class II aldolase;

when grown under autotrophic conditions, they accumulate primarily Class I aldolase. Similar results have now been obtained by Russell and Gibbs (37). Class II aldolases therefore may be utilized primarily in photosynthetic metabolism in this organism.

## Two Homologous Series of Class I Aldolases

An example of intraorganismic redundancy of Class I aldolase has been discovered in animal systems. In organisms with rudimentary or true livers, there exists a fructose diphosphate aldolase variant which shows somewhat greater divergence of properties than extraorganismic homologs (38, 39). Table II compares some of the characteristic features of rabbit liver aldolase, termed aldolase B, with those of rabbit muscle aldolase, termed aldolase A (the prototype of Class I aldolases) (38, 39, 35). The molecular weight and general subunit structure of these

TABLE II

PROPERTIES OF CLASS I FDP ALDOLASE HOMOLOGOUS VARIANTS

| Property | A (rabbit muscle) | B (rabbit liver) |
|---|---|---|
| Molecular weight | 147,000 | 154,000 |
| Peptide chains | (3) | (3) |
| Fingerprint patterns | Generally similar, but about 1/3 spots not coincident | |
| Immunological reaction with anti A | $+$ | $-$ |
| Immunological reaction with anti B | $-$ | $+$ |
| DHAP binding sites | 2 lysine | 2 lysine |
| Per cent residual FDP activity after carboxypeptidase treatment | 5 | 50 |
| FDP/FIP activity ratio | 50 | 1 |
| $V_{max}$ FDP cleavage | 5300 | 460 |
| $V_{max}$ FDP synthesis | 10,000 | 3000 |
| $K_M$ (M): FDP | $6.1 \times 10^{-5}$ | $2.3 \times 10^{-6}$ |
| FIP | $1.2 \times 10^{-2}$ | $8.3 \times 10^{-4}$ |
| DHAP | $2.1 \times 10^{-3}$ | $3.7 \times 10^{-4}$ |
| GA3P | $1.1 \times 10^{-3}$ | $3.0 \times 10^{-4}$ |

proteins are similar, but there is a significant difference in substrate specificity and the kinetic properties of the enzyme relative to its substrates. Aldolase A is apparently tailored for breakdown of FDP, whereas aldolase B is more effective in synthesis of FDP from small molecules and, in addition, has a broader substrate specificity. Aldolase B, for example, can effectively catalyze the aldol cleavage of fructose-1-phosphate, an obligatory intermediate in the metabolism of fructose in liver tissue. Even though these molecules have generally similar molecular characteristics, they have a distinct amino acid sequence. Antibodies prepared against aldolase A do not cross-react with aldolase B, and, conversely, antibodies prepared against aldolase B do not cross-react significantly with aldolase A (5). Fingerprints of the two enzymes, although grossly similar, show distinct differences in the peptides formed by treatment with trypsin and chymotrypsin. About a third of the peptide spots are not coincident (38). This suggests that at least parts of the two molecules have different amino acid sequences and are presumably therefore defined by separate regions on the genome. The question whether there are common subunits in aldolases A and B—as with hemoglobin (23) and lactic dehydrogenase variants (3, 31, 8)—has not been decisively resolved.

The phenomenon of intraorganismic redundancy observed with aldolases A and B is similar to that discovered with hemoglobin variants. Because of the general similarity in molecular structure and catalytic properties of members of both series, an evolutionary relationship seems probable. Gene duplication has been proposed as a reasonable mechanism for the origin of these variants from the parent genetic segment (22, 54, 40). It is perhaps significant that the Class I and Class II aldolases in *Euglena* and *Chlamydomonas,* and aldolases A and B in mammalian systems, are apparently utilized for a specific physiological function. Where there is intraorganismic duplicity, metabolically meaningful variants may tend to develop in phylogeny.

## Possible Evolutionary Relationships with Others Aldolases

The observed phyletic distribution of Class I and Class II aldolases suggests that the origin of Class I aldolases occurred after considerable organismic evolution. The existence of both analogous aldolase variants in *Euglena* and *Chlamydomonas* is consistent with the postulate that a primitive progenitor of these organisms (whose ancestors produced only the Class II aldolase) suddenly acquired the ability to produce the Class I aldolase. This metabolic redundancy may have been used to physiological advantage in one segment of progeny, while the other segment, the one in the more direct phylogenetic line to the higher organisms, subsequently lost the ability to produce Class I aldolase.

There are many possible mechanisms for the evolutionary origin of the genetic segment which defines the structure of the Class I aldolases, but it is of special interest to ascertain whether this enzyme class arose as a result of random modifications of an essentially useless genomic segment, i.e., a "creative event," or, alternatively, was derived by "adaptation" of a genomic segment defining a protein with many of the important features of the new catalyst (40). Although it may be difficult to distinguish rigorously between these two possibilities, the latter appears the more probable mechanism, especially since a number of enzymes which catalyze more or less similar reaction types to the aldolases are known. This fact is emphasized in Fig. 2. An extragenomic segment, perhaps formed by gene duplication of a region coded for the amino acid sequence of a related enzyme, might in the course of evolution be "adapted" to allow altered substrate specificity of the gene product while conserving, to a high degree, the fairly important features of the catalytically active site. If this argument were true, homologous families of enzymes might be recognized by the similarity in over-all catalytic and over-all molecular properties as well as by congruence of amino acid sequence in certain regions of the molecule.

A preliminary attempt to classify other enzymes facilitating other aldol-type reactions by comparison with the properties of fructose diphosphate aldolases is presented in Table III.

With the exception of enzymes mediated by biotin and pyridoxal phosphate (which probably belong to other evolutionary families), the properties of enzymes catalyzing aldolase-type reactions appear to be similar to those of Class I aldolases, perhaps having lysine at the active site, or to those of Class II aldolases, requiring divalent metal ions for catalytic activity. The majority if not all of the Class II enzymes listed also require the presence of SH compounds for maximal activity. Horecker and associates have isolated a lysine peptide presumably involved in Schiff base formation with the substrates from transaldolase (21) and have presented evidence for a similar active site in keto-3-deoxy-6-phosphogluconate (KDPG) aldolase and deoxyribose-5-phosphate aldolase (15). Presumptive evidence has been presented for a similar intermediate in the reactions catalyzed by the other Class I aldolases. It is significant that transaldolase, KDPG aldolase, and deoxyribose-5-phosphate aldolase are found in microbiological species which contain Class II aldolase, but not Class I aldolase. It is possible, therefore, that these enzymes are more "primitive" than the Class I aldolases, and are evolutionarily related to a gene system adapted during evolution to produce the FDP aldolase. In contrast, the fuculose-1-phosphate aldolase (13) is a divalent metal ion enzyme similar in many respects to the Class II aldolases. The pentose and hexose phosphate aldolases can be thus tentatively segregated into "lysine" and "metal ion" aldolase classes. More distant relationships might be expected to exhibit increasingly blurred correlations; therefore, it is remarkable that the properties of less obviously related enzymes catalyzing aldolase-type reactions usually appear similar to the properties of one or the other FDP aldolase class.

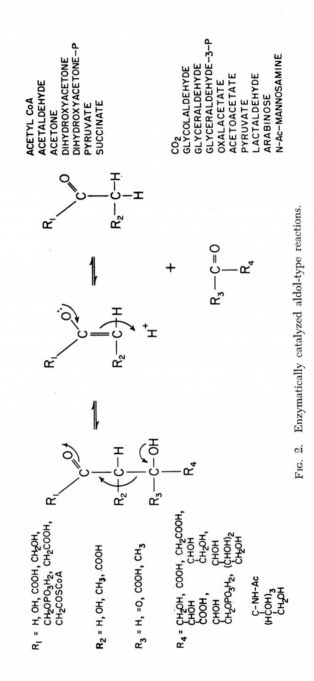

FIG. 2.   Enzymatically catalyzed aldol-type reactions.

TABLE III

ENZYMES CATALYZING ALDOL-TYPE REACTIONS:
POSSIBLE ANALOGOUS FAMILIES

| I<br>"Lysine aldolases" | II<br>"Metallo aldolases" |
|---|---|
| Fructose-1,6-diphosphate (A, B) | Fructose-1,6-diphosphate |
| 2-Keto-3-deoxy-6-phosphogluconate (15) | Fuculose-1-phosphate (13) |
| Deoxyribose-5-phosphate (34, 15) | 2-Keto-3-deoxyglucarate (6) |
| (N-Acylneuraminic acid) (9, 7) | |
| (2-Keto-3-deoxyoctanic acid) (14) | |
| | 2, Keto-4-hydroxy-4-methylglutarate (45) |
| | 2 Keto-4-hydroxyglutarate (29) |
| Citrate condensing enzyme (47) | Isocitrate lyase (10) |
| (Citrate cleavage enzyme) (46) | Citrate lyase (47) |
| | 3-Hydroxy-3-methylglutaryl CoA cleavage enzyme (4) |
| Acetoacetic decarboxylase (53) | Oxalacetic decarboxylase (20) |

Some of the enzymes facilitating aldol cleavage of dicarboxylic acids and their derivatives are divalent metal ion enzymes. The available evidence concerning the properties of isocitric lyase (10) and citric lyase (47) suggests a role of a divalent metal ion in the catalytic process. In contrast, citrate-cleaving (46) and condensing enzymes give no indication of being metalloproteins. For many of these enzymes there is little information available on the nature of the active site, and the placement here is only tentative. Srere suggests (47) that lysine may be involved at the active site of the citrate-condensing enzyme because acylation probably at specific lysine residues causes severe loss of catalytic activity. Preliminary attempts to produce a stabile inactive form of this enzyme by reducing in the presence of both substrates with sodium borohydride have given ambiguous results. Because of the complexity of the reaction catalyzed by the condensing enzyme, it might be expected that the catalytic site would differ considerably from the other enzymes in this family of aldolases.

Similarity with the two classes of aldolases may be found in the β-keto decarboxylases. There is good evidence suggesting that the mechanism of action of oxalacetate decarboxylase involves a metal ion complex with the substrate (20, 48, 26). It has also been known for some time, however, that acetoacetic decarboxylase is not a metalloprotein (17). Recently, Westheimer and Fridovich (53) have implicated lysine in the reaction mechanism by the sodium borohydride reduction technique. Presumably in this case, too, lysine may form a Schiff base intermediate with the substrate during the reaction sequence.

It is thus conceivable, though certainly not yet established, that two basic catalytic sites may be utilized in most enzymes which facilitate aldol-type reactions in biological systems and that these represent two homologous families of enzymes.

The possibility that there are a finite number of "active configurations" and that these have been reached by "convergent evolution" should not be dismissed. It would perhaps be possible to distinguish between these alternatives by a more comprehensive study of other molecular properties —over-all amino acid sequence, subunit structure, etc.

## Other Analogous and Homologous Relationships

Previous comparative analyses of functionally similar proteins have indicated strong conservation of structure and catalytic properties in intraspecies variants (2). The remarkable similarity in the amino acid sequence of cytochrome c from yeast to mammalian species (30) demonstrates the degree of homology which may occur in phylogeny. The finding by Allison and Kaplan (1) of immunological cross-reactivity between triosephosphate dehydrogenases as widely divergent as yeast and lobster, together with the demonstration by Perham and Harris (33) of congruity in the amino acid sequence of a cysteine peptide present at the active site, indicates strong conservation of structure of this enzyme throughout the phylogenetic scale. Considerably greater disparity was found in the structure of cysteine peptides obtained from yeast and horse alcohol dehydrogenases (18).

The evidence for distinct classes of fructose diphosphate aldolase raises the question whether this is an isolated phenomenon. The available evidence suggests there may be other examples of "analogous" enzyme variants. Hartley has proposed (19) four distinctive classes of "proteinases," based on mechanism of action: (a) serine proteinases, (b) thiol proteinases, (c) acid proteinases, and (d) metal proteinases. A good case for homology of "serine" proteinases can already be made from available molecular and catalytic properties. Trypsinogen and chymotrypsinogen have been recognized as homologous proteins (52). The possibility of analogous forms of carbamyl phosphate synthetase and diphosphoglycerate mutase has already been discussed (40). The concept that many enzymes catalyzing essentially similar reactions may do so by similar catalytic mechanisms was emphasized by the discovery that both peptidases and esterases are inhibited by diisopropyl fluorophosphonate and contain a similar serine peptide at the active site. The major question remains whether these enzyme families are homologous in the evolutionary sense. Besides the present suggestions on the two classes of aldolase, evidence of homology among the dehydrogenases has been presented by Harris (18) and by Kaplan (25). It seems possible that the large number of enzymes present in biological systems may have evolved by "adaptation" of a small number of primitive gene systems.

The recognizable conservation of molecular properties in a given series suggests that a comprehensive analysis of structure of proteins may provide a basis for the development of a coherent, if not compelling, model of evolutionary relationships.

### Acknowledgments

The experimental work described in this paper was supported in part by U.S. Public Health Service Grant H 1250. It is a pleasure to acknowledge the collaboration of O. C. Richards, W. E. Groves, R. E. Blostein, B. M. Woodfin, T. Rajkumar, and J. Hunsley on various aspects of this problem.

### References

1. ALLISON, W. S., AND KAPLAN, N. O., *J. Biol. Chem.*, **239**, 2140 (1964).
2. ANFINSEN, C., "The Molecular Basis of Evolution," Wiley, New York, 1960.
3. APPELLA, E., AND MARKERT, C. L., *Biochem. Biophys. Res. Commun.*, **6**, 171 (1961).

4. BACHAWAT, B. K., ROBINSON, W. G., AND COON, M. J., *J. Biol. Chem.*, **216**, 727 (1955).
5. BLOSTEIN, R. E., AND RUTTER, W. J., *J. Biol. Chem.*, **238**, 3280 (1963).
6. BLUMENTHAL, H. J., AND FISH, D. C., *Biochem. Biophys. Res. Commun.*, **11**, 239 (1963).
7. BRUNETTI, P., JOURDIAN, G. W., AND ROSEMAN, S., *J. Biol. Chem.*, **237**, 2447 (1962).
8. CAHN, R. D., KAPLAN, N. O., LEVINE, L., AND ZWILLING, E., *Science*, **136**, 1 (1962).
9. COMB, D. G., AND ROSEMAN, S., *J. Biol. Chem.*, **235**, 2529 (1960).
10. DARON, HARLOW, Ph.D. Dissertation, University of Illinois, 1961.
11. DEAL, W. C., RUTTER, W. J., AND VAN HOLDE, K. E., *Biochemistry*, **2**, 246 (1963).
12. DRECHSLER, E. R., BOYER, P. D., AND KOWALSKY, A. G., *J. Biol. Chem.*, **234**, 2627 (1959).
13. GHALAMBOR, M. A., AND HEATH, E. C., *J. Biol. Chem.*, **237**, 2427 (1942).
14. GHALAMBOR, M. A., AND HEATH, E. C., *Biochem. Biophys. Res. Commun.*, **11**, 288 (1963).
15. GRAZI, E., MELOCHE, H., MARTINEZ, G., WOOD, W. A., AND HORECKER, B. L., *Biochem. Biophys. Res. Commun.*, **10**, 4 (1963).
16. GROVES, W. E., Ph.D. Dissertation, University of Illinois, 1962.
17. HAMILTON, G. A., AND WESTHEIMER, F. H., *J. Am. Chem. Soc.*, **81**, 2277 (1959).
18. HARRIS, I., *Nature*, **203**, 30 (1964).
19. HARTLEY, B. S., *Ann. Rev. Biochem.*, **29**, 45 (1960).
20. HERBERT, D., *Symp. Soc. Exptl. Biol.*, **5**, 52 (1951).
21. HORECKER, B. L., ROWLEY, P. T., GRAZI, E., CHENG T., AND TCHOLA, O., *Biochem. Z.*, **338**, 36 (1963).
22. INGRAM, V. M., *Nature*, **189**, 704 (1961).
23. INGRAM, V. M., "The Hemoglobins in Genetics and Evolution," Columbia Univ. Press, New York, 1963.
24. JAGANMATHAN, V., SINGH, K., AND DAMODARAN, M., *Biochem. J.*, **63**, 94 (1956).
25. KAPLAN, N. O., this volume.
26. KORNBERG, A., OCHOA, S., AND MEHLER, A. H., *J. Biol. Chem.*, **174**, 159 (1948).
27. KOWALSKY, A. G., AND BOYER, P. D., *J. Biol. Chem.*, **235**, 604 (1960).
28. LEVENBOOK, L., AND SHIGEMATSU, H., LEVENBOOK, L., AND RUTTER, W. J., unpublished observations.
29. MAITRA, A., AND DEKKER, E., *J. Biol. Chem.*, **239**, 1485 (1964).
30. MARGOLIASH, E., AND SMITH, E. L., this volume.
31. MARKERT, C. L., *Science*, **140**, 1329 (1963).
32. NIRENBERG, M., AND LEDER, P., *Science*, **145**, 1399 (1964).
33. PERHAM, R. N., AND HARRIS, J. I., *J. Mol. Biol.*, **7**, 316 (1963).
34. PRICER, W. E., JR., AND HORECHER, B. L., *J. Biol. Chem.*, **235**, 1292 (1960).
35. RAJKUMAR, T., CLARK, W., AND RUTTER, W. J., unpublished observation.
36. RICHARDS, O. C., AND RUTTER, W. J., *J. Biol. Chem.*, **236**, 3185 (1961).
37. RUSSELL, G. K., AND GIBBS, M., *AIBS Abstr.*, Boulder, Colorado, 1964.
38. RUTTER, W. J., WOODFIN, B. M., AND BLOSTEIN, R. E., *Acta Chem. Scand.*, **17**, 226 (1963).
39. RUTTER, W. J., BLOSTEIN, R. E., WOODFIN, B. M., AND WEBER, C. S., *in* "Advances in Enzyme Regulation" (G. Weber, ed.), p. 39, Macmillan (Pergamon), New York, 1963.

40. RUTTER, W. J., *Federation Proc.*, **23**, 1248 (1964).
41. RUTTER, W. J., *Abstr., 6th Intern. Congr. Biochem., Vol.* VI, 487 (1964).
42. RUTTER, W. J., AND GROVES, W. E., *in* "Taxonomic Biochemistry, Physiology and Serology," (C. A. Leone, ed.), p. 417, Ronald Press, New York, 1964.
43. RUTTER, W. J., AND HUNSLEY, J., unpublished observations.
44. RUTTER, W. J., unpublished observations.
45. SHANNON, L. M., AND MARCUS, A., *J. Biol. Chem.*, **237**, 3342, 3348 (1962).
46. SRERE, P., *J. Biol. Chem.*, **234**, 2544 (1959).
47. SRERE, P., private communication.
48. STEINBERG, R., AND WESTHEIMER, F. H., *J. Am. Chem. Soc.*, **73**, 429 (1951).
49. STELLWAGEN, E., AND SCHACHMAN, H. K., *Biochemistry*, **1**, 1056 (1962).
50. STUMPF, P. K., *J. Biol. Chem.*, **176**, 223 (1948).
51. VOGEL, H. J., BRYSON, V., AND LAMPEN, J. O. (eds.), "Informational Macromolecules," The Genetic Code, Part IV, VII, pp. 175-239, 435-499, Academic Press, New York, 1963.
52. WALSH, K. A., AND NEURATH, H., *Proc. Natl. Acad. Sci. U.S.*, **52**, 884 (1964).
53. WESTHEIMER, F. A., AND FRIDOVICH, I., *J. Am. Chem. Soc.*, **84**, 3209 (1962).
54. ZUCKERKANDL, E., AND PAULING, L., *in* "Horizons in Biochemistry" (M. Kasha and B. Pullman, eds.), p. 189, Academic Press, New York, 1962.

# Discussion of Part IV

E. L. SMITH, E. MAYR, P. SIEKEVITZ, T. H. JUKES,
N. O. KAPLAN, E. L. TATUM

CHAIRMAN SMITH: I will now call for a discussion.

DR. MAYR: The discussion this afternoon was most heartwarming to a taxonomist when he is told that he can give comfort to the biochemist. Just think of the horseshoe crab!

Unfortunately, I can also bring up all sorts of things that might destroy this confidence. In a phylogeny of the reptiles—and I might say that phylogenetically the birds are just one of the branches of the reptiles —you find that birds and crocodiles are just two twigs of a single branch, while the turtles branched off at least 50 or 100 million years earlier and are on quite a different branch from birds and crocodilians.

Again, one must emphasize that branching is only one of the two phylogenetic events. Amount of phylogenetic change is equally, or in many cases, more important.

I would like to make two short comments on the paper of Dr. Margoliash. I think we are agreed on two things. One is that the earlier two lines separate from each other, the greater the probability of residue replacement.

The second one is that most likely the replacement of residues must have been controlled by natural selection, even though we do not yet know the function of most residues.

Let us now look a little more closely at some of the values (number of residue replacements). We find, that within a group of related forms, these values do not necessarily parallel degree of relationship. Man and horse differ by 12 replacements. Man and kangaroo—and everybody agrees that the marsupials are much more distantly related to man than are the perissodactyls—differ by only eight.

Pig, sheep, and cow seem to have the same cytochrome structure, even though the pig, in spite of being an artiodactyl, is only rather distantly related to sheep and cow.

Thus, the generalization that residue replacement parallels phylogeny is true only in a very loose way. Let us not claim too much for it. Particularly, let us not read this correlation backward and say that "as proved by the amino acid replacements," man and horse are more distantly related than man and kangaroo. Single-character classifications never work.

I want to emphasize one other very important point. In some of the statements, it was implied, although I am sure this was not meant, that every 7 million years or every 11 million years we have one mutation occurring in this or that enzyme.

Actually, what we have is a replacement. Considering that most of these species have millions of individuals, and that about 40 million years, let us say, are available for the pig-cow difference to develop, the DNA programming the residues must have produced literally millions of mutations. The few that are incorporated are those which selection let go through.

It is very important to remember this because, with mutations undoubtedly happening all the time at the DNA sites responsible for all the residues, the fact that pig, sheep, and cow are completely uniform indicates that all the residues for which no functional significance has so far been found must have a tremendous selective value. Only a steady, tremendous selection pressure could have kept them the same in all these independent phyletic lines. Otherwise, each of the species would have evolved its own species-specific cytochrome *c*.

DR. SIEKEVITZ: I would like to comment on what was said with regard to that amino acid sequence in cytochrome *c* which is invariant. I think one other explanation is that we tend to forget that cytochrome *c* only has a function when it is part of a lipoprotein matrix in the mitochondria. It has to be attached to specific sites in the mitochondria, and it could be that this particular sequence "means" mitochondria. Perhaps this sequence signifies that the mitochondrial site had not changed for millions of years.

It might be good to look at some mitochondria from cells, such as the ameba or paramecium, in which you have a different internal structure of mitochondria. You might have a different sequence in this region of cytochrome *c*.

DR. JUKES: Drs. Margoliash and Smith have presented a fascinating series of results showing that the similarities and differences in the cytochrome *c* isolated from a wide variety of living species may be interpreted as being due to a series of base changes in the corresponding structural genes that have taken place more or less steadily during hundreds of millions of years. As a result, there will be a divergence between different living species in the primary structure of their cytochromes *c*, and the divergence will increase with time. The divergence is expressed in amino acid differences scattered through the length of the cytochrome *c* molecule which reflect single-base changes in the corresponding structural genes. The amino acid changes will at first correspond to single-base changes in the coding triplets because they will be widely scattered. However, as time goes on, some of the triplets will receive more than one "hit," so that amino acid changes corresponding to the alteration of two bases in a coding triplet will be seen when the amino acid sequences are compared. In this postulation, we have assumed that the mutational events in the base sequence of the gene occur in a random distribution, and that natural selection eliminates the mutations that give rise to biochemically defective phenotypes. The amino acid substitutions were examined in the light of the triplet assignments in the accompanying table for the amino acid code. These are based on a previous summary [T. H. Jukes, *Biochem. Biophys. Res. Comm.*, **10**, 155 (1963)] but are rearranged to correspond to the recent findings that GUU is a code for valine, UGU for cysteine, and UUG for leucine [P. Leder and M. W. Nirenberg, *Proc. Natl. Acad. Sci. U.S.*, **52**, 420 and 1521 (1964); F. Cramer, H. Küntzel, and J. H. Matthaei, *Angew. Chemie*, **76**, 716 (1964)]. These findings make it necessary to replace the base in the first position that was previously assigned to the third position in all codes [T. H. Jukes, *Biochem. Biophys. Res. Comm.*, **10**, 155 (1963)].

POSSIBLE BASE SEQUENCES IN THE AMINO ACID CODE
( Derived from GUU = val, UUG = leu, UGU = cys, and linked mutations )

| Ala | GCA, GCC, GCU | Leu | UUA, UUG, CUC, CUU |
|-----|---------------|-----|--------------------|
| Arg | AGA, CGC, CGU | Lys | AAA |
| AsN | AAC | Met | AUG |
| Asp | AGC, AGU | Phe | UUC, UUU |
| Cys | UGU | Pro | CCA, CCC, CCU |
| GlN | CAA, CUA, AGG | Ser | GAC, UCC, UCU |
| Glu | GAA, GAU | Thr | ACA, ACC |
| Gly | GGA, GGC, GGU | Try | UGG |
| His | CAC, CAU | Tyr | UAC, UAU |
| Ilu | AUA, AUU | Val | GUU |

When tuna cytochrome *c* is compared with the "warm-blooded" cytochromes *c* (human, horse, chicken), there is an average of 85 unchanged amino acid sites. There is an average of 11 substitutions that represent single-base changes and 8 that correspond to changes of two or more bases in the coding triplets. When yeast cytochrome *c* is compared with the vertebrate cytochromes *c*, the corresponding figures are 64 unchanged sites, 23 single-base changes and 16 changes of two or more bases. The comparatively high incidence of changes involving two or more bases leads to the statistical conclusion that only about 60 to 65 of the 104 sites in the cytochrome *c* chain are subject to mutational changes that enable the molecule to "survive."

Margoliash and Smith have reported that seven different amino acids can occupy residue 89 in various cytochromes *c*. If a code of AAC is assigned to asparagine, 5 of the 7 amino acids that occupy this locus in various species may be represented as being interrelated by transitional (purine/purine and pyrimidine/pyrimidine) single-base changes. Several of the interrelationships are concordant with mutations in various proteins as follows: asN/ser, asN/asp, asp/gly, and glu/gly. The sixth and seventh amino acid at site 89 are lys and thr; in terms of the accompanying table, it is necessary to postulate pu/py interchanges to relate lys and thr to any of the other amino acids at this locus, such as AAC/ACC, asN/thr, and AAC/AAA, asN/lys. The seven different amino acids at residue 89 may therefore represent a total of only five base interchanges in the coding triplet for this locus; A $\rightleftharpoons$ G in the first base of the triplet, C $\rightleftharpoons$ A $\rightleftharpoons$ G in the second base, and A $\rightleftharpoons$ C $\rightleftharpoons$ U (T) in the third.

(Dr. Margoliash kindly furnished a copy of the manuscript by himself and Dr. Smith after the meeting, thus enabling me to expand my comments.)

DR. KAPLAN: I would like to make a comment about the immunological method; when you go from the chicken to the reptiles that is quite a distance. It is hard to tell smaller differences within the reptiles with an antibody prepared against a chicken enzyme.

If you want to see differences between the caiman and the turtle, you make an antibody to the caiman and then you can see the differences from the turtle. In other words, the absolute numbers don't mean as much the further away you get from the chicken.

CHAIRMAN SMITH: I would like to make a very strong point, as co-author of one of the papers presented, that I don't think this is a very good way to do taxonomy. Taxonomy has all been done. What we are looking at are individual proteins.

I think the greater significance to this is to help us in the structure-function correlations. This is the important aspect of it. If you examine some of the cytochrome data in detail, it is utter nonsense from a biological standpoint. For example, the mammal which is closest to the rattlesnake in amino acid sequence is man. You can draw your own conclusions from this. But this is biological nonsense from a taxonomic standpoint.

There is one region, for example, which is identical in human and rattlesnake, and no other cytochrome even resembles this. Clearly, this is accidental and has nothing to do with evolution or taxonomy whatsoever. These are random events. They are compatible with some selection pressure in terms of the whole mitochondrial complex.

I don't disagree with Dr. Siekevitz. I think what we are groping for is to learn something of the significance of protein structure, really. The evolutionary consequences of this tell us what we have already known about evolution—in fact, when they tell us anything at all.

DR. TATUM: I can't resist making one point. which may or may not have some validity. In all the explanations and suggestions as to the role of mutation and selection in maintenance of active sites and other properties of enzymes, I haven't heard yet—although perhaps it will come up in relation to tomorrow's discussion—any suggestions that selection may not always operate at the level of the protein itself but might operate at the level of nucleic acid.

If there are genic hot spots, there must be cold spots. There may be structural regions in the gene itself which cannot be varied without upsetting the replication or some other essential functional process.

I just want to raise this point because I think without this our considerations on evolution, selection, and survival of proteins and enzymes are somewhat incomplete.

CHAIRMAN SMITH: Some evidence may be presented on this subject tomorrow.

PART V

# EVOLUTION OF PROTEINS III

# Chairman's Remarks

PHILIP H. ABELSON

*Geophysical Laboratory,*
*Carnegie Institution of Washington,*
*Washington, D.C.*

I will use the five minutes for Chairman's Remarks to tell of some work that Dr. Ed Hare and I have been doing on the proteins of molluscan shells. The molluscs are represented by 80,000 species. Among them are a number of so-called living fossils, which extant today are evidently not much changed from ancestors of 500,000,000 years ago. Abundant shells of past living forms have given rise to an excellent fossil record. Also included among the molluscs are highly evolved forms, some of which are changing even today. Virtually all the species secrete shells consisting principally of calcium carbonate. The mineral crystals of the shells are bonded by layers of protein.

Dr. Hare and I have studied the amino acid content of shells from about 100 different species and find that the proteins of closely related species are similar in composition (Chart A). These chromatograms from

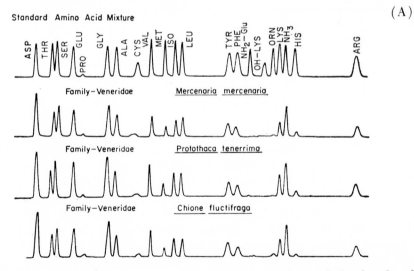

(A)

the amino acid analyzer were prepared from members of the family of Veneridae (clams). You can note that there is a close relationship in the proportion of the various amino acids in shells of this family.

If we examine shells of various families among the bivalves, some remarkable differences can be seen (Chart B). The variation in the ratio of the glycine to alanine is significant as are the differences among methionine, isoleucine, and leucine, from the various species. We have noted that relative amino acid contents can vary by factors as much as 10.

While we have observed these large differences, for instance, among the bivalves, we have also observed some great similarities among certain species of different classes of molluscs. Students of molluscs have long

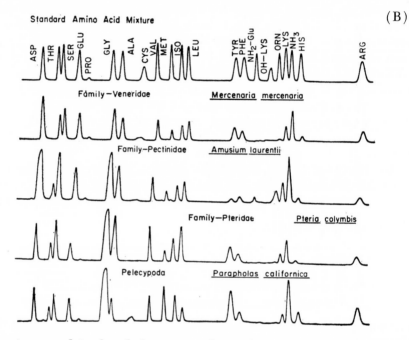

been interested in the phylogenetic relationships among the classes and families. From an examination of the soft parts, and embryological studies some families can be classified as primitive; indeed, shells similar to those of present day forms may be found early in the fossil record.

On the basis of this comparative anatomy and paleontological evidence, many authorities have leaned to the suggestion that all molluscs descended from a common ancestor. Accordingly, it was interesting to compare proteins and amino acids in a series of representatives of very old families. In Chart C are shown chromatograms of proteins from descendants of these ancient forms.

At the top of the figure is a chromatogram from shell protein of an archeogastropod, a very ancient snail *Perotrocus* which is comparatively unchanged from 500,000,000 years ago. The second chart from the top is from *Astrea*, another archeogastropod. The middle charts are derived from two primitive pelecypods. At the bottom is a chromatogram from *Nautilus pompilius*.

It can be seen that differences among these ancient forms are compara-tively small especially in the light of differences, for example, among those bivalves shown in Chart B.

From both the paleontological evidence and evidence obtained from studies of the proteins in shells, we are led to believe that evolution is not inevitable, that proteins having the same function can remain

Archeogastropoda (C)

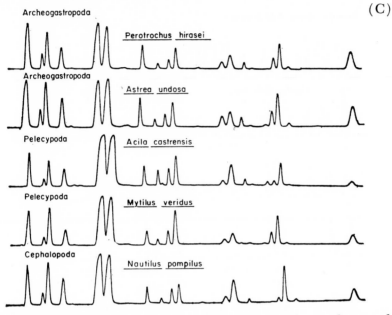

unchanged for long periods of time. On the other hand, we also see that proteins having the same function can change very rapidly; thus it seems unrealistic to try to base a time scale on rates of change in some proteins.

Here is another example in which a phylogeny, based solely on proteins of the shell, would lead one to believe that some of the old cephalopods and gastropods are closely related, while suggesting that some of the clams are more distantly related. Few zoologists would accept such a view and I would not wish to urge it.

We can now proceed with the first paper of the morning. I note the authors listed are D. M. Bonner, J. A. DeMoss, and S. E. Mills.

This has been a very stimulating symposium, but I am sure that virtually all of you would have enjoyed it more if Dave Bonner had been alive and here. Few biologists have enjoyed as much esteem or had more friends than Dave Bonner. His courage, his cheerfulness, his imagination, and his constructive attitude struck a warm response in all.

# The Evolution of an Enzyme

David M. Bonner,[1] J. A. DeMoss, and Stanley E. Mills

Biology Department, University of California, La Jolla, California

As an extension of Darwin's theory that the species have a common origin, the concept of biochemical unity has gradually evolved. It has become clear that superimposed on this common biochemical organization is a diversity at the molecular level. Thus, the results of comparative studies on the primary structure of specific proteins from various sources have provided the raw material for speculations on the nature of the variations which have occurred at the biochemical level during evolution (2). Such speculations usually invoke the notion that mutations, leading to alterations in the specificity or in the stability of proteins, are preserved or eliminated by natural selective forces. This notion is based on our knowledge from studies on gene–enzyme relationships that mutations can lead to alteration of substrate affinities, of thermolability, of sensitivity to metal ions, and of antigenic structure of specific proteins or enzymes.

Studies with the tryptophan synthetase system of *Escherichia coli* and *Neurospora crassa* have been particularly fruitful in establishing the types of alterations which may occur in the properties of a protein as a result of mutation (23, 3), and the alterations have been correlated directly with changes in the primary structure of the protein in certain cases (11, 13). The extensive studies carried out on the tryptophan synthetases from these two organisms, in addition to establishing numerous similarities, have uncovered some unexpected differences in the physical properties and gene–enzyme relationships in these systems and pose some interesting questions regarding the origin of these diverse properties.

The most striking differences between the tryptophan synthetase systems of *E. coli* and *N. crassa* are the number of genetic and protein components involved in the expression of this enzyme activity. As shown by the studies of Yanofsky and his colleagues, tryptophan synthetase in *E. coli* is composed of two distinct protein components, each being the product of a distinct cistron. These components, designated A and B, have molecular weights of 29,500 (12) and 117,000 (22),

---

[1] Deceased.

respectively. In contrast, the tryptophan synthetase from *N. crassa* is controlled by a single genetic locus (20, 16). This enzyme has a molecular weight of 110,000 (7) and has resisted all attempts to separate it into distinct protein components.

It was surprising to find that two such drastically different systems are responsible for the same biochemical functions. A number of interesting questions were posed by these observations. How related are the two enzyme systems with respect to the details of the reaction they catalyze? How different are the active catalytic centers of these proteins and the mechanisms of the reactions catalyzed therein? Have these two gene–enzyme systems evolved independently? Or do they represent two stages in a series of events which have altered this gene–enzyme system during evolution? What are the advantages or disadvantages of these systems which might have led to their preservation or elimination during evolution of the two organisms? While none of these questions can be answered at the present time, a consideration of the results of biochemical, genetic, and immunochemical studies carried out an these two systems provides some clues and even more areas for speculation.

When the biochemical properties of the tryptophan synthetases from *E. coli* and *N. crassa* are examined, it becomes clear that their active catalytic centers must be very similar. Both catalyze the three reactions illustrated in Fig. 1. The relative rates at which these reactions are catalyzed are remarkably similar (Table I) when the active A–B complex of *E. coli* is compared to the *N. crassa* enzyme.

When the A and B components of the *E. coli* system are separated, neither is capable of catalyzing reaction 1, and the rates of reactions 2 and 3 are severely reduced (24). However, component A retains the ability to catalyze reaction 3, and component B retains the ability to catalyze reaction 2, each to a very limited extent. As suggested by these findings, each component possesses a distinct indole binding site (10), one specific for reaction 3 in component A, and one specific for reaction 2 in component B. The association of A and B then activates the reaction catalyzed by each of the separated components and creates an active catalytic site for reaction 1. The active centers of the two compounds are apparently organized in a very specific manner in the complex, since InGP is converted to tryptophan without free indole participating as an intermediate (4).

Our detailed biochemical analysis of the component reactions (5) has demonstrated the following properties for the *N. crassa* enzyme: (a) Two distinct indole binding sites are present, one specific for reaction 3 and one specific for reaction 2. (b) Reactions 2 and 3 exhibit

an interdependence which suggests that, while each reaction is catalyzed at a distinct site, the two sites are organized so that some interaction between them occurs. (c) Although reactions 2 and 3 each
appear to be catalyzed by distinct sites, InGP is converted to tryptophan
in reaction 1 without the free indole participating as an obligatory intermediate. Thus, the active catalytic sites of the *E. coli* and *N. crassa*

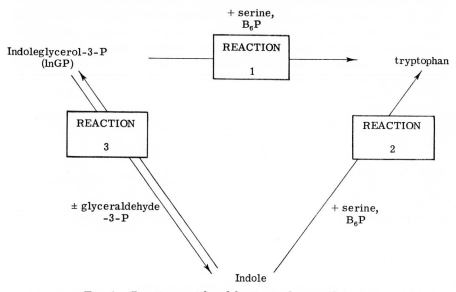

Fig. 1.   Reactions catalyzed by tryptophan synthetase.

TABLE I
Relative Rates of Reactions[a] Catalyzed by Tryptophan Synthetase

| Organism | | Reaction 1 (InGP → T) | Reaction 2 (Ind → T) | Reaction 3 (InGP ⇄ Ind) |
|---|---|---|---|---|
| *Escherichia coli*[b] | A + excess B | 1.0 | 2.2 | 0.07 |
| | B + excess A | 1.0 | 2.2 | 0.07 |
| *Neurospora crassa*[c] | | 1.0 | 2.2 | 0.02 |

[a] The rate of reaction 1 is arbitrarily adjusted to 1.0, and the other activities are
calculated on that basis.
[b] Yanofsky (23).
[c] DeMoss (5).

enzymes are very similar in that each appears to be composed of two
distinct catalytic components which interact to catalyze the three
reactions at their maximum rate.

Are the enzymes from these two sources functionally identical except
that the *E. coli* enzyme is dissociable while the *N. crassa* enzyme is not?

An analysis of the types of functional alteration which can result from mutation in each system has provided us with some insight into the relationship between these two systems. Yanofsky and his colleagues have clearly demonstrated that the A and B components of the *E. coli* system are coded by independent but adjacent cistrons (23). Point mutations in either cistron alter only the product of that cistron, leaving the other component unaltered and capable of catalyzing its partial reaction. The partial activity retained in such mutants, i.e., reaction 2 in altered A mutants and reaction 3 in altered B mutants, is usually of considerable magnitude, since the unaltered component which remains will catalyze its partial reaction at essentially wild-type rates, when it is associated with the altered component (23).

TABLE II

EFFECTS OF GENETIC ALTERATION ON TRYPTOPHAN SYNTHETASE OF *N. crassa*

| | Enzyme activity | | | |
|---|---|---|---|---|
| Immunochemical cross-reaction | Reaction 1 (InGP → T) | Reaction 2 (Ind → T) | Reaction 3 (InGP → Ind) | Type designation |
| CRM+ (neutralizing) | 0 | + | 0 | Indole utilizers (A) |
| | 0 | 0 | + | Indole accumulators (B) |
| | 0 | 0 | 0 | Profound (C) |
| CRM− (neutralizing) | 0 | 0 | 0 | (D) |

In Table II, the mutant types which have been characterized in *N. crassa* are presented (3, 14). All the mutants have in common the inability to catalyze reaction 1. The mutants can be separated into two groups (CRM+ and CRM−) according to their ability to neutralize antibodies which specifically inhibit the wild-type enzyme activity. Among those mutants which are CRM+, mutant groups analogous to those obtained in *E. coli* are obvious. One group (A class) retains the ability to catalyze reaction 2 (analogous to an A mutant of *E. coli*), and another (B class) retains the ability to catalyze reaction 3 (analogous to a B mutant of *E. coli*). In addition, a third class of mutants is found among the CRM+ mutants, the profound class. These mutants, although possessing gene products which react with neutralizing antibodies directed against tryptophan synthetase, are not able to catalyze any of the three reactions. This group is important, since a similar type of mutant has not been found in *E. coli*. Mapping of these mutants by recombination analysis (20, 16, 15) has revealed a very interesting distribution of the mutations within the *td* locus (Fig. 2). Specific mutants are identified only by their phenotype designation, and the distribution determined by prototroph frequency is drawn approximately to scale (14). The most striking feature of this map is the clustering of the various CRM+ mutants. Type A and B mutants fall into two distinct regions of the map, and the profound mutants (type C) map in a restricted region between the A and B types. The CRM⁻ mutants, many of them point mutations, are distributed randomly throughout the map and are devoid of all three reactions. Thus, no part of the locus possesses the autonomy exhibited by the A and B genes of E. coli. From these observations, the td locus of N. crassa can be interpreted as consisting of two functional regions which are analogous to the A and

FIG. 2. The distribution of mutant types in the td locus of N. crassa, drawn approximately to scale. For the letter designations, see Table II.

B cistrons of E. coli. These regions would appear to be divided by a small region (region C) in which mutations may alter functionally both the A and B regions.

Following the success in preparing essentially pure tryptophan synthetase from N. crassa, Kaplan et al. (14) have been able to carry out a detailed immunochemical study on the gene products of CRM⁻ mutants. Through the use of antiserum prepared against the purified enzyme and the quantitative complement fixation technique, they have demonstrated that most of the CRM⁻ mutants form td-gene products which cross-react with the nonneutralizing fraction of the antiserum. Of greatest interest here is the fact that they were able to detect an apparent regional autonomy in the polypeptide chain by this analysis. The antiserum, prepared against tryptophan synthetase purified from mutant td 141, gives the standard complement fixation curve illustrated in Fig. 3 with either the purified or the crude enzyme from td 141 or with the crude enzyme from the wild-type strain. The amount of enzyme in each case is calculated from the specific activity of tryptophan synthetase in the preparation and the specific activity of the purified preparation. Several basic features have been demonstrated for this system: (a) The system behaves as a single antigen–antibody system on the basis of several immunochemical criteria. (b) The enzyme purified from td 141 is identical, immunochemically, to the wild-type (strain 74A) enzyme. (c) Crude extracts of two of the ten CRM⁻ strains examined exhibit no detectable cross-reaction, demonstrating that the complement fixation being observed is specific to the gene products of the *td* locus.

Of the ten CRM⁻ strains examined, eight exhibit cross-reaction in the complement fixation test, but none are identical to wild type (Fig. 4). In contrast to the standard system, peak fixation of complement is reduced, and the shape of the fixation curve varies significantly. The most exciting feature of these results is the fact that the nature of the fixation curve is dependent on the location of the mutants in the genetic map. Thus, CRM⁻ mutants located in the far left-hand region

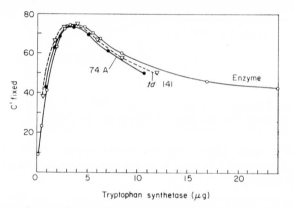

Fig. 3. Complement fixation curves for the purified enzyme and crude extracts of strains *td* 141 and 74A run against anti-tryptophan synthetase (14). The number of units of complement fixed (C') are plotted against the amount of enzyme in micrograms.

of the genetic map in Table II exhibit curves which are similar to each other but significantly different from the wild-type system or that of the CRM⁻ mutants located in the right-hand region. The same is true of mutants located in the right-hand region. CRM⁻ mutants located in the center region exhibit curves that possess some of the features of both left-hand and right-hand regions and appear more like the standard systems.

All the CRM⁻ mutants referred to here (except *td* 120) behave as point mutants, both in recombination and in reversion studies (15). It seems likely that the type of change which occurs in the protein products of such mutants, i.e., loss of ability to react with neutralizing antibodies, involves changes in the tertiary structure of the protein. The fact that mutants located at each extreme of the genetic map retain partial, but characteristic, features of the standard system indicates that these regions possess some autonomy in specifying the immunochemical structure of the protein product.

On the basis of these biochemical, genetic, and immunochemical studies, then, we conclude that the tryptophan synthetase systems from *E. coli* and *N. crassa* are very similar. It would appear that, in each case, this enzyme is composed of two autonomous or semiautonomous regions which interact to produce an active enzyme (Fig. 5). The main point of departure between the two systems would appear to be that in *N. crassa* these two regions are linked in a single polypeptide chain

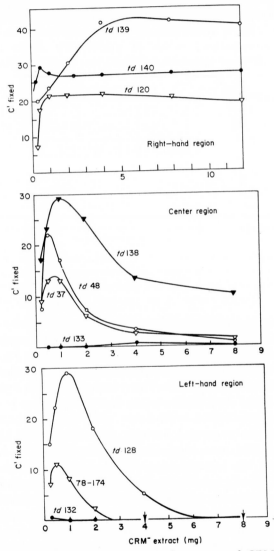

Fig. 4.   Complement fixation curves for crude extracts of CRM⁻ mutants run against anti-tryptophan synthetase (14). The region designations refer to the relative location of the mutants in the scale genetic map shown in Fig. 2.

and under the control of a single genetic locus. Lesions in the area of linkage account for the profound mutant class which is specific to the *N. crassa* system.

From the numerous similarities we feel that these forms represent two different stages in a series of alterations which have occurred in this gene–enzyme system during the course of evolution. Can we marshal any information which would add weight to such an argument? Studies on the properties of tryptophan synthetases from various other organisms (17, 18; E. Balbinder, personal communication; K. Sakaguchi, personal communication), while in preliminary stages in most cases, provide us with some interesting information in this regard (Table III).

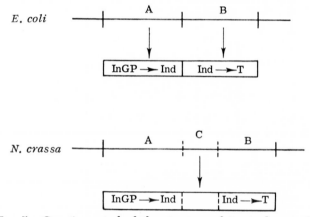

FIG. 5.   Genetic control of the structure of tryptophan synthetase.

The tryptophan synthetase from yeast is controlled by a single genetic locus, and the enzyme appears to be a single component in preliminary purification steps. Moreover, the enzyme is inhibited by antiserum prepared against *Neurospora* tryptophan synthetase (T. Manney, personal communication). The yeast tryptophan synthetase therefore appears to be very similar to the *N. crassa* system.

The other tryptophan synthetases are two-component systems, including those from several bacteria, the blue-green alga, *Anabaena variabilis*, and the green alga, *Chlorella ellipsoidea*.

In addition, the tryptophan synthetases from *Bacillus subtilis, Anabaena,* and *Chlorella* exhibit one feature in common which is not found in the other bacterial tryptophan synthetases. While the association of the A and B components is still essential for reaction 1 activity (InGP → tryptophan) and for maximal activity in reaction 3 (InGP → Ind), the B component in each case exhibits maximal activity in reaction 2 (Ind → tryptophan) by itself.

The pattern of complementation of the A and B components from

## TABLE III

### PROPERTIES OF TRYPTOPHAN SYNTHETASES OF VARIOUS ORGANISMS

| Organism | Number of cistrons | Number of components | Complement with: | | Inhibition of antiserum to: | | Enhancement of component B (Ind → T) by component A |
|---|---|---|---|---|---|---|---|
| | | | coli A | coli B | Salmonella B | N. crassa | |
| Escherichia coli | 2 | 2 | + | + | + + | 0 | + |
| Salmonella typhimurium[a] | 2 | 2 | + + | + + | + + | 0 | + |
| Bacillus subtilis[b] | — | 2 | — | — | — | — | 0 |
| Anabaena variabilis[c] | — | 2 | + + | 0 | + (weak) | 0 | 0 |
| Chlorella ellipsoidea[c] | — | 2 | + | 0 | 0 | + (weak) | 0 |
| Saccharomyces cerevisiae[d] | 1 | 1 | — | — | 0 | + | + |
| Neurospora crassa | 1 | 1 | 0 | 0 | 0 | + | + |

[a] E. Balbinder, unpublished results.
[b] Schwartz and Bonner (18).
[c] K. Sakaguchi, unpublished results.
[d] Manney (17), and personal communication.

*E. coli* with the components from some of the other organisms is also presented in Table III. It is interesting that, while there is very effective complementation between the components of *Salmonella typhimurium* and *E. coli,* only the A component of *E. coli* will complement with *Anabaena* and *Chlorella.* The B component of *E. coli* will not complement with the two algal systems.

To test for possible immunochemical relationships, the pattern of inhibition has been examined by using antisera prepared against either *Salmonella* B component or *Neurospora.* The inhibition of the enzyme from *E. coli* by the *Salmonella* antiserum is to be expected, but it is interesting that the *Anabaena* enzyme is also weakly inhibited by this antiserum. On the other hand, *N. crassa* antiserum inhibits the yeast enzyme and the *Chlorella* enzyme. The inhibition of the *Chlorella* enzyme by the antiserum is very weak but significant. The *Chlorella* system therefore exhibits some relationship to both the *E. coli* and the *N. crassa* systems.

On the basis of the properties of this limited number of organisms, the tryptophan synthetases appear to fall into three general classes, represented in Fig. 6. If these classes are considered to represent various stages of a sequence of change which has occurred during evolution, it seems reasonable that the change would be in the direction of greater interdependence of the two components. One extreme of this sequence would be the complete independence of the two components, as indicated at the top of Fig. 6. It is conceivable that interaction of the chains would lend a stability to the system which would have some selective advantage. Once such an interaction became obligatory, the coordinated control of the formation of the individual components would become important. In the evolution of organisms such as *Neurospora* and yeast where, in general, the genetic loci controlling related biochemical functions are distributed randomly on different chromosomes, the most effective system of coordination would be to combine the two loci into one. This presumably would result finally in the evolution of a single polypeptide system.

While this sequence is not to be taken seriously, several features suggested by it should be emphasized for consideration in any general scheme of biochemical evolution. (a) The interaction of nonidentical polypeptide chains may well play an important role in the expression of enzyme activities in cellular metabolism. (b) The components of such an interaction may be converted to a single genetic unit–single polypeptide system during the course of evolution.

Does our knowledge from other biochemical systems justify the suggestion that these features are of general importance? Our recent investigations into the early stages in tryptophan biosynthesis bear directly on this question. The biochemical steps specifically involved in tryptophan biosynthesis, excluding tryptophan synthetase, are presented schematically in Table IV. In *E. coli*, the work of several investigators (19, 8, 9, 6) has provided tentative evidence that four enzymatic steps are involved in the conversion of chorismic acid to InGP and that these reactions are controlled by four cistrons. On the other

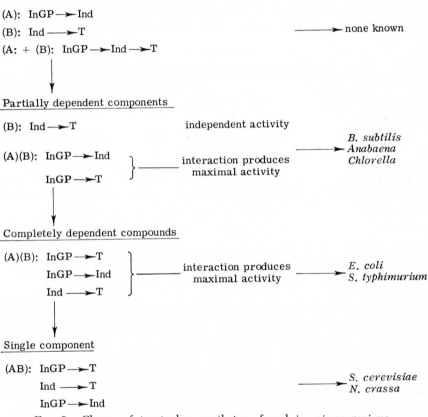

Completely independent components

(A):  InGP ⟶ Ind
(B):  Ind ⟶ T                                                    ⟶ none known
(A: + (B):  InGP ⟶ Ind ⟶ T

Partially dependent components

(B):  Ind ⟶ T                              independent activity

                                                                    *B. subtilis*
(A)(B):  InGP ⟶ Ind      ⎫                                        ⟶ *Anabaena*
                          ⎬── interaction produces                   *Chlorella*
        InGP ⟶ T         ⎭      maximal activity

Completely dependent compounds

(A)(B):  InGP ⟶ T        ⎫
        InGP ⟶ Ind       ⎬── interaction produces    ⟶  *E. coli*
        Ind ⟶ T          ⎭      maximal activity          *S. typhimurium*

Single component

(AB):  InGP ⟶ T
       Ind ⟶ T                                          ⟶ *S. cerevisiae*
       InGP ⟶ Ind                                          *N. crassa*

Fig. 6.   Classes of tryptophan synthetase found in microorganisms.

hand, genetic studies with *N. crassa* have demonstrated that only three genetic loci (*tryp 1, tryp 2, tryp 4*) control the same biochemical steps (1, 21). Our biochemical and genetic analyses of this system (J. Wegman and J. A. DeMoss, unpublished results) have established the following interesting points: (a) Reactions III and IV appear to be catalyzed by a single enzyme. Point mutations at the *tryp 1* locus lead to the loss of both reactions. (b) Point mutations at either the *tryp 1* locus or the *tryp 2* locus result in the loss of reaction I. One possible explanation of these facts was that a molecular complex between the gene products of the *tryp 1* and *tryp 2* loci catalyzes reactions I, III, and IV. Such a complex has now been purified 90-fold from wild-type *N. crassa*, and we have been unable to dissociate it into separate active components by column chromatography, zone centrifugation, or standard fractionation procedures.

The pathway in yeast provides an interesting contrast to both the *E. coli* and *N. crassa* systems. Manney (17) has demonstrated that four genetic loci are involved in the synthesis of InGP. Our biochemical analysis of these mutant classes has demonstrated the following per-

TABLE IV

GENETIC CONTROL OF TRYPTOPHAN BIOSYNTHESIS

| Organism | Number of cistrons | Biochemical reactions | | | |
|---|---|---|---|---|---|
| | | I | II | III | IV |
| *Escherichia coli* | 4 (?) | $CA^a$ ——→ AA ——→ PRA ——→ CDRP ——→ InGP | | | |
| *Saccharomgces cerevisiae* | 4 | tryp 2<br>tryp 3<br>CA ——→ AA | tryp 4<br>——→ PRA | tryp 1<br>——→ CDRP | tryp 3<br>——→ InGP |
| *Neurospora crassa* | 3 | tryp 1<br>tryp 2<br>CA ——→ AA | tryp 4<br>——→ PRA | tryp 1<br>——————————→ InGP<br>(CDRP) | |

$^a$ The following abbreviations are used: CA—chorismic acid; AA—anthranilic acid; PRA—$N$-(5′-phosphoribosyl) anthranilic acid; CDRP—1-($o$-carboxyphenyl-amino)-1-deoxyribulose 5-phosphate; InGP—indole-3-glycerol phosphate.

tinent features: (a) Reactions III and IV clearly are catalyzed by two distinct enzymes under the control of two distinct genetic loci, *tryp 1* and *tryp 3*, respectively. In this regard, the yeast system is analogous to the *E. coli* system. (b) Reaction I is lost as the result of mutation at either the *tryp 2* locus or the *tryp 3* locus. It would thus appear that in yeast a molecular complex between the *tryp 2* gene product and the *tryp 3* gene product catalyzes reactions I and IV.

In *E. coli*, an interaction between distinct loci would not appear to be necessary for reaction I, since mutations which lead to the loss of reaction IV have not been observed to lead to the loss of reactions I or III.

In these three organisms then, the other component enzymes of the tryptophan pathway would appear to involve varying degrees of interaction of the types previously discussed for the tryptophan synthetase system. An analysis of the enzymatic components by gel filtration on

Sephadex G-100 provides a direct demonstration of the varying degree of interaction involved (J. Wegman and J. A. DeMoss, unpublished results). In Fig. 7, the excluded volume of the gel bed is indicated by the vertical dotted line. The interaction of the enzymatic components

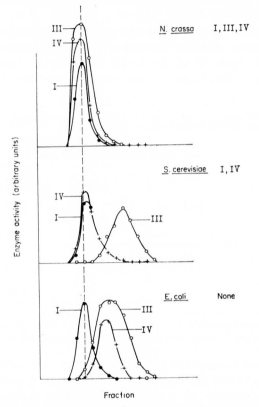

FIG. 7. The characterization of enzymes in the tryptophan pathway by gel filtration on Sephadex G-100. Activities are presented in arbitrary units. Reaction I is the conversion of chorismic acid to anthranilic acid, reaction III is the conversion of PRA to CDRP, and reaction IV is the conversion of CDRP to InGP. In each case, 1 ml of a crude extract prepared in 0.05 $M$ potassium phosphate buffer, pH 7.0, containing $10^{-4}$ $M$ EDTA was passed over a 1 × 22 — cm Sephadex G-100 column and eluted with the same buffer. Fractions of 1 ml were collected and assayed for the individual reaction (J. Wegman and J. A. DeMoss, in preparation).

suggested from the study of mutant classes is represented on the right side of the figure for comparison. In *E. coli*, reactions III and IV are catalyzed by proteins small enough to be retained by the gel, while the protein catalyzing reaction I is excluded by the gel. In yeast, the protein catalyzing reaction IV is large enough to be excluded by the gel, while the protein catalyzing reaction III is retained. In *N. crassa*, all three activities are excluded by the gel. In each case, the size of the component catalyzing each reaction appears to reflect the degree of interaction which was suggested by the studies of the mutant classes.

These results provide a clear indication that the interactions between distinct polypeptide chains are of considerable importance in the expression of enzyme activities. Furthermore, the degree of interaction between catalytic units observed in the tryptophan pathway of these three organisms provides a more sound basis for the argument that such polypeptide interactions, followed by eventual conversion to single polypeptide systems, have played an important role in the evolution of enzymes as we know them today.

## REFERENCES

1. AHMED, M., AND CATCHESIDE, D. G., *Heredity,* **15**, 55 (1960).
2. ANFINSEN, C. B., *The Molecular Basis of Evolution,* Wiley, New York, 1959.
3. BONNER, D. M., SUYAMA, Y., AND DEMOSS, J. A., *Federation Proc.,* **19**, 926 (1960).
4. CRAWFORD, I. P., AND YANOFSKY, C., *Proc. Natl. Acad. Sci. U.S.,* **44**, 1161 (1958).
5. DEMOSS, J. A., *Biochim. Biophys. Acta,* **62**, 279 (1962).
6. DOY, C. H., RIVERA, A., JR., AND SRINIVASAN, P. R., *Biochem. Biophys. Res. Commun.,* **4**, 83 (1961).
7. ENSIGN, S., KAPLAN, S., AND BONNER, D. M., *Biochim. Biophys. Acta,* **81**, 357 (1964).
8. GIBSON, F., AND YANOFSKY, C., *Biochim. Biophys. Acta,* **43**, 489 (1960).
9. GIBSON, M. I., AND GIBSON, F., *Biochem. J.,* **90**, 248 (1964).
10. HATANAKA, M., WHITE, E. A., HORIBATA, K., AND CRAWFORD, I. P., *Arch. Biochem. Biophys.* **97**, 596 (1962).
11. HELINSKI, D. R., AND YANOFSKY, C., *Proc. Natl. Acad. Sci. U.S.,* **48**, 173 (1962).
12. HENNING, U., HELINSKI, D. R., CHAO, F. C., AND YANOFSKY, C., *J. Biol. Chem.,* **237**, 1523 (1962).
13. HENNING, U., AND YANOFSKY, C., *Proc. Natl. Acad. Sci. U.S.,* **48**, 183 (1962).
14. KAPLAN, S., MILLS, S. E., ENSIGN, S., AND BONNER, D. M., *J. Mol. Biol.,* **8**, 801 (1964).
15. KAPLAN, S., SUYAMA, Y., AND BONNER, D. M., *Genet. Res.,* **4**, 470 (1963).
16. KAPLAN, S., SUYAMA, Y., AND BONNER, D. M., *Genetics,* **49**, 145 (1964).
17. MANNEY, T., Ph.D. Dissertation, University of California, Berkeley, 1964.
18. SCHWARTZ, A. K., AND BONNER, D. M., *Biochim. Biophys. Acta,* **89**, 337 (1964).
19. SMITH, O. H., AND YANOFSKY, C., *J. Biol. Chem.,* **235**, 2051 (1960).
20. SUYAMA, Y., LACY, A. M., AND BONNER, D. M., *Genetics,* **49**, 135 (1964).
21. WEGMAN, J., Ph.D. Dissertation, University of California, San Diego, 1964.
22. WILSON, D. A., AND CRAWFORD, I. P., *Bacteriol. Proc.,* p. 92 (1964).
23. YANOFSKY, C., *Bacteriol. Revs.,* **24**, 221 (1960).
24. YANOFSKY, C., HELINSKI, D. R., AND MALING, B., *Cold Spring Harbor Symp. Quant. Biol.,* **26**, 11 (1961).

# Enzyme Catalysis and Color of Light in Bioluminescent Reactions[1]

W. D. McElroy, H. H. Seliger, and M. DeLuca

*Department of Biology and McCollum Pratt Institute,*
*Johns Hopkins University,*
*Baltimore, Maryland*

Studies on the catalytic properties of firefly luciferase have indicated that the differences in the colors of the light emitted from various species are due to differences in the structures of the enzymes. In addition, the effect on the color of the *in vitro* light emission of pH, temperature, and various salts as well as of modifications in the structure of the substrates suggests that the strength and nature of the binding of the transient emitter to the enzyme are important factors in determining the allowed electronic transistions for light emission.

In the present paper we shall review the evidence which indicates that conformational changes in the luciferase not only are important for catalysis but also affect the resonance energy levels of the excited state.

## Catalytic Properties of Firefly Luciferase

Luciferase is defined as an enzyme that catalyzes an oxidative reaction in which one of the products emits light. In all cases which have been examined carefully in cell-free extracts, light emission requires a substrate, called luciferin, and molecular oxygen (3).

### Activation of Luciferin and Dehydroluciferin

The structures of firefly luciferin and dehydroluciferin (13) are shown in Fig. 1. When one starts with free luciferin and luciferase, it is necessary to add ATP and magnesium or manganese ions in order to obtain light emission. In the initial reaction there is an adenyl transfer from ATP to the carboxyl group of luciferin with the elimination of inorganic pyrophosphate. The reaction is analogous to the fatty-acid- and amino-acid-activating reaction (6). The luciferyl-adenylate ($LH_2$-

[1] The work that has been summarized in this paper has been supported by research funds from the Atomic Energy Commission, the National Science Foundation, and the National Institutes of Health.

319

AMP) remains tightly bound to the enzyme and subsequently reacts with molecular oxygen to give light emission as indicated in the following reactions:

$$E + LH_2 + ATP \xrightarrow{Mg^{++}} E \cdot LH_2\text{-}AMP + PP \tag{1}$$

$$E \cdot LH_2\text{-}AMP + O_2 \rightarrow \text{Products} + \text{light} \tag{2}$$

In addition to reactions 1 and 2, luciferase will catalyze the formation of dehydroluciferyl-adenylate (L-AMP) as shown in the following reaction:

$$E + L + ATP \xrightarrow{Mg^{++}} E \cdot L\text{-}AMP + PP \tag{3}$$

The properties of these reactions have been reported in detail (2, 4, 6).

### Utilization of Oxygen

Unfortunately we have not been able to identify the product of the oxidation reaction that leads to light emission. We have found that one

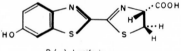

D (−)−Luciferin

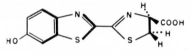

L (+)−Luciferin

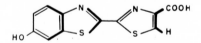

Dehydroluciferin

Fig. 1. Structures of firefly luciferin and dehydroluciferin, showing the D(−) and L(+) stereoisomers.

mole of oxygen is consumed per mole of luciferin utilized. Since one quantum of light is emitted for each luciferin destroyed, it seems likely that at least one atom of oxygen is incorporated into the product.

Recently we substituted deuterium for hydrogen on the carbon atom in the thiazolane ring, alpha to the carboxyl group. The initial rate of the reaction with the deutero analog was about one-half that observed with the normal substrate, suggesting that cleavage of the C—H bond may be the rate-limiting step in the enzymatic oxidation. This effect was observed only with LHD-AMP, not when deuterated luciferin and ATP were used as substrates. This is in agreement with previous studies in which it was found that the activating reaction proceeds at about one-tenth the rate of the light-emitting reaction.

## The Active Site of Luciferase

Recently the —SH content of luciferase has been determined with PMB (1). For three different preparations of the enzyme, between six and seven —SH groups per molecule were found to react with PMB. During sequential titration it was found that the relative inhibition of light emission by PMB was greater when $LH_2$-AMP and luciferase were reacted than when $LH_2$, ATP, and luciferase were reacted. This dif-

TABLE I

LOSS OF ENZYMATIC ACTIVITY AS A FUNCTION OF TIME OF
INCUBATION WITH PMB[a]

| | Control (%) | | | |
|---|---|---|---|---|
| | Activating and light-emitting (luciferin + ATP) | | Light-emitting (luciferyl-adenylate) | |
| PMB (moles/mole enzyme) | 30 min | 40 hr | 30 min | 40 hr |
| 0.5 | 82 | 79 | 74 | 72 |
| 1.0 | 75 | 67 | 64 | 63 |
| 1.5 | 63 | 45 | 44 | 45 |
| 2.0 | 51 | 37 | 39 | 40 |

[a] The samples contained approximately $3 \times 10^{-6}$ $M$ luciferase in 0.025 $M$ glycylglycine, pH 7.5. PMB was added as shown, and the samples were assayed 30 minutes after the addition of the PMB. They were stored at 0°C for 40 hours and reassayed. The activity is expressed as per cent of a control sample which was treated identically except that no PMB was added.

ference in loss of activity is dependent upon the length of time the enzyme is allowed to incubate with PMB prior to assay. The data in Table I show that after 30 minutes of incubation with PMB there is a real difference between the activities of the two reactions. If these samples are assayed after 40 hours, the per cent loss of activity for both reactions is the same. Both the initial and the gradual loss of activity are reversed almost completely by the addition of excess cysteine.

## Effect of Dehydroluciferyl-Adenylate on Reactive Sulfhydryls

The reaction of dehydroluciferin, ATP, and $Mg^{++}$ with luciferase results in the formation of a tightly bound dehydroluciferyl-adenylate–

enzyme complex. The dehydroluciferyl-adenylate is presumably bound at the same site as the normal substrate and is a potent competitive inhibitor. Several PMB titrations were carried out in the presence of dehydroluciferyl-adenylate to see if any of the protein —SH groups were prevented from reacting with PMB when dehydroluciferyl-adenylate was on the enzyme. These data are given in Table II. In each experiment

TABLE II

Effect of Dehydroluciferyl-Adenylate on the Number of Reactive —SH Groups Per Mole of Luciferase[a]

| Without dehydro- luciferyl- adenylate | With dehydro- luciferyl- adenylate | Difference |
|---|---|---|
| 6.1 | 4.1 | 2.0 |
| 7.1 | 5.0 | 2.1 |
| 6.7 | 4.1 | 2.6 |
| 6.8 | 3.9 | 2.9 |
| 7.0 | 4.0 | 3.0 |
| 6.0 | 4.0 | 2.0 |

[a] Stock luciferase (0.07 ml) was diluted to 1.0 ml with 0.023 $M$ Tris, pH 7.1. Where dehydroluciferyl-adenylate was present 3.2 mμmoles of dehydroluciferin, 4.5 mμmoles of ATP, and 5 μmoles of $MgSO_4$ were added. The enzyme was allowed to react for 30 minutes at 0°C with the dehydroluciferin, ATP, and $Mg^{++}$ before the titration was started.

two titrations were carried out simultaneously; one cuvette contained only enzyme and buffer, and the other contained in addition ATP, $Mg^{++}$, and a 6 $\times$ molar excess of dehydroluciferin. It can be seen that, in the presence of dehydroluciferyl-adenylate, two or three fewer —SH groups react with PMB. Several titrations were carried out in 6 $M$ urea, and in all cases six —SH groups per molecule of protein were found.

In subsequent experiments, advantage was taken of the ability of CoA to react with enzyme–dehydroluciferyl-adenylate to form dehydroluciferyl-CoA and free enzyme. The enzyme was first treated with dehydroluciferin, ATP, and $Mg^{++}$ as described in Table II; then 4 or 5 moles of PMB per mole of enzyme were added and allowed to react for 60 minutes at 0°C. Most of the enzyme activity was lost either with dehydroluciferyl-adenylate, dehydroluciferyl-adenylate and PMB, or PMB alone after this time of incubation. Approximately a 10 $\times$ molar excess of CoA was added, and the enzyme was assayed by flash height with luciferin and ATP. A similar sample of the enzyme was reacted with the same amount of PMB in the absence of dehydroluciferyl-adenylate. This sample served as a control, since the CoA would be expected to remove some of the PMB by nonspecific reaction as a sulfhydryl compound. The data in Table III show that the enzyme which was protected from PMB by dehydroluciferyl-adenylate (sample 2) recovers almost as much activity as the sample in which no PMB was added (sample 1). The unprotected enzyme treated only with PMB (sample 3) showed much less activity restored upon the addition of CoA.

In experiment II, Table III, sample 3 again shows further loss of activity upon prolonged incubation with PMB, even in the presence of

TABLE III

PROTECTION OF LUCIFERASE FROM PMB-INACTIVATION BY DEHYDROLUCIFERYL-ADENYLATE[a]

| Sample | Per cent of original activity | Per cent of original activity after addition of CoA (4 × excess) |
|---|---|---|
| *Experiment I* | | |
| 1. Enzyme, dehydroluciferyl-adenylate | 5, 6 | 100, 100 |
| 2. Enzyme, dehydroluciferyl-adenylate, PMB (4 × excess) | 2, 3 | 90, 90 |
| 3. Enzyme, PMB (4 × excess) | 1, 0 | 24, 28 |

| *Experiment II* | | 2 hr | 4.5 hr |
|---|---|---|---|
| 1. Enzyme, dehydroluciferyl-adenylate | 5 | 100 | 100 |
| 2. Enzyme, dehydroluciferyl-adenylate, PMB (5 × excess) | 2 | 74 | 84 |
| 3. Enzyme, PMB (5 × excess) | 1 | 23 | 13 |

[a] All samples contained 3 μmoles of luciferase; where indicated, 15 mμmoles of dehydroluciferin, 5 mμmoles of ATP, and 1 μmole of $MgSO_4$ were added to the enzyme prior to PMB. After the addition of PMB the reaction was allowed to proceed for 60 minutes at 0°C, and duplicate aliquots were removed and assayed. Coenzyme A was then added, and assays were performed at the times indicated. In experiment I, PMB was in 4 × molar excess and CoA was in 4 × molar excess. In experiment II, PMB was in 5 × molar excess of luciferase, and CoA was in 10 × molar excess. Assay was with luciferin and ATP.

CoA. This was not observed when the enzyme had been preincubated with dehydroluciferyl-adenylate (sample 2). All these samples showed complete recovery of activity upon the addition of excess cysteine.

The masking of two or three —SH groups of luciferase by the competitive inhibitor dehydroluciferyl-adenylate together with the almost complete recovery of activity from the protected enzyme gives strong support for the involvement of these —SH groups either in the catalytic activity of the enzyme or in the maintenance of a specific conformation at the active site. As in all such studies, this kind of evidence cannot be taken as proof for the direct participation of the —SH groups in catalysis; however, it can be stated with certainty that the four or five —SH groups not covered by the dehydroluciferyl-adenylate are not essential in any way to the activity of the enzyme, since 90% of the activity can be recovered with these —SH groups in the form of the mercaptide derivative of PMB.

The involvement of protein sulfhydryls in the catalytic activity of luciferase and the ability of CoA to react with E·L-AMP to form the thiol ester of dehydroluciferin and CoA suggested that the $LH_2$-AMP might be reacting with a sulfhydryl group of luciferase to form an intermediate $LH_2$—C—S—E compound which would then react with oxygen. If this were the case one might expect to observe a catalysis of free AMP into ATP in the presence of dehydroluciferin. This was studied carefully by using $C^{14}$-labeled AMP, and only a slow exchange was observed into both ATP and ADP. This was probably due to contaminating myokinase. Isolation of the E·L-AMP complex from Sephadex and exposure to labeled AMP in solution likewise showed no equilibration of solution AMP with the enzyme-bound adenylate. There is therefore no evidence that the anhydride link of luciferyl-adenylate is broken during the reaction.

## The Hydrolase Properties of Luciferase

When light emission is initiated by the injection of ATP into a reaction mixture containing excess luciferin, one observes a rapid rise in intensity followed by a rapid decrease in the first few seconds and then by a slow decay that may last for hours. This decrease in the rate of reaction can be shown to be due to product inhibition. The fact that the light intensity does not go completely to zero is due in part to the production of pyrophosphate initially which is sufficient to reverse the inhibition. If inorganic pyrophosphate is destroyed by added pyrophosphatase, then the light intensity rapidly decreases to less than 1% of the initial flash. However, the rate of production of inorganic pyrophosphate by the splitting of ATP is not depressed provided the pyrophosphate is hydrolyzed to prevent reversal of the activating reaction. This same property of the enzyme system is observed if luciferin is replaced by dehydroluciferin. The E·L-AMP complex is capable of catalyzing the breakdown of ATP to AMP and PP.

The results obtained thus far indicate that ATP does not favor the dissociation of L-AMP from the enzyme as free L-AMP, where it would hydrolyze gradually to form free L and AMP. Rather, in the presence of ATP the enzyme itself rapidly hydrolyzes L-AMP to form free L and

AMP. The results presented in Fig. 2 suggest that ATP causes the hydrolysis of enzyme-bound L-AMP, after which dehydroluciferin reacts with enzyme and ATP to release PP. If L-AMP is present in excess of the enzyme, then it apparently competes with L for the enzyme surface before ATP can react with it. Thus, under conditions where there is excess L-AMP over enzyme, the addition of ATP causes a rapid hydrolysis of L-AMP into L and AMP. Since the fluorescence of L is very much

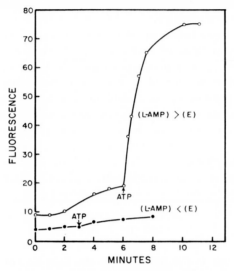

FIG. 2. Effect of ATP on hydrolysis of L-AMP. Fluorescence increase is due to hydrolysis of L-AMP to L and AMP. Excitation at 350 mμ. Emission measured at 540 mμ.

greater than that of L-AMP, we observe an increase of fluorescence under these conditions. When luciferin is also present it competes with dehydroluciferin for the enzyme surface, thus accounting for the low-level light production observed under these conditions.

*Stereochemical Specificity*

In the final step of the chemical synthesis of luciferin, 2-cyano-6-hydroxybenzthiazole is reacted with cysteine. When D-cysteine is used, a luciferin, $D(-)$-$LH_2$, is obtained that has all the chemical and biochemical properties of natural luciferin. On the other hand, when L-cysteine is used in the final step of synthesis, the resulting luciferin, $L(+)$-$LH_2$, appears to have all the chemical properties of natural luciferin except that no light emission is observed when it is mixed with enzyme, ATP, and $Mg^{++}$ (11).

However, the initial activation by ATP to form the adenylic acid derivative and pyrophosphate proceeds normally. In addition, L($+$)-LH$_2$ is a potent competitive inhibitor of luminescence. The data indicate that in the activation step the luciferase makes no distinction between D and L forms of luciferin. As discussed later, only D($-$)-luciferyl-adenylate is oxidized.

Both L- and D-luciferin can be converted to dehydroluciferin by heating in alkaline solution or by oxidation with ferricyanide. The chemical data establish with certainty that the oxidation products from the two forms of luciferin are identical.

As might be expected from the structure, it is possible to convert synthetic L-luciferin into DL-luciferin in an alkali-catalyzed isomerization. If L-luciferin is heated to approximately 80°C in 1 $N$ sodium hydroxide and in the absence of oxygen, one obtains significant amounts of D-luciferin as judged by its ability to produce bioluminescence. One can follow these isomeric changes by the measurement of optical rotation. In dimethylformamide solvent the synthetic D- and L-luciferins have specific rotations for the sodium D doublet of minus and plus approximately 30°, respectively.

We have found that the synthetically formed adenylic acid derivatives of luciferin are racemized more rapidly than luciferin alone.

The luminescence stereospecificity appears to be an unusual type of enzyme specificity in that both the D and L forms of luciferin combine with the enzyme in the activation process with the same affinity. Both forms have the same Briggs-Haldane constants. The stereospecificity seems to involve the oxidative step in which the enzyme–luciferyl-adenylate complex interacts with molecular oxygen to create, through an unknown organic reaction, the excited state.

The fluorescence emission peak of luciferin is at 538 mμ, and that of dehydroluciferin at 555 mμ. There appears to be a shoulder of blue fluorescence for dehydroluciferin at around 450 to 460 mμ at acid pH. It is of interest that, although the absorption peaks shift radically with changes in pH from acid to base, the fluorescence emission peaks are not altered. This would indicate that a particular ionic species of the molecule is responsible for the emission. Thus the ionic species present is a function of pH or, in the bioluminescence case, is dependent on the type of binding to the enzyme surface. The intramolecular transfer efficiency is reflected in the fluorescence yield of the luciferin and dehydroluciferin molecules (Fig. 3). The curve indicates that both luciferin and dehydroluciferin have the same ionizable groups, a carboxyl group showing a p$K$ between pH 3 and 4 and a phenolic OH group with a p$K$ at pH 8.25. The fluorescence yield exhibits the most dramatic change on ionization of the hydroxyl group, and it is most likely this group which is prevented effectively from ionizing when dehydroluciferin is bound on the enzyme surface, since the fluorescence of E·L-AMP relative to L shows the same relative decrease in intensity.

In none of these fluorescence measurements of luciferin and dehydroluciferin under the various conditions described have we observed a fluorescence emission exactly comparable to the bioluminescence emission spectrum. However, as the results in Fig. 4 indicate, the adenylic

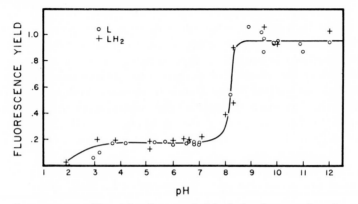

FIG. 3. Fluorescence yields of luciferin and dehydroluciferin as functions of pH.

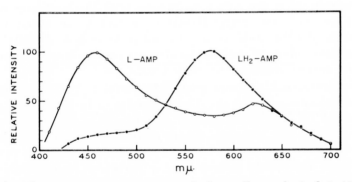

FIG. 4. Fluorescence emission spectra of chemically synthesized L-AMP and LH$_2$-AMP in acid solution. The emitting species have not been completely identified.

acid derivatives of luciferin and dehydroluciferin radically change the emission peaks. The LH$_2$-AMP acid fluorescence has an emission peak at 570 mµ, which corresponds closely with the bioluminescence emission curve. On the other hand, acid dehydroluciferyl-adenylate is presumably two molecular species with peaks around 460 mµ and 625 mµ. These species have not yet been identified.

FACTORS AFFECTING THE COLOR OF LIGHT

*Emission Spectrum in* Photinus pyralis

Figure 5 shows the true emission spectrum of the *Photinus pyralis* fire-fly light reaction *in vitro* in glycylglycine buffer at pH 7.6. The peak emission for the bioluminescence is 562 mμ, with the band ranging from 500 to 630 mμ. As an absolute minimum, therefore, the energy require-

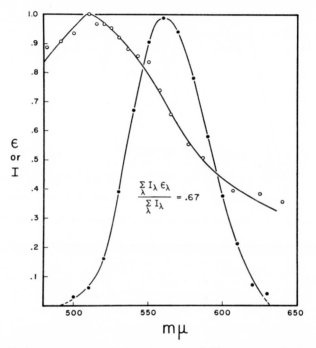

FIG. 5. Bioluminescence emission spectrum of *Photinus pyralis in vitro* enzyme reaction. The peak emission is at 562 mμ. Superimposed upon this emission spectrum is the normalized photon spectral efficiency of the photocathode of the phototube used in the measurements.

ment for the bioluminescence should exceed 57 kcal/mole. Measurements of the spectrum by using *P. pyralis* organs give the same emission peak. However, other fireflies show some shifts in their peak emissions, and the reasons for this are discussed below.

One might expect that some product would occur in the light-emitting step which would have a fluorescence spectrum similar to the bioluminescence emission spectrum and which could possibly be identified as the light-emitting species. The evidence indicates that the adenylic derivative of an oxidized product is the most likely emitter (5).

## Temperature, pH, and Metal Ions

As the pH of the *P. pyralis* extract is lowered, it can be observed that the intensity of the yellow-green bioluminescence decreases, leaving a dull brick-organe glow (7, 8). This variation in bioluminescence emission with pH is shown in Fig. 6. As can be seen at neutral (and alkaline) pH,

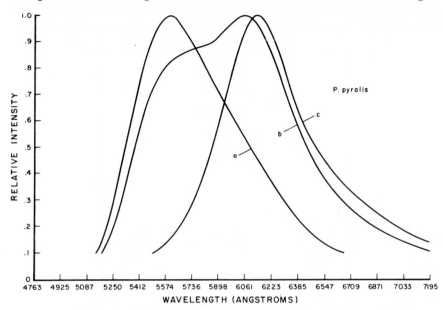

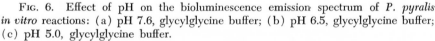

FIG. 6. Effect of pH on the bioluminescence emission spectrum of *P. pyralis* *in vitro* reactions: (a) pH 7.6, glycylglycine buffer; (b) pH 6.5, glycylglycine buffer; (c) pH 5.0, glycylglycine buffer.

there is a single emission band in the yellow-green region. At intermediate pH, a red emission band appears at 616 mµ, and at pH value below 5.5, the yellow-green emission is completely suppressed and only the red band is evident. At acid pH, the number of light quanta emitted per luciferin molecule oxidized is markedly lower than 1 and indicates a predominantly dark reaction. However, at alkaline pH, although the rate of light emission is reduced to a fraction of the rate of pH 7.6, the quantum yield is essentially unity. The change of yield with pH corresponds rather closely in form to the fluorescence yield of luciferin and dehydroluciferin at various pH's except for the fact that the pK has been shifted essentially one pH unit toward the acid range for the bioluminescence quantum yield. This may represent the interaction of the enzyme with the benzthiazole OH group or possibly the amino group of AMP, altering in effect the fluorescence or chemiluminescence properties of the bound intermediate which is essential for light emission.

Recently we have attempted to measure the pK of the red-light-emitting species by observing only the red light as a function of pH. Although the data are not conclusive, there is a suggestion that the pK is near 6.8. It is possible, therefore, that a histidine residue may be involved in the binding of the luciferyl-adenylic acid to the enzyme, which in turn may affect the pK of the excited state and consequently the color of the light emitted.

Except for the partial denaturation of the enzyme in acidic buffer, the pH effect on the emission spectrum shift is completely reversible. We have been able to observe these same reversible red shifts in emission spectra by increasing and then decreasing the temperature of the reac-

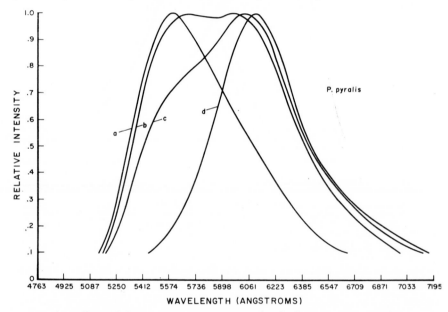

Fig. 7. Effect of $Zn^{++}$ concentration on the bioluminescence emission spectrum of *P. pyralis in vitro* reactions: (a) pH 7.6, no added $Zn^{++}$; (b) pH 7.6, $1.33 \times 10^{-4}$ *M* $Zn^{++}$; (c) pH 7.6, $3.95 \times 10^{-4}$ *M* $Zn^{++}$; (d) pH 7.6, $2.3 \times 10^{-3}$ *M* $Zn^{++}$.

tion, by carrying out the reaction in 0.2 *M* urea at normal pH values (7.6) in glycylglycine buffer, or by adding small concentrations of $Zn^{++}$, $Cd^{++}$, and $Hg^{++}$ cations, as chlorides. The normalized emission spectra of the *in vitro* bioluminescence of purified *P. pyralis* luciferase for various $Zn^{++}$ concentrations are shown in Fig. 7. The curves do not show absolute changes in intensities in going from the yellow-green to the red emission; there is actually a marked decrease in the efficiency of the light reaction under conditions where red light is emitted. The maximum red shifts obtained with *P. pyralis* luciferase at low pH, with $Zn^{++}$, and with $Cd^{++}$ are shown in Fig. 8, compared with the normal yellow-green emission. The temperature, urea, and $Hg^{++}$ effects are essentially the same. In the case of $Hg^{++}$ the concentrations required for the red shift were smaller than for both $Zn^{++}$ and $Cd^{++}$ by a factor of 100.

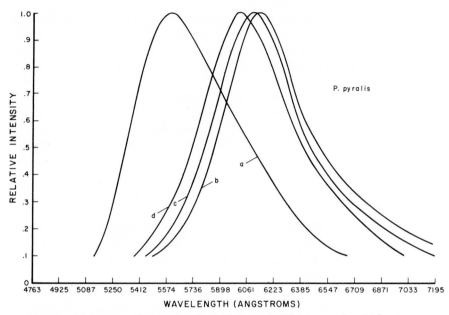

FIG. 8. Maximum effects of pH, $Zn^{++}$, and $Cd^{++}$ on the bioluminescence emission spectrum of *P. pyralis in vitro* reactions: (a) pH 7.6, no added metal ions; (b) pH 5.0, no added metal ions; (c) pH 7.6, $2.3 \times 10^{-3}$ $M$ $Zn^{++}$; (d) pH 7.6, $1.2 \times 10^{-2}$ $M$ $Cd^{++}$.

By the use of suitable blue-green-transmitting filters and red-transmitting filters we have been able to establish that there are two pH optima and two temperature optima for the bioluminescence emission, one each for the red and the yellow-green emissions. As would be expected, the red emission has a lower pH and higher temperature optimum.

## Changes in Substrate Structure

The above facts support the idea that the color of the emitted light depends upon the nature of the binding of the intermediate to the enzyme. It seemed likely, therefore, that a change in the structure of the substrate molecules (luciferin or ATP) may alter the binding and in turn affect the color of the light. Unfortunately it is not possible to change greatly the luciferin structure and still obtain an active light-emitting substrate. It turns out that the 6-aminobenzthiazole compound is an active substrate, and in this case a red emission instead of the yellow-green is observed even at neutral pH. This is additional evidence that the 6-hydroxy group in the normal luciferin has an effect on the nature of the emitting intermediate.

Until recently only adenosine triphosphate (ATP) was active for the enzymatic reaction leading to light emission. Deoxy ATP, UTP, CTP, GTP, ADP, and other pyrophosphate-containing nucleotides were inactive. Recently Leonard and associates prepared an ATP with the ribose attached to the 3 position of the adenine ring (3-isoATP) and made a sample available to us. This compound appears to be about 10 to 15% as effective in the light reaction as normal ATP. The additional interesting observation, however, is that at pH 7.5 a significant fraction of the light emitted is red when 3-isoATP is used. Thus the nature (stereochemistry) of the nucleotide attachment to luciferin and presumably to the enzyme is also of importance in determining the color of the light.

### Chemiluminescence

An investigation of the nonenzymatic chemiluminescence of luciferin-adenylate and other derivatives in the organic solvent dimethyl sulfoxide actually reveals that there are two fundamental emission peaks, i.e., two different emitting species (9).

Firefly luciferin was condensed with adenylic acid, metaphosphoric acid, or diazomethane in dry pyridine with dicyclohexylcarbodiimide, according to the method of Khorana. An aliquot was delivered to 2 ml of dimethyl sulfoxide in a 10- by 75-mm test tube mounted in front of a phototube. Chemiluminescence was obtained upon addition of a solid pellet of KOH, by the addition of a droplet of 10 $M$ NaOH, or by the addition of a drop of tertiary butyl alcohol solution in which a small amount of potassium metal had been dissolved so that tertiary butoxide ions were formed.

Except in the cases of the esters of luciferin, the observed chemiluminescence was of too low an intensity to permit an estimate of color. In the case of LH$_2$-AMP, as a drop of 10 $M$ NaOH was added to the test tube there was a yellow-green glow surrounding the drop as it sank to the bottom of the tube. If the tube was then shaken vigorously there appeared a brilliant red emission over the entire solution volume. This disappeared in 1 to 2 seconds, and there remained the very low-intensity steady emission characteristic of the NaOH and dimethyl sulfoxide reaction alone. This yellow-green light emission from LH$_2$-AMP was seen most clearly upon the initial introduction of the NaOH droplet. Upon successive additions of NaOH the chemiluminescence emission became more orange until only a red glow was visible. These results are consistent with the appearance of the red flash when either the NaOH or KOH was shaken vigorously in the solution and also with the red flash which was observed when the strongly basic tertiary butoxide ions were added to the solution; they show that the color of the chemiluminescence is strongly dependent on pH. This is analogous to the enzymatic reaction which depends upon pH for the color of the emission. The red emission spectrum in strongly basic dimethyl sulfoxide is shown in Fig. 9. The peak emission at 6255 A differs from the 6140-A peak in

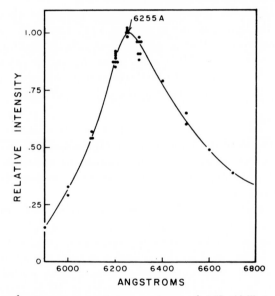

Fig. 9. Chemiluminescence emission spectrum of $LH_2$-AMP in dimethyl sulfoxide.

the enzymatic reaction. However, this is not unexpected, since in the case of luminol there was also a red shift in chemiluminescence emission from 4300 A in aqueous solution to 4800 A in dimethyl sulfoxide.

The unique character of the $LH_2$-AMP compound was shown by the fact that the methyl ester of luciferin, $LH_2$-$CH_3$, gave only a yellow-green color and $LH_2$-$PO_4$ gave only a red chemiluminescence under the same experimental conditions which caused $LH_2$-AMP emission to shift from yellow-green to red. Thus, the oxidized product of $LH_2$-AMP can exist in either of two fluorescent excited species, dependent on pH. These results indicate that an essential role of the enzyme in the oxidation of firefly luciferin is to permit, by virtue of the binding of the $LH_2$-AMP, the removal of a proton and the subsequent attack by oxygen. On the other hand, in the absence of enzyme the chemical environment would have to be so basic that $LH_2$-AMP would hydrolyze before oxygen attack could occur. By reacting the $LH_2$-AMP in dimethyl sulfoxide we have inhibited hydrolysis by chemical means even at high effective pH values, accomplishing what the enzyme can do at neutral pH. As might be expected, D-$LH_2$-AMP and L-$LH_2$-AMP do not show the stereospecificity in nonenzymatic chemiluminescence which was previously reported for the enzymatic reaction.

## Color of Light in Different Species of Fireflies

It has been known for some time that different species of fireflies emit different colors of bioluminescence, ranging from green through bright yellow. These are valid observations and are not visual artifacts due to selective cuticle absorption in the light organ. We have recently measured the *in vivo* emission spectra of twenty species of firefly, sixteen Jamaican and four native American species (12). The large range of *in vivo* spectral variations is summarized in Table IV. From the symmetric shapes and reasonably constant half-widths of the curves obtained it is improbable that peak emissions intermediate between green and yellow are due to mixtures of a green-emitting molecular species and a red-emitting molecular species. The emission is most likely due to a single excited enzyme–substrate complex.

We succeeded in collecting sufficient numbers of *Photuris pennsylvanica* (United States), *Photuris jamaicensis* (Jamaica), and *Pyrophorus plagiophthalamus* (Jamaica) to extract and partially purify both luciferase and luciferin from each species. The Jamaican elaterid beetle, *Pyrophorus plagiophthalamus*, has been described by Harvey (3) as being unique among the fireflies in possessing light organs which emit two different colors of light. A symmetric pair of dorsal organs on the anterior thorax light up with a constant bright *green* glow when the insect is resting or walking, or disturbed in captivity. These are extinguished when the insect is in flight. There is in addition a single large ventral organ, completely shielded in a cleft between the thorax and the first abdominal segment. When the insect is in flight the elytra are extended; the first abdominal segment is flexed, opening the cleft, and a constant bright yellow light is emitted. In a dark field a low-flying *Pyrophorus* illuminates the ground below much as do downward-directed landing lights of an airplane. When the insect alights or is batted down, the yellow light goes off, the elytra close, and the green "parking lights" go on. For this reason and because of the position and shape of the anterior thoracic organs, *P. plagiophthalamus* is also called the "automobile bug."

On the basis of paper chromatography, absorbance and fluorescence spectra, and the pH dependence of the relative fluorescence yield, all the isolated luciferins, including those isolated from the two different organs of *P. plagiophthalamus*, appear to be identical with *P. pyralis* luciferin. In the *in vitro* light reaction, regardless of the source of luciferin, the spectral distribution of the light emitted by each species corresponded

TABLE IV

FIREFLY SPECIES AND WAVELENGTH OF MAXIMUM INTENSITY
(PEAK WAVELENGTH) ARRANGED IN ORDER OF
INCREASING WAVELENGTH

| Species | Peak wavelength (A) |
|---|---|
| Photuris pennsylvanica | 5520 |
| Pyrophorus plagiophthalamus (dorsal organ) | 5430 |
| Diphotus sp. | 5550 |
| Photuris jamaicensis ♂, ♀ | 5550 |
| Photinus pardalus | 5600 |
| Photinus pyralis ♂, ♀ | 5620 |
| Photinus commissus | 5640 |
| Photinus marginellus | 5650 |
| Photinus pallens | 5650 |
| Photinus xanthophotus ♀ | 5670 |
| Photinus leucopyge | 5690 |
| Lecontea sp. | 5700 |
| Photinus lobatus | 5700 |
| Photinus evanescens | 5700 |
| Photinus melanurus | 5700 |
| Photinus nothus | 5700 |
| Photinus (new species) | 5700 |
| Photinus morbosus-ceratus | 5710 |
| Photinus gracilobus | 5720 |
| Photinus scintillans ♀ | 5750 |
| Photinus scintillans ♂ | 5750 |
| Pyrophorus plagiophthalamus (ventral organ) | 5820 |

with the *in vivo* emission measured previously. The data for *P. pyralis* are shown in Fig. 10. Similar studies have been made with *P. plagiophthalamus* luciferase. In each case the species enzyme alone determined the spectral distribution of the emitted light. The spectra in Fig. 10 are displaced one above the other in order to show the relative distributions more easily. In the case of *P. plagiophthalamus* there are slight shifts in the peak positions of the *in vivo* emissions relative to the *in vitro* emissions. This is probably due to the fact that the color of the light emitted by the particular *in vivo* specimens measured was actually slightly dif-

ferent from the average color due to the *in vitro* enzyme extract obtained
from the light organs of approximately 100 different insects. We found on
a subsequent collecting trip, where a large number of *P. plagiophthalamus* was caught, that in this presumably single species we can distinguish,
in different insects, three separate colors of *in vivo* emission from the
dorsal organs, namely green, yellow-green, and lemon yellow, and three

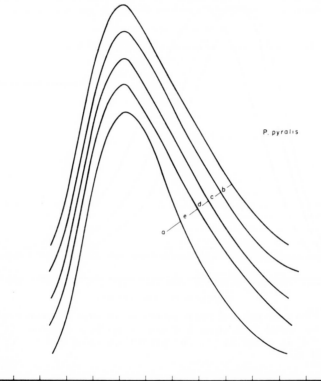

WAVELENGTH (ANGSTROMS)

FIG. 10.  Emission spectra of *P. pyralis:* (a) *in vivo;* (b) *in vitro, P. pyralis*
luciferase + *P. pyralis* luciferin; (c) *in vitro, P. pyralis* luciferase + synthetic luciferin; (d) *in vitro, P. pyralis* luciferase + *P. plagiophthalamus* dorsal light organ
luciferin; (e) *in vitro, P. pyralis* luciferase + *P. plagiophthalamus* ventral light
organ luciferin.

separate colors of *in vivo* emission from different ventral organs, namely
yellow-green, yellow, and orange. There is apparently no correlation
between ventral organ emission color and dorsal organ emission color.
In more than 1000 insects examined both dorsal organs emitted identical
colors of light without exception.

## Effects of pH and Metal Cations

The maximum effects of pH and metal cations on the *in vitro* emissions of *P. plagiophthalamus* dorsal organ luciferase are shown in Fig. 11. Qualitatively these spectral shifts are in the same direction as the *P. pyralis* effects, although the magnitudes of the shifts are much smaller. In none of our experiments were we able to observe a red-shift in the

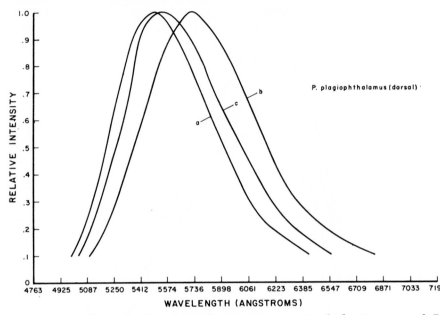

Fig. 11. Effects of pH and metal cations on *in vitro* bioluminescence of *P. plagiophthalamus* dorsal light organ luciferase + synthetic luciferin: (a) normal reaction, pH 7.6, no added $Zn^{++}$; (b) pH 6.0, no added $Zn^{++}$; (c) pH 7.6, $5.5 \times 10^{-4}$ $M$ $Zn^{++}$.

emission from *P. plagiophthalamus* ventral organ luciferase. However, as shown in Fig. 12, *basic solutions* and, separately, the addition of metal cations produced a *"blue-shift,"* opposite to that observed from both the *P. plagiophthalamus* dorsal organ and from *P. pyralis*.

### DISCUSSION

From a consideration of the influence of temperature, inhibitors, and pressure on enzyme-catalyzed reactions, one was led to suspect early that changes in the secondary and tertiary structure of biocatalysts were of great importance in determining not only the rate of catalysis but also the reactivity of transients formed in the reaction. The stimulation of enzyme by hydrogen-bond-breaking molecules and the activators and inhibitors which combine at sites other than the "catalytic center" (allosteric) presumably function in this manner. There is much direct evidence that proteins can undergo specific and reversible configurational changes, but it is only recently that one suspected that these may be the same changes that occur during catalysis. The effect of ATP in stimulating the hydrolysis of L-AMP by luciferase suggests that binding of ATP to the enzyme results in a conformational change which increases the reactivity of bound L-AMP with water. It is interesting also that PMB or $Cd^{++}$ stimulates the release of free L from the $E \cdot L$-AMP complex

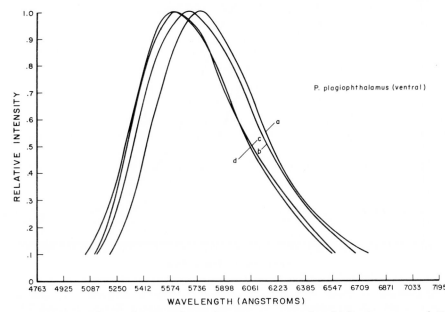

FIG. 12. Effects of pH and metal cations on *in vitro* bioluminescence of *P. plagiophthalamus* ventral light organ luciferase + synthetic luciferin: (a) normal reaction, pH 7.6, no added $Zn^{++}$ or $Cd^{++}$; (b) pH 9, no added $Zn^{++}$ or $Cd^{++}$; (c) pH 7.6, $5.5 \times 10^{-4}$ $M$ $Zn^{++}$; (d) pH 7.6, $8 \times 10^{-5}$ $M$ $Cd^{++}$.

only in the presence of ATP, indicating that the sensitive —SH groups are not accessible unless the ATP is bound to the protein and in some way is modifying the structure of the complex. The dehydroluciferyl-adenylate is much less reactive when bound to the enzyme than as a free molecule in solution. At neutral pH, luciferyl-adenylate reacts rapidly with nucleophilic compounds such as cystine, hydroxylamine, and water; however, on the enzyme it remains stable for hours at room temperature. The only compounds which will react with $E \cdot L$-AMP are inorganic pyrophosphate, which is the other product of the reaction in the activating step, or coenzyme A. Even dephospho-coenzyme A is completely inactive in stimulating the breakdown of enzyme-bound L-AMP. The effect of PMB, Cd, and other inhibitors indicate that at least two —SH groups must be involved in this catalytic activity. Thus the results suggest that both the nature of the binding and the shape of the enzyme molecule are important in determining quantitatively and qualitatively the catalytic powers of the enzyme. Modification of the protein structure may alter the nature of the reaction catalyzed.

It is interesting that in the case of the light-emitting catalytic process these same properties are important in determining the allowed electronic transitions. Using purified enzyme and substrates, we know that the following factors are important in determining the color of the *in vitro* light emission: luciferin and ATP structure, luciferase structure, pH, temperature, metals, salts, and various inhibitors that can combine with specific groups on the enzyme. All these results indicate that the strength and nature of the binding of the transient emitter are the important factors that determine the color of the light. Since the luciferin and other cofactors are identical in the various fireflies analyzed, it is clear that the variation in color among species must be due to a difference in enzyme structure (10).

The presence of two different luciferases in the light organs of the same organism, the "automobile bug," indicated the interesting possibility that we are dealing with isozymes. As indicated previously, we have noted differences in the color of light emitted from the ventral and dorsal groups. This suggests that genetic as well as developmental differences may be important in the synthesis of specific luciferases. Unfortunately, inadequate material at this time has prevented us from looking more carefully at the physical structure of the luciferases from this organism.

It is obvious that much more knowledge concerning the structure of the luciferase molecule and the nature of the binding and active catalytic sites is necessary before we can give an adequate explanation of these striking effects. These observations do suggest that discrete fluorescence changes of small molecules attached to protein will be extremely valuable for studying conformational changes that may occur during catalysis or function.

### REFERENCES

1. DeLuca, M., Wirtz, G. W., and McElroy, W. D., *Biochemistry*, **3**, 935 (1964).
2. Green, Arda, A., and McElroy, W. D., *Biochim. Biophys. Acta*, **20**, 170 (1956).
3. Harvey, E. N., "Bioluminescence," Academic Press, New York, 1952.
4. McElroy, W. D., and Seliger, H. H., *Federation Proc.*, **21**, 1006 (1963).

5. McELROY, W. D., AND SELIGER, H. H., *Advan. Enzymol.*, **25**, 119 (1963).

6. RHODES, W. C., AND McELROY, W. D., *J. Biol. Chem.*, **233**, 1528 (1958).

7. SELIGER, H. H., AND McELROY, W. D., *Radiation Res.*, Suppl. 2, 528 (1960).

8. SELIGER, H. H., AND McELROY, W. D., *Arch. Biochem. Biophys.*, **88**, 136 (1960).

9. SELIGER, H. H., AND McELROY, W. D., *Science*, **138**, 683 (1962).

10. SELIGER, H. H., AND McELROY, W. D., *Proc. Natl. Acad. Sci. U.S.*, **52**, 75 (1964).

11. SELIGER, H. H., AND McELROY, W. D., WHITE, E. H., AND FIELD, G. F., *Proc. Natl. Acad. Sci. U.S.*, **47**, 1129 (1961).

12. SELIGER, H. H., BUCK, J. B., FASTIE, W. G., AND McELROY, W. D., *J. Gen. Physiol.*, **48**, 95 (1964).

13. WHITE, E. H., McCAPRA, F., FIELD, G. F., AND McELROY, W. D., *J. Am. Chem. Soc.*, **83**, 2402 (1961).

# The Role of Mutations
# in Evolution

Ernst Freese and Akira Yoshida

*Laboratory of Molecular Biology,*
*National Institute of Neurological Diseases and Blindness,*
*National Institutes of Health,*
*Bethesda, Maryland*

Classical hypotheses of evolution have been derived by a comparison of the morphological and other phenotypic properties of many different organisms. The more information was accumulated and carefully evaluated, the fewer hypotheses remained likely. More recently, evolution became explainable in molecular terms, owing to the rapidly accumulating knowledge of the possible alterations of DNA, the information transfer from DNA to RNA and proteins, and the chemical and functional properties of proteins. This knowledge allows one to state general rules about the evolution of macromolecules, rules that hold for both simple and complex organisms. Some hypotheses of evolution can thus be eliminated already by *deduction* from molecular principles rather than by *induction* from many phenotypic observations. A complete theory of evolution probably can be obtained only by a *combination* of both inductive and deductive reasoning.

In the following we shall limit ourselves to the mutational aspect of molecular evolution and not discuss recombination. We shall first analyze rules of DNA evolution and then regard their consequences for the evolution of proteins.

## A. Evidence for the Evolution of DNA

The evolution of DNA is most apparent in microorganisms, since they can rapidly duplicate and thus build up large populations from a single cell. Bacteria, for example, have very different base frequencies (25), and yet the DNA in a given bacterial species is rather homogeneous in base composition when compared to another species (29). Since the frequency of GC pairs varies from 0.75 to 0.3 (25), the DNA of some bacteria must have changed at least 45% of its bases, since the bacteria have evolved from a common ancestor. The assumption of a common ancestor is reasonable on the following grounds:

1. The composition of different bacteria is similar: ribosomes, SRNA, membranes are similar in properties; cell walls vary but have many common features.

2. The biochemical pathways in different bacteria are practically the same.

3. The deviation from randomness of the dinucleotide frequencies in DNA varies systematically with the base ratio (7, 13).

In higher organisms the variation of DNA is much less pronounced, so that by base ratio or CsCl analysis no significant differences can be observed for the DNA of different organisms. Nevertheless, differences have been found by hybridization experiments with DNA, such that more closely related organisms have more closely similar DNA sequences (1).

## B. Alterations of DNA Leading to Its Evolution

1. It seems clear that the change in the base composition of DNA did not occur suddenly but by many consecutive alterations of individual bases:

a. There is no evidence that base sequences can suddenly change during their replication, since the base composition of an organism with a given phenotype seems to remain constant when determined at different times.

b. Even the presently known *in vitro* systems of DNA synthesis reproduce faithfully both the base- and the nearest-neighbor frequency of their template (12). The occurrence of slippage, observed during polymer synthesis in the absence of one triphosphate (16), provides an exception which might have played a role in extending the length of DNA during evolution; but this mechanism could not have altered the base composition of DNA regions that carry information.

c. Since the DNA of bacteria of a given phenotype has a rather homogeneous base composition, many vital genes would probably have been altered at the same time by a sudden change from one base composition to a very different one. Thus practically all biochemical functions would have been affected at the same time, with lethal results for the organism. Only if different genes had changed one at a time could those changes which did not alter a vital function be retained by natural selection.

d. The known mechanisms of mutations and their biological effects indicate that only very small DNA alterations have a good chance to survive evolution.

2. Let us look in more detail at the different possible types of alterations that affect the hereditary material. Experimentally, the extent
of DNA alterations has been determined by chemical and genetic investigations on phages, transforming DNA, and bacteria; whereas the
nature of chromosomal alterations has been discovered by cytological
methods. As a result of these studies, one can roughly subdivide DNA
alterations into predominantly lethal and predominantly mutagenic
alterations.

a. Predominantly lethal alterations of DNA are illustrated in Fig. 1.
If these alterations are induced in chromosomal DNA within a cell,
some and maybe all of them can be occasionally repaired by special

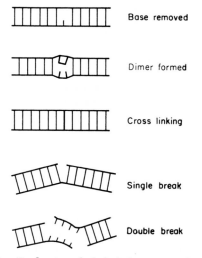

FIG. 1.   Predominantly lethal alterations of DNA.

enzymes, as has been most clearly shown for the repair of ultraviolet-
induced thymine dimers (26). It is also well known (30) that broken
chromosomes behave as if they have sticky ends which can cause the
attachment of two broken ends from the same or from two different
chromosomes. Various large chromosomal alterations can thus be
induced, such as deletions and translocations, of which most are
apparently lethal or at least disadvantageous to the cell or organism.
Occasionally, however, a large alteration, like a duplication, may
have no significant immediate effect on the organism. If it undergoes
further small alterations it may acquire additional information, thus
adding to the store of functional properties.

The predominantly lethal or large alterations could not significantly contribute to the evolutionary drift of the DNA base composition.

b. Predominantly mutagenic alterations of DNA are shown in Fig. 2. They involve the change of only one DNA base pair.

*Deletions and insertions* of single bases within a structural gene should shift the reading frame of protein synthesis, thus changing in the corresponding proteins all amino acids distal to the alteration (4). Most of such mutations occurring in a vital gene would therefore be lethal (except when the alteration is so close to the C-terminal

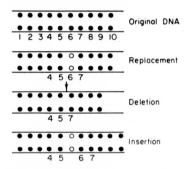

FIG. 2.    Types of single base pair changes in DNA.

end of the protein that its function is not affected). The alteration could survive only if it occurred in a genetically inert region or if the altered protein was not absolutely necessary for the organism.

*Base pair replacements* are expected to cause the substitution of only one (or no) amino acid in a protein (except for rare nonsense mutations). Since such a substitution often does not seem to significantly alter the functional property of the protein, many mutants of this type would survive, even if the mutation involved a vital protein.

Base pair replacements can be further subdivided into transitions and transversions (Fig. 3). A *transition* can be initiated by a minor alteration of a single DNA base; the altered base pairs sometimes or always with the wrong complementary base, during subsequent DNA duplications (8). In contrast, all other small DNA alterations require much more drastic reactions and are therefore expected to occur usually much less frequently. *Transversions* could come about, e.g., by the mistaken pairing of one purine with either another purine or with a gap produced by depurination (or of one pyrimidine with another pyrimidine), or perhaps by a mistake in a repair process. Deletions and insertions would require skipping or adding of bases during DNA duplication, especially by mistakes in recombination (18).

These reasons suggest that most of the surviving evolutionary base pair changes are probably caused by base pair transitions. This assumption would predict that most spontaneous mutants, whose DNA alteration is small enough to be able to revert, can be induced to revert by agents which induce only transitions, e.g., by highly mutage-

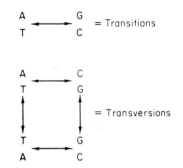

FIG. 3.   Types of base pair replacements.

nic base analogs. This assumption is apparently correct for bacteria (20). [Phages T4 are an exception to the rule, since only 20% of their spontaneous mutations are of the transition type (8); this may be due to the many rounds of recombination which phage DNA undergoes during its duplication.]

## C. The Preferential Direction of Base Pair Transitions during Evolution

1. The homogeneity of the DNA base composition in different bacteria shows that base pair changes occurred nearly randomly in all DNA regions; special regions that may have kept their sequence because of natural selection must be small compared to the size of the commonly isolated DNA pieces. Nevertheless, unaltered DNA regions apparently do exist, since one can show that a completely random occurrence of base pair changes in DNA would give rise to a narrower distribution in CsCl than has been observed (7, 28). Furthermore, some inhomogeneity of DNA has been directly demonstrated (6). In higher organisms the inhomogeneity is even more pronounced (29).

2. But why do different bacteria have different average base frequencies? The answer to this question depends on the knowledge of two figures: (a) the *number, τ, of base pair changes* which the DNA of a given bacterium DNA has undergone since it diverged from the

common ancestor of all bacteria; (b) the average probability, g, with which the base pair transitions occurred from GC to AT rather than in the opposite direction (whose probability is $1 - g$); i.e., $g = \gamma/\alpha$ if

$$GC \underset{\alpha}{\overset{\gamma}{\rightleftharpoons}} AT.$$

From the extreme values of the base frequencies, one can estimate that at least for some bacteria $\tau$ must be equal or larger than one-half times the number of base pairs in a bacterium; i.e., $\tau \geqslant 10^6$. If $\tau$ were orders of magnitude larger than this number, the present DNA could represent the equilibrium state of transitions from GC to AT and vice versa. In this case the observed frequency of AT pairs would be equal to g. This possibility seems unlikely, because the mutation probabilities, g, could in this case range only from 0.25 to 0.7; i.e., the probability of transitions from GC to AT would be within a factor of 3 the same as those from AT to GC, and that for all bacteria. For all we know about the specificity of mutagenesis, this possibility is extremely unlikely: (a) Most mutagens exhibit a strong specificity toward one of the two types of base pairs (8). (b) Spontaneous mutation rates are controlled both by the environment and by the genetic constitution of the organism. Mutator genes are known to increase greatly the mutation frequency in different organisms (5). Even if the relative mutation rates would have a g value in the above range for some organisms, a change of environment or a mutation affecting the rate of base pair changes would be likely to move this value out of the range.

We conclude for all organisms that the base pair changes from GC to AT are not yet in equilibrium with the opposite changes from AT to GC. On the contrary, base pairs continue to change preferentially in one of the two directions. Consequently, bacteria differ in their base frequency because they have experienced different numbers, $\tau$, of base pair changes. For bacteria whose DNA base frequencies are on one end of the scale (e.g., high GC), both $\tau$ and the present spontaneous mutation rates should be much smaller than for those on the other end of the scale (e.g., low GC) (except for those in which a recent mutation has greatly altered the spontaneous mutation rate).

3. Having seen that spontaneous transitions must preferentially occur in one direction, from GC to AT or vice versa, we now want to know which this direction is. For bacteria or other organisms, not enough data are available at this time to argue either way. But we do have data both on the mutagenic specificity of various mutagens and on spontaneous mutation rates in phage T4 (8). Figure 4 shows the results of a combination of chemical and mutagenic experiments in phage T4. It is apparent that all chemical mutagens which can attack resting DNA

react preferentially with either G or C and thus cause base pair transitions from GC to AT. In the opposite direction only nitrous acid exhibits an appreciable though smaller effect. The two highly mutagenic base analogs BUdR and AP, which act on duplicating DNA, can alter either base pair; but BUdR preferentially affects GC, so that only AP seems to alter both base pairs with about equal frequency.

| Agent | Base Pair Change |
|---|---|
| 2-aminopurine | A ⇄ G<br>T ⇄ C |
| 5-bromodeoxyuridine | G → A<br>C ⇠ T |
| nitrous acid | G → A<br>C ⇠ T |
| hydroxylamine | G → A<br>C → T |
| ethylating agents | G → A<br>C ⇠ T |
| low pH | G → A<br>C ⇠ T |
| spontaneous | G → A<br>C ⇠ T |

FIG. 4. Preferred direction of transition mutation induction by different mutagens.

*Experiments on bacteria (24) and on pollen and seeds (3)* suggest that spontaneous mutations may occur without DNA duplication. Even in duplicating bacteria spontaneous mutations have sometimes been found to increase linearly with time rather than with the number of DNA duplications (23). Furthermore, some of the known mutagenic chemicals, such as nitrous acid and hydroxylamine, are actually produced metabolically.

Altogether, it seems likely that spontaneous base pair changes occur mostly from GC to AT. In agreement with this assumption one finds that transition mutants in phage T4 revert spontaneously much more frequently if their mutant site has a GC pair than if it has an AT pair (8).

## D. Nonrandomness of Mutations

The frequency with which a base pair, say a GC pair, is spontaneously substituted depends not only on the mutagenic agents in the cell but also on the position of the base pair in DNA. This position effect would not influence the direction of phenotypic changes in evolution if it were the same whether a given DNA region were functionally active or not. For in this case the relative mutation rate of different DNA sites, and therefore of different functional properties, would be independent of the environment to which the organism is exposed. There is, however, the distinct possibility that the functional activity of a DNA region may influence its mutational activity.

1. Functionally inactive DNA regions tend to be condensed into a small area, presumably by means of basic proteins. This may render them less accessible to chemical agents.

2. Certain agents (e.g., hydroxylamine) mutate single-stranded DNA regions much more effectively than double-stranded regions (10). Any uncoiling of a given DNA region may therefore increase its mutagenic response.

3. In particular, the DNA double strands probably must open while the DNA functions, i.e., while it serves as a template for RNA formation. Although we have not observed a large difference of the rate of mutation induction by hydroxylamine for the tryptophan region of repressed and constitutive bacteria (9), a small difference (within a factor of 3) may nevertheless exist. More experiments along this line, especially for spontaneous mutations, are clearly necessary.

If the rate of mutagenesis would depend on the functional activity of a DNA region, natural selection and random fluctuations of gene frequencies might not be the only factors determining the adaptation of populations to their environment. Let us regard, for example, the evolution of a biochemical pathway. A gene controlling an early reaction in the pathway might have evolved by the duplication and subsequent mutation of another gene that controls a later step in the pathway, i.e., by retrogression (11). Since the lack of a biochemical end product usually derepresses the functional activity of the corresponding genes, all these genes, including the duplicated one, might be more exposed to mutagenic effects than other repressed genes. This effect could therefore favor a mutation to the required new property. Although this possibility would by no means imply an inheritance of acquired characters, it would nevertheless influence evolution in this direction. The directional effect would be more important in microorganisms than in higher organisms in which gametes are well protected from environmental influences and mutations play but a minor role when compared to recombination (21).

## E. Evolution of Proteins

The evolutionary alteration of the base composition of DNA entails an alteration in the amino acid sequence of proteins. This follows directly from the fact that the code is essentially uniform (31). Consequently, bacteria with different DNA base frequencies must also have different amino acid compositions (27). Nevertheless, certain base pair changes may not alter the corresponding amino acid because the code is degenerate; i.e., most amino acids can be coded by more than one combination of bases (22). Such base pair changes will be hard to discover. The degeneracy may be useful for the organism, in order to avoid excessive mutations of some important amino acids.

## 1. Retention of Functional Properties

In spite of the many amino acid changes which a given protein undergoes during evolution, its functional property has to be retained if the protein is vital to the organism. Such functionally active spontaneous mutants of a given enzyme do apparently occur quite frequently, as shown by several examples in this Symposium (cf. 2). A comparison of many such mutants indicates that certain amino acids are retained, apparently because they are indispensable for the functional specificity of the protein. However, many amino acids can be altered without a serious impairment of the functional property, although apparently not completely randomly. The restrictions imposed on these alterations are probably twofold.

a. Each amino acid could usually be altered only into three other amino acids, if transitions were the only base pair changes that occurred with reasonable frequency; the number of possible alterations would be even less for certain amino acids (e.g., containing AT pairs in their code) if transitions occurred preferentially in one *direction* (e.g., from GC → AT).

b. Certain amino acid substitutions change the protein configuration too drastically, such as the introduction of a kink by the appearance of proline, the change of disulfide bonding by a cysteine, or the exchange of hydrophobic by hydrophilic groups or vice versa, which would tend to turn the inside of the enzyme out (19).

## 2. Alterations of Functional Properties

Not only do enzymes evolve under preservation of their essential original specificity, but they can apparently also change into new enzymes with different specificity. The original enzymic activity may be lost during this process or it may be retained, if the original gene is first duplicated and then one of the two copies is altered to produce enzymes with new specificity. Indications for this type of evolution are plentiful, although little is known in detail. For example, enzymes having the same cofactor seem also to have other features that indicate their common origins; such enzymes are transaminases requiring pyridoxal phosphate, dehydrogenases requiring NAD or NADP (14), flavoproteins, etc. In addition, enzymes of a given biochemical pathway are probably related by evolution (11).

A clear example of evolutionary relatedness is shown by the similarity of some amino acid sequences of trypsin and chymotrypsin (32), presumably needed for the functionally active regions of the enzymes.

We want to mention, in this connection, some of our results which suggest an evolutionary relationship between three dehydrogenases isolated from *Bacillus subtilis* (34-36). These enzymes, alanine (AlD), malic (MDH), and lactic (LDH) dehydrogenase, have been obtained in crystalline form, and the preparations are homogeneous in several columns, in the ultracentrifuge, and electrophoretically. Their common features are revealed by the following properties: (a) Upon dilution of the enzyme AlD and LDH lose part of their activity, while MDH is completely inactivated under similar conditions (except when NAD is present). (b) Although the molecular weights are different, the sub-

TABLE I

PROPERTIES OF CRYSTALLINE DEHYDROGENASES OF *B. subtilis*

|  | AlD | MDH | LDH |
|---|---|---|---|
| Molecular weight | 228,000 | 150,000 | 145,000 |
| Number of subunits | 6 | 4 | 4 |
| Subunit molecular weight | 38,000 | 37,000 | 36,000 |
| Anti-AlD | +++ | ++ | + |
| Anti-MDH | ++ | +++ | + |
| Anti-LDH | + | + | +++ |

+     = Complement fixation.
++    = Complement fixation or capillary precipitation.
+++   = Complement fixation or capillary or Ochterlony plates.

units have approximately the same size (Table I). (c) AlD and MDH show some immunological cross reaction (that with LDH being much weaker). (d) By fingerprinting AlD and MDH have at least four spots in common (see Fig. 5, spots marked 1, 2, 3, 4), with the same amino acid composition, and even LDH has two (1 and 2) of these spots in common with the other two enzymes. (e) For all three enzymes the Michaelis constants with respect to NAD and NADH are of the same order of magnitude. In addition, the NAD analogs, 3-acetyl- and 3-acetyldeaminopyridine adenine dinucleotide, are better substrates than NAD, whereas thionicotinamide adenine dinucleotide is not a substrate.

Several of these properties are significantly different from the corresponding animal dehydrogenases. (a) No cross reaction between the bacterial and animal dehydrogenases has been found. (b) The affinities to NAD analogs are distinctly different, since the acetylated analogs of NAD are less effective than NAD itself, and thionicotinamide adenine dinucleotide is a rather good substrate (15, 33). These observations suggest the possibility that the different bacterial dehydrogenases may have evolved from a common DNA region *after* the evolutionary branching had occurred between the precursor of the present bacteria and that of the present animals.

## F. Deduction of the DNA Sequence from the Amino Acid Sequence of a Protein

It will soon be possible to assign to each triplet of RNA, and hence DNA, bases a certain amino acid (or no amino acid) (17). If the code were not degenerate, one could therefore derive the sequence of DNA bases in a gene from that of the amino acids in the corresponding protein. But even with degeneracy, a partial, if not a complete, sequence determination appears feasible if the amino acid sequence of many different mutants is available such as for hemoglobin.

As an example let us assume that an isolated amino acid in one protein has been changed into another amino acid in a mutant protein. If each of the two amino acids would correspond to three possible triplets, altogether nine associations of triplets would be possible. In order to decide which of these associations is the correct one, we would have to make assumptions about the mutations which can convert one triplet into the other. Thus the earlier analysis of probable types of mutations becomes very helpful. The following assumptions, made in this sequence, will enable us to uniquely determine the initial and final base triplet:

1. Only a single base pair has been changed.
2. The change was of the transition type.
3. The change occurred from GC to AT.

The third and sometimes even the second assumption may not be necessary to assign unique triplets; the result obtained without them can then be used to decide whether or not the assumptions are elsewhere reasonable, that is, whether really transitions and in particular those from GC → AT are the most frequent base pair changes in DNA.

## Summary

1. Single base pair changes of DNA occur much more frequently than large alterations. Each of these changes alters the structure of only one (or no) protein.

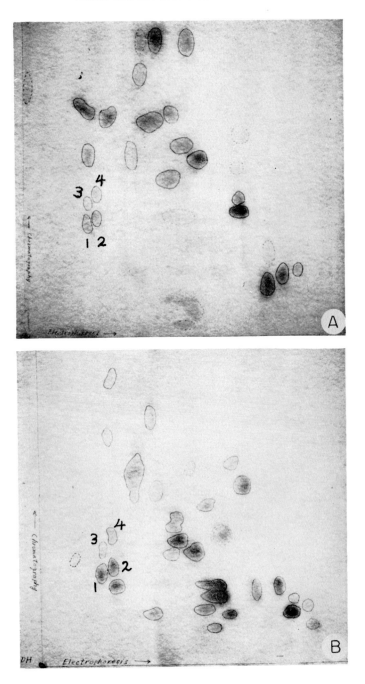

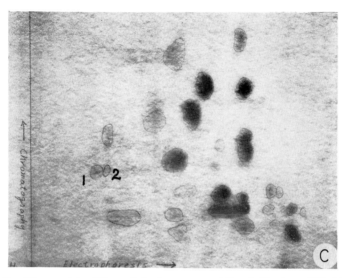

Fig. 5. Fingerprints of three dehydrogenases of *B. subtilis*. A = AlD, B = BDH, C = MDH; vertical axis = chromatography; horizontal axis = electrophoresis.

2. Most surviving base pair changes are of the transition type. Only one amino acid is therefore altered in any corresponding protein.

3. Base pair transitions occur preferentially in one direction, probably from GC to AT. Since the code is apparently uniform, there should be a corresponding drift toward certain amino acids; this drift is blurred by the degeneracy of the code.

4. The relative mutation rates of different DNA sites probably are nearly independent of the environment of the cell. Populations therefore adapt to changing environments mostly by natural selection or genetic drift, although a mutational bias toward useful characters may exist.

5. Many base pair changes cause only minor or no changes in the functional property of a protein. Some changes give rise to a protein with new but related functional properties. Such an evolutionary relatedness is indicated for three dehydrogenases of *B. subtilis*, as shown by a brief outline of the evidence.

6. Rules concerning the preferred types of spontaneous mutations can be employed to deduce the base sequence of normal and mutant genes from the amino acid sequences of the corresponding proteins.

## REFERENCES

1. BOLTON, E. T., AND HOYER, B. H., this volume.
2. BRAUNITZER, G., *in* "Haemoglobin Colloquium" (H. Lehmann and K. Betke, eds.), p. 15, Thieme, Stuttgart, 1962.

3. CARTLEDGE, J. L., AND BLAKESLEE, A. F., *Proc. Natl. Acad. Sci. U.S.*, **20**, 103 (1934); D'AMATO, F., AND HOFFMAN-OSTENHOF, O., *Advan. Genet.*, **8**, 1 (1956).

4. CRICK, F. S., BARNETT, L., BRENNER, S., AND WATTS-TOBIN, R. J., *Nature*, **192**, 1227 (1961).

5. DEMEREC, M., *Genetics*, **22**, 469 (1937); MIYAKI, T., ibid., **45**, 111 (1959); KIRCHNER, C. W. J., *J. Mol. Biol.*, **2**, 331 (1960).

6. DOTY, P., MARMUR, J., AND SUEOKA, N., *Brookhaven Symp. Biol.*, **12**, 1 (1959); ROGER, M., AND HOTCHKISS, R. D., *Proc. Natl. Acad. Sci. U.S.*, **47**, 653 (1961); ROLFE, R., AND EPHRUSSI-TAYLOR, H., *ibid.*, **47**, 653 (1961); GUILD, W. R., *J. Mol. Biol.*, **6**, 214 (1963).

7. FREESE, E., *J. Theoret. Biol.*, **3**, 82 (1962).

8. FREESE, E., in "Molecular Genetics" (J. H. Taylor, ed.), p. 207, Academic Press, New York, 1963.

9. FREESE, E., in "Genetics Today," *Proc. XI Intern. Congr. Genetics*, p. 297, Pergamon Press, 1964.

10. FREESE, E., AND STRACK, H. B., *Proc. Natl. Acad. Sci. U.S.*, **48**, 1796 (1962); STRACK, H. B., FREESE, E. B., AND FREESE, E., *Mutation Res.*, **1**, 10 (1964).

11. HOROWITZ, N., this volume.

12. JOSSE, J., KAISER, A. D., AND KORNBERG, A., *J. Biol. Chem.*, **236**, 864 (1961).

13. KAISER, A. D., AND BALDWIN, R. L., *J. Mol. Biol.*, **4**, 418 (1962).

14. KAPLAN, N. O., this volume.

15. KAPLAN, N. O., CIOTTI, M. M., HAMOLSKY, M., AND BIEBER, R. E., *Science*, **131**, 392 (1960); CAHN, R. D., KAPLAN, N. O., LEVINE, L., AND ZWILLING, E., *ibid.*, **136**, 962 (1962).

16. KORNBERG, A., this volume.

17. LEDER, P., AND NIRENBERG, M., *Proc. Natl. Acad. Sci. U.S.*, **52**, 420 (1964); NIRENBERG, M., AND LEDER, P., *Science*, **145**, 1399 (1964).

18. LERMAN, L. S., *J. Mol. Biol.*, **3**, 18 (1961); *Proc. Natl. Acad. Sci. U.S.*, **49**, 94 (1963).

19. MARGOLIASH, E., *Proc. Natl. Acad. Sci. U.S.*, **50**, 672 (1963); EPSTEIN, C. J., *Nature*, **203**, 1350 (1964).

20. MARGOLIN, P., AND MUKAI, F. H., *Z. Vererbungslehre*, **92**, 330 (1961); KIRCHNER, C. W. J., *J. Mol. Biol.*, **2**, 331 (1960).

21. MAYR, E., "Animal Species and Evolution," Belknap Press, Harvard University, Cambridge, 1963.

22. NIRENBERG, M. W., AND JONES, O. W., in "Informational Macromolecules" (H. Vogel, V. Bryson, and J. O. Lampen, eds.), p. 451, Academic Press, New York, 1963.

23. NOVICK, A., AND SZILARD, L., *Proc. Natl. Acad. Sci. U.S.*, **36**, 708 (1950); NOVICK, A., *Brookhaven Symp. Biol.*, **8**, 201 (1956).

24. RYAN, F., *Ann. N.Y. Acad. Sci.*, **19**, 515 (1957); *J. Gen. Microbiol.*, **21**, 530 (1959).

25. SCHILDKRAUT, C. L., MARMUR, J., AND DOTY, P., *J. Mol. Biol.*, **4**, 430 (1962).

26. SETLOW, R. B., AND CARRIER, W. L., *Proc. Natl. Acad. Sci. U.S.*, **51**, 226 (1964); BOYCE, R. P., AND HOWARD-FLANDERS, P., *ibid.*, **51**, 293 (1964).

27. SUEOKA, N., *Proc. Natl. Acad. Sci. U.S.*, **47**, 1141 (1961).

28. SUEOKA, N., *Proc. Natl. Acad. Sci. U.S.*, **48**, 582 (1962).

29. SUEOKA, N., MARMUR, J., AND DOTY, P., *Nature*, **183**, 1429 (1959); ROLFE, R., AND MESELSON, M., *Proc. Natl. Acad. Sci. U.S.*, **45**, 1039 (1959).

30. Swanson, C. P., "Cytology and Cytogenetics," Prentice-Hall, Englewood Cliffs, New Jersey, 1957.
31. Von Ehrenstein, G., and Lipmann, F., Proc. Natl. Acad. Sci. U.S., **47**, 941 (1961); Signer, E. R., Torriani, A., and Levinthal, C., Cold Spring Harbor Symp. Quant. Biol., **26**, 31 (1961); Abel, P., and Trautner, T. A., Z. Vererbungslehre, **95**, 66 (1964).
32. Walsh, K. A., and Neurath, H., Proc. Natl. Acad. Sci. U.S., **52**, 884 (1964).
33. Wiggert, B. O., and Villee, C. A., J. Biol. Chem., **239**, 444 (1964).
34. Yoshida, A., J. Biol. Chem., **240**, 1113 (1965); ibid., **240**, 1118 (1965).
35. Yoshida, A., and Freese, E., Biochim. Biophys. Acta, in press; Yoshida, A., Biochim. Biophys. Acta, in press.
36. Yoshida, A., and Freese, E., Biochim. Biophys. Acta, **92**, 33 (1964); ibid., **96**, 248 (1965).

# On the Evolution of the Lactose Utilization Gene System in Enteric Bacteria

S. E. Luria

*Department of Biology,*
*Massachusetts Institute of Technology,*
*Cambridge, Massachusetts*

An interesting case history in gene evolution is that of the lactose utilization system in enteric bacteria—an old darling of molecular biology. The lactose-utilizing members of the group, such as *Escherichia coli*, have β-D-galactosidase and galactoside permease (plus galactoside transacetylase) determined by adjacent genes, $z^+$ and $y^+$, members of the *lac* operon. This operon is subject to functional control by its repressor-producing neighbor gene $i^+$ (3). *Shigella dysenteriae* is a very close relative of *E. coli*, and genetic transfers, followed by genetic integration, occur rather freely among organisms of these two species (4, 6). Yet, *S. dysenteriae* is typically *lac⁻*: several strains examined have the *i* and the *z* genes but have neither galactoside permease nor transacetylase and, by genetic analysis, appear to lack the *y* gene altogether, no $y^+$ recombination being obtained from transductions or crosses between *S. dysenteriae* and $y^-$ point mutants of *E. coli* (2, 5, 7).

The absence of the permease and the resulting inability to use lactose effectively appear to have played some remarkable evolutionary tricks on the rest of the lactose-utilizing gene set. The $z^+$ genes of *S. dysenteriae* strains are more or less ineffectual, producing levels of galactosidase activity between 0 and 20% of those produced by the $z^+$ gene of *E. coli*. Yet, the *z* genes are still homologous: intragenic recombination is readily observed in genetic transfers between *E. coli* $z^-$ and *S. dysenteriae*, albeit at lower frequencies than in crosses between $z^-$ mutants of *E. coli* (2, 5). Even more significant, the galactosidases of *S. dysenteriae* appear to be proteins resembling that of *E. coli* in molecular size and kinetics of enzyme action, but with a lower turnover number (8). Also, the *dysenteriae* galactosidases are more heat-sensitive than the *coli* enzyme, both in their stability to heat treatment and in the range of temperatures within which they are synthesized. A similar situation has been described in *Paracolobactron aerogenoides*, another distant relative of *E. coli* (1).

By contrast, the $i^+$ (repressor) gene of *S. dysenteriae* is perfectly functional, and any $i^+$ gene, irrespective of its origin, is equally effective in causing repression of the *lac* operons of either *E. coli* or *S. dysenteriae*. So are the $i^+$ genes formed by recombination between $i^-$ mutants of *E. coli* and of *S. dysenteriae* (8).

An attractive interpretation of these findings is that the loss of permease has played the key role in the evolution of the *lac* region by rendering the galactosidase inoperative in lactose utilization and thereby permitting accumulation of a variety of mutations within the *z* gene. The $i^+$ gene, of course, has retained and even increased its usefulness, since it prevents the wasteful biosynthesis of a now useless protein, the galactosidase, which if derepressed would constitute up to 5% of the total cellular protein. The evolutionary reasons for the loss of the permease gene in *Shigella* remain a most interesting puzzle.

## REFERENCES

1. ANDERSON, J. M., AND RICKENBERG, H. V., *J. Bacteriol.*, **80**, 297 (1960).
2. FRANKLIN, N., AND LURIA, S. E., *Virology*, **15**, 290 (1961).
3. JACOB, F., AND MONOD, J., *Cold Spring Harbor Symp. Quant. Biol.*, **26**, 193 (1961).
4. LENNOX, E. S., *Virology*, **1**, 190 (1955).
5. LURIA, S. E., ADAMS, M. J., AND TING, R. C., *Virology*, **12**, 358 (1960).
6. LURIA, S. E., AND BURROUS, J. W., *J. Bacteriol.*, **74**, 461 (1957).
7. RICKENBERG, H. V., *J. Bacteriol.*, **80**, 421 (1960).
8. SARKAR, S., Ph.D. Thesis, Massachusetts Institute of Technology, 1963.

# Experiments Suggesting Evolution to Protein[1]

SIDNEY W. FOX

*Institute of Molecular Evolution,*
*University of Miami, Coral Gables, Florida, and*
*Department of Chemistry, Florida State University,*
*Tallahassee, Florida*

J. D. Bernal has stated recently, "Questions of origin have a logic of their own" (1). The special logic of questions of origin applies to, and was applied by Bernal to, methods of answering those questions. When those questions are answered, one should anticipate that the answers must not have an existence of their own, but should ultimately fit into a conceptual continuum. When the questions concern the origin of protein, or of other biochemical systems, the continuum must span prebiological molecular evolution and Darwinian organismic evolution unless one assumes a discontinuity between pre-life and life. Theoretical constructions which do not comport with pertinent parts of such a continuum can hardly be valid models. For instance, the validity of any simulated primitive synthesis of amino acids should be evaluated by the ease with which the process can be reconciled with the necessary subsequent step of condensation polymerization.

Experiments which have been performed in the context of the origin of life, or of the origin of protein, have several relationships to the subject matter of this conference. These relationships involve (a) the background of knowledge of evolution of protein molecules in organisms, which provides clues to the conceptual origin of protein[2] (7), (b) the employment of knowledge of the properties of contemporary protein as a test of the validity of experimental models of primitive protein, and (c) conceptual answers to some of the problems of primordial protein. The first protein was of course the starting point for evolving proteins. The original protein may well have been closely related to

---

[1] This work was aided by Grants NsG-173-62 and NsG-689 of the National Aeronautics and Space Administration. Contribution 040 of the Institute of Molecular Evolution.

[2] Protein is used instead of the term proteins to connote the theoretical concept of a family of protein molecules related in an evolutionary manner.

the starting point of gene-controlled enzymes and of polymerases. One purpose of this paper will be to suggest the relationship of earliest protein to the protocell. Both proteins and genes may have required the simultaneous evolution of the cell (cf. 28).

Studies in our laboratory of the organismic evolution of proteins began with considerations of applying sequential and terminal residue methods to tracing evolution of primary structure of protein molecules (5, 7, 15, 43). Porter and Sanger were the first to provide information for such possibilities (39). Some of the concepts which emerged from these studies in our laboratory were: a Darwinian explanation of microheterogeneity (6) of protein preparations (again recently shown not to be entirely explainable as artifacts (4), demonstration that the evolution of protein has proceeded to yield only a minute fraction of the theoretical possibilities (7), an explanation of the similarities between protein molecules (7, 15) as related to slow stepwise substitution of residues, the use of such techniques in chemical taxonomy (43), and detailed analyses of genealogy of homologous and heterologous proteins (43).

Studies of genealogical relationships of proteins posed the possibility that the results might harbor clues of the origin of the first protein. In particular, the presence of disproportionately large ratios of the dicarboxylic amino acids (as acids plus amides) invited attention. This feature suggested the possibility that these contents are an evolutionary reflection of relatively high proportions of these amino acids in the first protein and, correspondingly, of the molecular matrix which may have yielded the first protein (10). Experiments were accordingly constructed to test the effect of sufficient proportions of glutamic acid, glutamine (17), aspartic acid, or asparagine on the anhydrocopolymerization of amino acids. When sufficient proportions of these were heated in dry mixtures of the eighteen amino acids common to protein, genuine polyanhydro-α-amino acids resulted (17, 18). This result is in contrast to the long-known pyrolytic behavior of amino acids as depicted on the left in Fig. 1. Clean polymers can be produced by heating dry in the molten state to temperatures such as 170°C followed by purification of the products from water through salting out with ammonium sulfate (right side of Fig. 1). The polymer shown on the right in Fig. 1 can be produced from mixtures of the eighteen amino acids common to protein; the polymers contain some of each of the eighteen, plus amide groups. The polymerization under these conditions can accommodate more or less than eighteen types of amino acid. In such heteropolyamino acids, the proportion of each neutral or basic amino acid can be high enough that it overlaps the proportion found typically in proteins (24).

Although the proportion of aspartic acid tends to be considerably above the usual per cent found in protein, fractions having less aspartic acid have been isolated (36). For those polymers having relatively large proportions of aspartic acid, the polymer is of course acidic in reaction. These acid protein-like polymers (acid *proteinoids*) typically have weights of many thousands. Their properties have been studied

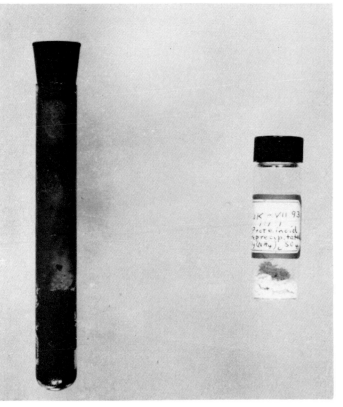

Fig. 1. The effects of heating dry amino acids above the boiling point of water. On the *left*—the usual result. On the *right*—with sufficient proportions of aspartic acid and of glutamic acid. This polymer has, in addition, been repurified by salting out the aqueous solution with ammonium sulfate.

extensively and reported a number of times. In this paper, the key properties which have been compared with those of protein are collected, with relevant references, in Table I.

In comparing the thermal proteinoids with contemporary proteins, one should recall that, inasmuch as no one protein has all the pertinent structure and properties usually imputed to proteins as a class, a comparison with proteinoids requires that the latter be scrutinized also as a class. In the case of each class of polymer, more data are clearly yet to be accumulated.

Besides comparing proteinoids with contemporary protein, one may attempt also to compare proteinoids with primitive organismic protein. Since no sure example of primitive protein exists, this comparison requires an indirect approach. The approach can conceptually be made through theoretical identification of the evolutionary pathways leading to and from primordial protein. Difficult as this may be to do with certainty, interpretable data are at hand. Of the many laboratory models of the prebiological synthesis of amino acids, one has been found to

TABLE I

PROPERTIES OF THERMAL POLY-α-AMINO ACIDS COMPARED
TO PROPERTIES OF PROTEINS

| Property | Reference |
|---|---|
| Qualitative composition | (17, 18, 24, 33) |
| Quantitative composition | (18, 19, 29, 30, 33) |
| Range of molecular weight | (18, 22) |
| Color tests | (17, 18, 33) |
| Solubilities | (17, 18, 33) |
| Inclusion of nonamino acid groups | (22) |
| Optical activity | (22, 40) |
| Salting-in and salting-out properties | (18, 22) |
| Precipitability by protein reagents | (18, 33) |
| Hypochromicity | (40) |
| Infrared absorption maxima | (18, 22) |
| Recoverability of amino acids on hydrolysis | (24) |
| Susceptibility to proteolytic enzymes | (18, 33, 34) |
| Catalytic activity | (22, 40) |
| Inactivatability by heating in aqueous solution | (40) |
| "Nonrandom" (nonuniform) sequential distribution of residues | (9, 10, 23) |
| Nutritive quality | (18, 35) |
| Morphogenicity | (10) |

produce almost all the amino acids common to protein and no other amino acids. This model is the thermal one, which, from a geological perspective, comports most easily with a continuum in which the next evolutionary step of anhydrocopolymerization is also thermal (31).

Properties of protein that one would ordinarily think of, and which have not yet been shown to be present in the thermal poly-α-amino acids, are antigenicity and helicity. Hypochromicity has been found, however. This hypochromicity has been shown to be correlated with the splitting in water of the somewhat unstable aspartimide linkage (40), so the question of helicity is yet unanswered. The properties of anti-genicity and helicity have been shown to be controllably introduced into the Leuchs type of poly-α-amino acid (41); attempts to find these in thermal polymers have been incomplete as yet. Some proteins lack these properties. Accordingly, attempts to distinguish biosynthetic protein on Mars from spontaneously generated thermal poly-α-amino acids (27) by remote monitoring of tests could not be based on any qualitatively distinctive criteria. The similarities of the chemically synthetic and the biosynthetic polymers are emphasized by this evaluation in a context of comparative planetology.

Recent data which are not documented to the degree of those in the table show that thermal proteinoids have weak but appreciable activity for the breakdown of a natural substrate, D-glucose, to glucuronic acid, and that this product is then decarboxylated (25). These weak activities were reliably demonstrated with aseptically prepared proteinoid and U-C$^{14}$-glucose. Weak catalytic activities sufficient to launch an evolutionary succession of organisms are all that would be needed at first. The evolutionist would anticipate that such primitive activities would be enriched by Darwinian selection to provide the powerful enzymes of contemporary organisms (3).

Another unpublished study, reported to the International Congress of Biochemistry in 1964 (36), included the report that a crude proteinoid can be fractionated on columns to yield many fractions each of which contains all the amino acids common both to protein and to the unfractionated proteinoid.

The geological locales in which the anhydropolymerization of "spontaneous" amino acids could occur have been discussed (8, 12, 25). The ways in which the amino acids themselves might arise geologically have been reviewed (11). A salient feature of the experiments suggesting the origin of amino acids is the frequency and extent to which the key aspartic acid appears among the reaction products (27).

The property listed last in Table I is that of morphogenicity. The self-organizing properties of macromolecules have been invoked in a biological context (28). Wald in particular has suggested that these may have been crucial in the emergence of the first cell (44). Also remarkable was the foresight of C. R. Darwin, who stated in 1871 (10):

It is often said that all the conditions for the first production of a living organism are now present, which could ever have been present. But if (and oh! what a big if!) we could conceive in some warm little pond, with all sorts of ammonia and phosphoric salts, light, heat, electricity &c present, that a proteine compound was chemically formed ready to undergo still more complex changes . . .

Darwin's remarkable insight is borne out by the model, if one defers the pond until the "proteine compound" is formed in an anhydrous or hypohydrous environment. By intrusion of water into the hot mixture of anhydropolymerized amino acids, vast numbers of microscopic units having many of the properties of cells are formed (14). These properties cannot be adequately evaluated without review of the visible consequences of these and other simple experiments. Such pictures are now in the literature. Two examples will be presented here. The quite fully documented properties of these units are set forth in Table II. A study

### TABLE II
#### PROPERTIES OF MICROPARTICLES SPONTANEOUSLY ORGANIZED FROM THERMAL POLY-α-AMINO ACIDS

| Property | Reference |
| --- | --- |
| Stability (to standing, centrifugation, sectioning) | (20, 21) |
| Microscopic size | (10, 20, 21) |
| Variability in shape: spheres, "buds," filaments | (27, 28) |
| Uniformity of size | (21) |
| Numerousness | (27) |
| Stainability | (26) |
| Producibility as gram-positive or gram-negative particles | (26) |
| Solubility parallel to that of bacteria | (26) |
| Shrinkability in hypertonic solution | (21) |
| Swellability in hypotonic solution | (21) |
| Simulation of cell division | (28) |
| Electron micrographability | (16) |
| Presence of boundary | (16) |
| Selectivity of boundary | (28) |
| Bilamellarity of boundary | (16) |
| ATP-splitting activity (by suitable inclusion of Zn) | (13) |
| Structured associations (algal-like) | (27) |

of these properties indicates that natural experiments could have converted "primordial gases" such as methane, ammonia, and water to amino acids, amino acids to early protein, and the primitive protein to protocells with which natural experiments could have continued (28).

Two examples of the kind of self-organizing propensity in the thermal poly-α-amino acids are presented. In Fig. 2 is seen a photomicrograph of proteinoid microspheres in a suspension in which the pH of 3.0 has been raised by allowing a drop of McIlwain buffer of pH 6.5 to diffuse in under the cover glass of a microscope slide. The self-organized microspheres (27) are thus reorganized (28). The relationship depicted raises the question of whether the units appearing to have septa result from fusion or fission of the simpler spherical units. This question has been answered by many time-lapse cinematographic studies. The studies indicate that the process is fission (28) in these particular experiments.

Another example of self-organizing properties is found in Fig. 3. This photograph shows proteinoid microspheres which have undergone

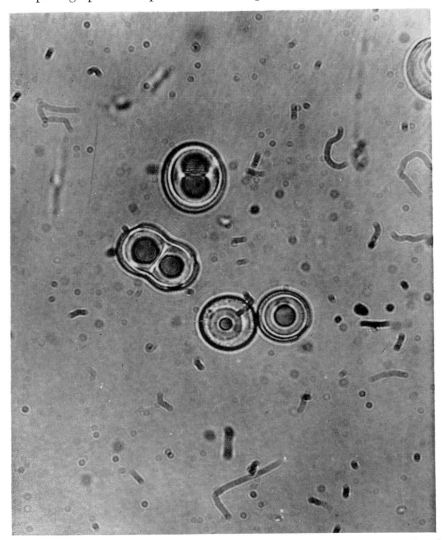

Fig. 2. Proteinoid microspheres in which septate division has been induced by elevation of pH.

the pH increase of Fig. 2 and have been stained with osmic acid, sectioned, and electron-micrographed (16). In the photograph may be seen a double layer (16) such as had been believed to characterize living cells (38). The examples presented illustrate the many cell-like properties found in and documented for the proteinoid microspheres. The experiments which serve as a model of evolutionary processes thus deal with evolution to and beyond the first protein.

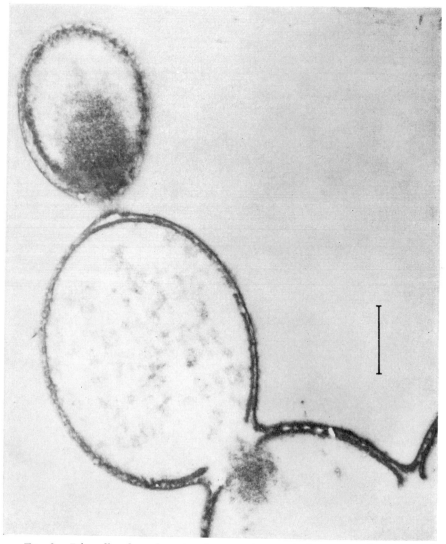

Fig. 3. Bilamellar boundary in electron-micrographed section of osmic acid-stained thermal acid proteinoid microsphere. Marker indicates 1 micron.

Clearly, the proteinoid produced by heating differs from protein in at least the fact that the mechanism of its production is thermal. The synthesis of protein biologically requires, at least at present, ATP-dependent reactions. The way in which the more primitive kind of synthesis may have been supplanted by the more modern one is suggested by the fact that the known ATP-splitting ability of Zn salts (42) can be built into microspheres so that they split ATP at 40°C. Such experiments have been performed in our laboratory by Joseph and Wiggert (13).

The fact that near-protein can be obtained in the fashion indicated resolves an old dilemma which has hindered the development of a theory of spontaneous generation. The concepts that (a) the production of cells required protein and that (b) the production of protein required the pre-existence of the cell (2, 32, 37) have been a barrier to a conceptual continuum.

The pathway that has been suggested by laboratory studies involves first the production of molecules very much like those of protein, in the geological vessel rather than in a cell. The similarity of such poly-α-amino acid to protein is manifest in many characteristics, and especially in the tendency to form a kind of cell, at least as the cell is minimally defined. The experiments also demonstrate how such units can be made to approach, in steps, the viable contemporary cell. The basic dilemma of the evolutionary pathway to the first protein, and beyond to a precellular form, is now solved in principle.[3] The sequence emerging from the experiments poses the possibility that the evolution of genes and enzymes should be examined in the context of evolving proteins, cells, and genes.

## ACKNOWLEDGMENT

The author is indebted to numerous associates who are named in the bibliography.

## REFERENCES

1. BERNAL, J. D., in "The Origins of Prebiological Systems" (S. W. Fox, ed.), p. 52, Academic Press, New York, 1965.
2. BLUM, H., "Time's Arrow and Evolution," 2nd ed., p. 170, Princeton Univ. Press, Princeton, New Jersey, 1955.
3. CALVIN, M., Science, 130, 1170 (1959).
4. FOSTER, J. F., SOGAMI, M., AND PETERSEN, H. A., Sixth Intern. Congr. Biochem. Abstr. II-60 (1964).
5. Fox, S. W., Advan. Protein Chem., 2, 155 (1945).
6. Fox, S. W., Am. Naturalist, 87, 253 (1953).

---

[3] A thermal pathway to polynucleotides has been suggested also [Schwartz, A., and Fox, S. W., Biochim. Biophys. Acta, 87, 694 (1964)].

7. Fox, S. W., *Am. Scientist,* **44**, 347 (1956).
8. Fox, S. W., *J. Chem. Educ.,* **34**, 472 (1957).
9. Fox, S. W., *Bull. Am. Inst. Biol. Sci.,* **9**, 20 (1959).
10. Fox, S. W., *Science,* **132**, 200 (1960).
11. Fox, S. W., *in* "Organic Geochemistry" (I. A. Breger, ed.), p. 36, Macmillan, New York, 1963.
12. Fox, S. W., *Nature,* **201**, 336 (1964).
13. Fox, S. W., *in* "The Origins of Prebiological Systems" (S. W. Fox, ed.), p. 361, Academic Press, New York, 1965.
14. Fox, S. W., *in* "Proceedings of a Conference on Theoretical Biology" (G. J. Jacobs, ed.), NASA Special Report, in press, 1965.
15. Fox, S. W., AND FOSTER, J. F., *in* "Introduction to Protein Chemistry," p. 429, Wiley, New York, 1957.
16. Fox, S. W., AND FUKUSHIMA, S., *in* "Problems of Evolutionary and Industrial Biochemistry" (V. L. Kretovich, T. E. Pavlovskaya, and G. A. Deborin, eds.), p. 93, U.S.S.R. Publishing House, Moscow, 1964.
17. Fox, S. W., AND HARADA, K., *Science,* **128**, 1214 (1958).
18. Fox, S. W., AND HARADA, K., *J. Am. Chem. Soc.,* **82**, 3745 (1960).
19. Fox, S. W., AND HARADA, K., *Arch. Biochem. Biophys.,* **86**, 281 (1960).
20. Fox, S. W., HARADA, K., AND KENDRICK, J., *Science,* **129**, 1221 (1959).
21. Fox, S. W., HARADA, K., AND KENDRICK, J., *in* "International Oceanographic Congress Preprints" (M. Sears, ed.), p. 80, Amer. Assoc. Adv. Sci., Washington, D.C., 1959.
22. Fox, S. W., HARADA, K., AND ROHLFING, D. L., *in* "Polyamino Acids, Polypeptides, and Proteins" (H. Stahmann, ed.), p. 47, Univ. of Wisconsin Press, Madison, 1962.
23. Fox, S. W., HARADA, K., AND VEGOTSKY, A., *Experientia,* **15**, 81 (1959).
24. Fox, S. W., HARADA, K., WOODS, K. R., AND WINDSOR, C. R., *Arch. Biochem. Biophys.,* **102**, 439 (1963).
25. Fox, S. W., AND KRAMPITZ, G., in Friday Evening lecture, Woods Hole Marine Biological Laboratory, 24 July 1964. *Nature,* **205**, 328 (1965).
26. Fox, S. W., AND YUYAMA, S., *J. Bacteriol.,* **85**, 279 (1963).
27. Fox, S. W., AND YUYAMA, S., *Ann. N.Y. Acad. Sci.,* **108**, 487 (1963).
28. Fox, S. W., AND YUYAMA, S., *Comp. Biochem. Physiol.,* **11**, 317 (1964).
29. HARADA, K., AND FOX, S. W., *J. Am. Chem. Soc.,* **80**, 2694 (1958).
30. HARADA, K., AND FOX, S. W., *Arch. Biochem. Biophys.* **86**, 274 (1960).
31. HARADA, K., AND FOX, S. W., *Nature,* **201**, 335 (1964).
32. JIRGENSONS, B., "Natural Organic Macromolecules" p. 437, Macmillan (Pergamon), New York, 1962.
33. KRAMPITZ, G., *Naturwissenschaften,* **46**, 558 (1959).
34. KRAMPITZ, G., *in* "Polyamino Acids, Polypeptides, and Proteins" (M. Stahmann, ed.), p. 55, Univ. of Wisconsin Press, Madison, Wisconsin, 1962.
35. KRAMPITZ, G., AND KNAPPEN, F., *Nature,* **195**, 385 (1962).
36. KRAMPITZ, G., AND FOX, S. W., *Sixth Intern. Congr. Biochem. Abstr.* II-101 (1964).
37. OPARIN, A. I., "The Origin of Life on the Earth," 3rd ed., p. 217, Academic Press, New York, 1957.
38. PICKEN, L., "The Organization of Cells," pp. 243, 335, 348, Clarendon Press, Oxford, Britain, 1960.
39. PORTER, R. R., AND SANGER, F., *Biochem. J.,* **42**, 287 (1948).

40. ROHLFING, D. L., Ph.D. Dissertation, Florida State University, 1964.
41. STAHMANN, M. (ed.), "Polyamino Acids, Polypeptides, and Proteins," Univ. of Wisconsin Press, Madison, Wisconsin, 1962.
42. TETAS, M., AND LOWENSTEIN, J. M., *Biochemistry*, **2**, 350 (1963).
43. VEGOTSKY, A., AND FOX, S. W., *in* "Comparative Biochemistry" (M. Florkin and H. S. Mason, eds.), Vol. 4, p. 185, Academic Press, New York, 1962.
44. WALD, G., *Sci. Am.*, p. 50 (August 1954).

# Discussion of Part V

W. D. McElroy, A. Bendich, C. Yanofsky, T. H. Jukes, N. O. Kaplan

Dr. McElroy: I would like to make an observation. Unfortunately we do not know all the amino acid sequences in the various luciferases; but one would presume, on the basis of present knowledge, that the secondary and tertiary structure of proteins depend upon the amino acid sequence. Consequently, the changes in luciferase must be due to a change in the amino acid sequence. These subtle changes in luciferase bring out functional differences as illustrated by a change in the color of light emitted. Other catalytic properties of the enzyme, including specificity of the substrate, have not been changed. The important thing from an evolutionary standpoint is that even this subtle difference has been used adaptively by the organism as a means of identification.

Once we are able to study other enzymes from a functional standpoint it is possible that very discrete changes in an enzyme structure can be observed to alter behavioral characteristics even though the apparent catalytic property of the enzyme has not changed. Alterations of sites concerned with regulation of enzyme activity may be greatly affected by small changes in the secondary and tertiary structure. Such changes may or may not influence the "catalytic site."

Dr. Bendich: It seems to me that there is little question but that, in the several instances discussed here and in the literature, mutations can be described in terms of altered proteins or enzymes in which a single amino acid (or more) has been changed. There is also little question but that the chemical mutagenic agents discussed this morning by Dr. Freese can exert chemical effects on components of DNA and RNA.

The assumption is made that these chemically induced mutations involve an actual change in the genetic material to which alterations in amino acids (or in their sequences) can be ascribed.

There may be a flaw in the argument though, and that is, in no case (unless there is something new that has come up since the discussion this morning) has there ever been an example offered in which an actual chemical change in the genetic determinants has been demonstrated following chemical treatment which has been maintained in future generations in the offspring of mutated bacteria, bacteriophage, and so on. There have been a couple of hundred mutant forms of TMV or phage studied, for example. These have been induced by six or seven chemically unrelated mutagens, and in some instances the same changes frequently occur regardless of the chemical nature of the mutagen.

The chemistry of the mutational events is supposed to be well worked out. In some instances, for the proteins which have been isolated from the mutant TMV's, as many as 10 percent of the amino acids have been changed in position, or in kind. And yet in no instance has there been a chemically or experimentally significant change observed in the base composition of the RNA in the TMV's examined.

Does anyone here know of any example of a chemical change in the prime genetic material following chemically induced mutation?

DR. YANOFSKY: If you could tell us how to isolate a single gene or a messenger corresponding to a single gene, and how to detect single nucleotide changes in nucleic acid fragments, then we probably could provide the answer.

DR. BENDICH: If we were to define the term "gene" chemically, it might be easier to find a method for isolation. In the TMV situation, there are a couple of hundred mutants studied, some of which showed rather massive changes in amino acid composition, and yet there has not been even as much as a one percent change in base composition. I feel one should expect some changes if we take into account currently held views concerning the relationship between base composition and amino acid composition.

On the other hand, there have been several examples, not presented here, in which there have been massive substitutions of one base by another in the nucleic acids of a variety of microbiological forms. For example, it is possible to replace 30 percent of the uracil in TMV RNA by fluorouracil. The resulting virus is still functional. My understanding, from Gordon's work, is that no mutations have appeared in the case of TMV (or *Escherichia coli*). It is possible to replace quite a bit of the thymine by 5-bromouracil in phage and *coli* nucleic acids without demonstrable genetic change.

If I remember from the work in which all the thymine of a particular phage was replaced by bromouracil, the resulting phage was still functional. So there are examples of specific base changes without corresponding genetic change. For my money, evidence for chemical change in the genetic material has not yet come forth, yet we all assume a specific chemical alteration following treatment with a chemical mutagen.

DR. JUKES: Regarding the point raised by Dr. Bendich, there is certainly an extensive literature on base changes in TMV occasioned by nitrous acid. This is paralleled, of course, by changes in the coat protein, although there has not been a base sequence isolated and characterized that reflects the exact change in coat proteins. Obviously, the surviving particles are those that have a very small number of changes, and most of the particles treated with nitrous acid lose their viability. Treatment of synthetic polyribonucleotides with nitrous acid changes their coding properties in a manner predictable from deamination, for example, poly UA (5:1) codes for valine (2U, 1G) after, but not before, $HNO_2$ treatment [C. Basilio, A. J. Wahba, P. Lengyel, J. F. Speyer, and S. Ochoa, *Proc. Natl. Acad. Sci. U.S.*, **48**, 613 (1962)].

DR. BENDICH: What I am referring to, Tom, is actual analysis of base composition on mutant forms and we have not yet found a mutant RNA which is chemically different from the parent nucleic acid. This is not only true of TMV RNA, but it holds also for those bacteriophages in which mutation has been induced by chemical agents. DNA of the offspring phage, the mutant phage, has the same base composition as the original so far as one can tell. This does not mean that they are identical. Perhaps the base sequences are altered. The point I am making is that the evidence is not in yet that the genetic material has undergone those chemical changes we might infer from our scanty knowledge of the reactions involved. Let us not forget that nitrous acid induces cross-linking in "double-stranded" DNA, yet what is stressed is that nitrous acid converts an amino base into an hydroxy base. Very recently, nitrous acid has been shown to convert guanosine to "2-nitro-inosine" [R. Shapiro, *J. Am. Chem. Soc.*, **86**, 2948 (1964)], as well as to xanthosine. Who is to say what change has actually occurred in the genetic material in the absence of pertinent chemical evidence?

DR. KAPLAN: I would just like to re-emphasize some of the points which Dr. McElroy brought up. I think what he has found is very important. The investigation of the effect of protein conformation on functional properties is, at least to a biochemist, one of the most fascinating approaches to evolution.

For example, one just has to look at what happens when one boils a lobster—the change of color. Dr. Jencks has been studying the effects of change of protein structure with various reagents, such as urea and guanidine, and he has found that the absorption of this lobster pigment can change anywhere from around 400 m$\mu$ to 630 m$\mu$, going from the red to the blue, depending on the conformation of the protein [see *Arch. Biochem. Biophys.*, **167**, 511 (1964)].

From a functional point of view, this is very important in evolution, because, as Dr. McElroy emphasized, a slight change in protein structure will give changes in color. You even see this with some of the co-enzymes that are involved in oxido-reduction reactions, such as flavins; when the flavin adenine dinucleotide is bound to different proteins, the potential of the flavin may change as much as 0.3 millivolt. We can see that the protein structure has a very important part in evolution.

## PART VI
# EVENING LECTURE
DeWitt Stetten, Jr., *Presiding*

# Degeneracy of the Genetic Code: Extent, Nature, and Genetic Implications

T. M. Sonneborn[1]

*Zoology Department, Indiana University, Bloomington, Indiana*

## Summary

Part I of this paper deals with the amount of degeneracy in the genetic code or, looked at in reverse, the amount of nonsense. Section A considers the experimental evidence and suggests (a) that technical difficulties have prevented assigning meaning to the still unassigned triplets and (b) that the validity of the earlier evidences for nonsense triplets may be questioned in the light of recent discoveries. Complete degeneracy of the code and total absence of nonsense have not yet been excluded. Section B comes to the conclusion, on the basis of general evolutionary considerations, that natural selection would be expected to establish and preserve a completely degenerate code. Section C points out that different nondegenerate codes differ greatly in the built-in frequency of nonsense mutations by single base substitutions.

Part II deals with the nature of degeneracy in the existing code. The high frequency of shared doublets between "synonyms" (i.e., codons for the same amino acid) suggests that they are "connected," that is, interconvertible by altering one base only. Among the sets of synonyms thus far reported, some *must* be completely connected, and, in the absence of knowledge of the order of the bases, the synonyms of *each* set could be ordered so as to be completely connected. Current knowledge leads to the expectation of either complete connectedness or a high degree of connectedness among synonyms.

---

[1] Publication No. 759 from the Department of Zoology, Indiana University. At the Symposium, only Part III of this paper was presented, and in very abbreviated form, because of the lateness of the hour. I thank the editors for permitting and encouraging me to include the full paper in the printed record. This work was supported by Contract COO-235-15 of the Atomic Energy Commission and Grant E81G of the American Cancer Society.

Part III explores the consequences of complete connectedness between synonyms; the consequences would be modified only quantitatively, not qualitatively, if connectedness is less than complete. Section A discusses "silent" mutations, i.e., single-base changes that yield a synonym. These *must* occur in the code as now known. Their frequency (if equal probability of all base substitutions is assumed) depends on the number of synonyms in a set, on the way in which the synonyms are connected, and on whether the various synonyms are used equally or unequally. By selecting one synonym of a set for almost exclusive usage, the minimal percentage of silent mutations stays constant at 11.1% in sets of two or more synonyms, but the maximum increases steadily with set size up to 100% in sets of ten or more. If the synonyms of a set are equally used, the pattern of connection that yields the highest frequency of silent mutations gives peaks for sets of four, seven, and ten synonyms. It would not be surprising if 20% or more of all single-base mutations were silent unless the frequency of transversions is greatly restricted. Comparable analyses can be made of a quadruplet code. The frequency of mutations to synonyms is not enough to account fully for modulatory mutations, but it is enough to constitute a potential source of error in certain amino acid replacement studies. Section B points out that the degeneracy of the existing code implies as an evolutionary consequence a molecular orthogenesis, that is, marked built-in differences among the synonyms of a set in their possible amino acid replacements by single-base mutations. Section C shows the surprising fact that crossing over between synonyms *must* in certain cases yield recombinant codons for a different amino acid. Although likely to be scored as mutations, these recombinations would be much more frequent than true mutations. The advantage of connected synonymy is opposed by the disadvantage of these recombinational pseudomutations. Possible ways out of this paradox are discussed.

## I. The Amount of Degeneracy in the Code

### A. *Experimental Considerations*

In 1963, Crick (4) and Woese (25) critically examined the evidences for degeneracy of the code and concluded that they demonstrated the existence of some degeneracy and indicated a high degree of degeneracy. With this conclusion a number of others (e.g., 6, 18) agree. Evidences for more codons have meanwhile appeared; more than 50 are listed (see Table II) in the papers of Nirenberg *et al.* (13) and Speyer *et al.* (18). The strength of the evidence varies from codon to codon. Some codons may have to be changed or dropped. On the other hand, some presently unassigned triplets may, for technical reasons, have escaped recognition as codons. About half of them are triplets containing two G's. These, as well as GGG, would be difficult to detect with artificial messengers because polynucleotides with a high G content are believed to acquire secondary structure which interferes with translation (17). The remaining triplets not recognized as codons, all of which contain G (23), are triplets with three different bases. These, too, are specially difficult to identify as codons by the usual synthetic messenger technique (4). And there are other technical difficulties. So far as the deciphering analysis is concerned, therefore, *complete* degeneracy of the code—every one of the 64 possible triplets coding for an amino acid—is by no means excluded.

Doubt as to the complete degeneracy of the code comes, not from evidence that any particular triplet is nonsense, i.e., fails to code for an amino acid, but from studies of a very different sort which have been interpreted as indicating the existence of (unspecified) nonsense triplets (3, 7, 16). The facts are of two kinds: (a) a certain class of mutations yields abbreviated polypeptides, the length of the polypeptide formed being correlated with the position of the mutated site in the cistron; (b) all mutations of a certain class fail to function in one genetic background, but all function more or less normally in another genetic background. Failure to function and the production of incomplete polypeptides are interpreted as due to a nonsense mutation which stops translation at the mutant site. Correction of the defect in organisms of another genotype is held to be due to their possession of a transfer RNA which matches the mutant triplet and so makes sense (or missense) of it, permitting a more or less normal complete polypeptide to form. Mutations to this triplet anywhere in the genome would form a class all of which could be corrected by the same sRNA, one missing in the first but present in the other (suppressor) strain. The triplet is thus held to be nonsense in the former, but to be a meaningful codon in the latter strain.

This interpretation was based on the assumption, plausible at that time, that the progression and specificity of the translation of a message depended only on the sequence of triplets in mRNA and the presence of a matching triplet in the proper place on corresponding amino-acid-charged sRNA's. But matters are no longer so simple. As Gorini and Kataja (8) and Davies et al. (5) point out, mutations altering ribosomes may also block, and relieve the block to, translation. Nirenberg and Leder (14) suggest other mechanisms that could affect translation in these ways, without a change in the sequence of bases at all. Modulation is another relevant complication (1, 19). Further, one could imagine mutations that introduce or remove secondary structure which, as already mentioned, similarly affects translation. In short, as more is discovered about "the transfer of genetic information," more previously unsuspected complications and more ways of interrupting and restoring translation come to light. At the very least, therefore, the evidence for the existence of nonsense triplets has become less convincing. Better evidence than any now available can reasonably be demanded before the interpretation is accepted. I shall not be content to accept it until a given specified triplet is shown not to code for any amino acid in some normal organism. My skepticism is based not only on the lack of critical evidence for nonsense but also on evolutionary considerations which lead me to expect no nonsense whatever in the code, as I shall try to show in the next section.

## B. *Evolutionary Considerations*

A century of study of evolution has resulted in general agreement that it takes place in the main by selection of mutations each of which individually has slight effects. Such "small" mutations may now be viewed as of two principal kinds: single-base substitutions and cistron repeats. The former (in translatable cistrons) should result directly in no more than a single amino acid replacement in a single polypeptide. A cistron repeat, i.e., inclusion in the genome of an extra copy of a cistron, would be expected to have initially only minor quantitative effects; but it is of great potential evolutionary importance in providing a "spare part" which is freer to mutate so long as one of the two (or more) duplicate cistrons continues to function normally.

Mutation rates, low though they be, are sufficiently high to introduce into the large populations composing a species, in the course of the passage of generations, virtually all possible elementary mutations, i.e., each of the three possible base substitutions at each site. Those that confer upon their possessors a reproductive disadvantage would tend to be eliminated at rates proportional to the disadvantage. Their frequency in the population would depend upon their rate of origination by mutation and of elimination by natural selection. Those mutations that confer upon their possessors a reproductive advantage would tend to increase, the original form of the cistron declining to a low equilibrium frequency, the converse of the previous case. Estimations of selective forces must of course in principle take into account the totality of conditions to which the organism is subjected and the totality of the effects of the mutation in all the existing genetic backgrounds (i.e., the rest of the genome). If any mutations failed to confer upon some of their possessors under some conditions either a reproductive advantage or disadvantage, the mutant would reach and maintain an equilibrium frequency in the population which depends upon the relative rates of mutation to and from it. Although it is not possible to state the absolute value of the equilibrium frequency with the information now available, certain facts and principles make it possible to give a first approximation, at least at the level of the underlying nucleotide changes. Because of the equality of C and G and of A and T in DNA, amino acid replacements due to back and forth mutations between C and G and between A and T should be equally frequent unless there is some unsuspected inequality in the rates of these mutations in the two strands of DNA. Hence, significant departures from 50% frequency for alleles due to such single-base differences would imply the operation of selective forces. The same would be true for *all* single-base alternatives in organisms characterized by about 50% G + C. If the organism has an extreme G + C percentage, e.g. 30% or 70%, the apparent constancy of the value for any one organism implies that the number of mutations from G to A or T or from C to A or T is exactly balanced by the number of mutations in the reverse directions. However, since there are fewer (or more) G and C than there are A and T, the *rates* of mutation must differ correspondingly in the two directions in order to yield equal *numbers* of mutations. Nevertheless, such differences still result in equilibrium values of more than 25% for the amino acid coded when the rarer base is present at a particular position in the codon. Values significantly less than 25% thus imply the operation of selective forces. Obviously by being based upon the over-all constancy of the G + C proportion, this reasoning does not exclude marked local deviations from the average, but it does hold that the deviations must exactly compensate if the G + C proportion is to remain constant.

These considerations of population genetics have extremely important implications for the primary structure of polypeptides. Of the nine possible codons due to single-base mutations in a particular codon, some would necessarily code for different amino acids. If these are not found with considerable frequency at the relevant position in the polypeptide, their presence there must be considered to be on the whole detrimental under present or recently existing natural conditions. Otherwise they would have arisen and not have been kept rare by elimination of the recurrent mutations. Of the nine possible direct mutations, some might not result in amino acid replacements (see Section III.A) and might have little or no detrimental effect. They would then persist and increase until reaching mutational equilibrium, thus providing further mutational possibilities including additional amino acid replacements (see Section III.B). This would broaden the spectrum of possible amino acid replacements which could be assessed as to detrimental effect on the basis of rarity.

Obviously the test of population rarity cannot legitimately be applied to laboratory populations. In them, mutant alternatives are exposed to the very *un*natural selection of the investigator's tender loving care. Their detection, maintenance, and multiplication by him bear witness only to their possibility of occurrence in nature and underscore their inability to succeed there. This comment applies equally to mutations which show no detectable alteration of a particular (e.g., an enzymatic or serological) feature and to those which show no detectable decrease in growth rate or fertility *under the limited range of conditions examined in the laboratory.* Natural selection is not limited to those features of a genic product on which an investigator chooses to concentrate or to those degrees of effect which are experimentally detectable or to those conditions or extents of time which are within his limited domain of examination. Its operation can be reliably inferred from rarity. Very rare alleles are detrimental whether we can identify their detrimental effects or not. Hence, if variations in the primary structure of a coded polypeptide in an organism are usually very rare, a point on which more critical and extensive evidence is much needed, we cannot escape the important conclusion that the possible single amino acid substitutions in it are on the whole more or less detrimental under the totality of conditions prevailing where this organism occurs in nature.

This formulation of the situation is not as dismal and evolution-blocking as appears at first thought. There are conditions under which rare mutations can become represented in increasing portions of the population. Under such conditions, the degree of detriment of the mutation has decreased or has even been converted into a positive advantage. One of these conditions is a change in selective action due to change of external conditions. That is what an investigator does in the laboratory when he nurtures and multiplies a detrimental mutant isolated from competitors. Another is the formation, by recombination with another mutant or by a second mutation, of a more fortunate genotype. Combination of mutation with suppressor is one familiar example. Introduction of a duplicate of the original unmutated cistron is another possibility.

The chances of occurrence of such lucky combinations that reduce or eliminate detriment or confer advantage would obviously vary with the degree of persistence of the individual mutations. The lesser their individual detriment, the greater is their persistence; or, in reverse, the greater their detriment, the less is the chance of their persisting long enough to result in a compensatory genic combination.

These considerations have crucial bearing on degeneracy and nonsense. A nonsense mutation resulting in nontranslation of all codons distal to it would as a rule be enormously more detrimental (and therefore more rapidly eliminated) than a sensible (or mis-sensible) mutation which permits translation of the entire message. Hence, neutralizing the detriment of a nonsense mutation by a second mutation or a genic recombination is very much less likely. In short, such nonsense mutations would with high probability have no evolutionary future, and they would by virtue of their detriment be prime targets for elimination by natural selection. On the other hand, mis-sense mutations could sometimes have relatively little detrimental effect and therefore a relatively long persistence and correspondingly greater chance to enter into a lucky genic combination by further mutation or recombination. Natural selection should consequently operate to minimize nonsense and maximize sense. The chance for a sensible or mis-sensible mutation increases and the chance for a nonsense mutation correspondingly decreases, the more triplets have meaning, as has been pointed out by Speyer *et al.* (18). Having more than 20 meaningful triplets can obviously be accomplished only by degeneracy.

If nonsense is as detrimental and as subject to selective elimination as I have indicated, then each and every nonsense triplet would be selected against. Even only one nonsense triplet among the 64 possible triplets would be accompanied by a degree of mutational detriment, and this would be true even if the triplet had some other function, such as punctuation. Mispunctuation could often have effects comparable to nonsense (25). Therefore I am of the opinion that if punctuation is needed—as seems likely—then natural selection would favor means of accomplishing it without reserving triplets for it. Happily, other means are conceivable, as discussed, for example, by Nirenberg and Leder (14). In short, I find it difficult to escape the conclusion that evolutionary considerations lead to the expectation of a completely degenerate code, every triplet coding for an amino acid.

These considerations do not necessarily imply, however, that a completely degenerate code evolved from a nondegenerate or less degenerate code. The earlier evolutionary stages of the code, whatever they may have been, are irrelevant to the argument that natural selection would favor maximal degeneracy and minimal nonsense once evolution had reached the stage of organisms as complex as bacteria. If maximal degeneracy already existed, arguments identical with those already developed lead to the conclusion that selection would maintain it and operate against the development of nonsense simply because as a rule nonsense is more detrimental than mis-sense. Further, selection against nonsense implies selection against genotypes in which mutational nonsense would be unavoidable, such as those which use a particular codon so rarely that it becomes dispensable. Although these extremes might be expected to exist, if at all, in organisms with extreme G + C proportions, the available evidence (23) provides no indication that the set of codon meanings differs in them. In other words, although certain codons must be used relatively rarely by them, they did not become nonsense and then acquire a different meaning.

If this reasoning is sound, as I think it is, then we are led to the important corollary that the code became frozen by the time that the ancestors of existing organisms had become as complex as bacteria. This conclusion has also been reached (9, 10) and attacked (26) by others. However, I see only two possible bases for a contrary conclusion: (a) if more than one evolutionary sequence arrived at this level of complexity and is today represented by descendants; (b) if a single complex common ancestral organism was of a type to which different principles applied, as might for example be the case with syncytial organisms (15). Otherwise, I think natural selection would force the code to remain universal. Universal here means only that *within* all organisms the same triplet codes the same amino acid. Evolutionary changes in other parts of the coding machinery, e.g., other parts of the sRNA's or the enzymes involved, have apparently occurred, as shown by artificial mixtures of parts from different organisms. But these are irrelevant to universality in the sense to which it is here restricted, so long as the changes are compensated *within* each organism and result in the same set of relations between codons and amino acids.

Although, as set forth above, natural selection of a completely degenerate code is independent of whether the code was ever nondegenerate, it is amusing to note, as I shall in the next brief section, that if nondegenerate codes ever existed, selection against nonsense implies selection of a certain type of nondegenerate code.

## C. *Variations in the Probability of Nonsense Mutations in Nondegenerate Codes*

With only 20 sensible triplets out of 64 in a nondegenerate code, one might at first thought suppose that 44/64 of all mutations would be nonsense. That is by no means true. The proportion of nonsense mutations depends strongly on the system of codons. Consider a code such as the one represented in Table IA. This type of code is constructed by starting with a single letter triplet (e.g., AAA), adding the three codons with different letters in one position (e.g., position 3; see row 1), the 12 codons that differ from these four in another position (e.g., position 1; see rows 2, 3, 4), and finally 4 codons that differ from those in any one of the four rows by one and the same substitution in the remaining position (e.g., position 2, substituting U's for the A's in row 4; see row 5). It is easy to show that with such a code, if all one-step mutations are equally probable, the ratio of one-step nonsense to one-step missense mutations is not 44 to 20 or 2.2 to 1 but only 0.55 to 1. On the other hand, codes such as the one represented in Table IB have a ratio of 6.5

TABLE I

A. A SET OF 20 TRIPLET CODONS WITH MINIMAL PROBABILITY OF NONSENSE MUTATIONS BY SINGLE-BASE SUBSTITUTION

| AAA | AAC | AAG | AAU |
|-----|-----|-----|-----|
| CAA | CAC | CAG | CAU |
| GAA | GAC | GAG | GAU |
| UAA | UAC | UAG | UAU |
| UUA | UUC | UUG | UUU |

B. A SET OF 20 TRIPLET CODONS WITH MAXIMAL PROBABILITY OF NONSENSE MUTATIONS BY SINGLE BASE SUBSTITUTION

| AAA | CAC | GAG | UAU | AAC |
|-----|-----|-----|-----|-----|
| ACC | CCG | GCU | UCA | CUG |
| AGG | CGU | GGA | UGC | GAU |
| AUU | CUA | GUC | UUG | UCG |

nonsense mutations to 1 sensible mutation. This sort of code is constructed by forming 16 codons any 2 of which differ from each other by bases in at least two positions, and then adding 4 more codons to bring the set up to 20. A number of sets of codons of each of these two extreme types can of course be constructed on the same principles.

On the principle developed earlier, namely that natural selection operates to minimize nonsense, had it been faced with choices among diverse nondegenerate codes it would have favored codes most nearly approaching the kind with minimal frequency of nonsense mutations, i.e., the type illustrated in Table IA.

## II. THE NATURE OF THE DEGENERACY OF THE CODE

Codons for the same amino acid, i.e., *synonyms*, to use the convenient term employed by Muller (12) and by Leder and Nirenberg (11), by no means constitute random groups. This was indicated soon after synonyms began to be discovered, and increase of knowledge has only served to reinforce the early impression. The main fact is this: of the 53 possible combinations of pairs of synonyms, 47, or 88%, differ in only one base, i.e., have two of their bases in common, as can be verified by comparing all possible pairs of synonyms listed in Table II. Exceptions occur for only a few of the several possible comparisons within only three sets of synonyms, those for arginine, leucine, and serine. The question is: What does this high frequency of "shared doublets" mean for the relation between synonyms?

For present purposes, it is not necessary to deal with this question in full. That has been done critically by Crick (4) and by Woese (25). I shall be concerned with only one aspect of the matter, the degree to which synonyms are "connected." Crick (4) designates two triplets as *connected* if each can be converted into the other by altering one base only. The high proportion of shared doublets suggests, but does not re-

TABLE II

THE GENETIC CODE, WITHOUT ASSIGNING ORDER TO THE BASES IN THE CODON[a]

| Amino acid | N | S | Both | W |
|---|---|---|---|---|
| Alanine | | | ACG[x]; 2C,G; CGU[x] | |
| Arginine | ACG[x] | | 2A,G; 2C,G; CGU[x] | |
| Asparagine | | | 2A,C; 2A,U; ACU[x] | |
| Aspartic acid | 2A,G[x] | | ACG[x]; AGU | |
| Cysteine | | | G,2U | |
| Glutamic acid | ACG[x] | | 2A,G; AGU[x] | |
| Glutamine | | ACU | 2A,C | |
| Glycine | | | A,2G; C,2G; 2G,U | |
| Histidine | | | A,2C; ACU[x] | |
| Isoleucine | | ACU | 2A,U; A,2U | |
| Leucine | | | A,2U; 2C,U; C,2U; G,2U | |
| Lysine | | | 3A; 2A,U | |
| Methionine | | | AGU | |
| Phenylalanine | | | C,2U; 3U | |
| Proline | 2C,G[x] | | A,2C; 3C; 2C,U | |
| Serine | CGU[x] | | ACG; 2C,U; C,2U | |
| Threonine | | ACU | 2A,C; A,2C | |
| Tryptophan | | | 2G,U | |
| Tyrosine | | ACU | A,2U | |
| Valine | AGU[x] | | G,2U | 2G,U |

[a] Sources: N = Nirenberg *et al.* (13); S = Speyer *et al.* (18) and Wahba *et al.* (22); Both = N + S; W = Woese (25). Superscript x = reported as only "probable" by Nirenberg *et al.* A, C, G, and U = ribonucleotides bearing adenine, cytosine, guanine, and uracil, respectively, in the mRNA codons.

quire, a high degree of connectedness among synonyms of a set. So far as the sets of presently reported synonyms (Table II) are concerned, some of them *must* be completely connected. Thus, in the set of four synonyms for proline, the codon CCC must be connected to the other three (A,2C; G,2C; and U,2C) regardless of what position or positions are occupied by A, G, and U. Likewise, the two synonyms for lysine (AAA and U,2A) and the two synonyms for phenylalanine (UUU and C,2U) must be connected. Moreover, the bases of the synonyms of each set in

Table II *could* be arranged so that each set is completely connected; there is not a single exception. On the other hand, all of the sets except the three mentioned earlier can also be ordered in such a way as to include unconnected synonyms.

Eck (6), for example, has proposed a completely degenerate code in which some unconnected synonyms occur. His system orders synonyms by pairs, the two members of which differ in one position where a purine replaces a purine or a pyrimidine replaces a pyrimidine. When a set of synonyms includes more than one pair, those in one pair may differ in two positions from those in another pair. He presents four sets of synonyms in which complete connection fails in this way. All of the other sets are completely connected.

The question of whether all or only some sets of synonyms are completely connected will be answered when the order of bases in the codons becomes known. The new method of Leder and Nirenberg (11) should soon provide this knowledge, perhaps before this book is published. They are, of course, well aware of the importance of their method for settling the question. Concentration on only one or two of Eck's four exceptional sets of synonyms would go far toward confirming or eliminating his system. For example, Eck proposes the two pairs UAU–UGU and UUC–UCC for leucine, the first pair not being connected to the second. The set could, however, be connected as follows:

$$\begin{array}{l} \text{A, 2U} - \text{C, 2U} - \text{U, 2C} \\ \quad | \qquad \qquad \quad | \\ \text{G, 2U} \underline{\hspace{3.5em}} \end{array}$$

Any of the three possible orders for A,2U would fix a corresponding order for C,2U and G,2U and would exclude one of the three orders for U,2C. The set for arginine provides another excellent test. Leder and Nirenberg predict AGA and CGC for two of the synonyms and a middle position for G in a third synonym which also contains A and C. If these predictions are confirmed, this set of four is almost completely specified on the hypothesis of complete connection:

$$\begin{array}{l} \ulcorner \text{AGC (or CGA)} - \text{AGA} \\ \quad | \\ \text{CGC} - \text{UGC (or CGU)} \end{array}$$

Eck's scheme permits him to pair CGC with UGC (or CGU), but he will be forced to postulate two more synonyms to pair with AGC (or CGA) and AGA, making a total of six synonyms in this set. Because of comparable difficulties, he has already postulated a set of six for serine.

In spite of appreciating the reasons for caution and of expecting an early experimental decision, it is difficult to resist the temptation to postulate complete connectedness among the synonyms of each set. Everyone who has tried to formulate a code on the basis of recent knowledge comes out either with completely connected sets of synonyms, as does Woese (25) in his Table VI, p. 248, though on different grounds, or with sets most of which are completely connected, as does Eck (6). The hypothesis of completely connected synonyms is simpler (and less ambitious) than other current hypotheses, for it makes no restrictive assumptions as to the kinds or locations of permitted base differences among synonyms. Nor does it necessarily imply a purely random-connected relationship among synonyms, i.e., with purely random positions of the differences in a set. Woese's system has positional restrictions and is still completely connected. In the remainder of this paper, I shall explore the consequences of complete connectedness among synonyms. Unless and until the ascertainment of base orders demonstrates the contrary, a high degree of connectedness—if not complete—among synonyms can hardly be seriously doubted. If it should turn out that connectedness is not complete, the implications and consequences set forth below would be quantitatively, not qualitatively, different.

## III. Consequences of Complete Connectedness among Synonyms

### A. Silent Mutations

"Silent" mutations, mutations that result in no amino acid substitution, have been recognized as a possible consequence of shared doublets in synonyms. They *must* occur in at least certain cases. For example, if either A or G or U in the three codons A,2C; G,2C; and U,2C for proline mutates to C, the result would be CCC, another codon for proline.

The following paragraphs explore the relative frequency of silent mutations among all possible one-base mutations and how this varies with the size of connected sets of synonyms, with the nature of the connection among the synonyms, and with equality and inequality of usage of the synonyms of a set. As a first approximation, I have assumed that all base substitutions are equally frequent. Although transitional mutations are believed to be more common than transversions, we lack the information needed to allow for possible differences of this sort. In general, however, such restrictions would reduce the frequency of silent mutations in certain sets.

Obviously, the frequency of silent mutations would be zero for amino acids represented by only one codon, as is thus far the case for cysteine, methionine, and tryptophan (Table II). Each of five amino acids is now represented by two codons. If these are connected, they yield 11.1% silent mutations, as appears from the diagram

WXY
|
ZXY

where the four letters represent the four bases without specifying which one stands for which, and where the connecting line shows the silent base changes. In this and subsequent diagrams, each connecting line indicates one silent mutational possibility for each of the two letters it connects. The total number of possible single-base mutations is of course three times the total number of letters in the diagram if each base can mutate to all the other three. Hence, in the diagram above, the proportion of silent mutations is $2/18 = 11.1\%$.

Each of eight amino acids is represented by three codons. If these are completely connected, the percentage of silent mutations depends upon the nature of the connections. The limits are readily calculated by diagraming the extreme forms of complete connection, yielding minimal and maximal frequencies of silent mutation. The minimum is represented by a diagram of the following sort:

WXY   ZXY   ZXW

This yields 4 silent mutations among a total of 27, or 14.8%. The maximum is represented by a diagram of the following sort:

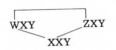

This yields 6/27, or 22.2% silent mutations.

Each of four amino acids is represented by four codons. The limiting cases for silent mutations are indicated by the following diagrams:

WXY   XXY   XXZ   XZZ

gives the minimum of 6/36, or 16.7% silent mutations;

WXY   WXZ
WXW   WXX

gives the maximum of $12/36 = 33.3\%$ silent mutations.

Although no amino acid is yet known to be represented by more than four codons, surprising results are obtained by examining what would happen if this did occur. The results with sets of five codons will be apparent by building on the diagrams for sets of four. The minimal diagram for four could be converted to a minimal diagram for five by introducing at the start WZY which is connected by its Z to the X of WXY. This introduces 2 new silent mutations among 9 new possible mutations; these, added to the previous 6/36, yield 8/45, or 17.8%

silent mutations. A maximal diagram is attained by adding, for example, WZY to the maximal diagram for a set of four; as before, the Z of this codon is connected to the X of WXY, and again 2 of the 9 new possible mutations are silent. Adding these to the previous 12/36 gives 14/45, or 31.1%. Thus the maximal value for a set of five is less than the maximum (33.3%) for a set of four. In like manner, it is readily shown that the maxima are 33.3 for sets of six, 38.1 for sets of seven, 36.1 for sets of eight, 37.1 for sets of nine, and 40.0 for sets of ten. The important point is that the maximal values are *lower* for sets of five than for sets of four, and lower for sets of eight and nine than for sets of seven.

The preceding calculations assume equal usage of all synonyms of a set. Inequalities in the frequencies with which different synonyms are actually used in the genome have no effect on sets of two connected synonyms, because the two must have identical percentages of silent mutations. The two diagrams above for sets of three synonyms show that the synonyms may have unequal (first of the two diagrams) or equal (second diagram) frequencies of silent mutations. In the former case, the middle codon (ZXY) has twice the frequency of each of the other two. If an organism kept all three codons but used WXY and/or ZXW almost exclusively, the minimum would approach 1/9 or 11.1%; if ZXY were used almost exclusively, the maximum would approach 2/9 or 22.2%, which is also the value for any one or all synonyms in the second three-synonym diagram.

The two diagrams above for sets of four synonyms show that unequal usage could reduce the frequency of silent mutations to approach 11.1% by almost exclusive use of either terminal codon (WXY or XZZ) in the first four-synonym diagram; the maximal frequency of 33.3% could be attained only in sets connected as in the second four-synonym diagram, but in such sets the frequency is the same regardless of whether the four synonyms are equally or unequally used.

Since no set is known to consist of more than four synonyms, and since less than 20 triplets remain for possible additions to the existing 20 sets, it should be quite safe to assume that no set will be found to contain more than ten, even if all triplets are codons. Let us then explore the effects of unequal usage on sets above four and up to ten. As already pointed out for smaller sets, the effects depend upon the manner in which the synonyms are connected. Minimal frequencies of silent mutations characterize the terminal codons in linear chains such as those represented in the first diagrams for sets of three and four synonyms. Such chains can easily be built up to ten synonyms, and the terminal codons always have 11.1% silent mutations. This then becomes the minimal value for all such sets and is approached as one or both terminal codons become almost exclusively used. The maximal value is always possessed by one or more codons in the cyclic type of diagram, such as the second diagrams for sets of three or four synonyms. This value increases steadily by increments of 11.1% as each new synonym is added, beginning with 11.1% for sets of two, and rising to 100% for sets of ten. The obvious basis lies in the addition successively of one new connection to the same codon until all nine possible connections have been made.

In view of these results, we may now try to estimate the frequency of silent mutations in the existing code. As a first approximation, we may simply take the unweighted means for the minimal and maximal values of the sets with one to four codons. With equal usage, the values are 12.0% and 18.3%; with unequal usage, 9.4% and 18.3%. These values would be reduced if transitions and transversions occur with unequal frequencies. On the other hand, the fact that a positive correlation exists between the size of a set and the frequency with which the amino acid coded by the set occurs in proteins (25) introduces a weighting factor that would shift the values toward the limits of the values for sets of four, i.e., 16.7% minimum and 33.3% maximum with equal usage of all synonyms, and 11.1% and 33.3% with unequal usage.

Some calculations in the preceding paragraph would of course be revised upward if further investigation demonstrates the existence of sets of more than four synonyms. With equal usage, the minimal values rise at a decreasing rate to 20% with sets of ten, but always stay at 11.1% with unequal usage. The irregular progression of the maxima with equal use and the steady rise of the maxima with unequal use as sets increase in size have already been noted. On the whole, of course, the percentage of silent mutations would be expected to be greater if some of the commoner amino acids prove to be coded by more than four synonyms. In this connection, Apgar and Holley (2) have reported at least five sRNA's for leucine in *E. coli*; but it is not yet known whether each of these corresponds to a different codon. Thus far, only four synonyms are reported for leucine (Table II), but in addition a codon for phenylalanine operates ambiguously with leucine in the *in vitro* studies.

In sum, taking everything into account, it would not be surprising if more than 20% of all single-base mutations are silent unless the restriction to transitions is considerable.

The same sort of analysis can readily be applied to a code with quadruplet codons. For example, a set of 13 connected and equally used quadruplet synonyms, which would be slightly above the average size of 12.8, yields a maximum of 30.8% silent mutations, i.e., slightly less than the 33.3% found above for a slightly above average size set (four) in a triplet code. However, it is possible to connect 13 quadruplet synonyms in such a way that one of them yields 100% silent mutations; this could then be approached by unequal usage. As pointed out above, this value requires only 10 triplet synonyms; but it is far above the maxima of 22.2 and 33.3% attainable with set sizes (three or four) nearest to the mean of 3.2 in the triplet code.

We shall now consider whether silent mutations are totally silent. Ames and Hartman (1) and Stent (19) review and discuss the evidence suggesting that synonyms may differ in their effects on the rate of translation of messenger or on the probability of stopping translation altogether at their site, perhaps by corresponding to an sRNA present in insufficient amounts. Ames and Hartman's indication that such mutations are common, running to about 50% of all mutations in their histidine operon, appears to be much too high to be accounted for solely by mutations to synonyms. Since one synonym in each set must be the "normal" one on this hypothesis, the maximal frequency of such modulatory mutations could not reach 33% and, taking the whole code into account, could hardly be much above 20%, if that much. Nevertheless, effects of this sort due to synonymy certainly cannot be excluded. Therefore, it may be better to cease calling mutations of this sort silent and instead use the objective term, synonymous mutations.

To the extent that synonymous mutations fail to affect even the quantity of genic product or its rate of synthesis, they would be neutral and not directly subject to natural selection. In this case, the relative frequencies of synonyms would be determined by mutational pressure, the relative rates of mutation to and from each synonym. This calls for a new kind of population genetics at the nucleotide level, and Sueoka (20) has indeed already initiated it in his brilliant attempt to deal with problems of variation in base composition of DNA.

Even if we assume that synonymous mutations are never entirely neutral, restriction of their effects to changes in rate of synthesis of genic product or to amount produced marks this class of mutations as the least detrimental of all single-base mutations. That is not to imply that such changes cannot on occasion be very damaging, but only to suggest that as a class they would on balance be less damaging than single amino acid substitutions or abbreviated polypeptides resulting from nonsense mutations. If so, then a maximally degenerate code with completely connected sets of synonyms, which maximize the protective effect of synonymous mutations against greater mutational damage, has selective value. Moreover, it increases stability without loss of ample opportunity for evolutionary change by nonsynonymous mutations.

The high frequency of synonymous mutations raises the question of whether amino acid replacement studies are subject to the risk of a

serious concealed technical error that could create difficulties in interpreting results. For example, in the magnificent studies of Yanofsky (27)
on mutations at a particular site coding for glycine, some 24 mutations
to arginine, glutamic acid, and valine have been found, and all are
assumed to have occurred in the same codon. But, if the three synonyms
of glycine are completely connected, 22.2% of the mutations in the
original codon could have been to a different synonym. At least several
should have occurred in the course of an investigation that detected
24 nonsynonymous mutations. However, the nonsynonymous mutations
were selected; without selection, the synonymous mutations would of
course be much less likely to have been picked up. Moreover, if—as is
not unlikely—the three synonyms for glycine differ at only one position
in the triplet, no error in interpretation would occur even if a synonymous
mutation had been picked up. It is unlikely, therefore, that this source
of error would enter into the one-step mutations from glycine. The
danger is greater in the second-step mutations from arginine, with a
set of four synonyms that must include base differences in more than
one position.

## B.  Molecular Orthogenesis

As is well known, the codon assignments are such that certain amino
acids cannot be replaced by certain other amino acids by a single-base
substitution. For example, proline, all of whose codons contain at least
2C, cannot mutate directly by a single-base change to lysine, cysteine,
methionine, tryptophan, or valine because all of their codons (so far as
now known) lack C completely. On the other hand, Speyer et al. (18)
and Tatum (21) have remarked that synonymy permits a greater flexibility or range of amino acid replacements. The situation may be put
even more significantly: synonymy requires different mutational patterns for different synonyms of a set. For example, the codon 2A,G for
arginine could mutate directly to lysine (3A), but not to proline, all of
whose codons contain at least 2C; whereas another codon for arginine
(2C,G) can mutate to proline (codon 3C and perhaps others), but not
to lysine, whose codons have at least 2A. A number of such differences
in the one-base mutational pathways open to synonyms can be cited
already, in spite of our present limited knowledge of the order of the
bases in the codons. When the orders of the bases become known, more
will probably be revealed.

This predetermined difference which distinguishes at the molecular
level the patterns of evolutionary possibilities open to different synonyms
implies that the synonyms of a set may be subject to a subtle, long-range
selective differential. For example, natural selection might favor those

synonyms whose nonsynonymous mutational pattern causes least detriment, perhaps such as those which result in replacing basic by basic or aromatic by aromatic amino acids. Nirenberg *et al.* (13) have indeed already noted that families of amino acids, the members of which have similar structure or similar *in vivo* synthetic pathways, tend to have families of similar codons. In any case, this built-in delimitation of the possible paths of evolution brings back to biology at the molecular level a sort of orthogenesis, a ghost long since believed to have been exorcised from biology.

## C. *Recombinational Pseudomutation*

Crossing over has been shown to occur within a codon, in heterozygotes bearing at the same site (in homologous chromosomes) codons for two different amino acids, and to yield recombinant codons for a third and different amino acid (27). Surprisingly, the same thing can happen in heterozygotes for two synonymous codons. Of course, it can happen only if the synonyms differ in bases at two positions. Among the synonym sets thus far known, some—those for arginine, leucine, and serine—*must* include pairs of synonyms differing in bases at two positions, and there may well be others, but that cannot be known until the order of the bases is known. Let us use leucine as an example. Its four synonyms are A,2U; 2C,U; C,2U; and G,2U. In a heterozygote for the two leucine synonyms A,2U and 2C,U, a single crossover can give rise to a triplet containing A, C and U, regardless of which of the nine conceivable combinations of the three A,2U orders (AUU, UAU, or UUA) with the three 2C,U orders (CCU, CUC or UCC) is the correct one. The set of synonyms for leucine does not include one containing A, C, and U; the six possible orders for triplets bearing those three bases are codons for glutamine, isoleucine, threonine, tyrosine, asparagine, and histidine. Thus, one or another of these six amino acids will be coded by a crossover between two synonyms for leucine.

Stated generally, two homozygous organisms, in both of whose genomes at a particular site there is a codon for the same amino acid, can form a hybrid which by normal crossing over yields offspring with an amino acid replacement. This would almost surely be scored as a mutation, for example in amino acid replacement studies; but it is only a recombinational pseudomutation. This is, I believe, a new concept for genetics, one which is implicit in the degeneracy of the code, but one which has to the best of my knowledge not hitherto been recognized.

From available information, such pseudomutations in appropriate heterozygotes would occur in frequencies orders of magnitude higher than true nonsynonymous mutations within the same triplet. Yanofsky

(27) reports that the frequency of intracodon crossing over in *E. coli* is about 2 to 4 per $10^5$.

Recombinational pseudomutation is not only surprising, but shocking and paradoxical. If synonyms serve not only to reduce damaging non-sense, but to increase stability by reducing the frequency of detrimental mutations to nonsynonyms, i.e., to amino acid changes, then the system is working at cross purposes in those situations in which synonyms permit amino acid changes by crossing over in frequencies which are orders of magnitude greater than those due to mutation. I think the situation would be much worse with a quadruplet code, with more chances of intracodon recombination by crossing over; but I have not fully worked this out. If so, this would be a good reason for selection to have rejected codons larger than triplets. In any case, the best that can be managed with a triplet code is to arrange matters so that the detriment due to recombinational pseudomutation, like that due to nonsynonymous mutation, is kept to a minimum and directed into least detrimental pathways. This could be achieved by having evolved the smallest practicable number of sets of synonyms with base differences at two positions and, among those that cannot be avoided, selecting them so that the crossovers will yield codons either for the same or for very similar amino acids, or by using preferentially within a set of synonyms those that differ at only one position.

The problems raised by recombinational pseudomutations bear also on Eck's system (6). It includes a considerable number of synonym combinations which not only differ in two positions but which yield by crossing over a high frequency of pseudomutations. As indicated above, I think natural selection would, if possible, have operated against such a system. Eck's system places great emphasis on transitional differences between synonyms. While transitional mutations may be more common than transversions, even much more common, selection could readily compensate for rarity of origin in the evolution of the code.

Earlier I mentioned that the idea of completely connected synonym sets was not to be confused with the idea of random-connected synonyms. Natural selection may well exert powerful forces restricting the system of connections. At several points in this paper, I have indicated the selective value of such restrictions. And none, it seems to me, would be more valuable than the kinds of restrictions that would minimize recombinational pseudomutations. Of course this does not imply, nor is anything else in this paper meant to imply, that it would be best to eliminate amino acid substitutions completely. These are a major source of evolutionary material. But more mutation does not necessarily mean more evolution. It is only necessary that the various amino acid and codon substitutions be present in amounts sufficient for selection to avail itself of them. Even with a maximally degenerate code and complete connectedness among synonyms, that need is amply satisfied. It is the great excess above what is needed that is detrimental to the species, and it is to the reduction of this that I have throughout this paper ascribed selective value. And, as I hope to have shown, consideration of natural selection has been a good guide in exposing the amount, the nature, and the consequences of degeneracy of the code, even leading to the revelation of some of its features that add both to its beauty and, in a minor way, to the corpus of genetic concepts.

## References

1. AMES, B. N., AND HARTMAN, P. E., Cold Spring Harbor Symp. Quant. Biol., 28, 349 (1963).
2. APGAR, J., AND HOLLEY, R. W., Biochem. Biophys. Res. Commun., 16, 121 (1964).
3. BENZER, S., AND CHAMPE, S. P., Proc. Natl. Acad. Sci. U.S., 48, 1114 (1962).
4. CRICK, F. H. C., Progr. Nucleic Acid Res., 1, 163 (1963).
5. DAVIS, J., GILBERT, W., AND GORINI, L., Proc. Natl. Acad. Sci. U.S., 51, 883 (1964).
6. ECK, R. V., Science, 140, 477 (1963).
7. GAREN, A., AND SIDDIQI, O., Proc. Natl. Acad. Sci. U.S., 48, 1121 (1962).
8. GORINI, L., AND KATAJA, E., Proc. Natl. Acad. Sci. U.S., 51, 487 (1964).
9. HINEGARDNER, R. T., AND ENGELBERG, J., Science, 142, 1083 (1963).
10. HINEGARDNER, R. T., AND ENGELBERG, J., Science, 144, 1031 (1964).
11. LEDER, P., AND NIRENBERG, M., Proc. Natl. Acad. Sci. U.S., 52, 420 & 1521 (1964).
12. MULLER, H. J., lecture at California Institute of Technology, June 4, 1963 (unpublished).
13. NIRENBERG, M. W., JONES, O. W., LEDER, P., CLARK, F. C., SLY, W. S., AND PESTKA, S., Cold Spring Harbor Symp. Quant. Biol., 28, 549 (1963).
14. NIRENBERG, M., AND LEDER, P., Science, 145, 1399 (1964).
15. PITTENGER, T. H., AND ATWOOD, K. C., Genetics, 41, 227 (1956).
16. SARABHAI, A. S., STRETTON, A. O. W., BRENNER, S., AND BOLLE, A., Nature, 201, 13 (1964).
17. SINGER, M. F., JONES, O. W., AND NIRENBERG, M. W., Proc. Natl. Acad. Sci. U.S., 49, 392 (1963).
18. SPEYER, J. F., LENGYEL, P., BASILIO, C., WAHBA, A. J., GARDNER, R. S., AND OCHOA, S., Cold Spring Harbor Symp. Quant. Biol., 28, 559 (1963).
19. STENT, G. S., Science, 144, 816 (1964).
20. SUEOKA, N., Proc. Natl. Acad. Sci. U.S., 48, 582 (1962).
21. TATUM, E. L., in "The Control of Human Heredity and Evolution" (T. M. Sonneborn, ed.), Chapter 2, Macmillan, New York, 1965.
22. WAHBA, A. J., GARDNER, R. S., BASILIO, C., MILLER, R. S., SPEYER, J. F., AND LENGYEL, P., Proc. Natl. Acad. Sci. U.S., 49, 116 (1963).
23. WAHBA, A. J., MILLER, R. S., BASILIO, C., LENGYEL, P., AND SPEYER, J. F., Proc. Natl. Acad. Sci. U.S., 49, 880 (1963).

24. WEINSTEIN, I. B., *Cold Spring Harbor Symp. Quant. Biol.*, **28**, 579 (1963).
25. WOESE, C. R., *ICSU Rev.*, **5**, 210 (1963).
26. WOESE, C. R., *Science*, **144**, 1030 (1964).
27. YANOFSKY, C., *Cold Spring Harbor Symp. Quant. Biol.*, **28**, 581 (1963).

PART VII

# EVOLUTION OF GENES I

# Chairman's Remarks

P. DOTY

*Department of Chemistry,*
*Harvard University,*
*Cambridge, Massachusetts*

From DNA molecules to human society, much can be learned from studying the conditions under which complementary pairs separate and re-form. In the four years that have passed since this phenomenon became recognized in DNA, certain aspects of the dynamics of behavioral interaction have become clear. Strands that have never been together before can unite in the Watson-Crick embrace if only their sequences are essentially complementary. With this condition met, even DNA and RNA combine with only a little distinction: miscegenation is quite acceptable at the molecular level. Dr. Kornberg will tell us of one consequence of this particular union, reiterative replication and its limitless possibilities. Dr. Bautz will then reveal how malocclusions between strands of DNA may have fostered mutational change and abetted the evolutionary process. Finally, Dr. Marmur will bring us the insight that comes from observing the generative powers of the separated strands of DNA. These studies only mark the beginning of a sociology of populations of individual nucleic acid strands, but before they are complete our own view of life, both in molecular detail and in evolutionary sweep, will surely be affected.

# Synthesis of DNA-Like Polymers
# *de novo* or by Reiterative
# Replication

Arthur Kornberg

*Department of Biochemistry,*
*Stanford University School of Medicine,*
*Palo Alto, California*

Modification or substitution of bases in DNA by standard chemical and physical mutagens leads to *in vivo* replication errors. Although this subject has been widely explored and discussed, as in the excellent preceding paper by Freese (5), *in vitro* studies on the mechanism of these reactions have been relatively scant.

Our own experience with the enzymatic replication of DNA under ordinary circumstances shows that errors, if they ever occur, are extremely rare. Replication of a DNA-like polymer which contains only adenine and thymine residues (dAT polymer)[1] revealed no detectable incorporation of guanine residues (17). The level of sensitivity of these experiments showed the frequency of "aberrant" guanine incorporation to be less than one residue per 500,000 adenine and thymine nucleotides polymerized. In the replication of an analogous polymer, dA$\overline{BU}$, containing the mutagen bromouracil in place of thymine, the incorporation of guanine was unequivocal (17). It occurred at a frequency in the range of 1 per 10,000 adenine and thymine (or bromouracil) nucleotides polymerized. Current theories of bromouracil mutagenesis, if applied to the replication of this polymer, would have predicted that the incorporation of guanine would be paired exclusively with bromouracil and therefore placed as a nearest neighbor to it in the chain. However, this location of guanine was true of only about half the residues incorporated and indicates that additional forces were controlling their insertion into

---

[1] Abbreviations used: A, adenine, deoxyadenosine or deoxyadenylate; DNA, deoxyribonucleic acid; T, thymine, deoxythymidine, or deoxythymidylate; dATP, dCTP, dGTP, and dTTP, deoxynucleoside triphosphates of adenine, cytosine, guanine, and thymine, respectively. Designations for a polynucleotide chain are those described in *J. Biol. Chem.*

the new chains. That other factors may also be operative is suggested by the discoveries of Goldberg and Rabinowitz (6) with RNA polymerase. They found, as would be expected, that when uridine was replaced by its analog, pseudouridine, the pairing was with adenine in the template, and the same nearest-neighbor relationships were formed. However, when both the uridine and pseudouridine nucleoside triphosphates were present together and competing for a place in the growing polymer, they paired with adenine but were fitted into distinctly different places in the chain. It is clear from this observation that the neighboring base in the template or in the synthesized chain does in fact influence the choice between a nucleotide and its analog. Comparable studies should now be attempted with deoxynucleotides and their analogs in replication of DNA by DNA polymerase.

We see that one purine may be substituted for another by mismatching with a base analog in the template, and a similar possibility for inserting a base analog into the newly developed chain creates the opportunity for mismatching in the next replication cycle. Possibilities also exist for more drastic substitutions as a purine for pyrimidine, or vice versa. In addition, circumstances may permit the insertion or deletion of a base. In these and related examples, altered sequences are created in DNA by the inclusion of an aberrant base or the deletion of a base.

I should like in this report to cite experiences with DNA replication *in vitro* which do not involve single base substitutions, but rather the inclusion in products of whole sequences in what appears to be the result of *reiteration* of segments of the template (9). The suggestion is made that such a mechanism might operate on occasion *in vivo* and would as a consequence have some significance for the natural evolution of DNA.

### De novo SYNTHESIS OF DNA-LIKE POLYMERS

The general rule regarding the action of the DNA-synthesizing enzymes (polymerases) is the requirement for a DNA template and the deoxynucleoside triphosphates necessary to make proper pairings with the bases in the template (8). The major exception to this rule has been the synthesis of certain polymers, after extensive lag periods, without any addition of template material (8). This synthesis *de novo* has been observed to produce the series of DNA-like polymers listed in Table I. These polymers have been useful in a variety of physical chemical and enzymological studies. To cite one example, it was of considerable interest that the viscosity of dAT solutions increased on melting instead of decreasing as is invariably observed during the helix-coil transition of naturally occurring DNA (7). A plausible explanation is now at hand as a result of Inman's electron microscopic examination of a dAĪŪ polymer, revealing it to be a highly branched structure (Fig. 1). It would seem that the viscosity of a branched helical dAĪŪ is exceptionally low to begin with compared to linear, unbranched DNA, and that the random coil form of dAĪŪ on melting is more extended and therefore more viscous than the helical molecule.

TABLE I
ENZYMATICALLY SYNTHESIZED DEOXYNUCLEOTIDE POLYMERS

| Designation | Components |
|---|---|
| Copolymers | |
| dAT | Adenine, thymine |
| dAU | Adenine, uracil |
| dABŪ | Adenine, bromouracil |
| dAĪŪ | Adenine, iodouracil |
| dMAT | Methyladenine, thymine |
| Homopolymers | |
| dGdC | Guanine, cytosine |
| dGdBC | Guanine, bromocytosine |
| dGdHMC | Guanine, hydroxymethylcytosine |
| dIdC | Hypoxanthine, cytosine |
| dAdT | Adenine, thymine |

Evidence suggests that the development of dAT does not proceed by continuous lengthening of polymer molecules until the substrate molecules are exhausted. Instead, the size of the polymer molecules, when the reaction is barely detectable and when far less than 1% of the substrates have been polymerized, is the same as that isolated at the end of the reaction (13). It seems clear that macromolecules are formed early and that available substrate molecules are used for replication of additional polymer molecules whose average size then remains relatively constant.

The kinetics of *de novo* dAT synthesis remain exponential from the earliest measurements up to the point when the majority of the substrate molecules have been consumed. Exponential kinetics in the phase of rapid synthesis, where the bulk of the reaction occurs, suggests that the autocatalytic process may originate early in the lag period where it remains obscured by the relative insensitivity of the methods used for measuring synthesis (11). The fact that exponential kinetics prevails throughout much of the lag period is indicated by the kinetics of primed synthesis. We have calculated from our data that midway in the lag period the concentration of dAT is of the order of $10^{-13}$ $M$, whereas that of polymerase is $10^{-8}$ $M$. The reaction therefore remains exponential until the polymer concentration reaches levels at which the enzyme is no longer in appreciable excess.

What have remained most obscure are the earlier events in *de novo* synthesis that surround the development of the first dAT molecules. We imagined that the polymer is started by a number of chance interactions of nucleotides catalyzed by the enzyme and that those products pos-

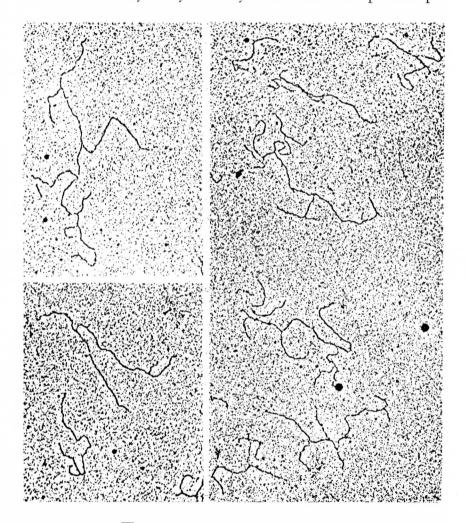

dAĪŪ -- Adenine-Iodouracil Copolymer

Fig. 1. Electron micrograph of dAĪŪ copolymer by the method of Kleinschmidt *et al.* as modified by Inman. This line photograph is available through the courtesy of Dr. Ross B. Inman.

sessing a simple and highly regular structure are then favored for further growth. Ordered polymerization continues until the molecule reaches an optimal size for serving as a template. Upon its replication each of the daughter molecules then becomes a template for further replication in a semiconservative fashion.

An opportunity to test this hypothesis was provided recently by the chemical synthesis by Khorana and his associates (18) of a series of deoxyAT oligomers of defined size and structure (Table II). Would

TABLE II
SYNTHETIC DEOXYOLIGONUCLEOTIDES (KHORANA)[a]

| | |
|---|---|
| pTpApTpApTpA | $(AT)_3$ |
| pTpA(pTpA)$_2$pTpA | $(AT)_4$ |
| TpA(pTpA)$_3$pTpA | $(AT)_5$ |
| TpA(pTpA)$_4$pTpA | $(AT)_6$ |
| TpA(pTpA)$_5$pTpA | $(AT)_7$ |
| TpTpTpTpTpTpTpTpTpTpT | $T_{11}$ |
| pApApApApApApA | $A_7$ |
| pCpT(pCpT)$_3$pCpT | $(CT)_5$ |
| pApG(pApG)$_3$pApG | $(AG)_5$ |

[a] These deoxyribo series of oligonucleotides are designated by these trivial notations for ease of reference in this paper.

such oligomers prime at all, and if so would they generate macromolecules of the size of the dAT polymer?

## PRIMING BY AT OLIGOMERS

In the presence of dATP, dTTP, and DNA polymerase (12), but in the absence of any added primer, there is, as mentioned, no apparent reaction for several hours; a rapid production of a high-molecular-weight dAT polymer then takes place. Figure 2a shows the results of testing a series of oligomers for their capacity to substitute for dAT polymer in priming dAT synthesis. The decrease in absorbancy, a measure of polymer synthesis, occurred promptly when $(AT)_7$, $(AT)_6$, or $(AT)_5$ was used, and considerably earlier than the *de novo* reaction when $(AT)_4$ was present. No significant effect on the lag time of the *de novo* reaction could be attributed to the use of $(AT)_3$ or $(AT)_2$. This priming effect of the oligomers $(AT)_{4-7}$ was indistinguishable from that of dAT in requiring the presence of both dATP and dTTP as well as DNA polymerase and $Mg^{++}$.

The kinetics of the oligomer-primed syntheses, the extent of these reactions, and the final destruction of polymer by the exonuclease II component of polymerase (10) upon exhaustion of the substrates were not distinguishable from the reactions primed by dAT. The product of the $(AT)_{4-7}$-primed reactions is a large molecule as judged by its complete acid-insolubility and nondialyzability. Evidence for its being a dAT copolymer is based on a CsCl density gradient analysis of a product of an $(AT)_4$-primed reaction. A single sharp band at the density of dAT was found both at pH 8 and at pH 12, which is beyond the alkaline-melting transition.

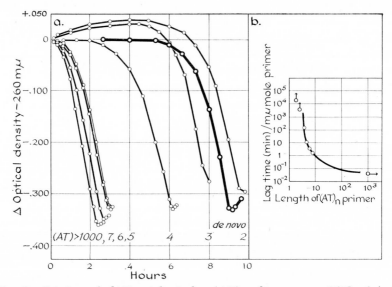

Fig. 2. Priming of dAT synthesis by $(AT)_n$ oligomers at 37°C. (*a*) The reaction mixtures were primed with 0.002 mμmole of dAT, 0.045 mμmole of $(AT)_7$, 0.075 mμmole of $(AT)_6$, or 0.21 mμmole of $(AT)_5$, 0.90 mμmole of $(AT)_4$, 15 mμmoles of $(AT)_3$, or 50 mμmoles of $(AT)_2$, and compared to a typical *de novo* synthesis curve at 37°C. (*b*) The length of $(AT)_n$ polymer refers to the number (*n*) of AT dinucleotide residues in the polymer. The amount of polymer in mμmoles was calculated from the $E_{260m\mu}$ for the polymers. The $E_{260m\mu}$ under reaction conditions for $(AT)_{2,4,5,7}$ were assumed to be 12,600, 12,600, 10,000, and 7,000, respectively. The symbols with an arrow attached are undetermined values that are at least greater than as represented on the graph.

The priming capacities of the $(AT)_n$ series of oligomers and of dAT polymer have been compared on the basis of the lag time per milli-micromole of primer (Fig. 2*b*). The lag time, arbitrarily defined as the time elapsed when an absorbancy decrease of 0.020 is reached (about 6% of the total reaction), is inversely proportional to the concentration of a given primer. For example, the lag times in an $(AT)_6$-primed reaction were 24, 42, and 83 minutes, respectively, with additions of 0.18, 0.12, and 0.06 millimicromole of primer. The lag time is markedly influenced by the size of the primer (Fig. 2*b*), with dAT being at least one hundred times as effective on this basis as the oligomers. It is not clear whether the greater effectiveness of a primer is due to more efficient binding by the enzyme or to its superior capacity to initiate and sustain replication.

The synthesis of a dAT polymer in response to an oligomer with an alternating sequence of deoxyadenylate and deoxythymidylate residues indicates that such an oligomer is being used as a template for the *E. coli* DNA polymerase. The lack of a 5′-phosphoryl terminal group in certain of these active oligomers indicates further that such a terminal grouping is not a requirement in the replication process. The kinetics of replication of the oligomers and the synthesis of exclusively large molecules suggest that a few oligomers have primed the synthesis of a few macromolecules which are then more rapidly replicated. These observations support the hypothesis that the *de novo* synthesis of dAT polymer starts with a random polymerization to produce a rare $(AT)_n$ oligomer. Just how this rare oligomer is put together in the first place remains unknown, but the fact that such an oligomer can lead to a large polymer is now established.

### INFLUENCE OF TEMPERATURE ON PRIMING CAPACITIES OF dAT AND OF THE $(AT)_n$ OLIGOMERS

All previous studies on the enzymatic replication of DNA have been carried out at 37°C. Under standard reaction conditions this temperature is 25 degrees below the $T_m$ of dAT, and it might be considered that variations between 0°C and 45°C attributable to the primer would not have a profound effect on dAT replication. However, even within the 0° to 45° range, there might still be significant changes in the degree of strand separation of the end of the dAT helix and very likely large effects on the secondary structure of the $(AT)_n$ oligomers. As seen in Fig. 3, the initial rates of replication are strikingly affected by temperature. With dAT as primer (Fig. 3*a*), the reaction at 20°C is far slower than at 37°C; at 10°C it is barely detectable. By contrast, the reaction with $(AT)_4$ as primer (Fig. 3*e*) is slightly faster at 20°C than at 37°C and more rapid still at 10°C. The replication rates of $(AT)_5$, $(AT)_6$, and $(AT)_7$ over the 10° to 45° range (Fig. 3*b*, *c*, *d*) show patterns that form a transition between those of $(AT)_4$ and dAT. The lag time of the *de novo* reaction varied from 6 to 12 hours at 37°C; no reaction was detectable during a 24-hour period at 20°C or a 72-hour period at 10°C; at 45°C the lag time was greater than 10 hours.

The fact that the priming by $(AT)_4$ was better at 10°C than at higher temperatures encouraged attempts to observe priming by $(AT)_3$ at low temperatures. Although no reaction was observed after a 72-hour incubation with $(AT)_3$ at either 10°C or 0°C, a subsequent elevation of the temperature to 37°C resulted in a prompt development of polymer (Fig. 3f). Controls which were preincubated for 72 to 144 hours at 0°C

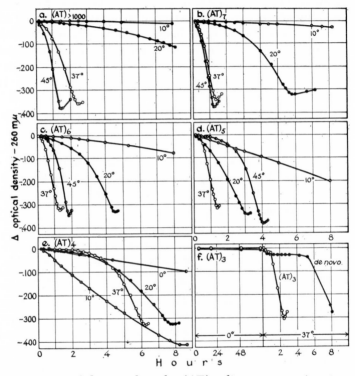

Fig. 3. Priming of dAT synthesis by $(AT)_n$ oligomers at various temperatures. Reaction mixtures as described were primed at the indicated temperatures with (a) 0.002 mμmole of dAT, (b) 0.13 mμmole of $(AT)_7$, (c) 0.22 mμmole of $(AT)_6$, and (d) 0.40 mμmole of $(AT)_5$. In (e) curves at 10°C, 20°C, and 37°C were obtained by priming with 0.9 mμmole of $(AT)_4$. The curve at 0°C was obtained with 0.5 mμmole of $(AT)_4$ and adjusted by a comparison with a curve obtained with this level of $(AT)_4$ at 10°. (f) Reaction mixtures, one primed with 15 mμmoles of $(AT)_3$ and one without any primer (de novo) were incubated at 0°C for 72 hours, then followed in the spectrophotometer at 37°C.

without enzyme or controls lacking $(AT)_3$ during the preincubation period showed the usual *de novo* lag period when placed at 37°C. These findings suggest that a few larger molecules were produced at 0°C which were unable to function effectively until the temperature was raised. A preliminary study of the kinetics of the $(AT)_3$-primed reaction at

0°C for 24, 48, and 72 hours showed a progressive decrease in lag time when the temperature was then raised to 37°C.

The relative rates at various temperatures for each of the $(AT)_n$ oligomers cited in Fig. 3 are compared in Fig. 4 on the basis of lag time. The temperatures in the 0° to 45° range were selected arbitrarily; measurements at temperatures above 45°C (e.g., 50°C) were complicated by extremely rapid rates for the dAT-primed reaction and by enzyme inactivation. It is clear from Fig. 4 that an optimal temperature has been approximated for the replication of each oligomer in the series and that there is a direct correlation between this temperature and the size of the oligomer.

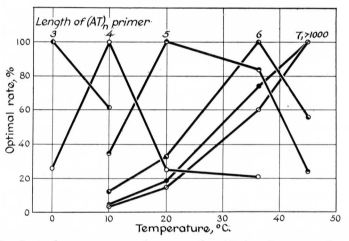

FIG. 4. Optimal temperatures of priming by $(AT)_n$ oligomers. The optimal rate of priming, defined as the minimum time required to produce a decrease of 0.020 in optical density at 260 mμ, was calculated from the data in Fig. 3 and set at 100. The entry for $(AT)_3$ at 10°C is based on the lag time at 37°C after a prior incubation for 72 hours at 10°C as compared with a sample preincubated at 0°C.

## PRIMING OF dAT SYNTHESIS BY DNA

The capacity of the relatively short AT sequences, as in the $(AT)_n$ oligomers, to prime dAT synthesis suggested the possibility that such sequences in DNA chains might also prime dAT synthesis. The crab testis DNA component, rich in AT copolymeric sequences but containing about 3% guanine and cytosine interspersed through the chains, initiated the prompt development of polymer (Fig. 5, No. 2). It may be inferred that the product is a dAT polymer, since dGTP and dCTP were excluded from the reaction mixture and the product displayed the buoyant density pattern in alkaline CsCl characteristic of dAT. DNA samples from yeast cytochrome b$_2$, *Tetrahymena patula*, and whole yeast also caused significant reductions in lag time (Fig. 5). On the other hand, T2 DNA, relatively rich in AT content (65% AT), failed to prime, whereas phage λ DNA, with a relatively low AT content (51%), appeared to do so.

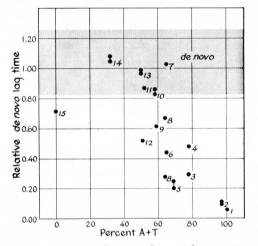

Fɪɢ. 5.   Influence of DNA on dAT synthesis. The reaction mixtures at 37°C contained polymer or DNA in the amount of 2 mμmoles (nucleotide residues) for (1) dAT and (2) crab testis, or 20 mμmoles (nucleotide residues) for (3) slime mole, (4) *T. patula*, (5) yeast cytochrome b$_2$, (6) *Paracentrotus lividus* (a sea urchin), (7) T2 phage, (8) whole yeast, (9) salmon sperm, (10) calf thymus, (11) T7 phage, (12) λ phage, (13) *E. coli*, (14) *Mycobacterium phlei*, and (15) dGdC. The lag time of *de novo* dAT synthesis (shaded area) was 360 to 545 minutes in an early series of experiments and 500 to 726 minutes in a later series; the median *de novo* value was set at 1.0 for each series. The double points for samples 2, 5, 8, 10, 13, and 14 represent separate experiments.

## A Suggested Mechanism of Replication Involving Reiteration of the Template

In considering the mechanism of AT oligomer replication to produce a dAT macromolecule, the most significant data available describe an optimal temperature distinctive for each oligomer in the series (Fig. 4). The fact that (AT)$_4$, for example, primes optimally at 10°C, whereas (AT)$_7$ is virtually inert at this temperature, argues against the stepwise extension of an (AT)$_4$ primer chain through intermediate stages which include (AT)$_7$. Unfortunately, definitive evidence to establish this point is lacking, and, as a consequence, several possible mechanisms can be entertained. A model which at this time appears plausible and offers a basis for discussion is described in Fig. 6. The first step involves replication of the template with a new strand starting from the 3'-hydroxyl end of the template. The second step entails the melting of this newly formed helix and its annealing to expose a segment of template for further replication. This second step in which reunion of the separated strands is correct in base pairing but displaced by one AT notch from perfect realignment may be regarded as a slippage process. An important assumption at this point is that the DNA polymerase binds the template in a way that distinguishes it from the growing replica; it might also be assumed that such an enzyme complex of template and

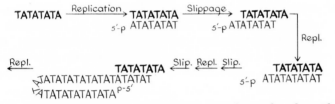

FIG. 6. A model for reiterative replication of oligonucleotides. The $(AT)_4$ template is designated in bold print. Replication proceeds from left to right; the initial unit of the newly synthesized strand, designated by standard print, is marked as a 5'-phosphoryl end group (pA. . .).

replica favors their union by hydrogen bonding. On the basis of this model we may consider that it is the slippage step of the reaction which is critically temperature-dependent. An $(AT)_4$ template after slippage would be linked to its replica by only six hydrogen bonds, a complex which would not be expected to be stable at 37°C but might be far more stable and effective at 10°C. By contrast, an $(AT)_7$ template linked by twelve hydrogen bonds to its slipped replica would be relatively more effective for replication at 37°C. However, at 10°C there is probably relatively little "breathing" in the $(AT)_7$ template–replica complex, and the system would therefore be almost frozen for further replication. This model, entailing successive steps of replication and slippage, would lead eventually to a continuous reiteration of the template and the development of a large dAT polymer. This scheme does not take into account the possibly important role played by helical hairpin structures which seem likely to develop in the growing replica (Fig. 6) and which may also be present in the larger oligomers, such as $(AT)_7$.

A model for polymer synthesis involving replication and slippage was first proposed by Chamberlin and Berg (2) to account for the development of polyriboadenylate by RNA polymerase. Their suggestion that short sequences of deoxythymidylate in the DNA template were reiterated was supported by the demonstration by Falaschi, Adler, and Khorana (4) that a synthetic deoxypolythymidylate with only five residues could serve as a template for polyriboadenylate synthesis. Recent studies have indicated that the reaction temperature has the same kind of influence on the replication of deoxythymidylate oligonucleotides by RNA polymerase as that described in the present report for the AT series by DNA polymerase.[2]

This model of reiterative replication by DNA polymerase has suggested several additional inquiries. One is the use of other oligomers which differ in base composition or in arrangement from the AT series. In current investigations, Khorana and his group (1) have found that reactions primed by $A_7$ and $T_{11}$ (Table II) or by $(CT)_5$ and $(AG)_5$ generate extensive synthesis of macromolecules. In the former case the product is the homopolymer pair of polydeoxyadenylate and polydeoxythymidylate dAdT; in the latter case a perfectly alternating copolymeric chain of CT and residues is matched to a corresponding chain of alternating A and G residues (dCT:dAG). The conjecture that the development of the AT polymer might in some way be due to the peculiar capacity of this polymer to fold back upon itself to form a hairpin-like structure clearly does not apply to the generation of the dCT:dAG polymer.

Another line of inquiry concerns the possibility that AT sequences in DNA would, in the absence of dGTP or dCTP, be reiterated sufficiently to prime the synthesis of a dAT polymer. The results already (Fig. 5) suggest that certain AT-rich DNA's do in fact prime dAT synthesis. Although a clear interpretation of these results is not at hand, it seems reasonable that the inability to copy a chain for lack of a matching G or C would predispose the looping out of a preceding synthesized TAT sequence. Given the possibility of such TAT loops and a reiteration of the ATA sequence in the template, the stage may be set for the initiation of an AT polymer. Conjectures of this kind lead to speculations that the origin of ATA or TAT sequences in natural DNA, so abundant in the crab testis DNA, for example, may be the consequence of such reiterative errors in replication. You may recall that DNA isolated from the testis of the common crab *Carcinus borealis* reveals two discrete and distinctive components (15). Upon density gradient centrifugation of DNA isolated from the testis and more recently from other tissues of this crustacean (3), Sueoka finds two components, the lighter one representing approximately 30% of the total DNA. Similar results have been obtained by Smith (14) with the Pacific coast representatives of this genus. The

---

[2] Personal communication from Dr. H. G. Khorana.

buoyant density of the main band corresponded to a G-C content of 42% which is characteristic of crab DNA. However, the buoyant density of the lesser band indicated a very low G-C content and was in fact at the level of the dAT polymer. Analysis of the nearest-neighbor frequency pattern (16) of this DNA indicated a frequency of dinucleotides containing G or C of only about 3%. Most remarkable was the finding that the A and T residues arranged in alternating sequence comprise 93% of the sequences. This crab DNA comes very close to being a dAT polymer with a peppering of G and C residues.

On the basis of the occurrence of this remarkable DNA in the crab, a wider search for this kind of polymer or other strikingly ordered polymers in animals, plants and bacteria appears desirable. It follows, too, that if such reiterative errors have occurred to create distinctive DNA's, there may also be associated distinctive mutational changes in amino acid sequences of the proteins reflecting repeated ATA, TAT, or other polymeric sequences.

Still another line of inquiry generated by these studies concerns the use of temperature to explore the nature of DNA replication. Would the activation energy of the DNA polymerase reaction, given an exposed strand of DNA for replication, resemble that of other enzyme-catalyzed reactions with a $Q_{10°}$ of about 2? If, however, replication requires that a given stretch of double helical DNA first be separated into its component strands, would the reaction be critically dependent on temperature with the involvement of very large activation energies? Recent experiments with DNA polymerase which distinguish the repair of a partially single-stranded helix from the synthesis of new strands provided an opportunity to test the influence of temperature on these two kinds of replication. The results indicate that when the temperature is lowered from 37°C to 20°C the repair process proceeds at a rate which is still a third to a half as great as at the higher temperature. By contrast, the new chain synthesis, which presumably requires the initial separation of the ends of the double helical template, is practically nil at 20°C.

## SUMMARY

1. In the presence of DNA polymerase and certain deoxynucleoside triphosphates but in the absence of template, novel polymers are synthesized after a lag period. Indications are that *de novo* synthesis of a macromolecular template occurs in the early part of this lag phase and that these molecules are then autocatalytically replicated. Electron micrographs reveal one of these polymers, a copolymer containing adenine and iodouracil, as a highly branched structure.

2. Oligonucleotides with sequences of six to fourteen alternating deoxyadenylate and deoxythymidylate residues [$(AT)_3$ to $(AT)_7$] prime the synthesis by *Escherichia coli* DNA polymerase of the high-molecular-weight deoxyadenylate–deoxythymidylate copolymer. At 37°C, the relative priming capacity of this series of $(AT)_n$ oligomers was directly related to their size. Temperature has a profound influence on the replication of the oligomers; in the range 0° to 45°C there is an optimal temperature distinctive for each oligomer in the series and a direct correlation between the size of the primer and the optimal temperature for its replication. For example, $(AT)_4$ is replicated most rapidly at 10°C, $(AT)_5$ at 20°C, and $(AT)_6$ at 37°C.

3. A model has been suggested in which replication of the oligomer template is followed by slippage of the resulting helix by an AT dinucleotide pair; such successive steps of replication and slippage many times would result in the continuous *reiteration* of the template and the synthesis of a large dAT copolymer. The possibility that AT sequences in DNA chains may also promote dAT synthesis is encouraged by the observed priming effect of several AT-rich DNA samples.

4. The suggestion is made that if reiterative events were to occur during *in vivo* replication it would result in DNA modifications which might under some circumstances be retained. This speculation is encouraged by the natural occurrence of a dAT-like polymer in the crab genus *Cancer* and invites a more intensive search for DNA's or DNA segments which contain reiterated sequences. If such reiterative events have occurred with any frequency in the evolution of DNA, they may be associated with distinctive mutational changes in the amino acid sequences of the proteins.

### Acknowledgment

This work was supported by grants from the United States Public Health Service, National Institutes of Health.

### References

1. Byrd, C., Ohtsuka, E., Moon, N. W., and Khorana, H. G., *Abstr. Meetings Natl. Acad. Sci. U.S., Madison, Wisconsin,* October 1964.
2. Chamberlin, M., and Berg, P., *Proc. Natl. Acad. Sci. U.S.* **48**, 81 (1962).
3. Cheng, T.-Y., and Sueoka, N., *Science,* **143**, 1442 (1964).
4. Falaschi, A., Adler, J., and Khorana, H. G., *J. Biol. Chem.* **238**, 3080 (1963).
5. Freese, E., this volume.
6. Goldberg, I. H., and Rabinowitz, M., *Biochem. Biophys. Res. Communs.,* **6**, 394 (1961).
7. Inman, R. B., and Baldwin, R. L., *J. Mol. Biol.,* **5**, 172 (1962).
8. Kornberg, A., "Enzymatic Synthesis of DNA," Ciba Lectures in Microbial Biochemistry, Wiley, New York, 1961.

9. KORNBERG, A., BERTSCH, L. L., JACKSON, J. F., AND KHORANA, H. G., *Proc. Natl. Acad. Sci. U.S.*, **51**, 315 (1964).
10. LEHMAN, I. R., AND RICHARDSON, C. C., *J. Biol. Chem.*, **239**, 242 (1964).
11. RADDING, C. M., AND KORNBERG, A., *J. Biol. Chem.*, **237**, 2877 (1962).
12. RICHARDSON, C. C., SCHILDKRAUT, C. L., APOSHIAN, H. V., AND KORNBERG, A., *J. Biol. Chem.*, **239**, 222 (1964).
13. SCHACHMAN, H. K., ADLER, J., RADDING, C. M., LEHMAN, I. R., AND KORNBERG, A., *J. Biol. Chem.*, **235**, 3242 (1960).
14. SMITH, M., *J. Mol. Biol.*, **9**, 17 (1964).
15. SUEOKA, N., *J. Mol. Biol.*, **3**, 31 (1961).
16. SWARTZ, M. N., TRAUTNER, T. A., AND KORNBERG, A., *J. Biol. Chem.* **237**, 1961 (1962).
17. TRAUTNER, T. A., SWARTZ, M. N., AND KORNBERG, A., *Proc. Natl. Acad. Sci. U.S.*, **48**, 449 (1962).
18. WEIMANN, G., SCHALLER, H., AND KHORANA, H. G., *J. Am. Chem. Soc.*, **85**, 3835 (1963).

# Evolutionary Aspects of the Distribution of Nucleotides in DNA and in RNA

Ekkehard K. F. Bautz

*Institute of Microbiology,*
*Rutgers University,*
*New Brunswick, New Jersey*

## Introduction

The variability of base content in DNA among different bacterial species represents one of the most extraordinary examples of how much variation nature can exhibit. This observation became even more puzzling when it was established that the only two RNA species known for some time, the transfer or soluble RNA (sRNA) and the ribosomal RNA (rRNA), showed no detectable variations in base composition even among the most distantly related bacterial species. A good part of the puzzle was resolved when fractions of metabolically unstable RNA molecules, now called messenger RNA (mRNA), were detected (Volkin and Astrachan, 26) which were identical in base composition with the DNA of the particular organism. From this finding one can draw the rather interesting conclusion that RNA species with no coding function have a fixed nucleotide composition, whereas those with coding function can exhibit extensive variations in nucleotide content. The now obligatory question whether the differences in DNA base composition among different bacterial species are reflected in the amino acid composition of the bacterial proteins was thoroughly investigated by Sueoka (25), and indeed a relationship with the G + C or the A + T content in DNA could be observed for a number of amino acids. It must be realized, however, that the correlation observed is on a very small scale, for an almost tenfold difference in the theoretical frequencies of some of the trinucleotides follows at best a twofold variation in the content of the most variable of the amino acids. The weakness of this correlation requires either that the bulk of the protein analyzed is specified by only a small portion of the bacterial genome which may not be variable in base composition, or that the distribution of nucleotides is *grossly* different from randomness, or that the genetic code is highly degenerate. Several lines of evidence now indicate that the last of the three possibilities suggested must be the correct one.

The extent of degeneracy is bound to influence greatly the distribution of nucleotides in DNA and in RNA, since the existence of many nonsense triplets would necessarily lead to a drastic reduction of certain nucleotide frequencies with a concomitant increase in frequencies belonging to sense triplets. If we assume the code to be completely degenerate, are we to expect complete randomness in the distribution of nucleotides in mRNA, provided, of course, that the number of messages is large enough for statistical purposes? The answer is, not quite, for one might argue that a message can carry sense only if it shows regularities, which means deviations from randomness, as is the case with our language, where no matter how large the sample of meaningful sentences may be, we shall always find some combinations of letters to be more frequent than others. In addition, the absolute amount of some letters will always be higher than that of others, a regularity that has its counterpart in the amino acid composition of proteins (Sueoka, 25). However, this deviation might not be reflected appreciably in the distribution of nucleotides in mRNA if we consider it likely that, during evolution of the present code, more triplets had been assigned to the more frequent amino acids (i.e., alanine) than to the less frequent ones.

Having discussed some of the factors likely to influence the distribution of nucleotides in mRNA, we come to the conclusion that, owing to the extensive degeneracy of the code, the frequencies of nearest neighbors in mRNA should not be far from random.

An extensive degeneracy of the genetic code also implies that any polynucleotide of random sequence is likely to function as a messenger (without, however, specifying useful polypeptides). If we allow, e.g., the existence of one nonsense triplet, a sufficiently large synthetic polynucleotide containing all four bases in equal molar quantities would then synthesize polypeptides of an average chain length of 63 amino acids before the nonsense triplet could put a stop to the growing chain. Therefore, in order to make an artificial nonmessenger molecule, we would have to synthesize a copolymer of a rather defined sequence, containing the nonsense triplet in quantities far above randomness. Thus it appears that, in the case of extensive or almost complete degeneracy, RNA molecules having other than messenger functions should be the unusual ones, showing strictly nonrandom distributions of nucleotides. However, a nonmessenger RNA molecule would not be required to possess any nonsense triplet if the messenger function were dependent only upon the secondary structure of RNA. From the extensive studies with cell-free extracts it is known that an increase in secondary structure in polynucleotides leads to a decrease in messenger activity (Singer *et al.*, 22). Therefore, a sequence of nucleotides causing the molecule to fold back on itself could be even more effective by not only keeping this sequence from being read but also preventing its own attachment to the ribosomes. Here again, as in our previous argument, the distribution of nucleotides is expected to be nonrandom.

The mid-point of helix–coil transition of fully or of partially ordered polynucleotides is directly related to their G + C content (Marmur and Doty 19; Fresco, 11). Therefore, the degree of ordered structure in RNA is expected to increase with increasing G + C content. The relatively high amount of G + C present in sRNA or in rRNA could then explain in part their observed inability to function as messengers *in vitro* (Nirenberg and Matthaei, 21; Bautz, 2). However, in some bacterial species, such as *Micrococcus lysodeikticus* and *M. phlei,* the G + C content of mRNA exceeds that of either sRNA or rRNA, and yet the messenger molecules are expected to be largely single-stranded in order to function properly. The question now arises whether a polynucleotide sequence, containing more than twice as much G + C as A + U, could be classified as a functional messenger, or whether in this case a nonrandom distribution of nucleotides might be required to effect a decrease in secondary structure. This question will be treated in some detail in connection with the discussion on helix stability.

## OLIGONUCLEOTIDE FREQUENCIES IN DIFFERENT TYPES OF RNA

Previous studies on the secondary structure of messenger RNA from phage T4 have convinced us that, with the methods presently available, it will hardly be possible to define structural variations between different RNA species by physical methods only. We have therefore focused our attention on the analysis of oligonucleotides obtained from a complete digest of RNA with pancreatic ribonuclease. Table I summarizes the di- and trinucleotide frequencies obtained from three different RNA species. The frequencies are presented as the ratios of the values found over those expected by a random distribution of nucleotides, calculated from the known base compositions. A comparison of the ratios for the four dinucleotides with the ones deduced from the corresponding nearest neighbors in T4 DNA (Josse *et al.*, 14) shows mRNA to be complementary and antiparallel to the coding DNA strand. This finding also implies that *in vitro* replication and *in vivo* transcription proceed by the same mechanism of reading. It is interesting to note that, al-

## TABLE I[a]

COMPARISON OF NEAREST-NEIGHBOR FREQUENCIES BETWEEN T4 mRNA AND T4 DNA, AND BETWEEN E. coli rRNA, PHAGE f2 RNA, AND E. coli DNA

| Nucleotide | T4 mRNA (found/random) | T4 DNA[b] (found/random) | | E. coli rRNA (found/random) | Phage f2 RNA (found/random) | E. coli DNA[b] (found/random), antiparallel |
|---|---|---|---|---|---|---|
| | | Antiparallel | Parallel | | | |
| ApCp | 0.87 | 0.90 | 1.09 | 0.94 | 1.04 | 0.87 |
| ApUp | 1.03 | 1.04 | 0.90 | 0.72 | 1.02 | 1.08 |
| GpCp | 1.11 | 1.13 | 0.84 | 1.05 | 1.00 | 1.34 |
| GpUp | 0.87 | 0.84 | 1.05 | 0.91 | 0.85 | 0.87 |
| ApApCp | 1.04 | 0.98 | 1.17 | 1.61 | 1.52 | 1.04 |
| ApApUp | 1.08 | 1.12 | 0.99 | 1.00 | 0.89 | 1.28 |
| GpApCp | 0.97 | 0.91 | 1.05 | 1.00 | 0.92 | 0.78 |
| ApGpCp | 1.27 | 1.08 | 0.86 | 1.30 | 1.00 | 1.17 |
| GpApUp | 1.25 | 1.06 | 0.87 | 1.00 | 0.91 | 0.96 |
| ApGpUp | 0.96 | 0.82 | 1.07 | 1.05 | 0.90 | 0.76 |
| GpGpCp | 1.18 | 1.12 | 0.84 | 0.88 | 1.19 | 1.21 |
| GpGpUp | 1.15 | 0.84 | 1.05 | 1.00 | 0.82 | 0.79 |

[a] From Bautz and Heding (4).
[b] Data from Josse et al. (14).

though the product of only one of the two DNA strands is analyzed, it resembles closely the dinucleotide frequencies of both DNA strands, indicating that there is little difference in the nearest-neighbor distribution between the coding strand and its complement.

The other two RNA species analyzed, *Escherichia coli* ribosomal RNA and the RNA from the *E. coli* phage f2 (Loeb and Zinder, 18), show little homology with *E. coli* DNA. This result is not surprising, since rRNA represents a rather homogeneous RNA species homologous only to a minute portion of the *E. coli* genome, and since phage f2 RNA is likewise homogeneous and, in addition, autonomously replicating; therefore, no direct correlation between these two RNA species and *E. coli* DNA is expected.

Since the DNA of *M. lysodeikticus* has a ratio of $A + T/G + C = 0.4$ (Lee *et al.*, 17) compared to a value of 1.0 for *E. coli* DNA (Smith and Wyatt, 23), it was of interest to compare the oligonucleotide frequencies

TABLE II

MONO-, DI-, AND TRINUCLEOTIDE FREQUENCIES IN RIBOSOMAL RNA
FROM *E. coli* AND FROM *M. lysodeikticus*[a]

| Nucleotide | *E. coli* | *M. lysodeikticus* | Nucleotide | *E. coli* | *M. lysodeikticus* |
|---|---|---|---|---|---|
| Cp | 10.0 | 10.6 | ApApCp | 2.8 | 2.6 |
| Up | 8.5 | 8.2 | ApApUp | 1.5 | 1.1 |
|  |  |  | GpApCp | 2.3 | 1.8 |
| ApCp | 4.5 | 4.8 | ApGpCp | 3.0 | 3.1 |
| ApUp | 3.1 | 3.8 | GpApUp | 2.1 | 2.2 |
| GpCp | 6.5 | 5.6 | ApGpUp | 2.3 | 2.8 |
| GpUp | 5.2 | 6.5 | GpGpCp . | 2.7 | 3.2 |

[a] Values given in mole per cent of total nucleotide.

in the rRNA's from these two species. The results shown in Table II suggests their structures to be similar, but not identical (the differences observed for GpCp and for GpUp are distinct).

Another problem that has so far been difficult to resolve in a decisive way is the question whether the two ribosomal subunits regularly encountered, the 50S and the 30S particles, contain structurally identical molecules. Small differences observed in nucleotide compositions of the two subunits have led different investigators to different conclusions (Spahr and Tissières, 24; Midgley, 20). More indicative were isotope dilution experiments, where the optical density and radioactivity profiles were compared after fragmentation and chromatography of cold and labeled RNA from 50S and 30S particles, respectively (Aronson, 1). We have likewise prepared $P^{32}$-labeled 30S ribosomal particles and extracted their RNA, which was degraded by pancreatic ribonuclease together with unlabeled RNA from a preparation of 50S ribosomes. In addition to the determination of the relative amounts of mono-, di-, and trinucleotides, the oligomers containing four and more nucleotides were collected and digested with T1 ribonuclease (Table III). A significant reduction in the amount of ApUp and GpUp in 30S particles can be observed, whereas the sequence PurineGAU occurs about twice as frequently in 30S as in 50S ribosomes. One can thus conclude with some degree of confidence that the two ribosomal subunits are indeed structurally different.

TABLE III

RELATIVE FREQUENCIES OF OLIGONUCLEOTIDES IN RNA
FROM 30S RIBOSOMES IN *E. coli*[a]

| From digest with pancreatic ribonuclease | | | | From T1 digest of oligonucleotides containing three or more purines | |
|---|---|---|---|---|---|
| Cp | 11.4 | ApApCp | 12.0 | (PuPuG)Cp | 7.9 |
| Up | 11.9 | ApApUp | 12.3 | (PuPuG)Up | 11.9 |
| | | GpApCp | 10.7 | Gp | 10.6 |
| ApCp | 11.6 | | | | |
| ApUp | 9.6 | ApGpCp ⎫ GpApUp ⎬ | 10.5 | (PuG)ApCp | 10.5 |
| | | | | (PuG)ApUp | 24.3 |
| GpCp | 10.5 | | | ApGp | 10.6 |
| GpUp | 8.2 | ApGpUp ⎫ GpGpCp ⎬ | 9.2 | (G)ApCp | 7.1 |
| | | | | (G)ApUp | 7.3 |
| | | GpGpUp | 9.3 | ApApGp | 10.6 |

[a] Numbers represent counts per minute of $P^{32}$ per millimicromole of nucleotide from 50S ribosomes.

The role of ribosomal RNA in protein synthesis is as yet unknown. One can speculate, however, that unique structural requirements exist for the function of rRNA, and that a rather tight relationship of rRNA structure with the function of the ribosomal subunits has prevented this type of RNA from participating in the drift of base composition observed in microorganisms.

Turning our attention to messenger RNA, let us assume that, as was shown to be the case for phage T4, we can accept the nearest-neighbor data on DNA by Josse *et al.* (14) in lieu of the dinucleotide frequencies in mRNA's from different species, which in most cases can be isolated only with extreme difficulty. On examining the nearest-neighbor data available from DNA species with widely varying base compositions, it appears that the frequencies show small but distinct deviations from randomness. It was also recognized (Kaiser and Baldwin, 15) that some of these deviations are dependent upon G + C content. There are several explanations possible for the observed deviations from randomness:

First, it can be argued, as we have in the Introduction, that sense requires nonrandomness. However, it was also pointed out that, owing to certain randomizing conditions, this deviation need be only very small. Hence, there appears to be room for two more possibilities, namely that either this species-specific distribution of nucleotides is related to the function of mRNA, or it reflects an evolutionary trend due to the fact that some mutagenic events occur more often than others. Evidence for and the extent of these two possibilities are the subject of the following discussion.

## HELIX STABILITY: ITS POSSIBLE ROLE IN MUTATIONS AND EVOLUTION

Although the hydrogen bonding between complementary bases represents the main reason for the helical structure of DNA, it must be realized that the stacking of the bases along the helix is greatly stabilized by Van der Waals forces, hydrophobic interactions, and others, their energy exceeding that of the hydrogen bonds between the base pairs (DeVoe and Tinoco, 9; Crothers and Zimm, 8). Owing to the quantitative differences in dipole moments and in mass of the four bases, there is little reason to assume that this stacking energy should be identical for all the sixteen possible combinations of dinucleotides. And indeed substantial differences in stacking energy have been suggested by DeVoe and Tinoco (9), based on the calculation of molecular orbitals in derivatives of purines and pyrimidines.

Working with the most thoroughly investigated model system of poly A–poly U complexes, we have designed experiments to show the existence of such differences directly on the oligo- and polynucleotide levels. In the first series of experiments oligonucleotides of the formulae $(Ap)_nC$, $(Ap)_nG$, and $(Ap)_nU$ ($n = 3, 4$) have been prepared, and their interactions with poly U investigated. Figure 1 shows the helix–coil transitions observed for mixtures of ApApApC + poly U, ApApApG + poly U, and ApApApU + poly U. The temperature mid-point of helix-coil transition ($T_m$) is approximately 7 degrees higher for ApApApC than for the corresponding oligomers terminating in either G or U. Because of the low melting temperatures of the oligomer–poly U complexes, it was technically preferable to measure the cooling rather than the heating profiles. Under the two conditions used throughout, 0.1 $M$ $Mg^{++}$ or 0.5 $M$ $Na^+$, helix formation proceeds almost instantaneously, since identical cooling profiles were obtained upon either fast or slow cooling. The $T_m$ values obtained with a number of oligonucleotides tested are summarized in Table IV.

In the presence of 0.1 $M$ $Mg^{++}$ the oligomers with three adenylic

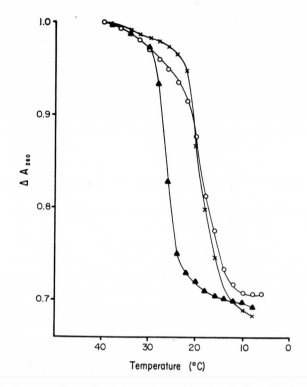

Fig. 1. Cooling profiles of ApApApC (—▲—), ApApApG (—o—), and ApApApU (—x—) in the presence of equimolar amounts of poly U in 0.1 $M$ MgCl$_2$. For experimental details see Bautz and Bautz (3).

TABLE IV

$T_m$ (°C) of Equimolar Mixtures of (Ap)$_n$X and Poly U, and of (Ap)$_n$Xp and Poly U

|              | In 0.5 $M$ Na+ | In 0.1 $M$ Mg++ |              | In 0.5 $M$ Na+ | In 0.1 $M$ Mg++ |
| ------------ | -------------- | --------------- | ------------ | -------------- | --------------- |
| (Ap)$_3$C    | 12             | 26              | (Ap)$_3$Cp   | 5              | 17              |
| (Ap)$_3$G    | 8              | 19              | (Ap)$_3$Gp   | < 4            | 13              |
| (Ap)$_3$U    |                | 19              |              |                |                 |
| (Ap)$_4$C    | 22             | 36              | (Ap)$_4$Cp   | 15             | 30              |
| (Ap)$_4$G    | 18             | 34              | (Ap)$_4$Gp   | 14             | 28              |
| (Ap)$_4$U    | 16             | 32              | (Ap)$_4$Up   | 13             |                 |

acid residues show the biggest differences; increasing chain length (or increasing $T_m$) diminishes the differences between C, G, and U. Addition of a phosphate to the 3′ position of the noncomplementary base also appears to reduce these differences. Under the conditions used in Fig. 1 the mixing curves show a minimum in absorption at 260 mμ at a molar concentration of A to poly U of 1 to 2 for $(Ap)_3C$, whereas $(Ap)_3G$ and $(Ap)_3U$ show a minimum at a ratio of oligomer to poly U closer to 1 to 1. Therefore, $(Ap)_3C$ seems to establish preferentially a triple-stranded structure together with two strands of poly U, under conditions where $(Ap)_3G$ and $(Ap)_3U$ appear to favor a double-stranded configuration involving only one strand of poly U (Fig. 2).

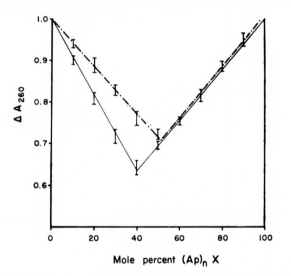

FIG. 2.   Mixing curves for $(Ap)_nX$ with poly U. The samples were mixed in the proportions given on the abscissa, transferred to cuvettes equilibrated for 10 minutes in the heating block precooled to 10°C, and read at 260 mμ.

————: $(Ap)_4C$ in 0.5 $M$ Na+; $(Ap)_3C$, $(Ap)_4C$, $(Ap)_4G$, $(Ap)_4U$ in 0.1 $M$ Mg++.

— · —: $(Ap)_3C$, $(Ap)_3G$, $(Ap)_3U$, $(Ap)_4G$, $(Ap)_4U$ in 0.5 $M$ Na+; $(Ap)_3G$, $(Ap)_3U$ in 0.1 $M$ Mg++.

To study the effect of the noncomplementary bases at the polymer level, four series of copolymers of poly A have been synthesized with a polynucleotide phosphorylase preparation from *M. lysodeikticus*, by using different input ratios of ADP versus either CDP, GDP, IDP, or UDP. The resulting copolymers had base compositions ranging from 70 to 100% of  adenylic acid residues. Each polymer was allowed to complex with poly U at a salt concentration of 0.5 $M$ NaCl, and the $T_m$ for each complex was determined by recording its heating profile. The $T_m$ values thus obtained were plotted against mole per cent A of the polymers. As shown in Fig. 3, poly AG and poly AI show slightly higher melting temperatures with poly U than the corresponding poly AU polymers,

which in turn melt out at higher temperatures than poly AC. Thus the
presence of cytidylic acid residues in poly A seems to weaken the stability
of the poly A–poly U complex the most, a result that appears to contradict
that data obtained from the oligonucleotides, where $(Ap)_nC$ showed
the highest $T_m$. The mixing curves in 0.5 $M$ NaCl shown in Fig. 4 are
similar to those obtained with $(Ap)_4C$ (Fig. 2), suggesting that, regardless of the nature of the nonmatching base, three stranded complexes are

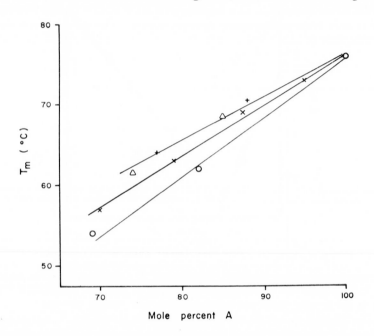

FIG. 3.   Dependence of $T_m$ upon A content of poly AX + U + U. For each
copolymer the heating profile in 0.5 $M$ NaCl + 0.01 $M$ Tris, pH 7.5, was determined
at a molar ratio of copolymer to poly U of 1–2. The $T_m$ values were plotted versus
the percentage of adenylic acid residues in the copolymers. +: poly AG; △: poly
AI; x: poly AU; O: poly AC.

preferred, and that the noncomplementary base does not titrate poly U.
   The most reasonable interpretation of the data obtained with the
oligonucleotides appears to be the following: Owing to the differences
in the pK values for C, G, and U, their ability to neutralize the net charge
of the complex is highest for C, and decreases in the order G and U. This
explanation, however, is compatible neither with the identical $T_m$ values
observed for the AG and AI copolymers, nor with the low $T_m$ values
observed for poly AC. Searching for possible explanations to fit the oligomer as well as the polymer data, we favor the following interpretation:

On the oligomer level, the melting temperature of an $(Ap)_3X$–poly U complex should be little or not affected if the noncomplementary base X does not interact with the neighboring A, but swings out freely, and it should be more affected if the extra base interacts strongly with the neighboring A, pulling it out of the helix and thereby weakening its hydrogen bonding with the opposite uridylic acid residue. In this latter case, the $T_m$ of $(Ap)_3X$ should be reduced markedly. According to this argument we propose that, in a sequence of nucleotides, U and G interact more strongly with a preceding A than does C. This assumption would

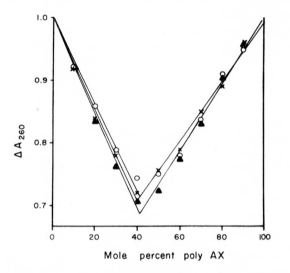

Fig. 4.   Mixing curves of poly U with: poly AC (82% A), —x—; poly AG (77%), —o—; poly AU (79% A), —△—. The mixtures had been allowed to equilibrate for one hour before reading.

then account for the low $T_m$ values observed for $(Ap)_3G$ and $(Ap)_3U$ compared to $(Ap)_3C$.

On the polymer level, an extra base interacting strongly with the preceding as well as the following A is likely to participate in stabilizing the helix and therefore should not lower the $T_m$ as much as a base that swings out freely and thereby in a way interrupts the continuity of the poly A strand.

These assumptions imply that an occasional guanylic acid residue, sandwiched between two stretches of A sequences, would be held in its place in the helix by the neighboring adenylic acid residues in spite of its inability to undergo hydrogen bonding with U. The failure of a single guanylic acid residue to loop out of the helix is expected to affect the structure of a poly A–poly U complex in one of the two following ways (Fig. 5-1): Either the U residue opposite a single G is forced to loop out of the poly U strand, leading to structure *a*, or it is pushed one place further in the helix to pair with the next A residue, leading to structure *b*. The two neighboring G residues in the bottom half of the complexes 1*a* and 1*b* are depicted as looping out according to the "helix with loop" model by Fresco and Alberts (12). In the poly AC–poly U complex (Fig. 5-2), all C residues are expected to loop out in accord with Fresco and Alberts' model. Although a model of the type 1*b* in Fig. 5 is favored through the data obtained from the mixing experiments (Fig. 4), an obstacle to such a model is the question whether the helix is flexible enough to counterbalance the distortion of the angles brought about by the stretching of one strand but not the other. Although this

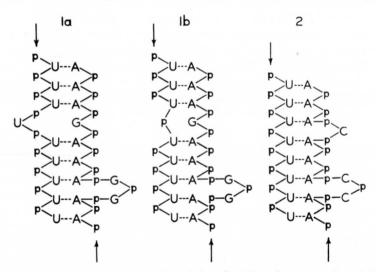

FIG. 5.   Hypothetical structure of a (1) poly AG–poly U complex, (2) poly AC–poly U complex.

question does not appear to lead to too serious complications as far as the building of molecular models is concerned, it cannot be entirely ruled out.

Let us consider now the bearing the discussed differences in helix stability are likely to have on the evolution of nucleotide sequences in DNA, and let us ask what consequences arise from this evolutionary trend to the structure and function of mRNA. Before entering a discussion on the results produced by selection pressures, we have to treat first the step initiating evolutionary processes, the occurrence of spontaneous mutations.

## The Effect of Helix Stability upon Mutation Rates

Point mutations are thought to arise through a change in the structure of DNA by either one of two mechanisms: (a) a mistake during replication of DNA leading from a wild-type parental strand to an altered (mutant) daughter half-molecule; or (b) a chemical alteration of a DNA base *in situ* into a derivative resembling in its hydrogen-bonding properties one of the three other bases rather than the original one. The mutagenic events of type (a) are likely to occur by either one of two possible ways: (i) the looping out of a base at the point of replication in the parental strand either causing the random incorporation of any one of the four bases leading to a base pair substitution, or, perhaps more likely (Brenner *et al.*, 6), causing the polymerizing enzyme to bypass the looped-out base, leading to a base pair deletion; (ii) the looping out of a base in the newly synthesized strand next to the growing point, leading to the insertion of a base pair (Fresco and Alberts, 12). The reiterative replication or "slippage mechanism" encountered with either DNA (Kornberg, 16) or RNA (Chamberlin and Berg, 7) polymerase leading to the addition of nucleotides to the newly synthesized strand may well represent an example of this latter case. It is important to note that the semiconservative mode of DNA replication requires the DNA to be single-stranded at the point of replication, which implies that the bases are held in a helical arrangement by planar interactions only, without the additional stabilization from the hydrogen bonds between the two complementary strands. Whereas the majority of mutations produced by base analogs or by acridines, or occurring spontaneously, are probably caused during replication of DNA (mechanism a), a number of chemical mutagens are known to react with resting DNA (mechanism b). For nitrous acid (Horn and Herriot, 13) as well as for hydroxylamine (Freese and Strack, 10) it has been shown that denatured DNA is far more reactive than native DNA, indicating partially denatured (labile) regions in DNA to be more susceptible to these mutagens.

A base interacting weakly with its two neighboring bases is likely to loop out with a higher frequency than a base interacting more strongly. From the arguments presented it follows that some sites are mutated at a higher rate than others, in agreement with the results from the analysis of the genetic fine structure of the rII region in phage T4, where it had been observed that the spontaneously arisen mutants are not randomly distributed throughout the two cistrons (Benzer, 5). The existence of only two very strong "hot spots" in the rII region indicates that the lability of the base at the hot-spot site is dependent not only upon the interactions with its nearest neighbors but also upon the interactions of these with their other neighbors; thus, the frequency of mutations at any one site is probably affected by a sequence of several nucleotides. Having concluded that helix stability is bound to cause mutation rates to be dependent upon the distribution of nucleotides, we can now turn to the question whether these mutational changes have indiscriminately been selected for during evolution.

## The Effect of Helix Stability upon the Evolution of Nucleotide Sequences

The high degree of degeneracy in the genetic code should allow a rather sizable drift in the distribution of nucleotides without necessitating adverse selection pressures. (For a discussion on this subject, see Sonneborn, this volume.) Owing to the higher mutability of labile sequences, the evolutionary trend of DNA structure is expected to lead toward more helix stability. On the other hand, as we know from the studies with cell-free extracts (Singer *et al.*, 22), messenger RNA is allowed to possess only a limited degree of secondary structure; it is therefore expected to counteract this trend, especially in those bacterial species where the messenger RNA has already a high degree of secondary structure due to a high $G + C$ content. If one accepts the structure–function relationship in mRNA as a major factor determining the evolutionary pressure on nucleotide distribution in DNA, then we could predict that the selection pressure working against greater helix stabilization is stronger in those species where the DNA is high in $G + C$, and weaker in those with a high $A + T$ content. Consequently, the most stable dinucleotide sequences should be relatively more abundant in high-AT than in high-GC DNA's. So far our experimental data do not suffice to warrant a comparison with the nearest-neighbor data (Josse *et al.*, 14); it is of interest to note, however, that the stabilizing purine–purine neighbors occur somewhat more frequently in high-AT than in high-GC DNA species.

### SUMMARY

In the present discussion an attempt has been made to combine two important aspects of DNA and RNA: their structural peculiarities and the requirements for their biological functions.

The notion we can accept with a reasonable degree of confidence is that RNA species having other than messenger functions are structurally the exception to the rule, and that their structural requirements have made them evolve into rather unique nucleotide sequences.

Model experiments with synthetic polynucleotides have shown that the effect of a noncomplementary base upon the interactions between complimentary sequences is quantitatively different for C, G, and U. These differences have led us to propose the hypothesis that nucleotide sequences of low helix stability undergo mutational changes more frequently than do the more stable regions; therefore, the evolutionary trend of base distribution in DNA is expected to lead from low to high helix stability. The structural requirements for the function of messenger RNA is thought to counteract this mutational trend in those species, where the secondary structure in the messenger molecules is expected to be strong due to a high $G + C$ content.

## ACKNOWLEDGMENT

This work was aided by Public Health Service Grant GM 10395 and National Science Foundation Grant GB 1882.

## REFERENCES

1. ARONSON, A. I., *J. Mol. Biol.*, **5**, 453 (1962).
2. BAUTZ, E. K. F., *in* "Informational Macromolecules" (H. J. Vogel, V. Bryson, and J. O. Lampen, eds.), p. 409, Academic Press, New York, 1963.
3. BAUTZ, E. K. F., AND BAUTZ, F. A., *Proc. Natl. Acad. Sci. U.S.*, **52**, 1476 (1964).
4. BAUTZ, E. K. F., AND HEDING, L., *Biochemistry*, **3**, 1010 (1964).
5. BENZER, S., *Proc. Natl. Acad. Sci. U.S.*, **47**, 403 (1961).
6. BRENNER, S., BARNETT, L., CRICK, F. H. C., AND ORGEL, A., *J. Mol. Biol.*, **3**, 121 (1961).
7. CHAMBERLIN, M., AND BERG, P., *J. Mol. Biol.*, **8**, 708 (1964).
8. CROTHERS, D. M., AND ZIMM, B. H., *J. Mol. Biol.*, **9**, 1 (1964).
9. DEVOE, H., AND TINOCO, I., JR., *J. Mol. Biol.*, **4**, 500 (1962).
10. FREESE, E., AND STRACK, H. B., *Proc. Natl. Acad. Sci. U.S.*, **48**, 1796 (1962).
11. FRESCO, J. R., *in* "Informational Macromolecules," (H. J. Vogel, V. Bryson, and J. O. Lampen, eds.), p. 121, Academic Press, New York, 1963.
12. FRESCO, J. R., AND ALBERTS, B. M., *Proc. Natl. Acad. Sci. U.S.*, **46**, 311 (1960).
13. HORN, E. E., AND HERRIOT, R. M., *Proc. Natl. Acad. Sci. U.S.*, **48**, 1409 (1962).
14. JOSSE, J., KAISER, A. D., AND KORNBERG, A., *J. Biol. Chem.*, **236**, 864 (1961).
15. KAISER, A. D., AND BALDWIN, R. L., *J. Mol. Biol.*, **4**, 418 (1962).
16. KORNBERG, A., this volume.
17. LEE, K. Y., WAHL, R., AND BARBU, E., *Ann. Inst. Pasteur*, **91**, 212 (1956).
18. LOEB, T., AND ZINDER, N. D., *Proc. Natl. Acad. Sci. U.S.*, **47**, 282 (1961).
19. MARMUR, J., AND DOTY, P., *Nature*, **183**, 1427 (1959).
20. MIDGLEY, J. E. M., *Biochim. Biophys. Acta*, **61**, 513 (1962).
21. NIRENBERG, M. W., AND MATTHAEI, J. H., *Proc. Natl. Acad. Sci. U.S.*, **47**, 1588 (1961).
22. SINGER, M. F., JONES, O. W., AND NIRENBERG, M. W., *Proc. Natl. Acad. Sci. U.S.*, **49**, 392 (1963).
23. SMITH, J. D., AND WYATT, G. R., *Biochem. J.*, **49**, 144 (1951).
24. SPAHR, P. F., AND TISSIÈRES, A., *J. Mol. Biol.*, **1**, 2 (1959).
25. SUEOKA, N., *Proc. Natl. Acad. Sci. U.S.*, **47**, 1141 (1961).
26. VOLKIN, E., AND ASTRACHAN, L., *Biochim. Biophys. Acta*, **29**, 536 (1956).

# Nature of Bacteriophages Induced in *Bacillus subtilis*[1]

T. V. Subbaiah, C. D. Goldthwaite, and J. Marmur

*Department of Biochemistry,*
*Albert Einstein College of Medicine,*
*Bronx, New York*

The origin of, and relationship between, extrachromosomal elements such as bacteriophages, bacteriocinogenic factors, sex factors, and resistance transfer factors in bacteria (15, 22) remains obscure. The specific properties of each can be traced to a unique polydeoxyribonucleotide sequence. In representative instances, it has been demonstrated that the extrachromosomal elements can replicate independently of the bacterial host genome. The possibility exists that the extrachromosomal elements, some of which have been demonstrated and studied in various bacteria, and all of which have been shown to exist in *Escherichia coli*, might represent part of an evolutionary spectrum. In such a spectrum, bacteriocins, some of which have been shown to be composed of single proteins, may occupy one end, and virulent bacteriophages, which possess an organized complex structure, the opposite end.

The deoxyribonucleic acids (DNA) of temperate bacteriophages appear to have similar nearest-neighbor base frequencies or contain a proportion of base sequences in common with the host DNA (6). This homology between regions of the viral and host genomes supports the concept that temperate bacteriophages may have evolved when a segment of the host genome acquired the ability to control its own duplication. Acquisition of bacteriophage-specific genes would in time decrease the extent of homology between host and bacteriophage nucleic acids, which may result in the appearance of obligatory virulent viruses. If this reasoning is correct, the "natural" hosts of temperate bacteriophages would be their respective lysogenic bacterial strains or ones closely related to them. On the other hand, it would be difficult to establish the identity of the natural host of virulent bacteriophages which have never been shown in the laboratory to have established cases of stable lysogeny,

[1] This work was supported by grants from the Atomic Energy Commission (AT-30-1-3311) and the National Science Foundation (GB-1869).

435

especially those whose over-all DNA base composition is different from that of bacterial strains capable of acting as a host for their reproduction.

All the *Bacillus subtilis* strains thus far studied in our laboratory harbor a variety of viruses which can best be described as highly defective lysogenic bacteriophages. It has been shown earlier (37) that upon induction of *B. subtilis* the cells lyse, liberating a mixture of virus-like particles containing DNA very similar to that of the host cell. These particles, designated as PBSX, are able to exert bacteriocidal action and have been shown to be genetically defective, i.e., unable to replicate in a sensitive host. The DNA extracted from PBSX particles resembles that of the host DNA with respect to physical, chemical, and biological properties.

The resemblance of some of the properties of phage particles PBSX to those of bacteriophages and bacteriocins offers a unique opportunity for the establishment of a basis of their common ancestry. In addition, the close identity between the bacteriophage and host DNA renders this system suitable for the study of evolution of bacteriophages. In this connection, studies have been made on the nature of the viral particles of PBSX and similar defective phages isolated from various strains of *B. subtilis*. Some of these results are presented, and their possible significance in the evolution of bacteriophages and bacteriocins is discussed.

Three strains of bacteria were used in the present investigations: (a) *B. subtilis* 168-2 ($try_2^-$ $leu^-$), a strain known to produce PBSX upon induction; (b) *B. subtilis* 168-2S, a suspected derivative of *B. subtilis* 168-2 and sensitive to PBSX; and (c) *B. subtilis* S31, a new wild-type isolate kindly supplied by P. Schaeffer, and also sensitive to PBSX.

Induction of the phage particles was generally achieved by treatment with mitomycin C, an antibiotic known to induce bacteriophages from lysogenic bacteria (33). Mitomycin C was added (0.2 to 1.0 µg/ml) to a log phase culture of a density of approximately $10^8$ cells/ml and incubated at 37°C with shaking for a period of 2 to 4 hours (10). Phages could also be induced if, after a 10-minute contact with mitomycin C, the cells were harvested, resuspended in fresh broth, and incubated at 37°C for a further period of 2 to 4 hours (37). In both procedures the turbidity of the culture increased to a maximum during the first 60 to 75 minutes. Lysis of the culture, followed by the liberation of the phage particles, occurred starting from 90 minutes after resuspension and incubation in the fresh medium. No apparent differences were observed between the phage particles produced by these two methods.

Phage particles could also be induced by exposure of the cultures to ultraviolet irradiation and to nalidixic acid, an antibacterial agent known to interfere with the synthesis of DNA in *E. coli* (17). Thymine deprivation or addition of 5-bromouracil (20 µg/ml) in place of thymine to a thymine auxotroph of *B. subtilis* 168 caused lysis and liberation of bacteriophage particles (23). No liberation of the phage particles was observed after treatment with heat (60°C for 30 minutes) or after exposure of the bacterial suspensions to chloroform. Spontaneous liberation of the phage occurred to a small extent in the stationary phase cultures. The results to be reported here concern only those phage particles induced with mitomycin C.

The lysates obtained after induction with mitomycin C were spun at $13,000 \times g$ to remove bacterial cell debris and were treated with 1 to 2 µg/ml of deoxyribonuclease (Worthington) in the presence of $5 \times 10^{-3}$ $M$ MgCl$_2$ for 60 to 90 minutes at 37°C. The phage lysates were then centrifuged in a Spinco Model L preparative ultracentrifuge for 90 minutes in the 21 rotor at 21,000 rpm, and the glassy, gelatinous phage pellet obtained was resuspended in approximately one hundredth of the original volume either in the synthetic medium described by Nomura (31) or in unsupplemented Spizizen minimal medium (38). The phage suspension was centrifuged at $12,000 \times g$ to remove any large particulate clumps and stored at 4°C over chloroform.

The susceptibility of bacterial strains to different phage particles was tested by placing drops of crude or processed lysates on a lawn of sensitive bacteria. The presence of phage could also be detected by cross streaking a sensitive bacterial strain on a nutrient agar plate against a streak of phage. The best results were obtained by incubating the plates for 14 to 16 hours at room temperature.

A semiquantitative assay of the crude or processed lysates of the phage particles was performed by a modification of the colicin ring test (16). Loopfuls of serial dilutions of the lysate were deposited on a lawn of a logarithmic phase culture of sensitive bacteria, and zones of inhibition of bacterial growth were observed. Unlike the success obtained with bacteriocins, this method was not sensitive enough to quantitatively titrate the lysates of phage, since the titrations yielded an abrupt end point at low dilutions of the concentrated lysate. Presumably, cooperative action of a large number of phage particles was necessary to cause a zone of inhibited growth. Assay by a bacteriocidal test in liquid medium, using an inoculum of about $10^7$ sensitive bacteria and determining the LD$_{50}$, was found to be more sensitive than the colicin ring test in the titration of the phage lysates.

All three strains, 168-2, 168-2S, and S31, liberated phage particles upon induction with mitomycin C. The particles produced upon induction of strain 168-2 are referred to as PBSX, a designation given in earlier studies (37). Strain 168-2S also released phage particles upon induction, and these phage particles are named PBSZ. Similarly, phage particles produced when S31 was induced are designated PBSY.

The three phages, PBSX, PBSZ, and PBSY, were unable to kill or lyse the homologous strains from which they were derived but were able to exert their bacteriocidal action on heterologous strains. The bacteriocidal activity of the phage lysates against heterologous sensitive strains was insensitive to trypsin when treated for 2 hours at a concentration of 250 µg/ml.

Attempts to lysogenize the sensitive strains by superinfection with heterologous phage have so far been unsuccessful. Similarly, efforts to isolate a host capable of supporting the replication of the inducible phages, allowing the formation of phages typical of virulent or lysogenic phages, have thus far failed.

No evidence could be obtained for the synthesis of any new phage-specific DNA upon induction with mitomycin C. Cells of strains 168-2S as well as S31 were grown for several generations in fully deuterated medium (7), harvested when they reached a cell density of approximately $10^7$/ml, and induced with mitomycin C upon transfer to $H_2O$ Penassay (Difco) medium. Phage lysates of PBSZ and PBSY thus obtained were processed and concentrated by centrifugation as described earlier. The DNA from these unfractionated phage lysates was extracted with phenol (28), and the phenol was removed by dialysis. The buoyant density of the DNA, determined by analytical CsCl density gradient centrifugation, corresponded to that of fully deuterated bacterial DNA. No hybrid or light DNA was observed. A similar result was obtained when PBSX was induced from B. subtilis SB25 (a 168 strain) grown in fully deuterated medium. It has also been found that PBSX can be induced in substantial yield in a thymineless strain of B. subtilis (12) in the absence of added thymine (23). These results confirm earlier findings (37) with respect to the origin of the DNA of PBSX and provide additional evidence that the nucleic acid incorporated into the phage particles is essentially pre-existing bacterial DNA packaged into newly synthesized phage-specific protein coats.

The DNA isolated from PBSX and PBSZ transformed competent B. subtilis strains to at least three markers carried by the host from which they were induced. Similarly, DNA isolated from PBSY transformed with respect to six of the host markers tested.

The incorporation into the phage particle of host DNA still retaining biological (transforming) activity suggests a unique degradation of host DNA by a nuclease, presumably activated or newly synthesized upon induction with mitomycin C. Increase in DNase activity of as yet un-identified nucleases and degradation of DNA have been shown to occur in *E. coli* (35) and *B. subtilis* (32) on treatment with mitomycin C. It has also been observed (26) that a significant increase in a unique DNase occurred in *E. coli* K12λ upon induction of λ by mitomycin C or by thymine deprivation, and also on λ infection. Similar investigations are being carried out to test for the appearance of any nucleases in strains 168-2, 168-2S, and S31 upon induction of phages PBSX, PBSZ, and PBSY, respectively, by mitomycin C.

The finding that the induction of *B. subtilis* phages results in the incorporation of pre-existing host DNA into the phage particles, and the subsequent discussion of findings in related systems, leads to the following tentative mechanism for the production of the *B. subtilis* phages: Any agent which inhibits DNA synthesis (e.g., thymine deprivation) and/or causes a distortion of the DNA molecule (e.g., mitomycin C or ultraviolet-induced crosslinking of DNA) activates or initiates the appearance of a nuclease leading to unique and limited degradation of the bacterial genome. At some point before the DNA is degraded into small pieces, the information encoded in the phage-specific polydeoxyribonucleotide sequence is expressed, leading to the formation of phage-specific structural proteins. The steps are programed so that the assembly of the completed phage particles takes place before the host DNA is extensively degraded by the new as well as the pre-existing nucleases. In the case of λ induction in *E. coli*, the nucleases may excise the λ-specific genome together with some attached host DNA. Since λ is capable of self-replication (a replicon) when dissociated from its host genome, it is λ DNA which, having the right size, is preferentially packaged into the phage head. It might not be surprising to find some particles after λ induction that possess bacterial DNA if, at some point in the packaging of DNA into the λ phage head, host DNA has been degraded by nucleases to a size equal to that of the phage genome.

In order to characterize the heterogeneous nature of the phages, concentrated phage lysates of PBSX, PBSZ, and PBSY, processed as described earlier, were each centrifuged to equilibrium in a CsCl density gradient (30). The density of the phage suspension was first adjusted to 1.380 gm/cc by the addition of solid CsCl (American Flouride), and the centrifugation (35,000 rpm) was carried out for 36 to 40 hours in a Spinco Model L preparative ultracentrifuge in the SW 39 rotor at 20° to 22°C. Before the fractions were collected, the bands were examined under transmitted light, and their positions were recorded. The Lusteroid tube was pierced with an insect mounting pin, and three drop fractions were collected. The refractive indices of several fractions of the gradient were measured and related to the density, and the density of the bands was estimated by interpolation. The fractions were diluted with 1 ml of Spizizen minimal medium, dialyzed against the same solution, and tested for bacteriocidal activity by the colicin ring test. The number of bands obtained with respect to each phage, the densities, and biological activity are presented in Table I.

It can be seen that most if not all the bacteriocidal activity exhibited by unfractionated lysates is now confined to the band of density 1.38 gm/cc which is obtained from phage PBSX, PBSY, and PBSZ lysates centrifuged in CsCl. Electron microscopic examination of the material in this band, kindly carried out by Dr. E. Holtzman (Department of Pathology of this Institute) by a modification of the phosphotungstic acid negative staining technique (5), revealed only intact phage particles. In contrast, similar examination of the unfractionated phage lysates prepared under the same conditions revealed what were apparently empty heads, phage ghosts, free tails, and bacterial flagella along with intact phage particles. Electron micrographs of the few specimens of phage lysates examined show that PBSX, PBSY, and PBSZ resemble each other closely. All possess a small head, long tail, tail sheath, and narrow head-to-tail connector. The dimensions are very similar to those of phages α and μ described below.

In their inducibility, bacteriocidal action, and morphology, phages PBSX, PBSZ, and PBSY resemble phage α (10) and phages μ and π (19), also derived from *B. subtilis*. Phage α (10) was induced either by ultraviolet irradiation or by mitomycin C and possessed a small head (430 A in diameter), a long cylindrical tail (70 × 2000 A), a tail plate (30 × 210 A) with four or five short fibers, a tail sheath (190 × 2000 A), and a narrow head-to-tail connector. Phages μ and π (19), two closely similar phages, were liberated on induction, respectively, from indole-requiring and threonine-requiring mutants of *B. subtilis* which killed sensitive heterologous strains but were inactive on the homologous strains. Phage μ possessed a small head (400 A in diameter) and a long tail (75 × 2200 A).

DNA obtained from phenol extraction (28) of phage preparations had a buoyant density of 1.703 gm/cc in the analytical CsCl density gradient, identical to that of *B. subtilis* DNA. The boundaries of the band obtained were slightly diffuse, indicative of partial degradation of DNA resulting from the induction by mitomycin C. No definite evidence of a satellite band at a higher or lower density has yet been observed.

The bacteriocidal action of phage particles PBSX, PBSY, and PBSZ resembles closely that of bacteriocins, which are known to kill sensitive cells rapidly upon contact. The properties that distinguish PBSX, PBSY, and PBSZ from the bacteriocins, however, are their characteristic bacteriophage morphology, the presence of DNA, their resistance to in-

TABLE I

CHARACTERIZATION OF BANDS OF CONCENTRATED *B. subtilis* PHAGE LYSATES FRACTIONATED IN CsCl DENSITY GRADIENTS

| Phage | | Band no. in preparative CsCl gradients:[a] | | | | | | | | | | |
|---|---|---|---|---|---|---|---|---|---|---|---|---|
| | | 1 | | | 2 | | | 3 | | | 4 | | |
| Inducible from *B. subtilis* strain | Type | Killing activity[b] | Presence of DNA[c] | Band density[d] | Killing activity | Presence of DNA | Band density | Killing activity | Presence of DNA | Band density | Killing activity | Presence of DNA | Band density |
| 168-2 | PBSX | — | — | 1.294 | — | ? | 1.325 | + | + | 1.375 | — | ? | 1.392 |
| S31 | PBSY | — | — | 1.295 | — | ? | 1.324 | + | + | 1.376 | | | |
| 168-2S | PBSZ | — | — | 1.293 | — | ? | 1.326 | + | + | 1.374 | | | |

[a] Centrifugations were carried out in the SW 39 rotor in the Spinco preparative ultracentrifuge at 35,000 rpm for 36 to 40 hours at 20°C.

[b] Bacteriocidal activity using heterologous sensitive strains, e.g. in the case of PBSX, strains 168-2S and S31.

[c] Presence of DNA after extraction of the respective band of the phage lysate with phenol (Mandell and Hershey, 1960) as judged by absorption at 260 mμ. The + sign also indicates that the DNA isolated from the phage possesses transforming activity.

[d] Density of the phage band in gm/cc. The densities are recorded only for those bands that are visible by scattered light.

activation by the proteolytic enzyme trypsin, and their easy sedimentability. However, exceptions to these properties among bacteriocins are not rare. Some of the E-group colicins (13, 14), megacins (20, 29), listeriocins (40), pyocin (24), and bacteriocin-like substances from *Streptomyces virginiae* (36) are known to be insensitive to the action of trypsin.

Particles resembling incomplete phage structures with only bacteriocidal activity are also known to occur. In a strain of *B. megaterium* producing an easily sedimentable killer particle, electron micrographs revealed a large number of uniform, spherical particles of approximately 55 mμ in diameter which could be incomplete phage structures of some kind (29). Electron microscopy of pyocin particles (24) has shown them to be uniform rods, about 100 mμ in length and about 15 mμ in width, which resemble phage tails. Incomplete phage structures have also been reported (3) when defective lysogenic strains derived from *E. coli* K12 were exposed to ultraviolet radiation.

Bacteriocidal action similar to that of bacteriocins is exhibited by phage ghosts of the T-even phages on phage-sensitive *E. coli* strains (8, 18, 31), and by *E. coli* phage P1Kc on *Pseudomonas aeruginosa* (9). Thus, except for the presence of DNA, other criteria of distinction between bacteriocins and the phage particles PBSX, PBSY, and PBSZ constitute only exceptions to the rule rather than the rule itself.

Phage particles PBSX, PBSY, and PBSZ, described here, and phage α and phages μ and II, described earlier, occur as inducible phages in *B. subtilis*. Similar particles have been observed in the lysates of *B. licheniformis* and *B. natto* (37) and of *B. cereus* (25), and from *B. circulans*, *B. polymyxa*, and *B. sphaericus* (10). All these particles are best described as extremely defective prophages sharing properties of both bacteriophages and bacteriocins. They may thus occupy a unique position in the evolutionary spectrum ranging between bacteriocins and bacteriophages.

It may be that bacteriocinogenic factors (some of which have been shown to be replicons) responsible for the synthesis of bacteriocins are extremely defective in that they are unable to code for the synthesis of all the necessary proteins and/or their subsequent assembly into an organized structure. A relatively complex structure such as a bacteriophage involves sophisticated programing in the synthesis and assembly of subunits, whose final construction contains a regular pattern of protein capsid enclosing a nucleic acid capable of initiating self-replication (11). The relatively low molecular weight protein of the bacteriocins retains the properties lethal to cells which are also known to be sensitive to the tails of some phages. Colicin K and tails of *E. coli* phage T6 compete for the same receptor site and exert similar bacteriocidal action (27).

In the case of pyocin, elongated structures similar to phage tails are seen under the electron microscope (24). The genome responsible for their production presumably is able to direct the formation of an organized structure devoid of infectious nucleic acid. If evolution has been proceeding in the direction from simpler to more complex structures, we have possibly encountered here a higher degree of development than the simpler bacteriocins. In the case of PBSX, PBSY, and PBSZ, the next step in the evolving process of subunit organization of the phages reflects an evolutionary position where the genome is able to code for the protein subunits but unable to replicate independently in a manner similar to other, less defective, prophages. In such a situation it is to the advantage of the symbiont to be present in a stable association with the host, the ideal state being permanent integration with the host genome. Such a situation, in which phage genes could form a continuous part of a bacterial chromosome, can be visualized if one considers the transducing particles, in which association of bacterial genes with phage genome is considered normal. Alternatively, a segment of the bacterial genome may have evolved to the extent that it is able to code for the complete coat protein of the phage particle; such a segment, which has not yet acquired the ability to multiply autonomously, could be present only as part of the normal chromosome of the host. Phage particles PBSX, PBSY, and PBSZ may thus represent another evolutionary stage, probably one close to the temperate phages.

In the case of defective *B. subtilis* phages, the phage genome is able to act as a template and code for the synthesis of the complete protein coat of the phage particle without autonomous multiplication, i.e., inability to function as a replicon. Presumably it is also able to direct the packaging of pre-existing, partially degraded, DNA into the protein shell, with the liberation, after induction, of complete phage particles which in their properties satisfy many of the criteria used to define phage. Whether the action of the induced nucleases on the host genome results in DNA molecules of an optimum size necessary for the condensation of DNA molecules into phage heads, and whether the formation of such phage heads is a prerequisite for the formation of completed phage particles, remains to be seen. This may be one of the explanations offered for the presence of a preponderance of empty heads and free tails observed in the unfractionated phage lysates if, at the time of their assembly, there was not enough DNA of the required size present to be incorporated into all the phage heads synthesized by the phage-specific template.

Phages PBSX, PBSY, and PBSZ are defective in two essential functions. They (a) are unable to infect sensitive cells and produce infectious progeny and (b) appear to lack the ability to multiply autonomously upon induction in a manner similar to other temperate bacteriophages.

The defect first cited could be due either to the failure of the phage to inject its DNA or to the "nonfunctionality" of the injected DNA.

The absence of autonomous multiplication of the viral genome of phages PBSX, PBSY, and PBSZ may be due to its loss by mutation. Alternatively, it may be analogous to the case of the non-inducible λ mutant, λ ind⁻ (21). However, unlike the λ ind⁻ case, the inducible phages of B. subtilis are capable of producing phage particles upon induction. It is also possible that the expression of the functions governed by the phage genome may be dependent on bacterial mutations which could affect the production of the repressor of vegetative phage growth (1, 4).

It may be that harboring of defective phages in a stably integrated state, of the kind reported here, is essential for the host, and their loss might be lethal. Whether the phage genome serves any essential functions during the normal reproduction of the host, as observed in the stable F′ strain of E. coli (34), remains to be seen.

The close similarities observed in the properties of the three phages PBSX, PBSY, and PBSZ may be due to their origin from a single bacterial strain. The differences observed in the host range of these phages could be due to alterations in their tail fibers. Such alterations are known to arise in other phages because of various mutations in the phage genome which affect the structural proteins of the phage (39).

It is conceivable that mutations in the phage genome affecting the structural proteins of the defective lysogenic phages PBSX, PBSY, and PBSZ may in some cases result in concomitant changes in the receptor sites of the host bacterium. The alterations in the protein coat or tail fibers of the phage particles may enable them to get adsorbed onto new receptor sites of bacterial strains previously resistant to the phage, and to exert their bacteriocidal action. The concomitant changes in the cell wall of the host, which produces the phage particles, may render it resistant to homologous phage. These alterations in the phage structure and in the cell wall receptors of the host may lead to changes in the host range pattern of the phage particles without the necessity of losing prophage. If this reasoning, which appears to be more suited to phages similar to PBSX, PBSY, and PBSZ, is correct, analysis of protein subunits of the induced phage particles from the strains 168-2, 168-2S, and S31 may reveal some differences. In addition, differences in cross-absorption titers between purified lysates and phage receptors isolated from the cell walls of the hosts may reveal the predicted changes in the receptor sites.

The changes in host sensitivities and production of different but closely related phages may also be explained as involving a sequential loss of prophages from a "polylysogenic" parent culture similar to that observed (1, 2) in a parent culture polylysogenic to bacteriophage λ.

## References

1. ARBER, W., *Virology*, **11**, 250 (1960).
2. ARBER, W., *in* "Symbiotic Associations" (P. S. Nutman and B. Mosse, eds.), p. 12, Cambridge Univ. Press, Cambridge, 1963.
3. ARBER, W., AND KELLENBERGER, G., *Virology*, **5**, 458 (1958).
4. BERTANI, L. E., *Virology*, **12**, 553 (1960).
5. BRENNER, S., AND HORNE, R. W., *Biochim. Biophys. Acta*, **34**, 103 (1959).
6. COWIE, D. B., AND MCCARTHY, B. J., *Proc. Natl. Acad. Sci. U.S.*, **50**, 537 (1963).
7. CRESPI, H. L., MARMUR, J., AND KATZ, J. J., *J. Am. Chem. Soc.*, **84**, 3489 (1962).
8. DEMARS, R. I., *Virology*, **1**, 83 (1955).
9. DEMEURISSE, G., AND SANABRIA, J., *Ann. Inst. Pasteur*, **106**, 449 (1964).
10. EISERLING, F. A., Doctoral Thesis, University of California of Los Angeles, 1964.
11. EPSTEIN, R. H., BOLLE, A., STEINBERG, C. M., KELLENBERGER, E., BOY DE LA TOUR, E., CHEVALLEY, R., EDGAR, R. S., SUSMAN, M., DENHARDT, G. H., AND LIELAUSIS, A., *Cold Spring Harbor Symp. Quant. Biol.*, **28**, 375 (1963).
12. FARMER, J. L., AND ROTHMAN, F., *J. Bacteriol.*, **89**, 262 (1965).
13. FREDERICQ, P., *Ann. Rev. Microbiol.*, **11**, 7 (1957).
14. FREDERICQ, P., *in* "Biological Replication of Macromolecules," p. 104, Academic Press, New York, 1958.
15. FREDERICQ, P., *J. Theoret. Biol.*, **4**, 159 (1963).
16. GOEBEL, W. F., AND BARRY, G. T., *J. Exptl. Med.*, **107**, 185 (1958).
17. GOSS, W. A., DIETZ, W. H., AND COOK, T. M., *J. Bacteriol.*, **89**, 1068 (1965).
18. HERRIOTT, R. M., AND BARLOW, J. L., *J. Gen. Physiol.*, **40**, 809 (1957).
19. IONESCO, H., RYTER, A., AND SCHAEFFER, P., *Ann. Inst. Pasteur*, **107**, 764 (1964).
20. IVANOVICS, G., NAGY, E., AND ALFOLDI, L., *Acta Microbiol. Hung.*, **6**, 161 (1959).
21. JACOB, F., AND CAMPBELL, A., *Compt. Rend. Acad. Sci.*, **248**, 219 (1959).
22. JACOB, F., SCHAEFFER, P., AND WOLLMAN, E. L., *in* "Microbial Genetics" (W. Hayes and R. C. Clowes, eds.), p. 67, Cambridge Univ. Press, Cambridge, 1960.
23. JANCZURA, E., personal communication.
24. KAGEYAMA, M., *J. Biochem. (Tokyo)*, **55**, 49 (1964).
25. KELLENBERGER, G., AND KELLENBERGER, E., *Schweiz. Z. Allgem. Pathol. Bakteriol.*, **15**, 225 (1952).
26. KORN, D., AND WEISSBACH, A., *J. Biol. Chem.*, **238**, 3390 (1963).
27. LATARJET, R., AND FREDERICQ, P., *Virology*, **1**, 100 (1955).
28. MANDELL, J. D., AND HERSHEY, A. D., *Anal. Biochem.*, **1**, 66 (1960).
29. MARJAI, E. H., AND IVANOVICS, G., *Acta Microbiol. Hung.*, **9**, 285 (1962).
30. MESELSON, M., STAHL, F. W., AND VINOGRAD, J., *Proc. Natl. Acad. Sci. U.S.* **43**, 581 (1957).
31. NOMURA, M., NATSUBARA, K., OKAMOTO, K., AND FUJIMURA, R., *J. Mol. Biol.*, **5**, 535 (1962).

32. NAKATA, Y., NAKATA, K., AND SAKAMOTO, Y., *Biochem. Biophys. Research Commun.*, **6**, 339 (1961).
33. OTSUJI, N., SEKIGUCHI, M., IIGIMA, T., AND TAKAGI, T., *Nature*, **184**, 1079 (1959).
34. PITTARD, J., AND RAMAKRISHNAN, T., *J. Bacteriol.*, **88**, 367 (1964).
35. REICH, E., SHATKIN, A. J., AND TATUM, E. L., *Biochim. Biophys. Acta*, **53**, 132 (1961).
36. ROELANTS, P., AND NAUDTS, F., *Antonie van Leeuwenhoek J. Microbiol. Serol.*, **30**, 45 (1964).
37. SEAMAN, E., TARMY, E., AND MARMUR, J., *Biochemistry*, **3**, 607 (1964).
38. SPIZIZEN, J., *Federation Proc.*, **18**, 957 (1959).
39. STREISINGER, G., AND FRANKLIN, N. C., *Cold Spring Harbor Symp. Quant. Biol.*, **21**, 103 (1956).
40. TUBYLEWICZ, H., *Bull. Acad. Polon. des Sci. Cl. II*, 519 (1963).

*Note added in proof:*

Particles that resemble bacteriophages in morphology and behave like bacteriocins in their bacteriocidal action have been shown to be induced by mitomycin C, azaserine, and other agents in *E. coli* 15WT and its substrains, which include *E. coli* 15 T$^-$ and 15 T$-$A$-$U$^-$ [Endo, H., Ayabe, K., Amako, K., and Takeya, K., *Virology*, **25**, 469 (1965); Sandoval, H. K., Reilly, H. C., and Tandler, B., *Nature*, **205**, 522 (1965)]. It is probable that "thymineless death" observed in the latter two strains is also due to the induction of bacteriophage-like particles under conditions of thymine deprivation. The drop in optical density and lysis after a period of thymine starvation and reintroduction of thymine [Mennigmann, H. D., *Biochem. Biophys. Research Commun.*, **16**, 373 (1964)] would be a result of induction and synthesis of the bacteriophage-like particles. These aspects of thymineless death thus form part of a general phenomenon of induction of bacteriophage-like particles such as accomplished by various means in *B. subtilis*.

# Discussion of Part VII

P. Doty, H. Harris, S. Spiegelman, C. A. Thomas,
M. V. Simpson, E. K. F. Bautz

Chairman Doty: We are short of time. If anybody would like to pull himself back to the mooring from which he has been loosened, by a question or two, those can be entertained.

Dr. Harris: This is strictly a question. As I remember the paper of Schildkraut and Doty (Dr. Doty can, no doubt, confirm this), dealing with artificial hybrids of polyribotides and polydeoxyribotides, the characteristics of the artificial hybrid were that it was resistant to both RNase and DNase and that it had a very great resistance to high temperatures, a much greater resistance to high temperatures than DNA-DNA hybrids.

I wonder whether you could give me some information about your natural RNA-DNA hybrids, especially in what way they are similar or different from the model system of Schildkraut and Doty.

Chairman Doty: The DNase level in that note wasn't high enough, so that result was incorrect.

Dr. Spiegelman: Let me point out something else that may not be obvious.

DNA strands hybridized to RNA are more resistant to DNase than free DNA. However, they are not absolutely resistant in the sense that you ever get a plateau.

As far as the melting temperature is concerned, is it very much higher, really?

Chairman Doty: That was the GC case. That was very special.

Dr. Spiegelman: Generally, this doesn't appear to hold for heteropolymers.

Dr. Thomas: I wonder if it had occurred to Dr. Kornberg that the evolutionary origin of sRNA cistrons might be the reiteration-replication process, which would put a reflection point in one strand, which would then give rise to a reflection point in the RNA strand, thus producing a structure similar to our notions of what sRNA molecules are like.

Dr. Simpson: Dr. Bautz, is model 1b likely?

Dr. Bautz: The problem is whether the energy gained by accommodating the G residues within the poly A protein of the helix is enough to offset the loss in energy due to the interruption of the poly U strand. This question is further complicated by the fact that the angle between the neighboring N-glycosidic bonds is opened up in the poly U part but not in the poly A part of the helix. Thus, energetically, model 1b doesn't look very attractive; however, lacking quantitative estimates on just exactly how much energy is gained or lost, we cannot presently disregard a structure like this, especially since it is the one that fits the experimental data better than the more reasonable looking model 1a.

CHAIRMAN DOTY: We must close now.

PART VIII

# EVOLUTION OF GENES II

# Chairman's Remarks

WERNER BRAUN

*Institute of Microbiology,*
*Rutgers University,*
*New Brunswick, New Jersey*

In the preceding papers, we heard about some aspects of the evolution of the basic cellular language for the specification of enzyme structure and function. This afternoon we shall consider some evolutionary aspects of the system responsible for the translation of the nucleic acid message into comprehensible and incomprehensible proteinaceous dialects.

In taking up this topic, we shall concern ourselves with a level of specificity production and product regulation that has fundamental significance for both the past evolution of gene action as well as the current evolution of a better understanding of these processes.

It is hardly necessary to point out to an audience such as this that it is at the level of these cellular events that many of the still remaining riddles of specification, recognition, and regulation may find an answer, and that it is also at this level that evolution has produced a major shift from what must have been a relatively monotonous basic tune to the spontaneous formation of a bewildering variety of etudes that eventually resulted in the selection of a multitude of melodious tunes. In fact, some current thinking suspects that one of the major and more recent evolutionary achievements, namely, the ability to respond specifically to many foreign stimuli, as represented in the formation of specific antibodies, may have evolved at or near the level of cellular activity that we are about to consider.

# Evolutionary Problems
# in the
# Synthesis of Proteins

ALEXANDER RICH

*Department of Biology, Massachusetts Institute of Technology,
Cambridge, Massachusetts*

There are two distinct areas to consider in discussing evolution and proteins. One of these is the study of the evolution of protein molecules. This study involves the determination of the amino acid sequence of a number of related proteins in an organism or of the same protein in related organisms. From this information and a knowledge of the evolutionary relations between the organisms, a reasonably consistent picture can be developed in which we learn something about the rate at which changes have taken place in the primary sequence of amino acids in various classes of proteins. However, this type of study must be differentiated sharply from a study of the evolution of the protein synthetic mechanism. In this latter activity, we would like to understand the way in which the protein synthetic machinery has been modified and evolved as a function of time both within a given organism and relative to different organisms. Although there is a rapidly expanding body of experimental information available on the evolution of protein structure, there is very little information dealing with the evolution of the protein synthetic machinery. This probably reflects the fact that the protein synthetic mechanism was largely stabilized at a comparatively early stage in evolution, so that few traces of its precursor have survived.

To gain some perspective on the nature of this problem let us first consider the general properties of the protein synthetic system as it is now understood. Our view of this process has come into focus sharply only within the last few years, and during this time period several fundamental discoveries have been made. It is quite likely that additional discoveries will be made in the next few years, but there is no expectation at the present time that the view which we now have will be altered in a fundamental way.

## An Outline of Protein Synthesis

According to our present understanding, the information which directs the sequential assembly of amino acids into proteins is found encoded in the sequence of nucleotides in the DNA molecules which constitute the major genetic storehouse (5). Synthesis of a protein is carried out by forming an RNA molecule which is complementary to one of the two DNA strands along a cistronic section of the DNA molecule. This molecule, called messenger RNA, directs the assembly of amino acids which are attached to the small-molecular-weight polynucleotides called transfer or soluble RNA (sRNA). The assembly takes place on the ribosomal particles which act to translate polynucleotide sequences into polyamino acid sequences. An important element in the translation system is a series of molecules called activating enzymes which have specificity toward individual amino acids and particular sRNA molecules. Information in the messenger RNA strand is believed to be encoded in the form of triplets of nucleotides (6) called codons, most of which are believed to specify a particular amino acid. The general nature of messenger RNA-directed protein synthesis was most strikingly demonstrated by Nirenberg and Matthaei (17), who showed that polyuridylic acid brought about the synthesis of polyphenylalanine. Recent experiments by Nirenberg and colleagues (14) have led to the direct assignment of specific nucleotide triplets for various amino acids. Most of the sixty-four possible triplets will undoubtedly code for amino acids, but it is likely that some of these sequences will carry out functions other than specifying amino acids. More than one triplet codes for a particular amino acid, and recent results suggest that this "degeneracy" arises out of a lack of complete specificity among one of the three bases in the codon (14). Other evidence of degeneracy has been the existence of more than one type of sRNA molecule which will accept a particular amino acid.

At the present time it is believed that the ribosome is a necessary component of any protein synthetic system. These particles appear to have a largely passive role in the protein synthetic process, and their function is usually described in manner analogous to that of a large enzyme-like unit acting to bring together messenger RNA and the amino acid–sRNA complex. Ribosomes are found in all living cells, and there is great similarity between the ribosomes obtained from a wide variety of living organisms, although they are not identical. In the electron microscope they appear as roughly spherical particles with a diameter slightly greater than 200 A. They consist of two unequal-sized subunits which combine to form a total particle with a molecular weight between

3 and 4 million, depending upon the particular source of the ribosomes. More than half of the mass is found in two macromolecular RNA molecules, the function of which is unknown.

The assembly of amino acids is initiated at the N-terminal end of the polypeptide chain and proceeds toward the C-terminal end (8). The growing or nascent chain remains attached to the ribosome through the C-terminal end where it is held onto the ribosome through a soluble RNA molecule (10), presumably the sRNA molecule associated with the most recently added amino acid at the C-terminus of the growing polypeptide chain. The sequential addition of amino acids occurs through a reading process, the detailed nature of which is not understood at the present time. It is likely that each codon triplet of bases on the messenger RNA strand combines with a complementary triplet of nucleotides on the sRNA strand called the anti-codon. Thus, the specificity for adding successive amino acids probably entails the formation of specific hydrogen bonds between purine and pyrimidine residues in much the same fashion that the specificity of DNA replication or messenger RNA synthesis involves the same bonding between these residues. However, since a regular helical structure is not being formed, it is possible that alternative types of hydrogen bonds could form between adenine and uracil residues (16).

The polypeptide chains found in proteins are of variable length. Thus we anticipate that the messenger RNA strands associated with their synthesis would also have variable lengths, and this is largely borne out by current research work. In synthesizing a protein such as hemoglobin, the polypeptide chains have approximately 150 amino acids, and we expect a polynucleotide messenger RNA strand containing about 450 nucleotides. In its stable configuration, the purine and pyrimidine residues are stacked on top of each other with a separation of 3.4 A, and this would lead us to anticipate a messenger RNA for hemoglobin with a length in the vicinity of 1500 A. This messenger RNA strand is long enough to accommodate several ribosomes, and this is the origin of the polyribosomal or polysomal structures which are the active protein synthetic units. Electron microscopic studies of hemoglobin synthesis show pentamers and hexamers of ribosomes in which there is an interribosomal spacing of 50 to 150 A and an over-all contour length near 1500 A (27). Electron micrographs of reticulocyte polyribosomes are shown in Fig. 1. Figure 1a shows shadowed polysomes, and Fig. 1b shows them stained with uranyl acetate. In addition to positively staining the RNA of the ribosomes, we can also see a thin thread passing between the ribosomes. It has a diameter of approximately 15 A, as would be expected of a single-stranded messenger RNA.

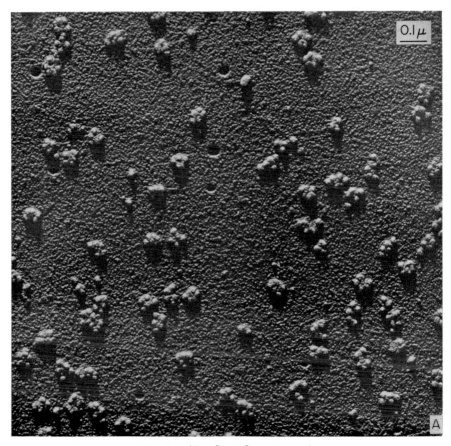

FIG. 1. (See legend next page.)

A schematic diagram of the mode of action of polysomes during protein synthesis is illustrated in Fig. 2 (see page 458). Protein synthesis begins by the attachment of ribosomes to the end of the messenger RNA strand. Recent work suggests that this may occur at the 3'-hydroxyl end of the messenger strand at a site which is specific for the attachment of ribosomes or the initiation of protein synthesis (9). Protein synthesis must be started by the attachment of the activated sRNA molecule associated with the N-terminal residue of the polypeptide chain. Once this has been attached, then the activated sRNA for the second amino acid is added, and the peptide bond is formed between them. A continuation of this process is associated both with the gradual elongation of the polypeptide chain and the gradual movement of ribosomes along the messenger strand. This is shown diagrammatically in Fig. 2 by the

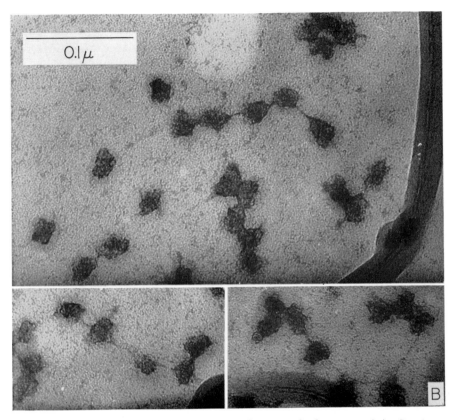

FIG. 1. Electron micrographs of reticulocyte polyribosomes. (*a*) Specimen shadowed with platinum (28). (*b*) Staining with uranyl acetate shows both ribosomes and messenger RNA molecule (22).

gradual elongation of the dotted polypeptide chains. The polypeptide chain is folded up to form both secondary and tertiary structure as the chain is elongated, as shown in Fig. 2. The best evidence for this is the detection of enzymatically active nascent protein molecules on polysomes, as they could have this activity only if they were largely in their native configuration (13).

Messenger RNA molecules have been studied which are polycistronic; that is, they contain structural sequence information for synthesizing more than one type of polypeptide chain. An example of this is seen in the synthesis of the enzymes associated with the induction of β-galactosidase. The existence of polycistronic messengers implies that there must be information in the polynucleotide strand which directs the release of polypeptide

chains once they are completed and also directs the initiation of the polypeptides which are found on the adjoining part of the messenger
molecule. Thus, it is likely that some of the sixty-four possible types
of polynucleotide triplets are used for functions other than those of
specifying particular amino acids. These functions include polypeptide
chain initiation and termination, and possibly ribosomal attachment sites
among others.

We do not as yet have a great deal of information concerning the
details of the interaction between ribosomes, messenger, and soluble
RNA molecules. It has been shown that free ribosomes have a binding
site for RNA which has the capacity to exchange single sRNA molecules
(4, 24). However, during the act of protein synthesis it has been shown
that ribosomes active in protein synthesis attached to polysomes have
two soluble RNA molecules per ribosome (26). Since one of these is
presumably occupied with holding the growing polypeptide chain, it is
likely that the other sRNA molecule holds the amino acid which is about
to be added to the chain. A diagrammatic illustration of a possible two-

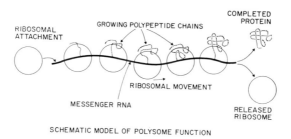

SCHEMATIC MODEL OF POLYSOME FUNCTION

Fig. 2.   A schematic model of polysome function.

site mechanism is shown in Fig. 3. The sRNA molecule is represented
by a hooklike structure with three lines representing the anti-codon
bases. Site A contains the activated amino acid, and the messenger RNA
codon triplet is shown hydrogen-bonded to the anti-codon nucleotides.
Attached to the adjoining site (P) is an sRNA molecule which holds the
growing polypeptide chain. Site A can be filled from the outside pool of
activated sRNA molecules, whereas site P can be filled only from site A.
The mechanism of protein synthesis may be schematically described in
terms of three coordinated activities: (1) The polypeptide chain is transferred from site P to site A, a new peptide bond is formed, and the freed
sRNA molecule is ejected from site P. (2) There is a movement of the
sRNA from site A to site P associated with (3) the simultaneous translation of the messenger RNA from site A to site P. This allows the sRNA
anti-codon and the messenger codon to remain in contact throughout

this process. Site A is then open for the addition of a new activated sRNA which is coded for by the adjoining triplet of nucleotides. The co-ordinated movements associated with (2) and (3) give rise to a displacement of the messenger strand relative to the ribosome, which represents, in a diagrammatic way, the molecular basis of the movement of ribosomes along messenger RNA. The scheme in Fig. 3 is, of course, highly diagrammatic, and the actual details of this mechanism have still to be elucidated.

The 3'-hydroxyl end of all sRNA molecules is terminated by the same triplet of nucleotides containing two cytidylic acid residues and

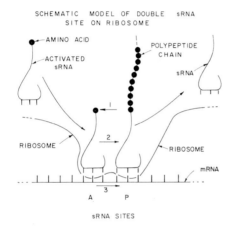

SCHEMATIC   MODEL OF DOUBLE   sRNA
SITE ON RIBOSOME

sRNA SITES

FIG. 3. Diagram illustrating the action of the sRNA sites during protein synthesis: (1) represents formation of the peptide bond; (2) and (3) represent the movement of sRNA and messenger from site A to site P.

a terminal adenylic acid residue onto which the amino acid is attached. The fact that this is common for all sRNA molecules suggests that it may be associated with a common function such as binding or movement. Recent work with digests of activated sRNA molecules has shown that this end of the sRNA molecule containing the common CCA sequence and the amino acid is able to terminate polypeptide chain synthesis by adding the amino acid and releasing the nascent chain (25). It is tempting to believe that this occurs because the sequence CCA is somehow associated with an attachment site whereby the ribosome is able to hold the activated sRNA and form the peptide bond. When this attachment site is released to facilitate movement of the sRNA molecule, in this abnormal situation it results in the release of the polypeptide chain attached to the fragment of the sRNA molecule.

It is quite likely that further research work over the next several years will bring out many of the subtle features of the protein synthetic machinery. Many of the functions described above which we now recognize as necessary will be translated into concrete molecular activities. However, the important point to consider is the fact that we probably understand the process of information flow and amino acid assembly in broad outline at the present time.

## UNIVERSALITY OF THE PROTEIN SYNTHETIC MECHANISM

From the information available at the present time, it seems likely that the same protein synthetic mechanism is used quite generally throughout all living systems. Polyribosomes have been observed in diverse species ranging from cabbage plants and slime molds to bacteria and man (19). The evidence all points to a rather similar system for bringing about the polymerization of amino acids into proteins.

Even more striking, however, is the evidence which suggests that not only is the mechanism the same but the code itself appears to be universal in that the same codons are used in vastly different species. This has been demonstrated most effectively in experiments in which heterologous components are used. Thus, for example, it has been shown that the aminoacyl sRNA from *Escherichia coli* serves adequately in bringing about the synthesis of hemoglobin in extracts of rabbit reticulocytes (26). This implies that the sRNA anti-codons of *E. coli* appropriately interpret the sequence of nucleotides on the rabbit messenger RNA. Likewise, the RNA obtained from the bacteriophage f2 can be used to direct the synthesis of f2 viral coat protein by using ribosomes and supernatant obtained from *Euglena* (21). Perhaps even more striking is the fact that DNA from a normally mammalian virus, vaccinia, can be placed into *B. subtilis,* and complete viruses can be obtained from this system (1). Thus, plant, bacterial, and mammalian systems seem to have the same codes. These observations are quite striking, since many of these species have been separated from each other for most of the last billion years. Another approach to the problem of universality involves the use of synthetic polynucleotides such as polyuridylic acid which promotes the incorporation of phenylalanine in cell-free systems. The results here also strongly suggest universality, since the same polynucleotides seem to promote incorporation of the same amino acid in a variety of cell-free systems. Thus, for example, mammalian systems and the alga *Chlamydomonas* seem to have similar coding properties (29).

The evidence suggesting the universality of the genetic code as well as the universality of the mechanism for assembling amino acids into protein raises several problems to which answers cannot be obtained at the present time. For example, we would like to know the nature of the mechanism which maintains the code. A suggestion has been put forward to the effect that there is a stereochemical interaction between each amino acid and the anti-codon nucleotides on its corresponding sRNA (29). A mechanism of this type involves a direct physical contact which might help to maintain universality independent of the enzymatic reactions which are important in amino acid activation. However, there is no evidence supporting this concept at the present time. Another possible alternative is that the universality of the code is maintained by the fact that any deviation from it would introduce so many alterations in the proteins of the organism that they would all be lethal. While this argument has some appeal, it is nonetheless difficult to see why it was not possible for some organisms to have made an escape from this over the long time period of evolution. However, it may be that such organisms which started to evolve utilizing a different code would for a considerable time period be so inefficient as to make it difficult for them to compete with the other organisms using the parental code, and hence they would not have survived the selection process. Alternatively, if the new code had greater survival value, organisms using the parental code would eventually disappear because of the continuity of the biosphere. Unfortunately, at the present time, we have no way of fully interpreting universality.

## EVOLUTION OF THE NUCLEIC ACIDS

We have no clear understanding of the nature of nucleic acid evolution, although several suggestions have been put forward (18). There is ample evidence that there has been a steady evolution among the nucleic acids of different organisms which is in many ways analogous to the evolution of the proteins. Considerable work has been done in the evolution of amino acid sequences in proteins. Detailed studies have been carried out on the evolution of the hemoglobins and on the evolution of the cytochrome $c$ molecule. By using paleontological evidence relating the time at which various species separated from each other, it is possible to obtain a time scale for the rate at which amino acid substitutions appear in these proteins. The results of these studies suggest that there has been one evolutionarily effective change in an amino acid every 2 to 11 million years, depending upon the protein (3, 15). This, of course, represents the rate at which a codon for one amino acid is changed into another, and not only does it involve a nucleotide change in the DNA of the organism, but also this change has to survive in the selection competition in which the entire organism is involved. Only in a very indirect manner does it tell us something about the rate at which nucleotides are changed in DNA chains.

Although there are good experimental data on amino acid substitutions incurred during the course of evolution, there is a paucity of information related to the changes in nucleotide sequence. There is, of course, some indirect information related to the over-all changes in guanine–cytosine versus adenine–thymine composition of DNA molecules from different species. However, these are gross alterations, and they have not been related to changes in the nucleotide sequence. In the protein synthetic system, there is evidence that there have been changes in the nucleotide composition of ribosomal RNA obtained from different species. However, these compositional changes have not been translated into sequence alterations as yet.

There is some information available regarding the evolution of soluble RNA molecules. This was obtained in the course of carrying out annealing studies between soluble RNA molecules and DNA molecules (11). In these experiments, radioactive soluble RNA from E. coli was prepared and added to unlabeled DNA from the same organism. The solution was then raised to an elevated temperature to melt both the DNA and the soluble RNA, and, following this, the mixture was slowly cooled, and the DNA was banded in a cesium chloride density gradient. The amount of sRNA attached to the DNA is measured by its radioactivity, and the amount which forms long stretches of complementary nucleotides is indicated by its resistance to ribonuclease treatment. When the DNA of the E. coli genome is fully saturated, the amount of bound sRNA has been used to estimate that there are about forty different types of sRNA molecules in the cell.

Having established the maximum number of E. coli sRNA molecules which could be annealed to E. coli DNA, it was then possible to carry out experiments to determine whether similar nucleotide sequences exist in other bacterial DNA's (11). Toward this end, seventeen types of DNA were obtained from five different bacterial families, as listed in Table I. These differ in their guanine–cytosine content, ranging from 38% to 72%. The amount of E. coli sRNA which could be annealed to these DNA samples was measured, and the results are plotted in Fig. 4. It can be seen that the maximum bonding is found with homologous molecules, that is, molecules in which E. coli B sRNA is annealed to the E. coli B DNA. A large number of related bacterial DNA's from the family Enterobacteriaceae annealed between 50 and 70% of the E. coli B sRNA. The somewhat distant member, Proteus vulgaris, annealed only about 30%

TABLE I
Types of DNA Used in Annealing Experiments as Shown in Fig. 4.

| Family | Species | % GC (20) |
|---|---|---|
| Bacillaceae | *Bacillus megaterium* | 38 |
| | *Bacillus cereus* (var. *mycoides*) | 39 |
| | *Bacillus subtilis* | 44 |
| Enterobacteriaceae | *Proteus vulgaris* | 39 |
| | *Escherichia coli* B | 51 |
| | *E. coli* K 12 (λ) | 51 |
| | *Proteus morganii* | 51 |
| | "*Aerobacter*" (1041) | 51.5 |
| | *E. freundii* | 53 |
| | *Salmonella typhimurium* | 53 |
| | *Paracolobactrum aerogenoides* | 54 |
| | *Klebsiella pneumoniae* | 56 |
| | *Serratia marcescens* | 59 |
| Brucellaceae | *Brucella abortus* | 56 |
| Pseudomonadaceae | *Pseudomonas fluorescens* | 62 |
| Micrococcaceae | *Micrococcus lysodeikticus* | 72 |
| | *Sarcina lutea* | 72 |

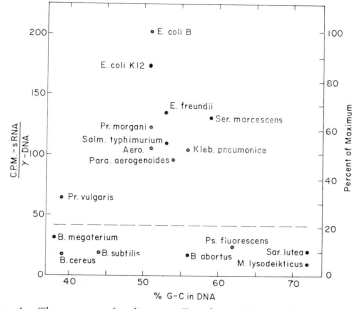

Fig. 4. The amount of radioactive *E. coli* B sRNA which can be annealed to various types of bacterial DNA. Although the data are plotted against per cent of guanine–cytosine in the DNA, it is clear that there is no relation between this value and the amount of annealed sRNA (11).

of that seen with *E. coli* B. However, all of the DNA's obtained from other bacterial families anneal between 5 and 15% of that seen for *E. coli* B itself. These experiments suggest that there has been a divergence in the polynucleotide sequences of sRNA as seen by examining a variety of closely related species. However, analogous experiments carried out with remote DNA, such as those found from T₂ bacteriophage or salmon sperm, show no ribonuclease-resistant *E. coli* sRNA annealing to the samples (11).

However, the proper way to perform this kind of experiment is to carry out with the sRNA molecule the type of study which is already under way in the case of the proteins. The nucleotide sequence of an alanine sRNA molecule has already been obtained (12). This has been a very difficult job in comparison to the work required to determine the amino acid sequence of proteins. However, it is likely that methods for carrying out polynucleotide sequence analysis will improve considerably in the future, and it may then be possible to determine the nucleotide sequence of alanine sRNA from a variety of different species. Then we will know which part of the molecule has been maintained constant and which parts have evolved in the course of time. If this work were carried out on species which have a well-defined paleontological history, it would enable us to obtain a time scale for these changes much in the same way as has been possible for proteins.

We cannot use the data in Fig. 4 in this way, since we do not know the rate at which various bacterial families separated from each other. However, investigation could be carried out on species which have a well-defined paleontological history. Selection pressures undoubtedly differ for different parts of the sRNA molecule. Evidence cited above suggests that the anti-codon nucleotides have not changed, but there is some evidence that activating enzymes have specialized somewhat and that they are not equally active with sRNA from other species (2). This suggests that the activating enzymes probably interact with more than just the sRNA anti-codon nucleotides. It also suggests that the rate of evolutionary changes in the sRNA nucleotides is somewhat coupled to the rate of evolutionary changes in the amino acids of the activating enzymes. Further experimentation will be necessary to test these two surmises. It is also possible that double helical segments of sRNA may be necessary for the molecule to function. If this is true, then it poses a further constraint on base alterations in that region, since only rare double mutants in which these regions remain intact will survive the selection process. Hence, these regions would evolve more slowly, and this can also be subjected to experimental test.

## PRIMITIVE SYSTEMS FOR PROTEIN SYNTHESIS

We have no direct experimental evidence regarding the precursors to the present system of protein synthesis. Accordingly, most of these comments must be speculative in nature. At the present time we see what appears to be a universal code for protein synthesis. If this is true, and if the code has not changed, it suggests that we can divide the evolutionary history of the protein synthetic mechanism into two periods, one before the establishment of this universal code and the other after it became the dominant mechanism. By studying the characteristics of the system during the latter period, it may be possible to infer something about the former stage.

It is of interest to note that modifications can be induced in the protein synthetic system. For example, lowering the magnesium concentration in cell-free systems promotes the incorporation of errors in the system (23). This represents a misreading which may be associated with less rigid binding near the ribosomal reading unit. Another interesting example of misreading is seen in the work associated with bacterial mutants which are sensitive or resistant to streptomycin. Streptomycin-sensitive mutants produce ribosomes which have the property of misreading messenger RNA sequences even at normal magnesium concentrations (7). The basis of this genetic alteration may be a modification of ribosomal proteins. These experiments suggest the possibility that the protein component of ribosomes may be largely responsible for the accuracy of the translation mechanism in the reading of messenger RNA strands. If this is true, we may imagine a precursor to the present system of protein synthesis as one in which the error level was substantially greater than that observed today. We might speculate that at this time there was a "noisy" translation of genetic messages resulting in a variety of polypeptide products and that the system did not have a precisely defined relation between messenger RNA and the polypeptide product. This could occur if the activating enzyme system had not evolved to a level of precise activity, or, alternatively, if it had not yet been developed at all. It is thus conceivable that a precursor to the present system of protein synthesis was one in which the functional role of the proteins themselves was of less importance than that seen today.

One of the peculiar properties of the information-transferring mechanism in biological systems is the fact that extensive use is made of the complementarity or hydrogen bonding between nucleotides. This is seen to be the controlling feature in DNA replication, in RNA synthesis, and probably also in the alignment of soluble RNA molecules on the messenger RNA strand. These are thus the major sequence-determining interactions. Proteins appear to be essential in this process in that they act as catalysts and are responsible for the precision in the translating mechanism, both through the action of the activating enzyme which precisely couples a particular sRNA molecule with a particular amino acid, and also possibly through the role of the ribosomal protein which may assist in an accurate positioning of sRNA molecules on the messenger strand. However, the dominant characteristic of this system is the fact that the major information-transferring reactions are those involving the formation of complementary purine–pyrimidine hydrogen–bonded pairs, and in one sense these reactions do not require the participation of the enzymatic specificities because they already have their own stereochemical basis for specificity. To be sure, the existence of protein enzymes substantially modifies the rate at which these reactions occur. But they are not basic in the sense that they may not be involved directly in the reading process.

Thus, our speculations regarding the nature of the early history of the protein synthesizing system have led us to the suggestion that there may have been a system in which the participation of protein molecules was much less important than that seen in contemporary biological systems and in which the nucleic acids played a correspondingly greater role. It is of course apparent that other materials, such as silicate surfaces, might have provided some of the catalytic role carried out with great precision by the protein enzymes today.

This speculation has the added advantage of leading directly to an explanation regarding the role of the large amount of macromolecular RNA which makes up the bulk of the ribosome. The function of this large RNA component has been continuously puzzling to workers in the field. It is not clear at all why such a large amount of RNA is necessary for ribosomal function. There is no evidence at the present time that the particular sequence of nucleotides is of great importance, and ribosomal RNA is usually given a vague structural role in acting as a "condensing" site for assembling the ribosomal proteins which are believed to be the important elements in carrying out an accurate translation of information. Our speculations suggest that we can understand the role of ribosomal RNA by referring to its evolutionary history. Perhaps in the early history of life a macromolecular RNA molecule served as a primitive ribosome, active in forming a molecular surface for condensing a messenger RNA strand with smaller RNA molecules which had amino acids (or even other molecules) attached to them. In short, these may have been active as primitive catalysts in a system which began to be effective in assembling a new polymeric species, the polyamino acids. This system may have evoked by having the products of the system take on an increasingly important role in increasing the precision of the reading system and the precision of the amino-acid-activating system. During evolution, the original macromolecular RNA molecules may have eventually become coated with protein to form the structure which is functionally active today. If this is true, it means that we can understand the composition and structure of the present-day ribosome only in terms of its evolutionary history.

It is only within the past five years that we have really achieved a coherent understanding of the process of information transfer which enables us to understand the mechanism of protein synthesis. Most of the research effort during this period has been devoted to the problem of trying to understand the subtleties of this mechanism. At the present time, our view of this process is reasonably coherent, and although further information will be forthcoming it would be surprising to find a radical change in our present concepts. Once our understanding of this process is reasonably complete, it may be that our attention will then turn to the problems of universality and to comparative studies of protein synthesis. This effort will undoubtedly yield results which may further elucidate the origin and evolution of the protein synthetic mechanism.

## References

1. ABEL, P., AND TRAUTNER, T. A., Z. *Verebungslehre,* **95**, 66 (1964).
2. BENNETT, T. P., GOLDSTEIN, J., AND LIPMANN, F., *Cold Spring Harbor Symp. Quant. Biol.,* **28**, 233 (1963).
3. BUETTNER-JANUSCH, J., AND HILL, R. L., *Science,* **147**, 836 (1965).
4. CANNON, M., KRUG, R., AND GILBERT, W., *J. Mol. Biol.,* **7**, 360 (1963).
5. *Cold Spring Harbor Symp. Quant. Biol.,* **28** (1963). The field of protein synthesis is vast, and it would be impossible to cite all relevant references. This general reference has many detailed papers relevant to the discussion.
6. CRICK, F. H. C., BARNETT, C. L., BRENNER, S., AND WATTS-TOBIN, R. J., *Nature,* **192**, 1227 (1961).
7. DAVIES, J., GILBERT, W., AND GORINI, L., *Proc. Natl. Acad. Sci. U.S.,* **51**, 883 (1964).
8. DINTZIS, H. M., *Proc. Natl. Acad. Sci. U.S.,* **48**, 247 (1961).
9. EIKENBERRY, E. F., AND RICH, A., *Proc. Natl. Acad. U.S.,* in press.
10. GILBERT, W., *J. Mol. Biol.,* **6**, 389 (1963).
11. GOODMAN, H. M., AND RICH, A., *Proc. Natl. Acad. Sci. U.S.,* **48**, 2101 (1962).
12. HOLLEY, R. W., APGAR, J., EVERETT, G. A., MADISON, J. T., MARQUISEE, M., MERRILL, S. H., PENSWICK, J. R., AND ZAMIR, A., *Science,* **147**, 1462 (1965).
13. KIHO, Y., AND RICH, A., *Proc. Natl. Acad. Sci. U.S.,* **51**, 111 (1964).
14. LEDER, P., AND NIRENBERG, M. W., *Proc. Natl. Acad. Sci. U.S.,* **52**, 1521 (1964).
15. MARGOLIASH, E., *Proc. Natl. Acad. Sci. U.S.,* **50**, 672 (1963).
16. MATHEWS, F. S., AND RICH, A., *J. Mol. Biol.,* **8**, 89 (1964).
17. NIRENBERG, M. W., AND MATTHAEI, H., *Proc. Natl. Acad. Sci. U.S.,* **47**, 1588 (1961).

18. RICH, A., in "Horizons in Biochemistry" (M. Kasha and B. Pullman, eds.), p. 103, Academic Press, New York, 1962.
19. RICH, A., WARNER, J. R., AND GOODMAN, H. M., *Cold Spring Harbor Symp. Quant. Biol.*, **28**, 269 (1963).
20. SCHILDKRAUT, C. L., MARMUR, J., AND DOTY, P. M., *J. Mol. Biol.*, **4**, 430 (1962).
21. SCHWARTZ, J. H., EISENSTADT, J. M., BRAWERMAN, G., AND ZINDER, N. D., *Proc. Natl. Acad. Sci. U.S.*, **53**, 195 (1965).
22. SLAYTER, H. S., WARNER, J. R., RICH, A., AND HALL, C. E., *J. Mol. Biol.*, **7**, 652 (1963).
23. SZER, W., AND OCHOA, S., *J. Mol. Biol.*, in press.
24. TAKANAMI, M., *Biochim. Biophys. Acta* **55**, 132 (1962).
25. TAKANAMI, M., *Proc. Natl. Acad. Sci. U.S.*, **52**, 1271 (1964).
26. VON EHRENSTEIN, G., AND LIPMANN, F., *Proc. Natl. Acad. Sci. U.S.*, **47**, 941 (1961).
27. WARNER, J. R., AND RICH, A., *Proc. Natl. Acad. Sci. U.S.*, **51**, 1134 (1964).
28. WARNER, J. R., RICH, A., AND HALL, C. E., *Science*, **138**, 1399 (1962).
29. WEINSTEIN, I. B., *Cold Spring Harbor Symp. Quant. Biol.*, **28**, 579 (1963).

# The Short-Lived RNA in the Cell Nucleus and its Possible Role in Evolution

HENRY HARRIS

*Sir William Dunn School of Pathology,*
*University of Oxford, England*

I first became interested in the RNA in the cell nucleus during one of those fleeting moments when an atmosphere of contented unanimity pervaded the literature on the subject. Hershey (16), Labaw, Mosley, and Wyckoff (20), and Davern and Meselson (3) had demonstrated that all the RNA in growing bacteria was stable; and Siminovitch and Graham (31) had produced evidence which indicated that this was also the case for animal cells growing in culture. Numerous workers had shown that when cells were exposed to a radioactive RNA precursor the RNA in the cell nucleus became labeled much more rapidly than the RNA in the cytoplasm; and when cells labeled in this way were transferred to non-radioactive medium it was observed that radioactivity disappeared from the nuclear RNA and appeared in the cytoplasmic RNA. These experiments were quite generally thought to indicate that the nuclear RNA which became labeled rapidly was the precursor of the cytoplasmic RNA; and the redistribution of radioactivity between nuclear and cytoplasmic RNA which occurred when labeled cells were transferred to nonradioactive medium was interpreted as evidence of the passage of labeled RNA from nucleus to cytoplasm.

In 1959, J. W. Watts and I, in a sceptical frame of mind, examined these experiments more closely and reached certain heretical conclusions. We found first that not all the RNA in animal cells was stable: we were able to show that some RNA fraction in the cell was being continuously synthesized and broken down. In one cell type this turnover was demonstrated formally by recovery of the end products of RNA breakdown (36). A little later in that year I carried out some autoradiographic experiments which indicated that the RNA involved in this rapid turnover was located in the cell nucleus (8); and subsequent work showed that the loss of radioactivity from the nuclear RNA which took place when labeled cells were transferred to nonradioactive medium could be accounted for, at least in part, by breakdown of the labeled nuclear RNA to acid-soluble end products (36, 15, 13).

Needless to say, my colleagues and I soon found ourselves immersed in the task of elucidating the biological role of these short-lived nuclear RNA molecules; and we began by attempting to find out first, what proportion of the RNA synthesized in the nucleus at any one time underwent subsequent breakdown within the cell, and second, whether the breakdown took place within the cell nucleus or whether this RNA was transferred to the cytoplasm before being broken down. While we were engaged on this exercise, in 1961 to be exact, short-lived RNA molecules suddenly became fashionable, and the idea that these molecules were the vectors of genetic information from the DNA to the cytoplasm of the cell gained wide popularity (24, 2, 6).

We worked very hard to convince ourselves that the short-lived nuclear RNA molecules which we had been studying were transferred to the cytoplasm of the cell before being broken down; but the evidence appeared to indicate that these molecules were broken down within the nucleus. We also came to hold the view that only a small proportion of the RNA made in the nucleus at any one time could be an immediate macromolecular precursor of the stable RNA in the cytoplasm.

May I summarize the main pieces of evidence which we have in support of these views?

1. When animal cells growing exponentially in culture are exposed to a suitable radioactive RNA base or nucleoside and are then transferred to nonradioactive medium containing the relevant unlabeled nucleosides, the specific activity of the cell RNA as a whole falls much more rapidly than can be accounted for by cell growth (35). This indicates that some fraction of the RNA in the cell is turning over.

2. When cells are exposed for a few minutes to a suitable radioactive RNA base or nucleoside and are then transferred to nonradioactive medium containing the relevant unlabeled nucleosides, much more radioactivity is lost from the nuclear RNA than appears in the cytoplasmic RNA (8, 13, 35). Under certain conditions it can be shown that more than ten times as much radioactivity is lost from the nuclear RNA as appears in the cytoplasmic RNA during the same time (13). This indicates that most of the rapidly labeled RNA in the cell nucleus undergoes breakdown within the cell. In liver cells, treatment with thioacetamide may produce a 30- to 40-fold increase in the rate of nuclear RNA synthesis and breakdown without affecting the rate at which radioactive

precursors enter the cytoplasmic RNA (19). In some cells it is possible to recover the end products of this nuclear RNA breakdown (36).

3. When cells are incubated with radioactive adenine, both the adenine and the guanine in the RNA become labeled, but the adenine much more rapidly than the guanine. When cells labeled in this way are transferred to nonradioactive medium, there is a gradual drift of radioactivity from RNA adenine to RNA guanine even under conditions where the amount of radioactivity in the RNA precursor pools is trivial relative to the amount of radioactivity in RNA (30, 29). This again indicates that some fraction of the RNA in the cells undergoes breakdown which permits the conversion of the released adenine to guanine.

4. In experiments in which cells exposed to radioactive adenine are transferred to nonradioactive medium, an analysis of the redistribution of radioactivity between nuclear and cytoplasmic RNA adenine and guanine reveals, under suitable conditions, that most of the radioactive adenine lost from the nuclear RNA appears in the cytoplasmic RNA not as adenine, but as guanine (9). This again indicates that most of the RNA made in the nucleus at any one time undergoes breakdown within the cell to acid-soluble end products.

Our reasons for supposing that the short-lived nuclear RNA is broken down within the nucleus are as follows:

1. No RNA having the kinetic characteristics of the short-lived nuclear RNA can be detected in the cytoplasm (13). Rapidly labeled polydisperse RNA fractions, usually with rather low sedimentation coefficients, have indeed been found in the cytoplasm of animal cells by some workers (27, 34, 25), but such fractions are found only when the cells are fractionated by mechanical homogenization and when preparations of ribosomes are prepared from the homogenate. Such fractions are not found in the cytoplasmic RNA when this is extracted directly from the cell by treatment with phenol in the absence of detergents (5, 28), or when a cell fractionation procedure is used which ensures that no nuclei are broken (13). The presence of rapidly labeled polydisperse RNA components in cytoplasmic preparations from animal cells may be taken as presumptive evidence of nuclei broken during the fractionation procedure.

2. A recent analysis by Scott and his colleagues (29) of the distribution of radioactivity in the nucleotides of RNA fractions from animal cells exposed to various radioactive RNA precursors reveals that the cytoplasm does not contain any RNA fraction with the distribution of radioactivity found in the short-lived nuclear RNA.

3. The breakdown of the short-lived nuclear RNA appears to release

5′-mononucleotides. This degradation is effected by an RNA-specific ex-onuclease (13) or a polynucleotide phosphorylase (10) or both. If nuclei are isolated from animal cells in such a way that they retain their normal complement of RNA, and are then incubated in medium which mimics the ionic composition of intracellular water, the nuclear RNA undergoes rapid breakdown to 5′-mononucleotides. No breakdown of cytoplasmic RNA components to 5′-nucleotides occurs under similar conditions (13, 17). This is taken to indicate that RNA in the forms in which it is nor-mally found in the cytoplasm is relatively insusceptible to these specific degradative enzymes, or that these enzymes are not present in an active form in the cytoplasm.

4. When RNA synthesis is stopped by actinomycin D or proflavine, the nuclear RNA undergoes rapid breakdown (11, 21, 26, 22). The RNA in the cytoplasm is much less susceptible to breakdown in the presence of actinomycin D (22), and the late breakdown of cytoplasmic RNA which may eventually take place has not been shown to release 5′-mono-nucleotides.

5. In cells in which the nuclei contain a large quantity of nuclear "sap," analysis of the RNA in the "sap" reveals that it varies greatly in amount from cell to cell and that it has a bizarre and very variable base composition (4). This is not what one would expect if most of the RNA made on the chromosomes were being transported through the nuclear "sap" to the cytoplasm. It is, however, precisely what one would expect if a large part of the RNA made in the nucleus underwent intra-nuclear breakdown. In the somatic cells of animals, the nuclei contain virtually no "sap," and studies on isolated nuclei suggest that the break-down of RNA occurs on the chromosomes (10).

It is, of course, difficult to accept the view that the cell makes all this RNA merely in order to break it down, so we have been forced to exercise our minds a great deal on what functions might possibly be served by intranuclear RNA turnover. Since so many people were urging the view that short-lived RNA molecules were the templates for the synthesis of proteins, we naturally examined the possibility that the short-lived nu-clear RNA which we had been studying might be a template for nuclear protein synthesis. We did this by comparing the rate of breakdown of the rapidly labeled nuclear RNA in the presence of actinomycin D with the fall in the rate of nuclear protein synthesis, and we came to the con-clusion that the two processes were not related in any simple way (12). Although the possibility that some of the short-lived nuclear RNA might be a template for some nuclear protein synthesis could not be excluded, our evidence appeared to indicate that on the whole the templates for protein synthesis in both nucleus and cytoplasm were very much more stable than the short-lived nuclear RNA. Under certain conditions it was found that more than half the rapidly labeled RNA in the cell nucleus could undergo breakdown without producing any detectable change in the over-all rate of nuclear protein synthesis (12). We also examined and, for a variety of reasons, rejected certain other possibilities, for example, that the short-lived nuclear RNA was directly involved in genetic regulation, or that the intranuclear RNA breakdown was a reflection of some form of imbalance between the synthesis of RNA and the synthesis of protein.

Having thus cursorily dismissed a number of things which I think the short-lived nuclear RNA is not doing, may I now hazard a tentative statement about what I think it is doing.

There is good reason to believe that very much more RNA is made in the cell nucleus than is used as a template for the synthesis of protein (12, 19, 18). Some recent experiments I have made on the synthesis of nuclear RNA at low temperatures lead me to suppose that there is in the nucleus some selective process which converts a small fraction of the rapidly labeled nuclear RNA into some form which renders it insusceptible to the intranuclear degradative enzymes (12). I like to think that it is this small fraction of the nuclear RNA which is transported to the cytoplasm to serve as a template for protein synthesis. The RNA which is not shielded from degradation, and which consequently undergoes intranuclear breakdown, I regard as RNA which has failed to assume the conformation necessary for function as a template.

The mechanism by which a small proportion of the nuclear RNA is protected from the action of the intranuclear degradative enzymes may involve coupling of the RNA with protein, or the assumption of an ordered secondary structure, or, more probably, both. M. E. Bramwell and I have been examining the secondary structure of the RNA in the cell nucleus and have found that, although almost all the nuclear RNA can be extracted as two components with sedimentation coefficients of 28S and 16S similar to those of the cytoplasmic ribosomal RNA, the nuclear RNA as a whole appears to be much more susceptible to degradation than the cytoplasmic ribosomal RNA. Since both polynucleotide phosphorylase and the RNA-specific exonuclease which appear to be responsible for the degradation of the short-lived RNA act only on single-stranded polyribonucleotides (32), the assumption of a high degree of order by a small proportion of the nuclear RNA might in itself be enough to protect this fraction from intranuclear degradation.

The view which I am advocating, then, is that the RNA which undergoes degradation is not the RNA which carries the information for
protein synthesis to the cytoplasm; this information is borne by that
small fraction of the nuclear RNA which is shielded from degradation.
This view implies that the templates for protein synthesis in the cytoplasm
are essentially stable and that they have a high order of secondary structure. Some of you might say that that sounds suspiciously like the
ribosomal RNA, and, if you did, I would be forced to confess that I am
one of those who remain unconvinced by the messenger-RNA hypothesis
and who still consider it possible that in the intact normal cell the
ribosomal RNA may yet prove to be the template for protein synthesis.
Those of us who have these reservations about the messenger-RNA
hypothesis tend to regard cell-free systems in which the synthesis of
specific polypeptides is induced by the addition of polynucleotides as
models not for the normal cell, but for the virus-infected cell in which
new templates produced by the virus become attached to existing cytoplasmic structures. However, my argument is not greatly affected by con-
troversy about the function of the ribosomal RNA. The essential requirement in the scheme which I am proposing is that the RNA which serves
as a template for protein synthesis should be in a form relatively insusceptible to intracellular degradation. This requirement is, of course, met
by the ribosomal RNA itself, but it would also be met by RNA tightly
bound to the ribosomes. It has been shown that, when polynucleotides
are introduced into cell-free systems, the components which become
degraded are those which fail to form a close attachment to the ribosomes;
those which become attached to the ribosomes and serve as templates
are relatively resistant to degradation by the polynucleotide phosphorylase
or RNA-specific exonuclease (1). A rapidly increasing body of experiment now supports the view that the cytoplasmic templates for protein
synthesis in animal and higher plant cells are essentially stable (14, 33);
and there is evidence that this may also be the case for at least some
templates in bacteria (14), and even in phage-infected bacteria (7).

My thesis is that short-lived RNA molecules are those which fail to
assume the conformation necessary for function as templates, and that in
animal and higher plant cells these molecules are eliminated within the
nucleus. But why should such ineffectual RNA be produced at all? And
here I should like to introduce the word "evolution" and thus justify my
having been invited to this Symposium.

Most students of genetics have long been puzzled by the fact that
the cells of all organisms from the highest to the lowest contain much
more DNA than appears to be necessary. In the case of animal and higher

plant cells the haploid amount of DNA may be some orders greater than any reasonable estimate for the amount of DNA required to specify the structure of cell proteins. The wide variability in the haploid amount of DNA in different species of animals and plants in itself suggests that much of the DNA does not contain genetic specifications for the synthesis of proteins. One can hardly suppose, for example, that the lily requires thirty times as much genetic information as the lupin (23), or that the salamander requires twenty to thirty times as much genetic information as man. In the giant salivary chromosomes of *Chironomus*, recent measurements have shown that the amount of DNA in a single chromomere, which is said to correspond in genetical terms to a single gene, is about a hundred times as great as the estimated amount of DNA necessary to specify the structure of a protein of average size (4). We do not know how much of the DNA in the cell nucleus is active in making RNA; but if the bulk of the DNA in an organism is never at any time responsible for the synthesis of a single RNA molecule, it is difficult to imagine what biological advantage the possession of so much totally inert DNA could confer. Indeed, one might rather suppose that even the smallest piece of permanently inert DNA would have been eliminated by natural selection. A more plausible view is that all the DNA in an organism is at some time responsible for the synthesis of some RNA molecules. My suggestion is that only the RNA molecules which assume a highly ordered secondary configuration serve as templates for protein synthesis, and that in animal and higher plant cells these RNA molecules normally constitute only a small proportion of the RNA made in the cell nucleus. The rest of the nuclear RNA may be the raw material on which evolution operates.

One must suppose that those RNA molecules which serve as templates for specific proteins have evolved as a result of prolonged selection. There is therefore a high probability that mutations at the loci which produce these molecules will prove to be disadvantageous to the cell; and this is borne out by observation. But mutations in those parts of the DNA which do not produce templates for protein synthesis may entail no disadvantage to the cell, since the RNA molecules made there are rapidly eliminated within the cell nucleus. Cumulative mutations in these areas could, however, when subjected to selection, eventually confer on the RNA made at one locus or another the ability to assume a configuration which protects it from degradation, and thus permit this RNA to function as a template. The passage of these new RNA molecules to the cytoplasm might then initiate the synthesis of a new protein. Selection would preserve the mutant if the possession of the new protein conferred a biological advantage.

In summary, then, my proposal, for want of a better, is as follows. Only a small proportion of the RNA made in the nucleus of animal and higher plant cells serves as a template for the synthesis of protein. This RNA is characterized by its ability to assume a form which protects it from intracellular degradation. Most of the nuclear RNA, however, is made on parts of the DNA which do not contain information for the synthesis of specific proteins. This RNA does not assume the configuration necessary for protection from degradation and is eliminated within the cell nucleus. It plays no role in the synthesis of cell protein, but serves as a background on which mutation and selection may operate to produce new templates for protein synthesis. These new templates are evolved by changes which gradually confer on the short-lived RNA the ability to resist degradation.

## REFERENCES

1. BARONDES, S. H., AND NIRENBERG, M. W., *Science*, **138**, 810 (1962).
2. BRENNER, S., JACOB, F., AND MESELSON, M., *Nature*, **190**, 576 (1961).
3. DAVERN, C. I., AND MESELSON, M., *J. Mol. Biol.*, **2**, 153 (1960).
4. EDSTRÖM, J.-E., *in* "The Role of Chromosomes in Development," 23rd Symposium of the Society for the Study of Development and Growth (M. Locke, ed.), Academic Press, New York, 1965.
5. FENWICK, M. L., *Virology*, **19**, 241 (1963).
6. GROS, F., HIATT, H. H., GILBERT, W., KURLAND, C. G., RISEBROUGH, R. W., AND WATSON, J. D., *Nature*, **190**, 581 (1961).
7. HALL, B. D., NYGAARD, A. P., AND GREEN, M. H., *J. Mol. Biol.*, **9**, 143 (1964).
8. HARRIS, H., *Biochem. J.*, **73**, 362 (1959).
9. HARRIS, H., *Nature*, **202**, 249 (1964).
10. HARRIS, H., *Proc. Roy. Soc.*, **B158**, 79 (1963).
11. HARRIS, H., *Nature*, **198**, 184 (1963).
12. HARRIS, H., *Nature*, **201**, 863 (1964).
13. HARRIS, H., FISHER, H. W., RODGERS, A. L., SPENCER, T., AND WATTS, J. W., *Proc. Roy. Soc.*, **B157**, 177 (1963).
14. HARRIS, H., AND SABATH, L. D., *Nature*, **202**, 1078 (1964).
15. HARRIS, H., AND WATTS, J. W., *Proc. Roy. Soc.*, **B156**, 109 (1962).
16. HERSHEY, A. D., *J. Gen. Physiol.*, **38**, 145 (1954).
17. HIATT, H. H., AND LAREAU, J., *in* "Regulation of Enzyme Activity and Synthesis in Normal and Neoplastic Liver (G. Weber, ed.), Pergamon Press, New York, 1962, p. 77.
18. KONRAD, C. G., *J. Cell Biol.*, **19**, 267 (1963).
19. KOULISH, S., AND KLEINFELD, R. G., *J. Cell Biol.*, **23**, 39 (1964).
20. LABAW, L. W., MOSLEY, V. M., AND WYCKOFF, W. G., *J. Bacteriol.*, **59**, 251 (1960).
21. LEVY, H. B., *Proc. Soc. Exptl. Biol. Med.*, **113**, 886 (1963).
22. LIEBERMAN, I., ABRAMS, R., AND OVE, P., *J. Biol. Chem.*, **238**, 2141 (1963).
23. McLEISH, J., AND SUNDERLAND, N., *Exptl. Cell Res.*, **24**, 527 (1961).
24. MONOD, J., AND JACOB, F., *J. Mol. Biol.* **3**, 318 (1961).
25. MUNRO, A. J., AND KORNER, A., *Nature*, **201**, 1194 (1964).
26. PAUL, J., AND STRUTHERS, M. G., *Biochem. Biophys. Res. Commun.*, **11**, 135 (1963).

27. PENMAN, S., SCHERRER, K., BECKER, Y., AND DARNELL, J. E., *Proc. Natl. Acad. Sci. U.S.*, **49**, 654 (1963).
28. RAKE, A. V., AND GRAHAM, A. F., *Biophys. J.*, **4**, 267 (1964).
29. SCOTT, J. F., KALTREIDER, H. B., BOEKER, F. A., AND TAFT, E. B., *Federation Proc.*, **23**, 168 (1964).
30. SCOTT, J. F., TAFT, E. B., AND LETOURNEAU, N. W., *Biochim. Biophys. Acta*, **61**, 62 (1962).
31. SIMINOVITCH, L., AND GRAHAM, A. F., *J. Histochem. Cytochem.*, **4**, 585 (1956).
32. SINGER, M. F., AND TOLBERT, G., *Science*, **145**, 593 (1964).
33. SPENCER, T., AND HARRIS, H., *Biochem. J.*, **91**, 282 (1964).
34. STAEHELIN, T., WETTSTEIN, F. O., OURA, H., AND NOLL, H., *Nature*, **201**, 264 (1964).
35. WATTS, J. W., *Biochem. J.*, **93**, 297 and 306 (1964).
36. WATTS, J. W., AND HARRIS, H., *Biochem. J.*, **72**, 147 (1959).

# On the Evolution of Informational Macromolecules

Noboru Sueoka

*Department of Biology, Princeton University,
Princeton, New Jersey*

In the preface of a now classic book (3), "The Molecular Basis of Evolution," Anfinsen (1959) states: "The writing of this book has been stimulated by the excitement and promise of contemporary protein chemistry and genetics and by the possibilities of integration of these fields toward a greater understanding of the fundamental forces underlying the evolutionary process." Today, the scope of the background has been widened so much by the progress in biochemistry of protein biosynthesis that the problem has become more dynamic than ever. Thus, the progress in the study of the mechanism of protein synthesis and the *in vitro* synthesis of polypeptide by using synthetic polyribonucleotides (28, 33) introduced such factors as messenger (mRNA) (20) and adaptor (sRNA) (9, 12, 17) between gene (DNA) and protein. Deeper insight into the molecular basis of evolution, therefore, can be attained only by the elucidation of the code translation mechanism and by the accumulation of information on similarities and differences in those factors involved in the mechanism.

In this chapter, our own experimental results relevant to the evolution of informational macromolecules will be reviewed. However, only by referring to the literature of others as indicated in each section can a more complete picture of the present status be envisaged.

## Distribution of DNA Base Composition

### Variation and Heterogeneity

Available data on the average DNA base composition of various organisms have been compiled and are presented in Fig. 1. The base composition has been conveniently expressed as a molar per cent of guanine plus cytosine (GC content) (15). The following points are evident.

1. Lower forms of life have more variability in DNA base composition.

479

2. The range of DNA base composition is approximately between 25% and 75% GC.

3. Phylogenetic relations are reflected in the mean GC content. For comprehensive treatment of these issues, see review articles (7, 10, 23, 37, 40). The third point was made much clearer by *in vitro* hybridization experiments between DNA (25) and between DNA and RNA (26).

Investigation of the compositional distribution of DNA molecules

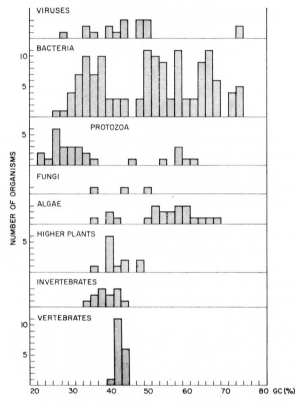

FIG. 1. Base composition of DNA of various organisms. For names of organisms and reference, see ref. 40.

of each organism became possible by finding the effect of GC content on the buoyant density (30, 44) and the thermal hyperchromic shift of DNA (24). An analysis of DNA distribution in CsCl density gradient (37) provided the following observations:

1. *The distribution of GC content of the DNA molecules of an organism is unimodal, and the range is relatively narrow.* Exceptions to the unimodality distribution are treated later.

2. *When the mean GC contents of DNA of two bacterial species are different by 10%, there are few DNA molecules of the same GC content common to the two species.*

This point is true for the level of $10^7$ molecular weight and is shown diagrammatically in Fig. 2. Although compositional heterogeneity is quite small compared with the range of compositional variation, the actual

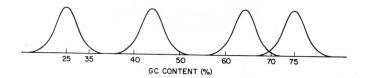

FIG. 2. A schematic representation of variation and heterogeneity of DNA base composition in bacteria.

heterogeneity is three times as large (in terms of standard deviation) in pneumococcus and ten times as large in calf thymus as that expected from random sequence of the bases (39).

3. *The small heterogeneity of the base composition among DNA molecules of an organism seems to be true for smaller regions within molecules.*

This statement was supported by an analysis of the distribution of sonicated calf thymus and pneumococcus (M.W. $\sim 10^6$) in CsCl density gradient (35). More recent analysis of still smaller molecules revealed a distinctly larger increase of heterogeneity than expected from random sequence of the bases (18, 27).

A closer examination of DNA base composition of various strains of the protozoa *Tetrahymena* gave further insight into the change in base composition (45). The experimental results are given in Fig. 3, indicating that the change in DNA base composition occurs uniformly in the whole genome rather than in a particular part of the genome. A schematic representation is given in Fig. 4.

*Extra Components of DNA*

The presence of extra components of DNA has been noticed in various organisms during analysis of the distribution of DNA molecules in density gradient centrifugation (37). A compilation of known cases is given in Table I.

The extra component found in several species of genus *Cancer* (marine crabs) (32, 37, 41, 42) represents an interesting problem (see

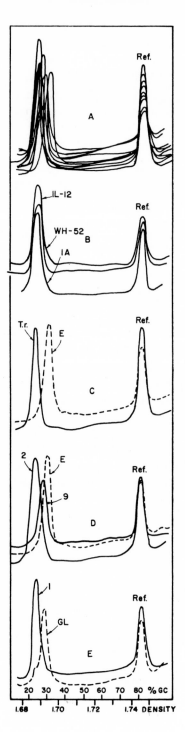

Fig. 3.    DNA distribution of various strains of *Tetrahymena*. Bacteria-free strains of *Tetrahymena* were cultured on 2 liters of 1% nutrient broth at 30°C with constant shaking. Cells were harvested as soon as they reached the concentration of about $5 \times 10^4$ cells/ml (2 to 3 days), washed once with a saline citrate solution (0.15 M NaCl plus 0.015 M sodium citrate), and suspended in the same solution with $2 \times 10^6$ cells/ml. Cells were lysed by adding sodium lauryl sulfate up to 2%. An aliquot of lysate containing about 1 to 2 μg of DNA was centrifuged at 44,770 rpm at 25°C for 20 hours in a cesium chloride solution with 1 μg of $N^{15}$-*Pseudomonas aeruginosa* DNA (density 1.746) as a density reference.

A, superimposed microdensitometer tracings of the ultraviolet absorption photographs of equilibrated DNA of various strains of *Tetrahymena pyriformis* and a strain of *Tetrahymena rostrata*. All tracings were matched at the reference DNA peak. B, superimposed tracings of the ultraviolet absorption pictures of DNA of three strains of *T. pyriformis* variety 1, which can mate freely with each other. C, superimposed tracings of the ultraviolet absorption pictures of DNA from *T. rostrata* and *T. pyriformis* variety E, which are most different in density. D, superimposed tracings of the ultraviolet absorption pictures of DNA from three varieties of *T. pyriformis*. Note how uniformly the density of DNA is different. E, a microdensitometer tracing of the ultraviolet absorption picture of variety GL of *T. pyriformis*. The tracing of variety 1 DNA is superimposed for comparison. From Sueoka and Nanney (45).

Table I). Structurally, the extra DNA of *Cancer borealis* contained 97% adenine and thymine (48) and was found in every tissue examined (11) (Fig. 5). The biological function of the DNA is not clear at present. However, the fact that the deoxyadenylate–thymidylate polymer can be synthesized *in vitro* (31) and that crab dAT contains a small amount (3%) of cytosine and guanine (48) suggests that generation of new DNA by a mechanism similar to the *in vitro* dAT polymer synthesis (22) may indeed occur in nature and could provide an origin of new DNA which may eventually develop into functional genetic material by base conversions.

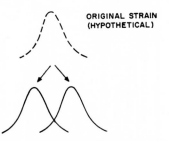

ORIGINAL STRAIN
(HYPOTHETICAL)

Fig. 4.    Schematic representation of the uniform change of DNA base composition in *Tetrahymena*.

TABLE I
SATELLITE DNA*

| Organism | Main DNA | | Satellite DNA | | | Notes | Ref. |
|---|---|---|---|---|---|---|---|
| | Density | GC (%) | Density | GC (%) | Amount (%) | | |
| *Serratia marscesens* with | | | | | | | |
|   *Escherichia coli* episome | 1.718 | 58 | 1.709 | 50 | 0.1–0.2 | *E. coli* episome | e |
| *Halobacterium salinarium* | 1.727 | 67 | 1.718 | 53 | 20 | | c |
| *Halobacterium cutirubrum* | | | | | | Small satellite | c |
| *Paramecium aurelia* | 1.689 | 29 | 1.696 | 36 | | Kappa particle | h |
| *Cancer borealis* | 1.702 | 42 | 1.681 | 2.7$^k$ | 30 | Analyzed by Swartz *et al.*$^k$ | j |
| *Cancer irroratus* | 1.700 | 42 | 1.680 | | 11 | | i |
| *Cancer antennaris* Stimpson | 1.700 | 42 | 1.677 | | 26 | | i |
| *Cancer gracilis* Dana | 1.700 | 42 | 1.680 | | 9 | | i |
| *Cancer magister* Dana | 1.701 | 42 | 1.677 | | 14 | | i |
| *Cancer productus* Randall | 1.701 | 42 | 1.679 | | 32 | | i |
| Calf thymus | 1.704 | 44 | 1.715 | 55 | | | a |
| Mouse testis and spleen | 1.702 | 43 | 1.692 | 33 | | | a |
| Guinea pig | 1.703 | 44 | 1.697 | 38 | | | d |
| *Escherichia coli, Bacillus subtilis, B. megaterium* | Rolfe$^f$ reports that in these bacteria DNA from exponentially growing cells show two satellite bands in CsCl density gradient centrifugation, one heavier than the main band, the other slightly lighter than the average of the main band. | | | | | | |
| *Chlamydomonas reinhardi, Euglena,* spinach | Chun *et al.*$^b$ find two satellite bands in these organisms, at least one of which may correspond to DNA in chloroplasts. | | | | | | |

* In order to make the density values of DNA comparable, the system$^g$ in which the density of *E. coli* DNA was taken as 1.710 was adopted in this table.

$^a$ Cheng, T. Y., and Sueoka, N., *Science*, **141**, 1194 (1963).
$^b$ Chun, E. H. L., Vaughan, M. H., Jr., and Rich, A., *J. Mol. Biol,* **7**, 130 (1963).
$^c$ Joshi, J. C., Guild, W. R., and Handler, P., *J. Mol. Biol.,* **6**, 34 (1963).
$^a$ Kit, S., *J. Mol. Biol.,* **3**, 711 (1961).
$^e$ Marmur, J., Rownd, R., Falkow, S., Baron, L. S., Schildkraut, C., and Doty, P., *Proc. Natl. Acad. Sci. U.S.,* **47**, 972 (1961).

$^f$ Rolfe, R., *Proc. Natl. Acad. Sci. U.S.,* **49**, 386 (1963).
$^g$ Schildkraut, C. L., Marmur, J., and Doty, P., *J. Mol. Biol.,* **4**, 430 (1962).
$^h$ Smith-Sonneborn, J., Green, L., and Marmur, J., *Nature,* **197**, 385 (1963).
$^i$ Smith, M., *Biochem. Biophys. Research Commun.,* **10**, 67 (1963).
$^j$ Sueoka, N., *J. Mol. Biol.,* **3**, 31 (1961).
$^k$ Swartz, M. N., Trautner, T. A., and Kornberg, A., *J. Biol. Chem.,* **237**, 1961 (1962).

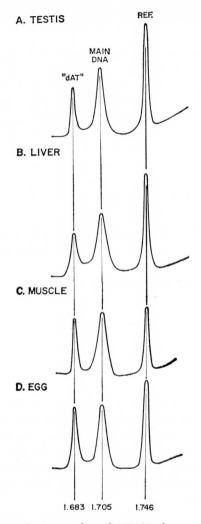

FIG. 5. Distribution of *Cancer borealis* DNA from various tissues in CsCl buoyant density gradient. DNA samples (2 to 3 μg) were centrifuged with 1 μg of $N^{15}$-*Pseudomonas aeruginosa* DNA as a reference at 44,770 rpm in 7.7 molal CsCl solution at 25°C for 20 hours. Ultraviolet absorption photographs of equilibrated DNA were traced by a microdensitometer. Densities of the peaks were calculated (8). The density values were calculated relative to the density of *Escherichia coli* B DNA (1.713). A, DNA from testes; B, DNA from liver; C, DNA from claw muscle; D, DNA from eggs. The horizontal axis indicates buoyant density. From Cheng and Sueoka (11).

*An Evolutionary Theory on the Variation and Heterogeneity of DNA*
*Base Composition*

A theory was proposed to account for the nature of the variation and heterogeneity of DNA base composition (16, 39). The cause for any change of the GC content of DNA must be found in conversions of base pairs from AT (adenine–thymine) to GC (guanine–cytosine), or vice versa. For present purposes, it is unnecessary to distinguish AT from TA and GC from CG. Consequently, AT and TA will be denoted as the $\alpha$ pairs, and GC and CG as the $\gamma$ pairs. Ideally, we assume that each pair undergoes conversion more or less independently. Further, the rates of conversion per generation per base pair, $u$ for $\alpha \rightarrow \gamma$ and $v$ for $\gamma \rightarrow \alpha$, are assumed to be rather uniform for all base pairs in the DNA molecules of an organism. In the present theory, this is the only major assumption. The theory predicts that the mean base composition expressed as the molar GC content $(\overline{p})$ will attain the equilibrium value $(\hat{p})$ and have a certain variance, $\sigma^2$, *if* the conversion rates, $u$ and $v$, remain constant during the evolution. Thus,

$$\hat{p} = \frac{v}{u + v}$$

$$\sigma^2 = \frac{\hat{p}(1 - \hat{p})}{b}$$

where $b$ is the average number of base pairs per DNA molecule isolated.

The actual variance has, however, a larger than theoretical prediction (39). This may not be surprising, because any deviation from the above assumptions will give larger heterogeneity. In this connection, data on the base composition of DNA molecules carrying various transforming markers of *Bacillus subtilis* in relation to their replication order may throw some light (29).

## COMPOSITIONAL CORRELATION BETWEEN DNA AND PROTEIN

The correlation between the base composition of DNA and the amino acid composition of total protein (cell membrane fraction excluded) has been examined in various bacteria and *Tetrahymena* with different GC content of DNA (36, 38). Several significant correlations were observed, and some examples are given in Fig. 6. The results were interpreted to mean that the code should be universal. It was also pointed out that, with the code being universal, the degeneracy of the code would explain the extent of the correlation (38).

The first experimental evidence for universality of the code showed that rabbit hemoglobin synthesized *in vitro* by using aminoacyl-sRNA's of *Escherichia coli* had a normal structure (49). Other experiments on the universality of the code can be found in reference 13. Recent experiments on animal viruses growing in *Bacillus subtilis* (1, 6) are a most remarkable demonstration of the universality of the code.

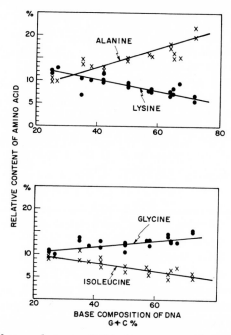

FIG. 6. Correlations between DNA base composition and amino acid composition of bulk protein in bacteria and *Tetrahymena*. The correlation is shown for alanine, lysine, glycine, and isoleucine. The relative molar content of each amino acid is expressed as a percentage of the amino acid content (molar) over the sum of "stable" amino acids: lysine, histidine, arginine, aspartic acid plus asparagine, glutamic acid and glutamine, proline, alanine, valine, leucine, tyrosine, and phenyl-alanine. The base composition of DNA is expressed as molar content (%) of guanine plus cytosine (GC). From Sueoka (36, 38).

In this light, variation of the DNA base composition seems to be best interpreted as the reflection of frequency difference among the codons for each amino acid in different organisms.

## SPECIFICITY BETWEEN sRNA AND AMINOACYL-sRNA SYNTHETASE

Involvement of sRNA as the adaptor in the translation of mRNA into polypeptide has been well established. The following are the main features of sRNA clarified in recent years.

1. sRNA accepting an amino acid is mostly heterogeneous. This multicomponent nature has been demonstrated by fractionation, using the countercurrent distribution technique (4, 14), and by methylated albumin column chromatography (46). The correspondence of different components of leucine acceptor RNA to different codons for leucine has been shown in *E. coli* (50).

2. The structure of sRNA is different among different organisms (47).

3. Interspecific cross reaction between sRNA and aminoacyl-sRNA synthetase can occur frequently between different organisms (8, 51). A more extensive survey is shown in Table II. The extent of cross reaction is definitely higher among bacteria than between bacteria and yeast or between bacteria and rabbit. Among bacteria, the interspecific cross reaction is remarkably well conserved despite the large difference in the average GC content of DNA. This gives support to the idea of a common evolutionary origin of bacteria. It is also surprising that cross reaction does occur and specificity is conserved even between organisms as remote as *E. coli* and rabbit. The nature of the product (aminoacyl-sRNA) from such cross reaction has been one of our main concerns (51). Direct comparisons of the product of cross reaction and that of control (homologous combination of sRNA and the synthetase of the same organism) in their profiles on the methylated albumin column have resulted in one of the following situations: (a) the same profile as that of normal aminoacyl-sRNA was obtained; (b) only some component or components of normal amino acid acceptor RNA were charged; (c) no cross reaction was observed; (d) an entirely different profile was noted. One example of each situation is presented in Fig. 7. For more instances, see reference 52. The first three are commonly observed. Thus, when cross reactions occur, normal components of sRNA for the particular amino acid are charged with the amino acid. A more extensive work will be reported elsewhere (54). The last situation occurs in only one case so far examined (52), where yeast leucyl-sRNA thus formed has an entirely different profile from those of normal yeast and *E. coli* leucyl-sRNA. However, the significance of this exception is not clear, since the leucyl-sRNA obtained constitutes only 1% of the normal yeast leucyl-sRNA. These results indicate that the specificity between sRNA and the synthetase for each amino acid is strikingly well conserved among different organisms. Recently, another exception was reported in phenylalanyl-sRNA formation between *E. coli* sRNA and *Neurospora crassa* synthetase (5). It was demonstrated by MAK column fractionation that the product includes three components in comparable quantities: normal phenylalanine acceptor sRNA of *E. coli*, alanine acceptor RNA of *E. coli*, and some unknown sRNA of *E. coli*. We have confirmed these

TABLE II

INTERSPECIES CROSS REACTION BETWEEN sRNA AND AMINOACYL-sRNA SYNTHETASE[a]

| sRNA | Enzyme | gly | leu | lys | phe | pro | ser | ileu |
|------|--------|-----|-----|-----|-----|-----|-----|------|
| E. coli | E. coli | +++ | +++ | +++ | +++ | +++ | +++ | |
| | A. aero. | +++ | +++ | ++ | +++ | +++ | +++ | |
| | S. typh. | +++ | +++ | ++ | +++ | +++ | +++ | |
| | M. lyso. | +++ | +++ | +++ | +++ | +++ | +++ | |
| | Yeast | ± | + | +++ | + | − | ++ | |
| | Rabbit | ± | + | + | − | − | +++ | |
| A. aero. | E. coli | +++ | +++ | +++ | +++ | +++ | +++ | |
| | A. aero. | +++ | +++ | +++ | +++ | +++ | +++ | |
| | S. typh. | +++ | ++ | + | +++ | +++ | +++ | |
| | M. lyso. | +++ | ++ | ++ | +++ | +++ | +++ | |
| | Yeast | − | + | ++ | − | ++ | + | |
| | Rabbit | − | + | + | − | − | ++ | |
| S. typh. | E. coli | +++ | +++ | +++ | +++ | +++ | +++ | |
| | A. aero. | +++ | +++ | +++ | +++ | +++ | +++ | |
| | S. typh. | +++ | +++ | +++ | +++ | +++ | +++ | |
| | M. lyso. | +++ | +++ | ++ | +++ | +++ | ++ | |
| | Yeast | ± | + | ++ | + | − | + | |
| | Rabbit | + | + | ++ | − | ± | + | |
| M. lyso. | E. coli | +++ | +++ | +++ | +++ | +++ | +++ | − |
| | A. aero. | +++ | + | +++ | ± | +++ | +++ | |
| | S. typh. | +++ | ++ | ++ | +++ | +++ | +++ | |
| | M. lyso. | +++ | +++ | +++ | +++ | +++ | +++ | +++ |
| | Yeast | − | ± | ++ | ± | − | − | − |
| Yeast | E. coli | + | ± | + | + | + | − | |
| | A. aero. | + | ± | + | + | ± | − | |
| | S. typh. | + | ± | + | + | + | − | |
| | M. lyso. | +++ | ± | + | ++ | +++ | + | |
| | Yeast | +++ | +++ | +++ | +++ | +++ | +++ | |
| | Rabbit | ++ | ++ | ++ | +++ | ++ | +++ | |
| Rabbit | E. coli | − | − | + | ± | − | − | − |
| | A. aero. | − | − | + | ± | − | − | |
| | S. typh. | − | − | + | ± | − | − | |
| | M. lyso. | + | − | ++ | + | +++ | + | ++ |
| | Yeast | +++ | +++ | +++ | ++ | +++ | +++ | |
| | Rabbit | +++ | +++ | +++ | +++ | +++ | +++ | +++ |

[a] The extent of the cross reaction is expressed as −, ±, +, ++, and +++ relative to the reaction between homologous combinations of sRNA and the synthetase. Approximate values corresponding to the signs are: +++, 70–100%; ++, 30–70%; +, 5–30%; ±, <5%; −, 0%. (The homologous combinations are taken as 100%.) Abbreviations: A. aero., Aerobacter aerogenes; S. typh., Salmonella typhimurium; M. lyso., Micrococcus lysodeikticus. From Yamane and Sueoka (54).

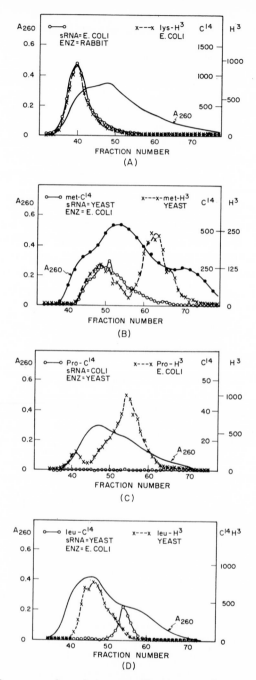

Fig. 7. A few examples of interspecific cross-combinations between sRNA and aminoacyl-sRNA synthetase for the formation of aminoacyl-sRNA. The enzyme preparations of *E. coli*, yeast, and rabbit liver had been freed of RNA by using a DEAE–cellulose column. In each case, aminoacyl-sRNA charged with homologous enzyme was added as the reference before sRNA fractionation on a methylated albumin column. From Yamane and Sueoka (54).

results and further found that enzymatic attachment of phenylalanine onto the second and third components can be completely inhibited by bentonite or polyvinal sulfate, while the first (normal) component accepts the amino acid under such conditions. This raises the possibility of another enzyme in *Neurospora* which catalyzes the phenylalanyl (illegitimate) attachment to the second and third components (19). Further studies are necessary before the significance of the phenomenon can be interpreted as to the heterologous specificity between sRNA and the synthetase.

4. In contrast to the multiple-component feature of sRNA, a single enzyme seems to exist in several cases examined. For leucine, only one enzyme appears to be responsible for charging all sRNA components of *E. coli*, as judged from kinetic evidence (21), first-order heat inactivation (Fig. 8), and the occurrence of transacylation between the components (Fig. 9) (53). The first-order heat inactivation kinetics has also been observed for valine and lysine.

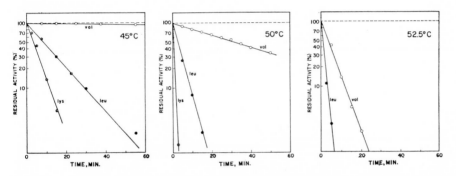

Fig. 8. Heat stability of *E. coli* aminoacyl-sRNA synthetase. Typical heat inactivation curves of valyl-, leucyl-, and lysyl-sRNA synthetases are shown. Enzyme activity was measured by the initial rate of aminoacyl-sRNA formation (incubation at 30°C for 5 minutes; saturation of sRNA with amino acid was reached after 15 minutes). From Yamane and Sueoka (53).

Another important aspect of the sRNA versus synthetase relationship is its possible role in the regulation of protein synthesis. This point has been only a matter of speculation (2, 34, 47, 55). Recently, modification of leucyl-sRNA of *E. coli* B upon phage T2 infection has been revealed (43). The modification is specific in that, among seventeen amino acids examined (all except asparagine, glutamine, and cysteine), only a component or two of leucine acceptor RNA are modified. T2 ghost adsorption or the presence of chloroamphenicol eliminates the modification. Thus, the modification started the third minute after

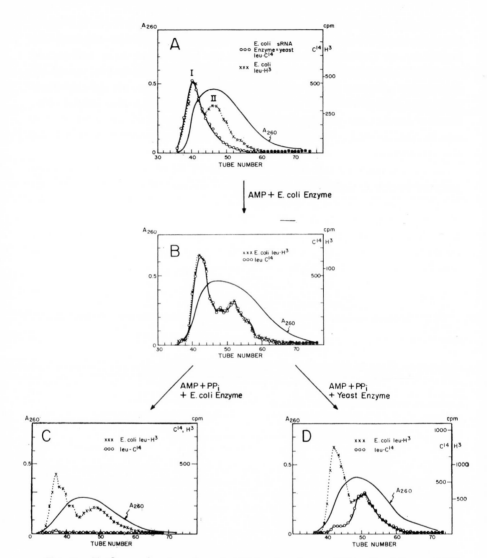

FIG. 9. Evidence for transfer of $C^{14}$-leucine from sRNA (leu)-I to sRNA (leu)-II. Comparison of the chromatographic profiles of *E. coli* total $H^3$-leucyl-sRNA and (A) *E. coli* ($C^{14}$-leucyl-sRNA) obtained by using yeast aminoacyl-sRNA synthetase; (B) $C^{14}$-leucyl-sRNA obtained by incubating *E. coli* ($C^{14}$-leucyl-sRNA) with *E. coli* aminoacyl-sRNA synthetase and AMP for 30 minutes at 30°C (81% of $C^{14}$ radioactivity was recovered from A); (C) $C^{14}$-leucyl-sRNA in (B) incubated with *E. coli* enzyme + AMP + PP*i* for 30 minutes at 30°C, reisolated, and rechromatographed; (D) $C^{14}$-leucyl-sRNA in (B) treated with yeast enzyme + AMP + PP*i* for 30 minutes at 30°C, reisolated, and rechromatographed (19% of $C^{14}$ radioactivity was recovered from B). From Yamane and Sueoka (53).

infection and was completed by the eighth minute (Fig. 10). The injection of phage DNA and protein synthesis, therefore, are required for modification. The theoretical basis for the experiment is as follows. If the codon recognition of a particular adaptor sRNA out of a set of degenerate adaptors for an amino acid is changed by structural modification, the mRNA of the genes which accommodate the codon cor-

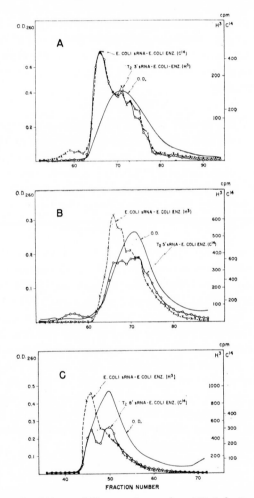

Fig. 10. Leucyl-sRNA at different times after T2 infection. The sRNA was taken from cells infected for 3 minutes, 5 minutes, and 8 minutes and charged by *E. coli* enzyme free from RNA. The profiles of the leucyl-sRNA were compared with that of *E. coli* by eluting them together on a MAK column. (*A*) T2 3-minute sRNA; (*B*) T2 5-minute sRNA; (*C*) T2 8-minute sRNA. From Sueoka and Kano-Sueoka (43).

responding to the modified adaptor should not be translated properly, while the mRNA of the other genes which do not accommodate the codon should be translated normally. This means that, by modifying a specific sRNA molecule, the function of some of the genes which are transcribed can be shut off, and the rest of the genes can be kept functional at the translation level. This, if true, should constitute one of the major principles in differentiation and may be called the adaptor *modification hypothesis*. This hypothesis may be applied to cases where a drastic change in the metabolic pattern is observed rather than to cases involving a change in a small number of enzymes. However, the true meaning of the modification of *E. coli* leucyl-sRNA by phage T2 infection remains to be seen.

## CONCLUSION

Universality of the genetic code is the outcome of experimental facts and was not obvious from *a priori* reasoning because of the presence of adaptors (sRNA). Without the adaptor, universality would have been the logical expectation from the stereospecificity between codon and amino acid. The adaptor hypothesis, however, disjoined the lock and key relationship between them and opened the basic properties of the code, *universality, degeneracy*, and the *size of codons*, to experimental investigations.

With the universal and degenerate code, variation and heterogeneity of DNA base composition are most readily understood as the reflection of frequency difference among the codons for each amino acid in different organisms. Thus, organisms with higher DNA GC content, more frequently than others, may have in their genomes codons with higher GC. The fact that the right kind of cross reaction between sRNA and aminoacyl-sRNA synthetase does occur between remotest organisms suggests that the present scheme of the code and its translation mechanism was established before the ramification of organisms. The significance of sRNA on the evolution of protein-synthesizing machinery is obviously important because of its role as the adaptor in the code translation mechanism. Further progress in this area should provide important clues for the evolution of the genetic code.

## ACKNOWLEDGMENT

This work was supported by the U.S. Public Health Service and the National Science Foundation.

## REFERENCES

1. ABEL, P., AND TRAUTNER, T. A., Z. *Vererbungslehre*, **95**, 66 (1964).
2. AMES, B. N., AND HARTMAN, P. E., *Cold Spring Harbor Symp. Quant. Biol.*, **28**, 349 (1963).

3. ANFINSEN, C. B., in "The Molecular Basis of Evolution," p. 228, Wiley, New York, 1959.
4. APGAR, J., HOLLEY, R. W., AND MERRILL, S. H., Biochim. Biophys. Acta, 53, 220 (1961).
5. BARNETT, W. E., AND JACOBSON, K. B., Proc. Natl. Acad. Sci. U.S., 51, 642 (1964).
6. BAYREUTHER, K. E., AND ROMIG, W. R., Science, 146, 778 (1964).
7. BELOZERSKY, A. N., AND SPIRIN, A. S., in "The Nucleic Acids" (E. Chargaff and J. Davidson, eds.), Vol. 3, p. 147, Academic Press, New York, 1960.
8. BENZER, S., AND WEISBLUM, B., Proc. Natl. Acad. Sci. U.S., 47, 1149 (1961).
9. BERG, P., AND OFENGAND, E. J., Proc. Natl. Acad. Sci. U.S., 44, 78 (1958).
10. CHARGAFF, E., in "The Nucleic Acids" (E. Chargaff and J. Davidson, eds.), Vol. 1, p. 307, Academic Press, New York, 1955.
11. CHENG, T. Y., AND SUEOKA, N., Science, 143, 1442 (1964).
12. CRICK, F. H. C., in "The Structure of Nucleic Acids and Their Role in Protein Synthesis," p. 25, Cambridge Univ. Press, Cambridge, 1957.
13. CRICK, F. H. C., Progr. Nucleic Acid Res. 1, 163 (1963).
14. DOCTOR, B. P., AND CONNELLY, C. M., Biochem. Biophys. Res. Commun., 6, 201 (1961).
15. DOTY, P., MARMUR, J., AND SUEOKA, N., Brookhaven Symp. Biol., 12, 1 (1959).
16. FREESE, E., J. Theoret. Biol., 3, 82 (1962).
17. HOAGLAND, M. B., STEPHENSON, M. L., SCOTT, J. F., HECHT, L. I., AND ZAMECNIK, P. C., J. Biol. Chem., 231, 241 (1958).
18. HOGNESS, D. S., AND SIMMONS, J. R., J. Mol. Biol., 9, 411 (1964).
19. IMAMOTO, F., YAMANE, T., AND SUEOKA, N., unpublished data.
20. JACOB, F., AND MONOD, J., J. Mol. Biol., 3, 318 (1961).
21. KELLER, E. B., AND ANTHONY, R. S., Federation Proc., 22, 231 (1963).
22. KORNBERG, A., BERTSCH, L. L., JACKSON, J. F., AND KHORANA, H. G., Proc. Natl. Acad. Sci. U.S., 51, 315 (1964).
23. LANNI, F., Perspectives Biol. Med., 3, 418 (1960).
24. MARMUR, J., AND DOTY, P., Nature, 183, 1427 (1959).
25. MARMUR, J., FALKOW, S., AND MANDEL, M., Ann. Rev. Microbiol., 17, 329 (1963).
26. McCARTHY, B. J., AND BOLTON, E. T., Proc. Natl. Acad. Sci. U.S., 50, 156 (1963).
27. MIYAZAWA, Y., AND THOMAS, C. A., J. Mol. Biol., 11, 223 (1965).
28. NIRENBERG, M. W., JONES, O. W., LEDER, P., CLARK, B. F. C., SLY, W. S., AND PESTKA, S., Cold Spring Harbor Symp. Quant. Biol., 28, 549 (1963).
29. O'SULLIVAN, A., YOSHIKAWA, H., AND SUEOKA, N., unpublished data.
30. ROLFE, R., AND MESELSON, M., Proc. Natl. Acad. Sci. U.S., 45, 1039 (1959).
31. SCHACHMAN, H. K., ADLER, J., RADDING, C. M., LEHMAN, I. R., AND KORNBERG, A., J. Biol. Chem., 235, 3242 (1960).
32. SMITH, M., Biochem. Biophys. Res. Commun., 10, 67 (1963).
33. SPEYER, J. F., LENGYEL, P., BASILIO, C., WAHBA, A. J., GARDNER, R. S., AND OCHOA, S., Cold Spring Harbor Symp. Quant. Biol., 28, 559 (1963).
34. STENT, G., Science, 144, 816 (1964).
35. SUEOKA, N., Proc. Natl. Acad. Sci. U.S., 45, 1480 (1959).
36. SUEOKA, N., Proc. Natl. Acad. Sci. U.S., 47, 1141 (1961).
37. SUEOKA, N., J. Mol. Biol., 3, 31 (1961).
38. SUEOKA, N., Cold Spring Harbor Symp. Quant. Biol., 26, 35 (1961).

39. Sueoka, N., *Proc. Natl. Acad. Sci. U.S.*, **48**, 582 (1962).
40. Sueoka, N., *in* "The Bacteria" (I. C. Gunsalus and R. Y. Stanier, eds.), Vol. 5, p. 419, Academic Press, New York, 1964.
41. Sueoka, N., and Cheng, T. Y., *J. Mol. Biol.*, **4**, 161 (1962).
42. Sueoka, N., and Cheng, T. Y., *Proc. Natl. Acad. Sci. U.S.*, **48**, 1851 (1962).
43. Sueoka, N., and Kano-Sueoka, T., *Proc. Natl. Acad. Sci. U.S.*, **52**, 1535 (1964).
44. Sueoka, N., Marmur, J., and Doty, P., *Nature*, **183**, 1429 (1959).
45. Sueoka, N., and Nanney, D. L., in preparation. Cited in Sueoka, N., *Cold Spring Harbor Symp. Quant. Biol.*, **26**, 35 (1961).
46. Sueoka, N., and Yamane, T., *Proc. Natl. Acad. Sci. U.S.*, **48**, 1454 (1962).
47. Sueoka, N., and Yamane, T., *in* "Informational Macromolecules" (H. J. Vogel, V. Bryson, and J. P. Lampen, eds.), p. 205, Academic Press, New York, 1963.
48. Swartz, M. N., Trautner, T. A., and Kornberg, A., *J. Biol. Chem.*, **237**, 1961 (1962).
49. von Ehrenstein, G., and Lipmann, F., *Proc. Natl. Acad. Sci. U.S.*, **47**, 941 (1961).
50. Weisblum, B., Benzer, S., and Holley, R. W., *Proc. Natl. Acad. Sci. U.S.*, **48**, 1449 (1962).
51. Yamane, T., Cheng, T. Y., and Sueoka, N., *Cold Spring Harbor Symp. Quant. Biol.*, **28**, 569 (1963).
52. Yamane, T., and Sueoka, N., *Proc. Natl. Acad. Sci. U.S.*, **50**, 1093 (1963).
53. Yamane, T., and Sueoka, N., *Proc. Natl. Acad. Sci. U.S.*, **51**, 1178 (1964).
54. Yamane, T., and Sueoka, N., in preparation.
55. Yanofsky, C., Helinski, D. R., and Maling, B. D., *Cold Spring Harbor Symp. Quant. Biol.*, **26**, 11 (1961).

# Discussion of Part VIII

W. Braun, C. B. Anfinsen, J. R. Warner, S. Spiegelman, P. Doty,
P. Siekevitz, R. Sager, H. Harris, L. Spetner, N. Sueoka

Chairman Braun: Are there any questions or comments?

Dr. Anfinsen: I would like to ask Dr. Warner about the β-galacto-sidase system. You seem rather certain that three chains are involved. There are about fifteen people knocking themselves out trying to determine whether it is two, three, or four. I think it is probably three.

Dr. Warner: I heard it from your laboratory.

Dr. Anfinsen: I am interested in the polycistronic message idea. If you visualize three chains for β-galactosidase and one for permease, you have four chains in all. Apparently, you would like to think of one chain per ribosome. Do you have any picture of how such a poly-cistronic message might be read, dropping off one chain at a time?

Dr. Warner: Well, that is about it. You read from one end, first at the left. We will say the operator end. That is the beginning of the messenger. You read through the $z$ genes and then you go and read the permease gene and the acetylase gene.

There is one real flaw in this. The acetylase seems to be made in a molar content at least 10-fold less than the galactosidase. You can invoke things to explain this—ribosomes falling off or something. But it is really only a speculation at this point.

Dr. Anfinsen: If there is one chain per ribosome, then you would have to have, if there were four cistrons being read, four starting points along this polycistronic message. It would mean that you might see, in your electron micrographs, strands with branching points or some other evidence of punctuation.

Dr. Warner: I don't think you would see branching points. It is a question of whether or not there is, let us say, a stop and then another start codon or something like that.

Dr. Spiegelman: I wanted to tell Anfinsen that excellent preparations of pure polycistronic messages are available in very large quantities in the form of RNA viruses. They have been examined very carefully under the electron microscope, and there are no stop-go's obvious on them.

Dr. Anfinsen: How do we work this out with Dr. Warner?

Dr. Spiegelman: I just don't believe that the ribosome starts at one end and drops off with a probability proportional to the distance traveled. This generates an obvious difficulty. If you need, say three peptides (e.g., for β-galactosidase) to put together, you have got to make them in equivalent quantities. If there is a probability of dropping off, then what are you going to do about the third one?

DR. DOTY: Or the first two.

DR. SIEKEVITZ: I had some slides, but I am not going to show them. But since Dr. Anfinsen brought up β-galactosidase, I wish to inject a note of caution in looking at the results of enzyme activities on the sucrose density gradient. We thought we would do an experiment to try to confirm the idea that the larger the size of the messenger, the larger the size of the so-called polysomes. We took guinea pig pancreas, made microsomes, treated them with low deoxycholate, spun down, suspended the residue, and put this on the sucrose density gradient. One peak of optical density was obtained, in the monomer region. We then took each tube and tested for amylase activity (M. W., $\sim 50,000$), chymotrypsinogen (M. W., $\sim 22,000$), and ribonuclease (M. W., $\sim 12,000$). We found that we obtained a distinct separation of activities, with the amylase coming toward the bottom of the gradient, then the chymotrypsinogen, then the ribonuclease, and then the monomer. But these activities do not mark where polysomes are. In the electron miscroscope, we found very small membrane-enclosed vesicles with ribosomes on them in these nonmonomer regions. The amylase seems to be inside the vesicles. If you do a pulse experiment, you find that the specific radioactivity of the amylase in the so-called polysome region is about the same as in the monomer region. Just one more point. If you do the same pulse-labeled experiment with high deoxycholate, put it on a sucrose density gradient, most of the RNA ($\sim 90\%$) resides in the monomer region. But there is always a pellet that comes down toward the bottom of the tube. When we took the pellet and looked for the radioactive amylase, we found a ten-fold higher amylase specific radioactivity there than in any other region where amylase was. What is down there at the bottom are ribosomes on membranes. Thus, the ribosomes which are active in protein synthesis are those very tightly tied to the membrane. I wish to say that the polysome contains something else besides a ribosome held together by messenger RNA, and that there is a membrane component which perhaps is involved in the last stage of protein synthesis.

DR. SAGER: I just want to understand from Dr. Harris what evidence he has about the fraction of the genome which is being copied in this fast-turning-over fraction. Is this really a copy of the whole genome or some small fraction represented here?

DR. HARRIS: Do you mean of a particular gene or of the whole of the DNA?

DR. SAGER: The whole.

DR. HARRIS: We don't have much information about that, unfortunately.

DR. SAGER: That is essential.

DR. HARRIS: I think I said in my paper that we do not know how much of the DNA actually gets copied. We can perhaps estimate how much is being copied at any one time, but that doesn't tell us very much.

In terms of the life of the cell, we have no way, at the moment, of knowing whether a little of the DNA gets copied or whether all of it gets copied. I wish I did know. I think the best discussion of this problem is in a recent paper by Edström on the giant salivary chromosomes but the question is far from solved.

DR. SPETNER: As a result of the last discussion, while Dr. Harris was speaking, it occurred to me that there might be some very useful function for the rapidly-breaking-down RNA within the nucleus. Since the RNA is an information carrier, it could do some computing housekeeping within the nucleus. Such a function would add a great deal of power to the computation.

It might be performing a housekeeping or control function by carrying information from one piece of a chromosome to another. And the resultant output, if I may talk in computer terms, would be just the stable RNA that gets out of the nucleus. Much more computing may be going on than is evident in the output.

DR. HARRIS: Yes, that is an idea we have entertained. The main reason why we don't really think that is what the RNA is doing rests on measurements of quantity. You see, if RNA is going to instruct a piece of DNA, it has to attach itself to DNA. So we must assume that RNA, attached to DNA, is either suppressing the function of that piece of DNA or is part of the process of expressing that function. If you look at the amount of RNA in the nuclei of animals and higher plants, relative to the amount of DNA, you find that in some cells the amount of DNA exceeds the amount of RNA by a factor of 20 or 30. Therefore, there must be large stretches of DNA which don't have any RNA attached to them at any one time. I haven't the time to go into this question in detail. What you suggest is quite plausible. We don't favor it, but it isn't something I have strong views about, really.

DR. SPIEGELMAN: I just want to ask one question. If the AT polymer in the crab is nuclear, we would have a test system for Dr. Harris because we should then find RNA complementary to the AT polymer. Is it nuclear, Dr. Sueoka?

DR. SUEOKA: We don't have any direct evidence on that. Regarding the amount of DNA per cell in higher organisms, I don't think there is any reason why it should be a constant or a minimum amount. For example, we know there can be a combination of two different genomes by crossing, and a retention of both genomes by duplication (amphidiploidy). I don't think that is the main issue there.

DR. HARRIS: I don't think that one will really wash. The genetics of higher plants is something that has been very carefully studied. If there were large numbers of duplicated genes, it would make nonsense of about nine-tenths of classical plant genetics.

# PART IX

# EVOLUTION OF GENES III

# Chairman's Remarks

ROLLIN D. HOTCHKISS

*The Rockefeller Institute,*
*New York, New York*

In trying to bridge this great gap from the eocene world to the unseen world—from the polyeonic to the polyanionic—the gap has sometimes seemed larger than it really is. Although the biologist has not been heard from here as much as hoped, his working method is essentially the same as that of the molecular biologist, I think.

This applies even to the extreme classical biologist-paleontologist, who indulges in worship of an ancestor that he creates out of a jawbone, while picking up interesting artifacts along the way; well, the molecular biologist does exactly the same thing. He uses his own jawbone, of course, but he, too, worships the bearer of that jawbone, in general, and he, too, picks up very interesting artifacts to show his fellows.

Dr. Williams yesterday reminded us that taxonomy and phylogeny were not the same thing, yet it seemed that we talked at times as though there were a true taxonomy, as though one would be the right one, and another the wrong one, as if the question were: Is this new molecular taxonomy going to be right?

I submit that taxonomy is not a thing that is subject to being right or wrong. It is a convenience, a way of thinking. Phylogeny might conceivably have a right pathway or several right pathways at different places and times. I believe that what the molecular biologist is trying to do is to ask questions not of right or wrong, but (when he is working at his best anyway): Is this a feasible hypothesis? Is this hypothesis more fitting than this other one?—not obsessed with the great conscience problem of rightness or wrongness.

One of our speakers may or may not bear this out. I think it was a brilliant stroke on the part of the planning committee to have Moses and Calvin collaborate. Moses, you remember, came back from a mountain retreat with a set of slides which fully documented his revealed philosophy. Calvin set up a running critique of this work, and together they have affected all our lives. Perhaps, too, it has tended to be forgotten that Moses was the first one who collected a small band in a high salt gradient and obtained some purification by that means.

We are lucky to have descendants of these remarkable people working together in our behalf.

# Homology and Divergence in Genetic Material of *Salmonella typhimurium* and *Escherichia coli*

M. DEMEREC

*Biology Department, Brookhaven National Laboratory, Upton, New York*

This paper will discuss our current work on two problems related to evolution in bacteria, one concerned with similarities and the other with divergencies in structure between the genetic materials of *Salmonella typhimurium* and *Escherichia coli*.

About two years ago, when Dr. K. E. Sanderson joined our group, we began intensive work on the preparation of a genetic map of the *S. typhimurium* chromosome, because such a map had become essential for efficient planning of our experiments and interpretation of results. Since that time, primarily through Dr. Sanderson's efforts, a basic map containing 133 gene loci has been compiled (6). A similar map for *E. coli* has recently been published (8). Comparison of the two maps reveals a strikingly high degree of homology between the two genomes in gross structure, that is, in the locations and functions of genes. Fifty-nine loci appearing on both maps have been thoroughly enough studied to permit the conclusion that they have the same functions in the two species; and all 59 of these loci occupy corresponding positions on the maps. So far, no well-substantiated case of chromosomal rearrangement has been found. I have no doubt that chromosomal rearrangements exist, and that ultimately we shall find some. But they must be rare, far more so than we might expect from speciation studies with other organisms, particularly *Drosophila*, in which inversions frequently differentiate strains of the same species inhabiting different localities. Taxonomists classify *Salmonella* and *Escherichia* not only as different genera but as members of different tribes of the enteric family of bacteria. Therefore, if evolutionary differentiation in these bacteria were related to chromosomal rearrangements, as it is in *Drosophila*, rearrangements should be found frequently.

Why this difference between bacteria (*Salmonella–Escherichia*) and a higher organism such as *Drosophila*? Is infrequency of rearrangements an attribute of more primitive organisms, or is it only a specific property of a certain group of bacteria?

An explanation of the phenomenon is suggested by results accumulated in studies of clustering of genes that control related functions. Shortly after we began work with S. *typhimurium* we observed that four tryptophan genes are located in a cluster (3), and soon thereafter P. E. Hartman found a cluster of four histidine genes (2). By now the analysis of mutants in our collection has progressed far enough to show that clustering is a frequent phenomenon in this species (1). It has been detected in 87 mutants, where 63 (72.5%) of the gene loci are located in 17 clusters. It appears probable that frequent clustering occurs in *E. coli* as well, but not in all bacteria, at least not to such an extent.

Where there is a mechanism capable of dispersing the genes of a cluster, they should, given sufficient time, become randomly distributed throughout a genome. We know of several mechanisms in bacteria that can bring about the separation of adjacent genes. If a cluster is to persist, therefore, the gene arrangement it represents must give some selective advantage to the organism. In *Salmonella,* such an advantage may derive from coordinated functioning of the clustered genes. If clusters offer selective advantage, chromosomal rearrangements, which are likely to break them up, would be selected against. Thus clusters, distributed along the chromosome as they are in *Salmonella,* should be instrumental in preserving the existing gene arrangement of a species; and the high degree of homology in gene arrangement found in S. *typhimurium* and *E. coli* could be explained by assuming that a progenitor of the two species also had clusters, which were responsible for perpetuating its gene arrangement in species derived from it.

It seems probable that extensive clustering occurs not in all bacteria but only in a certain group (enteric) or groups of bacteria. Thus, if clustering is responsible for homology of gene arrangements in related genera, homology may be a special condition not necessarily limited to lower organisms.

The second problem that I mentioned, concerning genetic divergence between S. *typhimurium* and *E. coli,* is being studied by analysis of recombination between genetic markers carried on the two chromosomes. For this purpose transduction is the most sensitive technique available. Phage serves as a vector to carry chromosomal fragments from donor into recipient bacteria. When appropriate genetic markers are located in a particular fragment, exchanges of material, due to incorporation of a donor segment in place of the homologous recipient segment, are detected. Since no phage is known that can grow in both S. *typhimurium* and *E. coli,* direct transduction experiments cannot be carried out. However, by conjugation between appropriate strains of S. *typhimurium* (recipient) and E. *coli* (donor), one can obtain hybrids whose chromosomes all consist partly of S. *typhimurium* and partly of E. *coli* material. *Salmonella*-transducing phage P22 is able to grow in some of these hybrids and can carry, without discrimination, fragments that are wholly *Salmonella* in origin, wholly E. *coli*, or a composite of both. With hybrids as donors, therefore, it is possible by transduction to determine frequencies of incorporation of E. *coli* material into the S. *typhimurium* chromosome, and to compare them with the frequencies of incorporation of comparable *Salmonella* material. Such studies have shown that, as a rule, E. *coli* markers are incorporated much less frequently than *Salmonella* markers. This finding is particularly well illustrated by the results of an early experiment, shown in Table I (4). For that experiment we selected a genetically well-known region of the *Salmonella* chromosome extending about 17% of its length. It contains the transducing fragment that carries a cluster of five cysteine loci (*cysC,D,H,I,J*), as well as markers representing seven other transducing fragments (*metC, argE, serA, lys–argB, phe, tyr,* and *purG–gly*). The experiment was done in two parts: part A with selected hybrids in which at least the entire *cysC* chromosomal region was of E. *coli* derivation; and part B with hybrids in which at least a specific part of the *cysC* region was E. *coli*. In different hybrids, of both the A and the B series, the E. *coli* segments presumably might differ in length and might include in addition to *cysC* other transducing fragments. The hybrids were analyzed by transduction. Phage P22 was grown in each hybrid (as well as in wild-type S. *typhimurium* as a control, top row of the table) and used to transduce the S. *typhimurium* mutant strains listed in the table heading.

The numbers record the frequencies of transductants detected. Every one of the hybrid donors gave rise to a much smaller number of transductants in crosses with cysteine mutants representing the five loci of the *cysC* cluster than in crosses with certain of the mutants representing nearby loci, or in the crosses between the *Salmonella* control donor and the *cysC* mutants. These results show that an E. *coli* chromosomal segment is incorporated much less frequently than a *Salmonella* segment into the *Salmonella* chromosome.

When we examine the results for transduction of markers located in fragments adjoining the *cysC* fragment, two classes are clearly discernible: one with low frequencies, similar to those observed within the *cysC* region, and the other with high frequencies comparable to those obtained in the control crosses. Moreover, when the mutants representing the adjacent loci are arranged in order according to whether they produced large or small numbers of transductants with different hybrids, the order

## TABLE I

Numbers of Transductants in Experiments with *S. typhimurium* Mutants as Recipients and *S. typhimurium* × *E. coli* Hybrids as Donors[a]

| Recipient: Donor | cysC −382 | metC −32 | argE −116 | serA −13 | lys −8 | argB −69 | cysC cluster dl-C −537 | dl-C −1021 | dl-CD −519 | dl-H −75 | dl-I −68 | dl-J −538 | phe −3 | tyr −3 | purG −303 | gly −1 |
|---|---|---|---|---|---|---|---|---|---|---|---|---|---|---|---|---|
| *Salmonella* + | 1260 | 555 | 485 | 446 | 960 | 740 | ~1400 | 377 | ~1000 | 1170 | ~1890 | ~1130 | ~3200 | ~2800 | ~2600 | ~3800 |
| Hybrids | | | | | | | | | | | | | | | | |
| A-18 | — | 85 | — | 129 | 176 | 126 | 0 | 7 | 12 | 12 | 4 | 13 | ~2000 | ~2400 | ~2600 | — |
| B-33 | 599 | 732 | 732 | 205 | 619 | 305 | 11 | 4 | — | — | — | 5 | 736 | 1362 | ~2840 | ~1336 |
| B-20 | — | — | — | — | 410 | 241 | 4 | 2 | 2 | 5 | 5 | 4 | ~1600 | ~1600 | ~1770 | — |
| A-57 | 451 | ~1470 | 385 | 282 | 5 | 0 | 0 | — | 1 | — | — | 0 | ~3000 | ~3000 | ~2200 | ~3000 |
| B-24 | 1320 | 18 | 92 | 433 | 8 | 1 | 0 | 1 | 1 | 0 | 2 | 2 | ~2600 | ~2600 | ~2600 | — |
| A-45 | ~1430 | 506 | 326 | 1 | 3 | 0 | 0 | — | 0 | — | — | 2 | ~3000 | ~3000 | ~2600 | ~3000 |
| B-11 | 541 | 893 | 96 | 1 | 4 | 0 | 0 | 0 | 0 | 0 | 0 | 0 | 0 | 2 | 25 | ~1277 |
| A-50 | — | 122 | 98 | 2 | 12 | 0 | 4 | 2 | 2 | 2 | 2 | 12 | ~1600 | — | — | — |
| A-14 | — | ~6000 | 0 | 1 | 0 | 0 | 0 | — | 0 | — | — | 2 | ~1500 | ~4800 | — | ~2750 |
| A-19 | — | 104 | 0 | 6 | 19 | 0 | 0 | 0 | — | — | 0 | 0 | 12 | 14 | 56 | 1480 |
| B-51 | 590 | 3 | 0 | 0 | 5 | 1 | 0 | 1 | 1 | 4 | 3 | 1 | 137 | 198 | 567 | 1663 |
| B-74 | 700 | 8 | 0 | 0 | 5 | 0 | 3 | 1 | 3 | 1 | 0 | 1 | 175 | 1229 | ~1280 | ~1450 |

[a] Recipient genes are located close together. (Two plates, $4 \times 10^8$ bacteria, phage multiplicity 5×, double-enriched medium.)

coincides with the genetic-map order indicated by the results of conjugation experiments. Thus it is justifiable to assume that low frequencies of transduction of certain genetic markers signify that the hybrid donors carried E. coli segments in the chromosomal regions where these markers are located. Evidently, this finding provides a means of differentiating between Salmonella and E. coli regions of a hybrid chromosome; and when known genetic markers are present in a section where such regions join, it is possible to establish the relative order of the markers. Thus hybrids can serve, in much the same way as overlapping deletions, for the mapping of genes. We are successfully using them for that purpose.

Is this low frequency of incorporation of E. coli material into the S. typhimurium genome, observed in the vicinity of the cysC region, limited to a certain section only, or does it obtain throughout the chromosome? There is evidence to show that the frequency varies in various chromosomal regions. Experiments like those described above but involving differently constituted hybrids as donors have shown the following transduction frequencies: in the cysC and try regions, about 1%; in the leu region, 3.5%; in argA,C,F,H, 7%; and in ser–thr, about 10%.

We are assuming that a lack (or a low degree) of homology is responsible for the observed failures of incorporation of E. coli material into the S. typhimurium chromosome. As such, it presents a sharp contrast to the high degree of over-all conformity in gene arrangement (gross structure) of the two genomes that was noted earlier. The most plausible explanation of such divergence seems to be that determinations of gross homology are concerned with whole gene loci, whereas in the studies of incorporation we deal with processes that occur at the subgenic, molecular level. Thus, genes may be homologous as far as their function is concerned and yet differ in their molecular structure.

This interpretation is supported by results of molecular in vitro hybridization of DNA carried out by two different methods. Schildkraut, Marmur, and Doty (7) did not detect any hybridization between DNA's of E. coli K12 and S. typhimurium; and McCarthy and Bolton (5), using a more sensitive technique, found such hybridization to be no more than about 70%.

It is also supported by the above-mentioned finding that frequency of incorporation is not uniform throughout the genome but varies considerably in different gene loci.

## SUMMARY

No well-substantiated case of chromosomal rearrangement has been discovered by comparison of the genetic maps of S. typhimurium and

*E. coli*, although more than a hundred genes have been mapped in each organism. Thus it appears that in the evolutionary differentiation between these two genera rearrangements have occurred much less frequently than in *Drosophila* and, presumably, other higher organisms. An explanation of the phenomenon is suggested by the finding that, in *S. typhimurium* and *E. coli*, genes controlling related functions are often clustered together. Seventeen such clusters, distributed along the genome, have been found in *S. typhimurium*. If a cluster is to persist, the gene arrangement it represents must offer some selective advantage to the organism, in which case chromosomal rearrangements, which are likely to break up clusters, would be selected against. Therefore the high degree of homology of gene arrangement observed in the two species can be explained by assuming that a common progenitor also had clusters, which were responsible for retention of its gene arrangement in species derived from it.

A technique has been developed for determining the frequency of incorporation of an *E. coli* genetic marker into the homologous region of the *S. typhimurium* chromosome. In general that frequency is considerably lower than the frequency of incorporation of the corresponding *S. typhimurium* marker. This finding has been interpreted as an indication of structural divergence between the chromosomes of the two genera. In view of the unexpectedly high degree of correspondence as far as gene order is concerned, it is inferred that the divergence detected by the incorporation studies is due to differences at the molecular level rather than to differences in gross chromosomal structure.

### ACKNOWLEDGMENT

This research was carried out at Brookhaven National Laboratory under the auspices of the U.S. Atomic Energy Commission. The help of Miss Agnes C. Fisher in editing the manuscript is acknowledged with gratitude.

### REFERENCES

1. DEMEREC, M., *Proc. Natl. Acad. Sci. U.S.*, **51**, 1057 (1964).
2. DEMEREC, M., HARTMAN, P. E., MOSER, H., KANAZIR, D., DEMEREC, Z. E., FITZGERALD, P. L., GLOVER, S. W., LAHR, E. L., WESTOVER, W. E., AND YURA, T., *Carnegie Inst. Wash. Yr. Bk.*, **54**, 219 (1955).
3. DEMEREC, M., MOSER, H., HEMMERLY, J., BLOMSTRAND, I., DEMEREC, Z. E., FITZGERALD, P. L., GLOVER, S. W., HANSON, J. F., NIELSEN, F. J., AND YURA, T., *Carnegie Inst. Wash. Yr. Bk.*, **53**, 225 (1954).
4. DEMEREC, M., AND OHTA, N., *Proc. Natl. Acad. Sci. U.S.*, **52**, 317 (1964).
5. McCARTHY, J. M., AND BOLTON, E. T., *Proc. Natl. Acad. Sci. U.S.*, **50**, 156 (1963).
6. SANDERSON, K. E., AND DEMEREC, M., *Genetics*, **51**, in press.
7. SCHILDKRAUT, C. L., MARMUR, J., AND DOTY, P., *J. Mol. Biol.*, **3**, 595 (1961).
8. TAYLOR, A. L., AND THOMAN, M. S., *Genetics*, **50**, 659 (1964).

# Molecular Regulation and Its Possible Evolutionary Significance

V. Moses and M. Calvin

*Lawrence Radiation Laboratory and Department of Chemistry,
University of California, Berkeley, California*

The model for the control of enzyme biosynthesis proposed by Jacob and Monod (16), which depends on repression and derepression of genetic expression, supposes in the case of inducible enzymes that the presence of a specific effector (or inducer) is required to initiate enzyme production. It is envisaged that only in the presence of inducer is transcription of the appropriate cistron of DNA carried out, with the formation of a corresponding RNA molecule. This so-called "messenger" RNA (mRNA) then carries the informational message for the synthesis of the specific protein to the ribosomes, where translation of the nucleic acid informational sequence to a polypeptide structure occurs. Much of the chemical and genetic evidence in support of this theory has been reviewed by Jacob and Monod (16). Recent additional pieces of evidence have been provided by measurement of the levels of specific mRNA in inducible cells, before and after induction with a specific effector, and in the corresponding constitutive strain (1, 2, 11).

The attainment within 3 minutes of a constant rate of specific enzyme synthesis following introduction of the inducer (18, 27) indicates that mRNA production starts very soon after the inducer is added. Similarly, studies by Kepes (18) have shown that enzyme synthesis ceases, also in about 3 minutes, after inducer is removed from the system or diluted to a concentration so low that it is no longer effective. This has led to the conclusion that, at least for the β-galactosidase system of *Escherichia coli*, mRNA is both rapidly synthesized and rapidly destroyed. Removal of the inducer results in almost instant cessation of mRNA synthesis, and the mRNA already existing at that time decays with a half-life of about 1 minute (18). Maintenance of enzyme synthesis thus requires continuous production of mRNA, and this, in turn, provides a very sensitive response to changes in the environment, since the removal of an inducing substance from the vicinity of the cells brings to a rapid halt the biosynthesis of the corresponding inducible enzymes.

Similar results for the formation and decay of mRNA in the β-galactosidase system of *E. coli* were obtained by Nakada and Magasanik (25),
who found a value of 2.5 minutes for the half-life of mRNA. In a study
of protein synthesis in *Bacillus subtilis* and its relation to mRNA formation, Levinthal, Keynan, and Higa (20) found that the incorporation of
$C^{14}$-valine into protein is rapidly inhibited shortly after the administration of actinomycin D. This antibiotic prevents the DNA-dependent
synthesis of RNA (15). Levinthal *et al.* (20) calculated a value of 2
minutes for the half-life of mRNA, and other authors have also assumed
or concluded that mRNA's decay with short half-lives (10, 23).

The widespread occurrence of genetic repression-depression phenomena, and their obvious potential importance as prime regulators of genetic
expression and cellular activity, has led to suggestions that the whole
enzymic apparatus of a cell may be subject to this sort of genetic regulation. Enzymes would be produced in response to the presence of environmental or intracellular inducers and repressors, and the production of
each protein might be envisaged as under a genetic regulating control
of the type postulated for β-galactosidase in *E. coli* (26). There may
thus be no fundamental genetic differences between inducible and constitutive enzymes in the sense originally intended by Karström (17), but
the apparent constancy of constitutive enzymes may be the consequence
of an unvarying balance of repressing and derepressing factors at a
genetic regulatory site. A short life for their mRNA's would then be an
important element in the exertion of fine control on the biosynthesis of
these phenotypically constitutive enzymes. The alternative possibility,
recognized by Pardee and Beckwith (26), was that certain enzymes
appear to be constitutive because of the absence of a control mechanism
involving inducers and repressors. The rate of synthesis of such an enzyme would then be constant in relation to the synthesis of all other
constitutive proteins in the cell, the actual rate being controlled, presumably, by some inherent feature of the coding of the structural gene
(19). Were this second possibility to be the case, one might question the
value of short-lived mRNA for constitutive enzymes, since the fine control of protein biosynthesis which may be achieved with unstable mRNA
for inducible enzyme synthesis is not relevant in the case of constitutive
enzyme formation.

It has already been recognized that all mRNA in all organisms cannot
be so unstable as to have a half-life of only 1 or 2 minutes. Spencer and
Harris (30) have shown that the biosynthesis and *regulation of biosynthesis* of some proteins may continue in cells of *Acetabularia crenulata*
many days after removal of the nucleus. This certainly suggests a very
great stability for the mRNA's involved. However, it must be borne in

mind that the algal cells contain a chloroplast, and it might be this organelle, rather than the nucleus, which in *Acetabularia* controls the biosynthesis of the enzymes studied; chloroplasts of some plants have been shown to contain DNA (4). No such reservation need be made in the case of the continuance of protein synthesis for several hours after the enucleation of various animal cells (9, 28, 29). In the case of *E. coli*, too, it has been suggested that not all mRNA is as short-lived as that for β-galactosidase (7). The induced synthesis of β-galactosidase in *E. coli* is preferentially inhibited by streptomycin compared with the total synthesis of protein. It was inferred from the data obtained that the synthesis of all proteins requiring the continuous formation of labile mRNA will be inhibited by streptomycin under appropriate circumstances, while the residual incorporation of labeled amino acids into the protein, which continues in the presence of streptomycin, may depend on a relatively stable mRNA (7).

The variation in stability of different mRNA's in the same organism may thus be of significance as a means of investigating the basic mechanism of phenotypic expression, with important consequences, for example, in the field of cellular differentiation. We have recently obtained evidence which may be interpreted as supporting the concept of varying lability for different mRNA's, and we will consider the significance of this data from an evolutionary point of view.

Three strains of *E. coli* have been used: C600-1 ($i^+y^-z^+$) (obtained from Dr. A. B. Pardee); 300U ($i^+y^-z^+$) and 230U ($i^-y^-z^+$) (from Dr. J. Monod). The organisms were all cultured on M63 medium, an inorganic salts medium containing glycerol and thiamine (27), at 37°C in air. The inducers used for β-galactosidase were isopropylthio-β-D-galactopyranoside (IPTG) (usually at $5 \times 10^{-4} M$) and methylthio-β-D-galactopyranoside (TMG) ($10^{-3} M$). Samples of cell suspension for enzyme assay were removed from the culture flasks, violently agitated with toluene, and assayed for enzyme activity as described by Kepes (18). Units of enzyme activity will be expressed as millimicromoles of o-nitrophenyl-β-D-galactoside hydrolyzed per minute per milliliter of cell suspension at 37°C.

Inoculation of the bacterium into the M63 medium results in a logarithmic growth pattern as measured by increase of optical density at 650 mμ (Fig. 1). The doubling time during this phase of growth varies on different occasions between about 65 and 85 minutes. Eventually growth stops, and the optical density remains constant. If after an hour or more of being in the stationary phase of growth a portion of the culture is rapidly added to several volumes of fresh culture medium, logarithmic growth starts again with no detectable lag, the first sample for optical density measurement being taken about 30 seconds after dilution to allow for thorough mixing. Growth in this medium stops as a result of exhaustion of the glycerol used as carbon and energy source (Fig. 2); a very great excess of ammonium nitrogen is present.

Addition of an inducer of β-galactosidase to *E. coli* growing logarithmically typically results in the sudden onset of the appearance of enzyme activity some 2.5 to 3 minutes later (Fig. 3) (5, 25, 27). The time

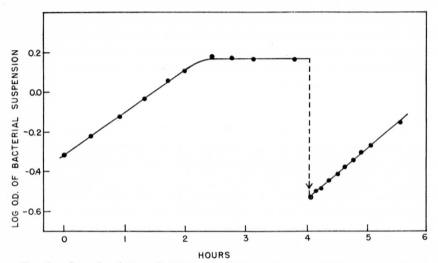

Fig. 1. Growth of *E. coli* C600-1 in M63 medium at 37°C. Optical density measured at 650 mμ in a Cary Model 14 spectrophotometer. At about 4 hours a portion of the stationary culture was diluted fivefold into fresh M63 medium.

required for the differential rate of enzyme synthesis (rate of enzyme synthesis versus rate of growth measured by optical density; 24) to increase from virtually zero to a constant value is very short, and the constant rate is always achieved within 3 minutes after the addition of inducer. However, if a culture in the stationary phase of growth is diluted into fresh medium already containing inducer (as in Fig. 1), a somewhat different kinetic course of enzyme synthesis is observed (Fig. 4). Although, as during normal logarithmic growth, the differential rate of enzyme synthesis begins to increase about 3 minutes after the first contact with inducer, the rate continues to increase for a considerable period and does not become constant until about 15 minutes have elapsed. Some variation is observed in the length of this period. Growth, however, is logarithmic from the time of dilution (Fig. 1). This finding suggests that an impairment of the enzyme induction and synthesis process has developed during the period of carbohydrate starva-

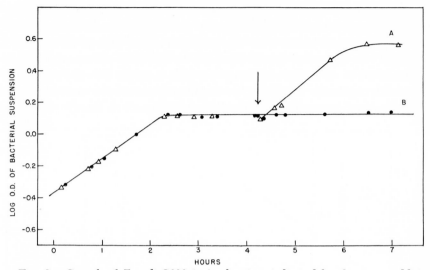

FIG. 2.   Growth of *E. coli* C600-1. At the time indicated by the arrow addition of glycerol (curve *A*) or ammonium sulfate (curve *B*) was made to the stationary culture.

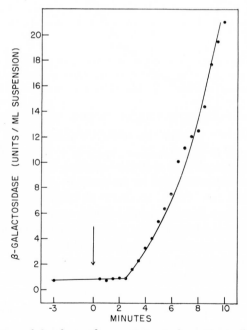

FIG. 3.   Induction of β-galactosidase activity in logarithmically growing *E. coli* C600-1 with TMG added as indicated by the arrow.

tion. Using Jacob and Monod's theory of induction (16), we might suppose that since the initial appearance of the enzyme is not delayed there
has been no interference with the initiation of DNA-dependent mRNA
synthesis. On the other hand, since the steady-state differential rate of
synthesis takes so long to become constant, it might be concluded that
essential components necessary for the over-all process of enzyme protein
synthesis have become depleted in the absence of a source of carbon

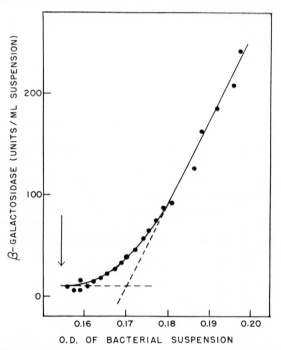

Fig. 4. Induction of β-galactosidase activity in *E. coli* 300U following dilution
of a stationary culture into fresh medium containing IPTG. Absorbance of culture
immediately after dilution indicated by the arrow.

and energy and that these are only slowly replaced. Such components
might be amino acids for protein synthesis or ribonucleotides for RNA
formation. It should be noted that dilution of a culture already growing
logarithmically into fresh medium containing inducer results in the characteristic 3-minute period to achieve a constant rate of synthesis (Fig. 5);
thus dilution per se is not responsible for the delay.

No absolute block to β-galactosidase synthesis develops during starvation which must first be overcome on the resumption of logarithmic
growth before enzyme induction can be effected. Such a block might be

envisaged as a consequence of catabolite repression (21) developing during starvation. However, the conditions of this starvation are completely reversed from those giving rise to catabolite repression; the latter effect is observed in conditions of carbohydrate surplus and nitrogen deficiency. Furthermore, β-galactosidase may be induced, albeit very slowly, during the starvation period itself (Fig. 6). Although the induction mechanism can be brought weakly into action during starvation, doing so does not potentiate enzyme synthesis during a subsequent re-

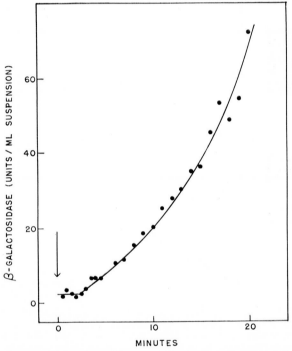

Fig. 5. Induction of β-galactosidase activity in *E. coli* 300U following dilution of an exponentially growing culture into fresh medium containing IPTG.

sumption of growth in the continued presence of inducer. This is true even if the inducer is added in the previous logarithmic phase of growth, hours before dilution takes place. Figure 7 illustrates an experiment in which stationary-state cells were diluted into fresh medium. The first contact with inducer in the upper curve was about 4 hours before dilution, 2.5 hours before the end of the earlier logarithmic phase. In the lower curve inducer was introduced at the time of dilution; in both cases the concentration of inducer was maintained constant at all times after it was first added to the cells. If no inducer was present before dilution, the differential rate of synthesis became constant about 14 minutes after dilution; when inducer was present before dilution, a constant rate of synthesis was reached about 18 minutes after dilution. From this we may conclude that decay of part of the enzyme synthesis mechanism takes place during starvation, and this would be consistent with the decay of labile mRNA when precursors and energy for its maintenance were not available.

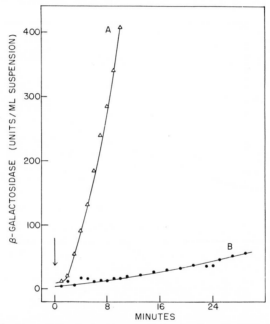

Fig. 6. Induction of β-galactosidase activity in *E. coli* C600-1 with IPTG: *A*, in exponentially growing culture; *B*, in stationary culture.

Freter and Ozawa (8) have shown that it is possible to obtain a second crop of bacteria by reinoculation into medium which had previously supported bacterial growth to stationary phase. The first crop of bacteria is removed by filtration or centrifugation, and these manipulations result in considerable aeration of the liquid. In this newly aerated condition the medium will support growth of a dilute culture which did not occur in the first very dense stationary culture. We have investigated the effects on induction of diluting a stationary culture into Millipore-filtered exhausted medium, the inducer being introduced at the time of dilution. Growth was indeed resumed at a very rapid rate with no lag (Fig. 8), the doubling time being only 24 minutes compared with 53 minutes for a control sample diluted into fresh medium. The rapid

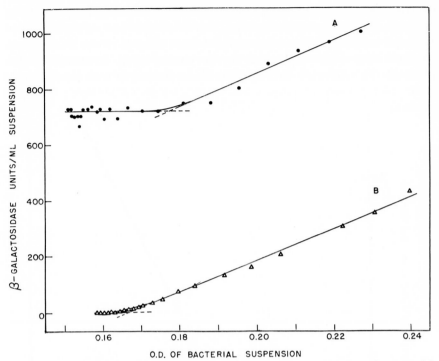

FIG. 7. Induction of β-galactosidase activity in *E. coli* C600-1 with IPTG following dilution from stationary phase into fresh medium: A, IPTG added 4 hours before dilution; B, IPTG added at time of dilution.

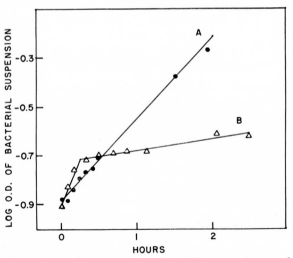

FIG. 8. Growth of *E. coli* C600-1 when diluted from stationary phase into fresh medium (A) or exhausted medium (B).

growth continued, however, for 15 minutes only, the doubling time then suddenly increasing to 362 minutes. The differential rate of enzyme synthesis became constant in exhausted medium (Fig. 9, curve *B*) in about the same time (16 minutes) as in the control (Fig. 9, curve *A*) (14 minutes). The delay of development of a constant rate of enzyme syn-

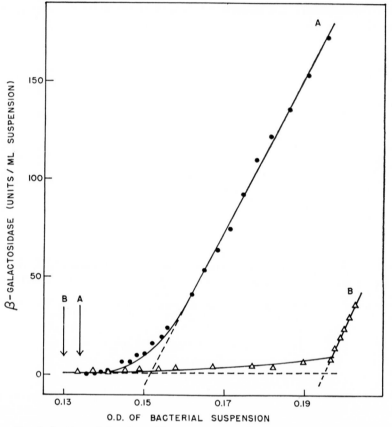

Fig. 9. Induction of β-galactosidase activity in the same experiment as shown in Fig. 8; in both cases IPTG added at time of dilution: *A*, fresh medium; *B*, exhausted medium. Arrows indicate absorbance of culture immediately after dilution.

thesis following dilution from a stationary state into fresh medium is therefore not the result of the need to overcome the effects of accumulation of an inhibitor in the medium as a result of growth.

Direct attempts to overcome a delay resulting from precursor deficiency by providing such precursors in the fresh medium at the time of dilution and introduction of the inducer were not effective in accelerating the attainment of a constant rate of synthesis. Neither the provision of enzymic hydrolyzate of casein (200 μg/ml) (Fig. 10), nor of a mixture (128 μg/ml each) of the 5′-diphosphates of adenosine, cytidine, guanosine, and uridine (Fig. 11), influenced the period required to achieve a constant differential rate of synthesis. While it is known that *E. coli* will concentrate amino acids from the medium (6), it is probable that nucleoside diphosphates are unable to penetrate through the cell membranes. Attempts were made to circumvent the barrier to nucleotides by

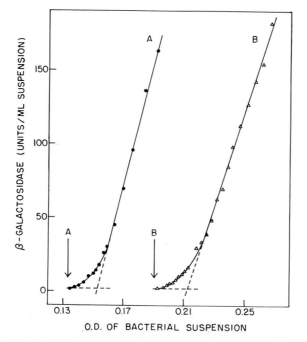

MUB-3986

Fig. 10.    Effect of casein hydrolysate on induction of β-galactosidase activity in *E. coli* C600-1 following dilution from stationary phase into fresh medium containing IPTG: A, control; B, plus casein hydrolysate (200 μg/ml).

supplying a mixture (50 μg/ml each) of adenosine, cytidine, guanosine, and uridine as free nucleosides. The result was rather unexpected (Fig. 12): in the presence of the nucleosides it took even longer (20 minutes) to reach a steady rate of synthesis than in the control (14 minutes), and the rate was only 20% of the control rate. This effect of the mixed nucleosides was probably related to some sort of catabolite repression and is being separately investigated. It must also be remembered that the free nucleosides are not normal metabolic intermediates in the biosynthesis of nucleotides.

As efforts to reduce the delay for constant enzyme synthesis were not successful, the approach was reversed and attempts were made to increase it by interfering with RNA synthesis. The inhibitor of choice of RNA synthesis, actinomycin D, is not active in *E. coli* (15), and it was therefore decided to use 6-azauracil, shown by Habermann (12) to inhibit RNA synthesis by being converted to 6-azauridine-5'-phosphate and blocking orotidylic acid decarboxylase, an enzyme in the biosyn-

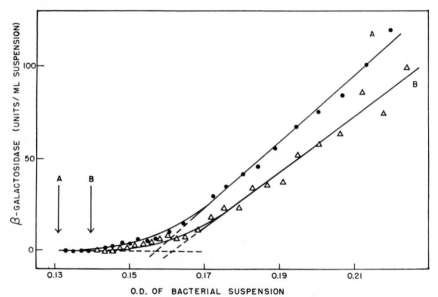

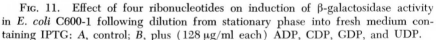

FIG. 11.   Effect of four ribonucleotides on induction of β-galactosidase activity in *E. coli* C600-1 following dilution from stationary phase into fresh medium containing IPTG: A, control; B, plus (128 µg/ml each) ADP, CDP, GDP, and UDP.

thetic pathway of pyrimidine ribotides. 6-Azauracil (25 µg/ml), added to a stationary culture 30 minutes before dilution, did not affect the immediate logarithmic increase of optical density of the culture after dilution into fresh medium still containing the same concentration of the inhibitor. However, about 44 minutes after dilution the doubling time suddenly increased from 56 to 160 minutes (Fig. 13). The differential rate of β-galactosidase synthesis in the presence of 6-azauracil was almost identical with that of the control for the first 27 minutes after dilution, the control rate becoming constant after 18 minutes. Thereafter in the period between 27 and 30 minutes the differential rate in the presence of 6-azauracil fell by 90% (Fig. 14). The relatively long time necessary for 6-azauracil to exert its effect precluded any inhibition of the initial increase in the rate of β-galactosidase synthesis. When it did be-

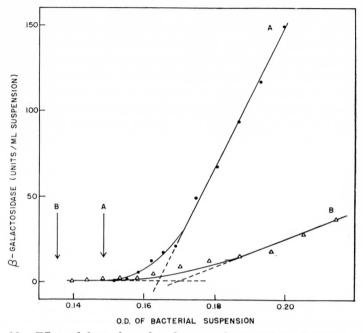

Fig. 12. Effect of four ribonucleosides on induction of β-galactosidase activity in *E. coli* C600-1 following dilution from stationary phase into fresh medium containing IPTG: A, control; B, plus (50 µg/ml each) adenosine, cytidine, guanosine, and uridine.

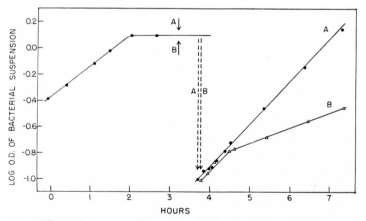

Fig. 13. Effect of 6-azauracil on growth of *E. coli* C600-1 following dilution from stationary phase to fresh medium: A, control; B, plus 6-azauracil (25 µg/ml). Azauracil added to B and water added to A as indicated by solid arrows; dilutions indicated by dashed arrows.

come effective it showed itself much more inhibitory to the synthesis of the inducible enzyme that it did toward growth in general, as illustrated by the large fall in the rate of *differential* enzyme synthesis. Addition of 6-azauracil to a logarithmically growing population similarly inhibited growth in about 30 minutes (Fig. 15), and enzyme synthesis a few minutes earlier (Fig. 16).

These data permit a number of conclusions to be reached concerning the response of the bacterial cell to a sudden transition from a stationary state of growth into fresh medium. The addition of inducer to a loga-

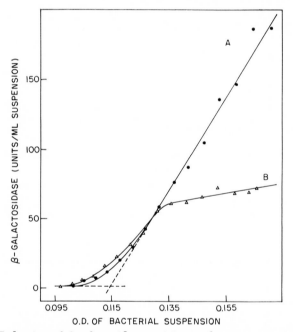

FIG 14.   Induction of β-galactosidase activity in the same experiment as shown in Fig. 13; in both cases IPTG added at time of dilution: A, control; B, plus 6-azauracil.

rithmically growing population results in a steady differential rate of enzyme synthesis being reached within 3 minutes (Fig. 3). This rate is maintained until growth stops owing to exhaustion of glycerol in the medium. In this condition of starvation mRNA specific for β-galactosidase is not readily synthesized, since addition of inducer during the stationary phase does not result in the immediate synthesis of enzyme when dilution takes place and the carbon and energy source again becomes plentiful. Pre-existing β-galactosidase mRNA breaks down during this stage, a conclusion reached because the continued presence of an inducer from a

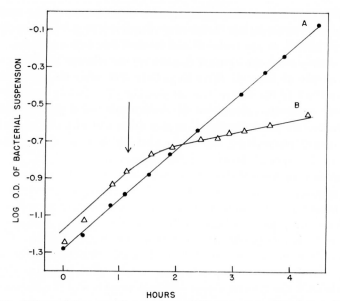

FIG. 15. Effect of 6-azauracil on exponentially growing cells of *E. coli* C600-1: *A*, control; *B*, 6-azauracil (25 μg/ml) added at arrow.

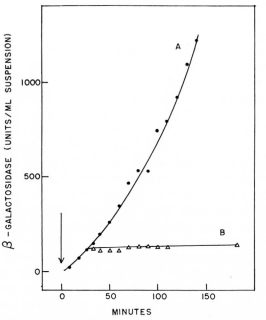

FIG. 16. Induction of β-galactosidase activity in the same experiment as shown in Fig. 15; IPTG added at arrow: *A*, control; *B*, 6-azauracil, added 2 minutes before IPTG.

previous period of enzyme synthesis also fails to ensure the synthesis of more enzyme immediately following dilution (Fig. 7). During starvation, then, mRNA is not formed, and labile mRNA decomposes.

Yet, with no lag, the optical density of the culture begins to increase logarithmically as soon as dilution occurs. We may thus pose two vital questions: (a) Is the lag in the attainment of a steady differential rate of enzyme synthesis related to the inducibility of β-galactosidase (i.e., the control of its synthesis by a regulator gene)? (b) What, in terms of various growth parameters, does a logarithmic increase immediately after dilution in the optical density of the culture signify?

If increase in optical density is related to growth, at least as far as protein synthesis is concerned, the mRNA's required to synthesize such protein must have survived from the previous growing period as, judged by the one for β-galactosidase, mRNA is not readily produced during starvation or immediately after dilution into fresh medium. Further, if β-galactosidase mRNA is unstable and must continuously be resynthesized to maintain enzyme production, while other proteins depend on stable mRNA's, the greater sensitivity to 6-azauracil of the β-galactosidase synthesis compared with growth becomes clear. 6-Azauracil eventually stops the formation of all mRNA. As the one for β-galactosidase synthesis is unstable, the synthesis of this protein rapidly stops. But other proteins, dependent on longer-lived mRNA's, are able to continue to be produced at a decreasing rate in the absence of mRNA transcription from DNA.

In the event that the above remarks on the instability of β-galactosidase mRNA and its lack of formation during starvation and immediately after dilution owing to a deficiency of precursors are correct, one would not expect to alter kinetics depending on mRNA stability by mutation of the regulator gene of the *lac* operon. Thus a corresponding $i^-$ strain of *E. coli* would also be expected to show a differential lag of β-galactosidase synthesis when it is diluted from stationary phase. This is indeed the case. There is no lag before the optical density of a constitutive culture, diluted from stationary phase into fresh medium, begins to increase logarithmically, but β-galactosidase formation shows the same sort of lag as in the inducible strain (Fig. 17). In this experiment the differential rate of synthesis was not constant until 42 minutes after dilution, though there was no lag in optical density increase. 6-Azauracil has an effect in the constitutive strain similar to that with the inducible: a zero rate of differential enzyme synthesis after 30 minutes (Fig. 17). In a logarithmically growing culture, too, 6-azauracil affects the constitutive strain as it affects the inducible: growth slows down (Fig. 18), and enzyme synthesis stops (Fig. 19) in about 30 minutes. It should be noted that the scatter of the experimental points is invariably greater in the constitutive experiments, as the proportional increase of enzyme activity for each minute of incubation is very much less than in the inducible strain shortly after induction is initiated.

An investigation was made of several aspects of growth following dilution in the presence and absence of 6-azauracil. In the first of these experiments (Fig. 20), the increase with time of the optical density of

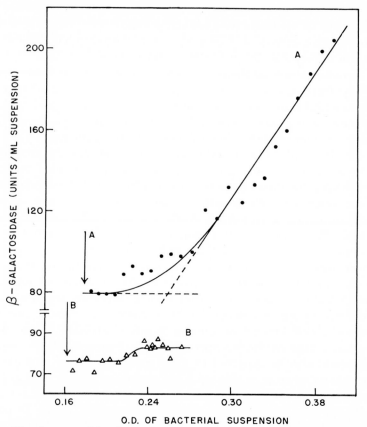

FIG. 17. Activity of β-galactosidase in *E. coli* 230U (*i⁻* constitutive) following dilution from stationary phase into fresh medium: A, control; B, plus 6-azauracil (25 µg/ml) added 30 minutes before dilution.

the culture was compared with the numbers of cells per milliliter and with the total volume of cellular material per milliliter of suspension. Cell number was measured in a suitably diluted aliquot of the culture with a Coulter particle counter (22). The size distribution of each population was obtained with a Coulter size distribution plotter, and the total volume of cells in the sample calculated in arbitrary units as the sum of the products of each channel number and the number of particles in that channel. An average cell volume was also calculated from these data. The results in Fig. 20 show that, in the absence of 6-azauracil, optical density increased logarithmically from the time of dilution as before, cell number showed no increase for 34 minutes and then increased logarithmically, while the total cell volume did not change for 19 minutes, when an exponential increase started. In the presence of 6-azauracil, the optical density increased rapidly for 30 minutes and then slowed down. There were low rates of increase of cell number and cell volume compared with the control, with delays of about 44 and 18 minutes, respec-

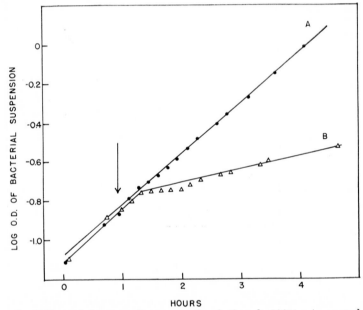

Fig. 18.    Effect of 6-azauracil on growth of *E. coli* 230U: A, control; B, 6-azauracil (25 μg/ml) added at arrow.

tively. Thus the exponential increase in optical density which starts immediately after dilution is directly related neither to the number of cells nor to the total volume of cells. This suggests that the optical density rise may result from an increase in the refractive index of the cells derived from an elevated internal level of certain macromolecules.

A second experiment was thus concerned with the levels of total DNA, RNA, and protein, again with and without 6-azauracil. For measurement of these substances, aliquots of the suspension were removed at intervals after resumption of growth into chilled trichloroacetic acid to give a final concentration of 6% trichloroacetic acid. Protein, DNA, and RNA were determined as described by Berrah and Konetzka (3). Since samples were collected initially at 2-minute intervals and very little increase was to be expected from one sample to the next, all volumetric measurements throughout this experiment were checked gravimetrically by using tared tubes, etc. The findings are presented in Fig. 21. As carefully as we can determine from the experimental data, there is in

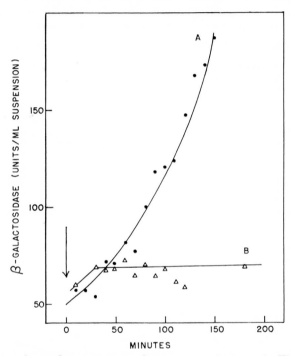

FIG. 19. β-Galactosidase activity in the same experiment as in Fig. 18: A, control; B, 6-azauracil (25 µg/ml) added at arrow.

the control series indeed no lag in the increase in protein (14), while a lag of 5.5 minutes was found for RNA and one of about 27 minutes for DNA. In the presence of 6-azauracil the initial lags for RNA and DNA were about the same as in the control, but production of these substances slowed down or stopped after 20 to 25 minutes. Protein increased very rapidly, and with no lag, for about 5 minutes, and then slowed down. The precise times reported in this experiment are certainly subject to appreciable error, but we see no way at this time of improving the accuracy of these experimental readings. It seemed desirable in addition to investigate the rate of formation of a particular identifiable protein, preferably a constitutive one, following dilution. Malic dehydrogenase was chosen, and this was determined by incubating toluene-treated cells with oxalacetate and NADPH$_2$ at 37°C in buffer at pH 7.4 and following the fall in optical density at 340 mμ with a Gilford Model 2000 Multiple Sample Absorbance Recorder. As with other measurements of the kinetics of formation of constitutive substances, considerable experimental scatter was found. Nevertheless the results shown in Fig. 22 demonstrate fairly

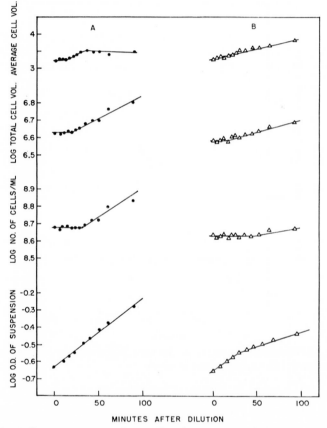

Fig. 20. Effect of 6-azauracil on cell enlargement and division following dilution of a stationary culture of *E. coli* C600-1 into fresh medium: Series *A*, control; series *B*, 6-azauracil (25 μg/ml) added 30 minutes before dilution.

convincingly that there is no lag in the increase in activity of this enzyme when the cells are placed in fresh medium. The line drawn in Fig. 22 was calculated by the least squares method to be the best fit for the points represented by solid circles; the open triangle points were excluded from the calculation.

All the evidence points, then, to the lag in β-galactosidase synthesis being due to a corresponding lag in the production of mRNA as a consequence of depletion of the nucleotide pools during starvation. Kepes (18) has divided the sequence of events between introduction of the inducer and appearance of active enzyme into six stages, and we may consider the β-galactosidase lag in these terms. Stages 1 and 2 concern

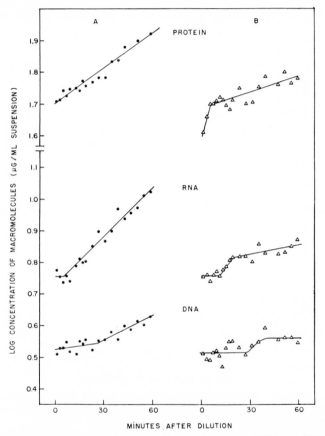

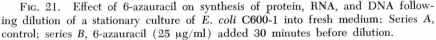

Fig. 21. Effect of 6-azauracil on synthesis of protein, RNA, and DNA following dilution of a stationary culture of *E. coli* C600-1 into fresh medium: Series *A*, control; series *B*, 6-azauracil (25 μg/ml) added 30 minutes before dilution.

the penetration of the inducer into the cell and its interaction with "repressor." These events cannot be responsible for the lag, since the constitutive strain, requiring no inducer, demonstrates the lag as markedly as does the inducible strain. Stages 5 and 6 refer to the synthesis of polypeptide using the information carried by mRNA and the establishment of secondary, tertiary, and quaternary structural characteristics associated with the enzymic activity of the protein. The lag cannot be ascribed to these phenomena, since other proteins, including malic dehydrogenase, are synthesized without lag, and no shortage of amino acids seems to result from starvation. We are thus left with stages 3 and 4: the transcription of DNA into mRNA and the transfer of the message to the ribosomes. The latter stage seems difficult to reconcile with the lag because there appears to be no hurdle to the transfer of

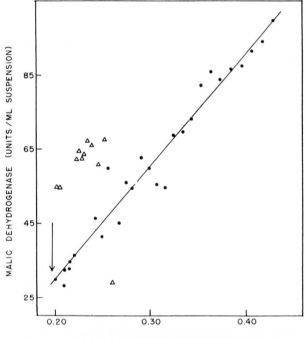

FIG. 22. Activity of malic dehydrogenase in *E. coli* C600-1 following dilution of a stationary culture into fresh medium. Open triangle points excluded from calculation of best-fitting straight line.

messages for other proteins to the ribosomes. Stage 3, then, remains the most likely origin of the lag, and this interpretation is supported by the lag in total RNA formation found experimentally (Fig. 21) and by the greater sensitivity of inducible enzyme formation compared with growth to agents interfering with RNA production. 6-Azauracil, as shown in the present study and by Habermann (12), inhibits the production of an inducible enzyme earlier and more severely than growth. The action of actinomycin D, as reported in the literature, is also in this direction. In

*Bacillus subtilis* the inducible formation of histidase is completely inhibited at 10 µg/ml (13), while at 0.2 µM actinomycin RNA synthesis is inhibited 90 to 95% and protein synthesis only 50 to 75%, and the base composition of the RNA produced does not resemble the normal base composition of *B. subtilis* RNA or DNA (15). The point of the latter observation was not lost on the authors. They remarked (15) that "the observation that RNA synthesis can be inhibited *in vivo* with only partial inhibition of protein synthesis . . . raises some questions concerning the nature of 'messenger' RNA, which, according to Jacob and Monod (16), should possess a short half-life. A possible explanation is that not all 'messenger' RNA molecules are short-lived but that some may act catalytically for a long time after the synthesis of new messenger is interrupted." We conclude that if the lag for inducible enzyme formation is to be ascribed to a lag in RNA production, including mRNA, and not associated with the induction process itself, then the absence of lag for other proteins reflects the continued presence of functional mRNA for these proteins remaining from the previous growth period. The latter mRNA is therefore not labile.

The evolutionary consequences of differential mRNA stability are intriguing if we consider that mRNA for inducible enzymes is labile and that for constitutive enzymes is stable. The high rates of formation and decay of inducible messenger give the cell a means of responding very sensitively to environmental changes by adapting its content of enzymes. This may well have become superfluous for more basic enzymes which need always to be present in about the same quantities, irrespective of the external environment. Such enzymes would most satisfactorily be truly constitutive because they would always be made whenever the cell was growing. Their mRNA's would similarly always need to be present, and no advantage would accrue to a cell which retained an inducible-type regulatory mechanism which was always switched on during growth. Rather this might be expected to be a disadvantage, resulting as it would in the continuous expenditure of energy to produce mRNA which was just as rapidly decomposed. We might expect that in evolutionary time such a disadvantage would have been selected against, and inducible control and labile mRNA for constitutive proteins to have died out in strains exposed to evolutionary pressure. The intracellular balance of constitutive enzymes might now be controlled in the manner proposed by Pardee and Beckwith (26). In the laboratory, where regulatory control can be removed by genetic mutation, we might still expect artificial constitutive proteins with short-lived mRNA, and this indeed appears to be the case with $i^-$ mutants of the *lac* operon in *E. coli*.

This leads to further questions concerning the differences in structure between stable and labile mRNA which permits one type to be destroyed but not the other. This, of course, is bound up further with the reasons for the apparent stability of the other forms of RNA which do not have a messenger function. Indeed the explanations of stability differences may be not so much in the differences of structure of the molecules themselves but perhaps in the different environments within the over-all cell structure in which they normally occur, and the varying spectrum of hydrolytic and other enzymes to which they are exposed. One way in which the difference between the short-lived and the long-lived molecules might be determined would be in their degree of association with particular organelles, especially the ribosomes. Thus, those types of mRNA which for some reason remain intimately a part of the ribosomes would be expected to resist the intracellular RNase much more than the free-living messenger molecules. The transition, then, from short to long life would involve the degree of association with the ribosomal protein and lipid.

If in evolutionary terms a change from inducible regulation to constitutive production of a protein, or vice versa, eventually results in a change in stability of the corresponding mRNA, we might expect that on occasion the cell has had to pay a price for an advantage gained. An alteration in stability would be expected ultimately to be dependent on a change in base sequence. This change might have no consequence other than a change in stability control, either directly or indirectly through the binding with ribosomes. On the other hand, the change might result sometimes in the protein's also having a slightly altered structure, an effect which in some cases might lead to enhanced activity of the protein and in other instances to diminished effectiveness. Evolutionary pressure in such a situation might lead to a whole series of compromises, from a sacrifice of the preferential means of control of biosynthesis, through the retention of mRNA with atypical stability for the type of biosynthetic control being used, to the production of a protein molecule which does not possess the most effective structure for the catalytic or other function which it performs. The testing of such ideas must await the development of more refined techniques for measuring the levels of many specific mRNA's, for determining nucleic acid structure, and for understanding how structure and function are intimately related in the nucleic acids and proteins.

### ACKNOWLEDGMENT

The preparation of this paper was sponsored by the U.S. Atomic Energy Commission.

## REFERENCES

1. ATTARDI, G., NAONO, S., GROS, F., BRENNER, S., AND JACOB, F., *Compt. Rend.* **255**, 2303 (1962).
2. ATTARDI, G., NAONO, S., GROS, F., BUTTIN, G., AND JACOB, F., *Compt. Rend.* **265**, 805 (1963).
3. BERRAH, G., AND KONETZKA, W. A., *J. Bacteriol.*, **83**, 738 (1962).
4. BIGGINS, J., AND PARK, R. B., *Nature*, **203**, 425 (1964).
5. BOEZI, J. A., AND COWIE, D. B., *Biophys. J.*, **1**, 639 (1961).
6. BRITTEN, R. J., AND MCCLURE, F. T., *Bacteriol. Rev.* **26**, 292 (1962).
7. ENGELBERG, H., AND ARTMAN, M., *Biochim. Biophys. Acta*, **80**, 256 (1964).
8. FRETTER, R., AND OZAWA, A., *J. Bacteriol.*, **86**, 904 (1963).
9. GOLDSTEIN, L., MICOU, J., AND CROCKER, T. T., *Biochim. Biophys. Acta*, **45**, 82 (1960).
10. GORMAN, J., TARUO, P., LABERGE, M., AND HALVORSON, H., *Biochem. Biophys. Res. Commun.*, **15**, 43 (1964).
11. GROS, F., *Biochem. J.*, **90**, 21P (1964).
12. HABERMANN, V., *Biochim. Biophys. Acta*, **49**, 204 (1961).
13. HARTWELL, L. H., AND MAGASANIK, B., *J. Mol. Biol.*, **7**, 401 (1963).
14. HERSHEY, A. D., *Proc. Soc. Exptl. Biol. Med.*, **38**, 127 (1938).
15. HURWITZ, J., FURTH, J. J., MALAMY, M., AND ALEXANDER, M., *Proc. Natl. Acad. Sci. U.S.*, **48**, 1222 (1962).
16. JACOB, F., AND MONOD, J., *J. Mol. Biol.*, **3**, 318 (1961).
17. KARSTRÖM, H., Uber die Enzymbildung in Bakterien, Thesis, Helsinki, 1930.
18. KEPES, A., *Biochim. Biophys. Acta*, **76**, 293 (1963).
19. LEE, N., AND ENGLESBERG, E., *Proc. Natl. Acad. Sci. U.S.*, **50**, 696 (1963).
20. LEVINTHAL, C., KEYNAN, A., AND HIGA, A., *Proc. Natl. Acad. Sci. U.S.*, **48**, 1631 (1962).
21. MAGASANIK, B., *in* "Informational Macromolecules" (H. J. Vogel, V. Bryson and J. O. Lampen, eds.), p. 271, Academic Press, New York and London, 1963.
22. MATTERN, C. F. T., BRACKETT, F. S., AND OLSON, B. J., *J. Appl. Phys.*, **10**, 56 (1957).
23. MCCARTHY, B. J., AND BOLTON, E. T., *J. Mol. Biol.*, **8**, 184 (1964).
24. MONOD, J., PAPPENHEIMER, A. M., JR., AND COHEN-BAZIRE, G., *Biochim. Biophys. Acta*, **9**, 648 (1952).
25. NAKADA, D., AND MAGASANIK, B., *J. Mol. Biol.*, **8**, 105 (1964).
26. PARDEE, A. B., AND BECKWITH, J. R., *in* "Informational Macromolecules" (H. J. Vogel, V. Bryson, and J. O. Lampen, eds.), p. 255, Academic Press, New York and London, 1963.
27. PARDEE, A. B., AND PRESTIDGE, L., *Biochim. Biophys. Acta*, **49**, 77 (1961).
28. PRESCOTT, D. M., *J. Biophys. Biochem. Cytol.*, **6**, 203 (1959).
29. PRESCOTT, D. M., *Exptl. Cell. Res.*, **19**, 29 (1960).
30. SPENCER, T., AND HARRIS, H., *Biochem. J.*, **91**, 282 (1964).

# The Relation of Ribosomal RNA
# to the Genome[1]

S. Spiegelman and S. A. Yankofsky

*University of Illinois,*
*Department of Microbiology,*
*Urbana, Illinois*

## Introduction

The Watson-Crick (53) model implies that in the replication of DNA each strand of the duplex serves as the template for the formation of a complementary copy. It is clear in retrospect that this in turn suggested a simple genetic transcription mechanism involving the synthesis of complementary RNA copies of the DNA. Nevertheless, some time elapsed before this implication was publicly proposed. The reasons for this lag are not hard to find. Comparison of the base compositions of the total RNA from cells of widely different base compositions did not encourage a belief in any such simple relation between RNA and its homologous DNA. In the extensive survey of Belozersky and Spirin (3) a slight correlation between the two was detected, indicating that only a comparatively minor component of the cellular RNA could possess a base composition similar to that of homologous DNA.

Examination of the RNA in a number of rather unrelated organisms revealed a surprisingly uniform picture. Three major components are universally found, and in bacteria they have sedimentation coefficients of 23S, 16S, and 4S. The 23S and 16S varieties are found in the ribosomes (Kurland, 24) and constitute approximately 85% of the total cellular RNA. If attention is confined to purified ribosomal RNA, even the slight correlation observed by Belozersky and Spirin disappears (Spiegelman, 47; Woese, 54). It is evident that the presence in bulk of this noncorrelating species of RNA served as a deterrent to many who might otherwise have been willing to predict the obvious.

Proof that the translatable RNA message fraction was complementary

[1] The experiments performed in the authors' laboratory were supported by Public Health Service Research Grant CA-01094 from the National Cancer Institute and a grant from the National Science Foundation.

to homologous RNA was first obtained with the DNA viruses by the use of DNA–RNA hybridization (Hall and Spiegelman, 19). This was followed by a similar demonstration for normal bacteria (Gros *et al.*, 18; Hayashi and Spiegelman, 20).

With these facts established it became of pressing importance to decide on the relation of the ribosomal RNA to the message fraction, since without this information the existence of a *unique* message fraction could not be rigorously concluded. For these and other obvious reasons, it became mandatory to undertake the design and performance of experiments which could resolve the issues involved. Essentially we wanted to know the answers to the following questions:

(1) Does DNA contain sequences complementary to ribosomal RNA?

(2) If so, how many are there per genome?

(3) Are the sequences of the 16S and 23S species the same or different?

(4) If there are many sequences, are they all clustered in the same region, or are they scattered?

As will be seen, much of the relevant information emerged from molecular hybridization in experiments which posed severe challenges to this test of sequence complementarity. In describing the experiments and the results obtained, we shall take the opportunity to detail the technical difficulties encountered in these and similar experiments. We shall also consider the devices initially employed to overcome them as well as more recent simpler solutions.

### The Question of Sequence Complementarity between Ribosomal RNA and Homologous DNA

Although clearly not exhaustive or mutually exclusive, two alternatives could be entertained for the origin of ribosomal RNA. One would assume generation by a DNA-dependent reaction, and the other would invoke a synthetic mechanism independent of DNA. The fact that the base composition of the ribosomal RNA shows no correlative tendency with homologous DNA is quite irrelevant to a choice between the two hypotheses. As was pointed out (47), the presumed DNA segment involved might be so small as to constitute a statistically inadequate sample of the over-all base composition. Further, only one of the two strands might be copied in this region.

It was because we posed the problem in the form of these two alternatives that we were led to consider the following question, pertinent to a decision and amenable to experimental resolution: *Does DNA contain a sequence complementary to homologous ribosomal RNA?* The obvious approach to an answer is to employ the hybridization technique using radioactively labeled material as developed by Hall and Spiegelman (19). Hybrid structures could then be identified by equilibrium centrifugation in density gradients of CsCl or by some of the other devices developed later.

The technical difficulties inherent in using hybridization to establish the existence of complementarity between ribosomal RNA and some sequence in the DNA have been discussed in some detail by Spiegelman (47). The major complications stem from the numerology of the situation. For example, the 23S RNA component of the ribosomes is $1.1 \times 10^6$ in molecular weight, so that, even if a specific complex were formed, it might involve as little as 0.02% of the DNA available in the genome of *Escherichia coli*. One is therefore faced with the problem of designing experiments which will detect hybridization at this level.

It is obvious that, unless the experiment is designed to attain this level of sensitivity, a negative answer is meaningless. This is clearly the case in earlier attempts (47) to detect hybridizations between ribosomal RNA and DNA, which failed. However, as was pointed out then, the specific activity of the RNA employed was so low that complexes could well have been missed, even if they had occurred and involved only 0.1% of the DNA.

Raising the sensitivity of the experiment can theoretically be accomplished by increasing the specific activity of the RNA used in the hybridization to suitable levels. Indeed, in principle, the test can be made definitive in both the positive and the negative sense. If the sensitivity were great enough to detect 0.01% of the DNA, and no hybrid structure were found, then the conclusion could be drawn with confidence that the relevant sequences do not exist in the DNA.

However, magnification of the sensitivity of hybrid detection by these means carries with it the attendant danger that complexes will be observed which are irrelevant to the question being examined. Apparent "hybrids" might represent any one of the following: (a) complexes between DNA and small amounts of RNA messages contaminating the ribosomal RNA preparations; (b) mechanical trapping of small amounts of ribosomal RNA in the strands of DNA; (c) partial hybridization resulting from accidental coincidences of complementarity over short sequences.

In view of these possible complications, the presence of labeled RNA accompanying the DNA in an equilibrium density centrifugation must be supplemented with independent information which establishes that the RNA found is indeed ribosomal and that it is specifically hybridized to the DNA.

## Preparation of Pure Radioactive Ribosomal RNA

Because of the polydisperse size distribution of the message fraction (19, 32, 44), there was little hope of physically eliminating it from the ribosomal material by either centrifugation or column chromatography. To obtain pure labeled ribosomal RNA, advantage was taken of the high turnover rate of RNA messages. Cells were grown for several generations in the presence of radioactive RNA precursors ($P^{32}$- or $H^3$-uridine) so that maximal labeling resulted, and then the growth was allowed to continue in the absence of the radioisotope. During this "chasing" period, radioactive message is degraded and irreversibly incorporated into newly synthesized ribosomal and sRNA fractions. Some dilution of the label in the ribosomal RNA would, of course, occur. However, this can be readily compensated for by ensuring an adequate initial level of labeling. Contamination of the radioactive ribosomal RNA preparations by non-radioactive message would be irrelevant to our purpose, since hybrid detection is achieved solely on the basis of the labeled RNA found in the complex.

Figure 1 compares the sucrose sedimentation patterns of two uniformly labeled and chased RNA preparations to that of an unchased "step-down" pulse (19) material. The radioactivity profiles show that, unlike the pulse preparation in Fig. 1C, the uniformly labeled preparations (Fig. 1A, $H^3$-RNA of *E. coli;* and Fig. 1B, $P^{32}$-RNA of *Pseudomonas aeruginosa*) track perfectly with the optical density profile in the ribosomal region. It would appear that the procedure adopted does, in fact, yield ribosomal RNA which is quite free from contamination with unstable radioactive RNA. Pooling the fractions indicated by the arrows in Figs. 1A and 1B yields pure 16S and 23S ribosomal RNA preparations. To obtain RNA message uncontaminated with ribosomal and soluble RNA, the indicated 8 to 12S region fractions of Fig. 1C are pooled for use.

## Base Composition of the RNA Complexed to DNA

In preliminary experiments, it was established that complex formation occurred between ribosomal RNA preparations isolated as above and homologous denatured DNA. Although there were excellent reasons for believing that the RNA so complexed was ribosomal in origin, it was nevertheless necessary to rule out the possibility that trace message RNA was involved. Base compositional analysis of the complexed RNA was therefore undertaken. For this purpose, *Pseudomonas aeruginosa* was chosen, since the base compositions of its ribosomal and message varieties are readily distinguished (52% versus 64% GC). P³²-labeled 23S RNA from *Pseudomonas aeruginosa* was heated and slow-cooled with homologous denatured DNA, and the reaction mixture was cen-

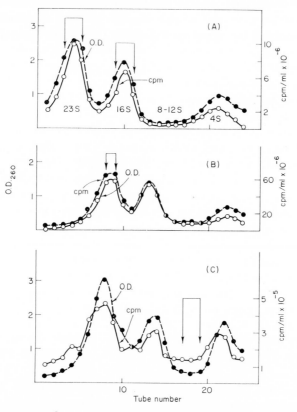

Fig. 1. Sucrose gradient separation of total cellular RNA. Centrifugation was carried out at 25,000 rpm and 10° to 15°C for 12 hours in each case. The arrows denote the fractions pooled for experimental use. A, uniformly labeled *E. coli* H³-RNA: 1550 μg having 6.4 × 10⁷ cpm in 1 ml of buffer was loaded on top of the gradient; 1.2-ml fractions were collected. B, uniformly labeled *Ps. aeruginosa* P³²-RNA: 728 μg having 6.1 × 10⁸ cpm loaded in 2 ml of buffer; 1.2-ml fractions were collected. C, step-down pulse labeled *E. coli* H³-RNA: 1750 μg having 8 × 10⁶ cpm loaded in 1 ml of buffer; 1.2-ml fractions were collected (Yankofsky and Spiegelman, 58).

trifuged to equilibrium in cesium chloride. In this experiment, a high concentration of single-stranded DNA was used to ensure that as much as possible of the RNA would be complexed. The resulting density gradient profile is shown in Fig. 2. It is clear that a considerable portion of the input RNA has become complexed to the DNA and moved into the DNA density region. This fact already argues against the supposition that only a minor contaminating component in the ribosomal RNA fraction is responsible for the complex observed.

The fact that there are no detectable alkali-stable radioactive materials present in any part of the density gradient eliminates the possibility of ascribing the apparent hybrid to DNA in the preparation.

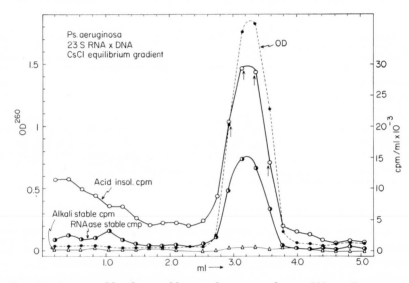

Fig. 2. Cesium chloride equilibrium density gradient: 800 µg *Ps. aeruginosa* heat-denatured DNA + 2.95 µg 23S-P³²-RNA (6 × 10⁵ cpm/µg) per milliliter in TMS slow-cooled from 55° to 34°C. The duration of the centrifuge run at 33,000 rpm and 25°C was 72 hours; 0.21-ml fractions were collected and diluted in 1.1 ml TM buffer. Aliquots were directly taken for digestion with 5 µg RNase per milliliter at 37°C for 30 minutes or 0.3 M NaOH at 30°C for 20 hours (Yankofsky and Spiegelman, 55).

It will be noted that the complex exhibits resistance to RNase digestion. The labeled material external to the hybrid region is sensitive to RNase, whereas the RNA in the region of the density is resistant. This is a characteristic of properly hybridized RNA (19), a feature which will be examined in much further detail below.

We now turn our attention to the question of whether the hybridized material is indeed ribosomal. To make completely certain, an analysis of the base composition of the pooled fractions indicated by the arrows in Fig. 2 was completed. The results of this analysis and a companion duplicate experiment are summarized in Table I. Comparison of the base compositions recorded leads to the conclusion that the RNA found in the DNA region of Fig. 2 is ribosomal.

The fact that more than 50% of the RNA actually entered the complex and the agreement in base composition both lend weight to the conclusion that the complex seen in Fig. 2 is a hybrid between DNA and ribosomal RNA.

TABLE I

BASE COMPOSITION OF *Pseudomonas* RNA HYBRIDIZED TO HOMOLOGOUS DNA[a]

| Nucleic acid | Moles per cent | | | | %GC | Pu/Pyr |
|---|---|---|---|---|---|---|
| | C | A | U(T) | G | | |
| Hybrid RNA: Expt. 1 | 19.3 | 25.4 | 21.1 | 34.2 | 53.5 | 1.48 |
| Expt. 2 | 21.0 | 25.8 | 20.4 | 32.8 | 53.8 | 1.42 |
| Ribosomal RNA | 22.4 | 26.8 | 20.7 | 30.3 | 53.3 | 1.30 |
| RNA messages | 30.3 | 20.9 | 19.0 | 29.8 | 60.1 | 1.02 |
| DNA | 32.0 | 18 | 18 | 32.0 | 64 | 1.00 |

[a] The material corresponding to experiment 1 came from the pooled fractions indicated by arrows in Fig. 1. Experiment 2 was an independently repeated hybridization. The base composition was determined chromatographically as described previously. The values for ribosomal RNA and informational RNA are those found earlier for *Ps. aeruginosa* (Yankofsky and Spiegelman, 55).

## The Specificity of the Complexes

It was next necessary to examine the specificity of the combination between the ribosomal RNA and the homologous DNA. We wished initially to avoid challenging with DNA which might conceivably contain ribosomal sequences, however remotely related they might be to those of bacteria, and as a consequence used viral DNA (bacteriophages T2 and T5). The ribosomal RNA used in these trials was a tritiated 23S preparation from *E. coli*. To minimize competition between DNA–RNA formation and DNA self-annealing, the incubation was carried out by holding the mixtures at 40°C for 36 hours. Under these conditions, homologous mixtures of *E. coli* single-stranded DNA and $H^3$-23S RNA complexed very well, as is evident by Fig. 3C. It is, however, clear from Figs. 3A and 3B that no complex formation could be detected between the ribosomal RNA of *E. coli* and the DNA of either of T2 or T5.

These findings clearly eliminated the possibility of mechanical trapping of RNA strands by DNA as a source of confusion. The results would appear to support the conclusion that the complex observed between homologous RNA and DNA is indeed specific and reflects a requirement for sequence complementarity. In view of the fact that the genome of T2 is approximately one-tenth that of *E. coli*, the number of different sorts of sequences being challenged is not so disparate in the homologous and heterologous situations. Hence, the different outcomes cannot readily be ascribed to a significantly richer variety of sequences in the bacterial as compared with the viral DNA.

It was of obvious interest to extend this examination to heterologous DNA, which would be expected to contain ribosomal cistrons. We started

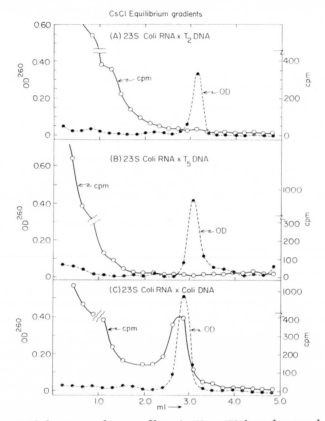

FIG. 3. CsCl density gradient profiles: *A*, 76 µg T2 heat-denatured DNA + 3.4 µg *E. coli* 23S-H³-RNA (4.8 × 10⁴ cpm/µg) per milliliter in TMS. *B*, 76 µg T5 heat-denatured DNA + 3.4 µg *E. coli* 23S-H³-RNA (4.8 × 10⁴ cpm/µg) per milliliter in TMS. *C*, 84 µg *E. coli* heat-denatured DNA + 3.4 µg 23S-H³-RNA (4.8 × 10⁴ cpm/µg) per milliliter in TMS. All three reaction mixtures were held at 40°C for 36 hours. Centrifugation was at 33,000 rpm and 25°C for 72 hours (Yankofsky and Spiegelman, 55).

by looking at material rather far removed from bacteria, and the results obtained will be illustrated with those found with calf thymus DNA. Figure 4 describes the results of a cesium chloride gradient density centrifugation of a hybridization between *E. coli* 23S RNA and heat-denatured calf thymus DNA. It is evident that a significant amount of an apparent hybrid formed. It should further be noted that very little (less than 1%) of this sort of complex is observed unless the mixture of the two nucleic acids is heated and slow-cooled, implying a requirement for hydrogen bond formation.

The existence of this heterologous complex makes it clear that the appearance of RNA in the DNA density region with one type of DNA and not another cannot per se be accepted as evidence of the extent

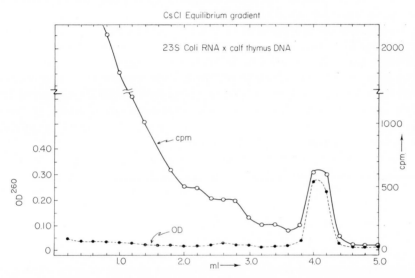

Fig. 4. CsCl density gradient profile: 84 μg heat-denatured calf thymus DNA + 3.4 μg 23S-H³-RNA (4.8 × 10⁴ cpm/μg) per milliliter in TMS; slow-cooled from 55° to 32°C. Centrifugation was at 33,000 rpm and 25°C for 74 hours (Yankofsky and Spiegelman, 55).

of the sequence correspondence. Even comparatively short stretches of matching complementarity might be sufficient to complex the RNA tightly enough to be carried with the DNA in a density gradient. This could imply that we are looking at the residues of sequence complementarity which remained in the course of the evolution of an original gene. In any case, other criteria must be developed if we are to interpret such complexes.

*Sensitivity to Ribonuclease as a Specificity Test of the Extent of Hybrid Formation*

It is important to recognize that we are here trying to distinguish between the following two possibilities:

1. Partial hybridization involving small scattered complementary segments of the corresponding sequences.

2. Complete hybridization between ribosomal RNA and a homologous complementary sequence in DNA.

Our previous studies would suggest the use of nucleolytic enzymes as a convenient differentiating device. The first possibility would predict that a major portion of each RNA strand in the complex is not actually involved in the hydrogen bonding and should therefore be accessible to degradation with ribonuclease. Complete hybrids involving essentially the entire sequence would be resistant.

To increase the sharpness of distinction, preliminary experiments were carried out first with T2-specific RNA and DNA to determine the minimal ionic strengths required to maintain the integrity of extensive RNA–DNA hybrids. This was done to permit enzyme treatment at near optimal conditions for RNase activity and to encourage instability of partial hybrids involving only short nucleotide sequences. As a result of these exploratory experiments, procedures for testing RNA–DNA complexes for RNase sensitivity were finally evolved (55).

To test whether the nucleolytic enzymes can distinguish between homologous and heterologous complexes, incubations were carried out with E. coli 23S RNA mixed with heat-denatured DNA of E. coli or of thymus. The hybrid regions of the cesium chloride gradients are shown in Figs. 5A and 5D, and it is clear that in both cases considerable amounts of RNA are found in the DNA density region.

In all tests for nucleolytic sensitivity, free ribosomal RNA was included as an internal control to monitor the enzyme activity. The control RNA was labeled with $P^{32}$, and the hybridized RNA with tritium, or vice versa. Examination of the data in Fig. 5 reveals an obvious difference between the sensitivities of the two complexes. In the case of homologous hybridization (Fig. 5C), there is a loss of counts in the first 5 minutes, but the residue is virtually completely resistant to RNase. On the other hand, in the case of the heterologous complex of thymus

---

Fig. 5. A, apparent hybrid in DNA region after CsCl density gradient centrifugation: 114 μg E. coli heat-denatured DNA + 3.1 μg E. coli 23S-$P^{32}$-RNA ($1.2 \times 10^5$ cpm/μg) per milliliter in TMS slow-cooled from 55° to 35°C. Centrifugation was at 33,000 rpm and 25°C for 72 hours. B, resistance of apparent hybrid (A) to digestion with RNase + DNase (A). C, RNase resistance of apparent hybrid (A). D, apparent hybrid in DNA region after CsCl density gradient centrifugation: 100 μg calf thymus heat-denatured DNA + 2.72 μg E. coli 23S-$H^3$-RNA ($4.8 \times 10^4$ cpm/μg) per milliliter in TMS, slow-cooled from 55° to 35°C. Centrifugation was at 33,000 rpm and 25°C for 97 hours. E, resistance of apparent hybrid shown in (D) to digestion with both RNase and DNase. F, resistance of apparent hybrid (D) to RNase digestion (Yankofsky and Spiegelman, 55).

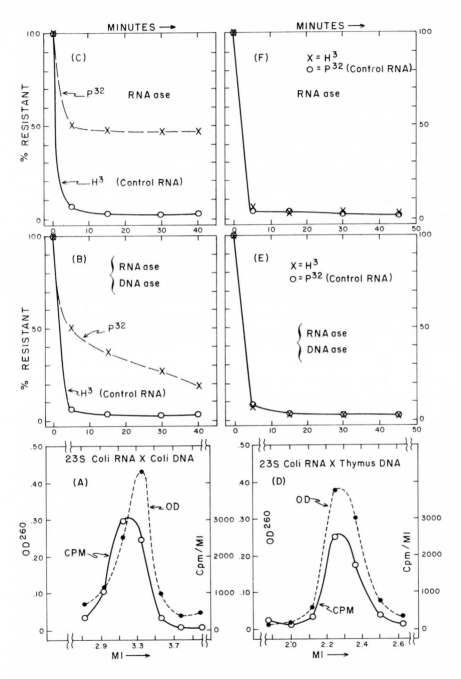

DNA with *E. coli* ribosomal RNA (Fig. 5F), it is impossible to distinguish the sensitivity of the apparently complexed RNA from that of the internal RNA control.

If we examine the sensitivity to the combined action of RNase and DNase, we see that essentially the same pattern is obtained. Again, in the case of the homologous hybrid (Fig. 5B), there is a rapid loss of counts in the first 5 minutes, bending off again at the 50% resistant residue. This is followed by a slow (3% of the free RNA) destruction of the hybridized RNA. Apparently, the presence of both enzymes exposes the hybrid material to a double jeopardy which makes complete stability impossible. Turning to the material derived from the heterologous incubation (Fig. 5E), we find again no detectable distinction between the sensitivity of the free $P^{32}$-labeled RNA and the apparently hybridized tritium-containing material.

It is evident from the experiments described that nuclease sensitivity at the ionic strengths employed permits a ready distinction between specific hybridization involving long sequences and the partial pairing of short segments. Density centrifugations to detect complexes combined with nuclease sensitivity tests have yielded completely consistent findings in examinations of the specificity of hybridization between DNA and RNA.

THE LENGTH OF THE DNA SEGMENT COMPLEMENTARY TO RIBOSOMAL RNA

The experiments just described lead to a number of testable predictions. Thus, the ratio of RNA to DNA in the specific complex should approach a maximum value at levels indicating the involvement of a minor fraction of the DNA in the specific ribonuclease-resistant complex. Further, the value at which the DNA saturates should provide a measure of the length of the DNA complementary to ribosomal RNA. Finally, nonribosomal RNA should not compete for the same sites.

The measurement of the saturation plateau requires the performance of experiments involving the following steps:

1. Mixtures containing fixed amounts of heat-denatured DNA and varying amounts of labeled ribosomal RNA are subjected to hybridization.

2. The resulting mixtures are then subjected to equilibrium density centrifugations in cesium chloride solutions to separate free RNA from that which is complexed to DNA.

The sorts of complexes seen are exemplified by the two cases depicted in Fig. 6. At the lower input level, most of the RNA in the reaction mixture is complexed to DNA. As is evident by a comparison of the two cases, the proportion of the input fixed decreases as the concentration of RNA is increased.

From our previous experience, it might be expected that binding involving coincidences over small regions will inevitably complicate such experiments, particularly at the higher concentrations of RNA. Fortu-

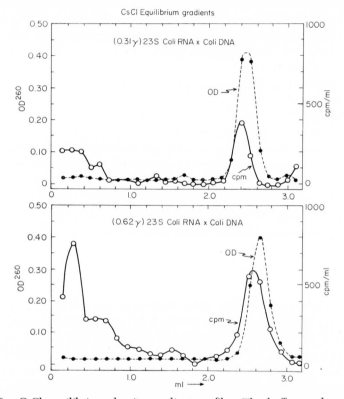

FIG. 6. CsCl equilibrium density gradient profiles. The buffer used was TMSV (0.03 $M$ Tris, pH 7.3; 0.001 $M$ MgCl$_2$; 0.3 $M$ NaCl; 0.005 $M$ EDTA). Both samples contained 71 µg of heat-denatured *E. coli* DNA per milliliter. The upper contained 0.31 µg and the lower contained 0.62 µg of P[32]-23S RNA (6.7 × 10[4] cpm/µg) of *E. coli*. Reaction mixtures were slow-cooled (about 13 hours) from 55° to 33°C. Mixtures were then brought to a density of 1.73 with CsCl and a total volume of 3 ml. Centrifugation was at 33,000 rpm and 25°C for 52 hours (Yankofsky and Spiegelman, 56).

nately, one can use ribonuclease sensitivity to distinguish between extensive and limited complexes. Fractions in the hybrid regions of the density gradient were pooled, dialyzed, and exposed to ribonuclease under standard conditions. The results obtained for four levels of H[3]-RNA are detailed in Fig. 7. In each case, free P[32]-labeled RNA was included as an internal control in the reaction mixture. The behavior of only one control is shown, since they are all identical. It will be seen that the free RNA is virtually completely solubilized in 5 minutes, whereas the tritium-labeled RNA from the hybrid regions exhibits RNase-resistant residues of varying percentages. The data shown in Fig. 7 are in agreement with what could have been expected from increasing amounts of limited complexing at higher concentration levels of RNA. The greater the input of RNA, the larger is the proportion of ribonuclease sensitive counts in the hybrid region.

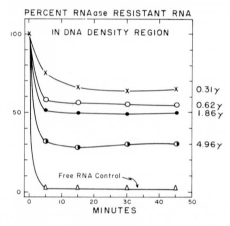

Fig. 7.    RNase resistance of RNA–DNA complexes: 109 µg of heat-denatured *E. coli* DNA per milliliter was slow-cooled in TMSV with the indicated concentrations of *E. coli* 23S-P$^{32}$-RNA (6.7 × 10$^4$ cpm/µg). After separation of hybrids by centrifugation as in Fig. 6, sensitivity to RNase was examined as described previously (Yankofsky and Spiegelman, 56).

A summary of the data obtained in such saturation experiments with the 23S ribosomal RNA of *E. coli* is plotted in Fig. 8, which compares the total RNA found in the DNA density region prior to RNase treatment with that which is RNase-resistant. It is clear that the behavior of these two is strikingly different. Initially, the "raw" hybrid structure tends to follow the RNase-resistant variety. However, beyond a certain input of RNA to DNA, there is striking divergence, and the total RNA shows no signs of saturation within the range of RNA inputs tested. However, the resistant residue clearly approaches a plateau corresponding approximately to an RNA–DNA ratio of 0.0015. The existence of this maximal level is consistent with the view that the DNA does indeed contain a restricted region capable of forming specific ribonuclease-resistant complexes with 23S ribosomal RNA.

Because of the nature of the experiments required to obtain it, the value of 0.0015 is more likely to be an underestimate than an overestimate. However, it provides us with an opportunity to calculate the minimum number of stretches in the DNA which are complementary to the 23S ribosomal RNA. *Escherichia coli* contains between 3 and $5 \times 10^9$ daltons of DNA per genome. If it is assumed that only one strand is transcribed (17, 21, 50), half these values must be taken. The molecular weight of the 23S RNA is about $1 \times 10^6$, and consequently, if the DNA contained only one complementary stretch of equivalent length, the

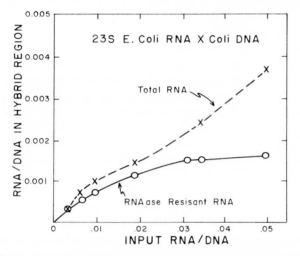

FIG. 8. Saturation curves of total and RNase-resistant counts in DNA region of CsCl equilibrium gradients. Details of incubations and centrifugation are as in Figs. 6 and 7 (Yankofsky and Spiegelman, 56).

saturation plateau should have come out between 0.00067 and 0.00045. The observed value of 0.0015 suggests, therefore, that there are at least two or three such sequences in the DNA. The existence of multiple sequences is of some interest, and we shall return to this issue after we have examined additional relevant data with other biological material.

### COMPETITIVE INTERACTION AS A TEST FOR SPECIFICITY OF HYBRID FORMATION

Competition experiments can also be employed to examine the specificity of the localized interaction between ribosomal RNA and its homologous DNA. Indeed, such experiments can in principle constitute rather sensitive tests for slight divergences in sequence. In any event, they can provide a direct answer to the following pertinent question: *Can non-*

*ribosomal RNA complex as effectively for the same sequences in the DNA which can form RNase-resistant hybrids with the ribosomal species?*

In the present system, competitive interaction can be studied by using two identifying isotopic labels on the two RNA preparations being tested. If the two RNA molecules are competing for the same site and the total concentration is at or near the saturation level, one label should displace the other as its proportion is increased in the hybridizing reaction mixture. If they do not compete for the same site, fixation to the DNA of one will be essentially indifferent to the presence of the other.

To examine questions of this nature it was first necessary to perform a control experiment to see whether competition is observed when it is expected. In these, mixtures containing fixed amounts of DNA and $P^{32}$-23S RNA at saturation levels are annealed in the presence of varying amounts of $H^3$-23S RNA. The amounts of each label hybridized in a RNase-resistant complex were then determined by centrifugation in CsCl gradients. The results are summarized in Fig. 9A, which shows clear evidence of displacement of the $P^{32}$ as more of the $H^3$-RNA is incorporated into the complex. Further, as is evident from the summation of the $P^{32}$ and $H^5$ (solid circles of Fig. 9C), the sum approaches the expected plateau value of about 0.0015. These data therefore establish the validity of such tests for competitive interaction.

To see whether nonribosomal RNA can compete, similar experiments were carried out with tritium-labeled message fractions taken from the 8 to 12S region (Fig. 1). The message fraction was chosen, since it was known to complex well with DNA and thus provides a test for the specificity of the ribosomal combination with DNA.

Again, in these experiments, to avoid confusion with irrelevant complexes involving short regions of complementarity, the fractions in the hybrid regions were always pooled, and the RNase-resistant residue of the complexed radioactivity was determined.

Figure 10 gives two examples of hybrid regions observed in CsCl gradients from reaction mixtures of this experiment. It is evident that both types ($P^{32}$-23S RNA and $H^3$-mRNA) have hybridized, with, however, an interesting and consistent difference. The tritium-labeled message RNA appears to be symmetrically distributed among the denatured strands of the DNA, and this is clearly not the case with the ribosomal complex, which is distinctly displaced toward the heavy side of the mean density of the denatured DNA.

Figure 9B summarizes the data obtained in competition tests between ribosomal and mRNA. In contrast to the results observed in the control experiment (Fig. 9A), the hybridization of the $H^3$-mRNA to the DNA has no effect on the ability of the DNA to combine with the $P^{32}$-labeled

23S RNA. In addition, it is clear (from Fig. 9C) that there is no evidence of saturation with the message fraction within the concentration range tested. The difference in saturation behavior between the control and the experimental hybridization is most strikingly illustrated in Fig. 9C, in which the sum of the P³² and H³ complexed is plotted against the total RNA in the mixture in the two experimental situations. Where ribosomal RNA alone is present, the expected saturation plateau is obtained. None

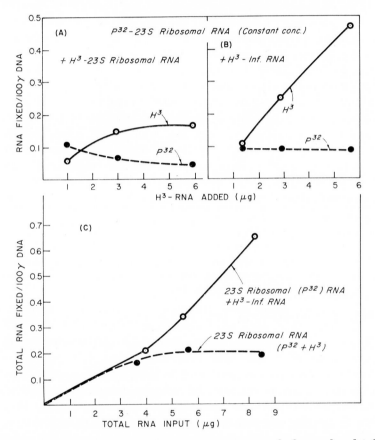

Fig. 9.  Tests for competitive interactions in mixtures of ribosomal and informational RNA molecules. A, All mixtures contained 63 μg of heat-denatured *E. coli* DNA and 2.66 μg of *E. coli* P³²-23S ribosomal RNA per milliliter. H³-23S ribosomal RNA of *E. coli* varied as shown. B, DNA and P³²-RNA same as in (A) except that H³-informational RNA was added in the amounts indicated. C, The same preparations as in (A) and (B). The plot here is total (P³² + H³) RNase-stable counts per 100 μg of DNA as a function of total input of RNA. All incubations during slow cooling and equilibrium centrifugation were carried out as described in Fig. 6 (Yankofsky and Spiegelman, 56).

is observed in the mixture containing mRNA. This, of course, does not mean that no such plateau is attainable. In point of fact, plateaus with mRNA have been obtained when about 50% of the DNA is occupied.

The data detailed establish that specific complexes occur between specific regions of the DNA and ribosomal RNA and that these regions are not occupiable by mRNA.

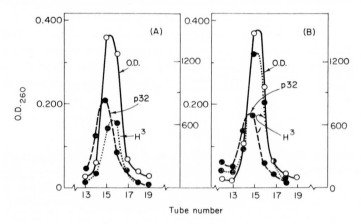

FIG. 10. Hybrid regions in CsCl gradients of mixtures containing ribosomal and informational RNA. Both incubation mixtures contained 63 µg of heat-denatured *E. coli* DNA and 2.66 µg of *E. coli* P³²-23S-RNA per milliliter. A, contained in addition 2.9 µg of H³-informational RNA per milliliter. B, contained in addition 5.7 µg of H³-informational RNA per milliliter. Details of incubations and centrifugations as in Figs. 6 and 7 (Yankofsky and Spiegelman, 56).

## THE RELATION BETWEEN THE 16S AND 23S RIBOSOMAL RNA COMPONENTS

All the experiments described so far were carried out with the 23S ribosomal RNA of *E. coli*, and they left unanswered the question of whether these findings hold for the 16S RNA component. We now turn our attention to the problem of the relation between the 16S and 23S RNA's. The similarity in base composition and the fact that the molecular weights of the 23S and 16S are almost in the relation of 2 to 1 suggest the possibility of a common origin, the 23S perhaps being a dimer of the 16S RNA. The crucial question which must be answered is whether or not they have the same sequence, and this can, of course, be answered by the sort of hybridization experiments we have already discussed.

The following sorts of information are pertinent to a resolution: (a) *saturation plateaus:* if the 16S and 23S ribosomal RNA's are derived from the same sequence, the RNA-to-DNA ratio (µg/µg) found in the hybrid at saturation should be the same for each RNA; (b) *addi-*

*tivity:* at the saturation ratio (RNA to DNA) of either, the addition of the other should lead to no further complex formation if they are derived from the same sequence. If, however, the sequences of origin are different, additional hybrids should be observed; (c) *competitive interaction:* by employing two identifying isotopic labels on the 16S and 23S, the presence or absence of competition during hybridization can be established. Absence of competitive interaction during hybridization would indicate distinct sequences, and its existence would argue for identity.

Experiments to settle these questions were undertaken with *Bacillus megaterium*, since we had not thus far examined the situation in an organism with a low (38%) GC content. The strain employed was a pyrimidine-requiring mutant, making it possible to prepare ribosomal RNA labeled at high specific activities with $H^3$-uridine.

## Purification of the Ribosomal RNA Subclasses

As in previous studies, all the RNA used in these studies was prepared from uniformly labeled cells followed by a "chase" in an unlabeled medium to remove contaminating labeled mRNA. To obtain purified preparations of each ribosomal RNA component freed of significant cross-contamination by the other, use was made of repeated chromatography (26, 27) on MAK columns (methylated albumin coated on kieselguhr columns). The purification was monitored by centrifugation in linear density gradients of sucrose with unlabeled bulk RNA of *E. coli* added as size markers. The degree of cross-contamination is readily determined by comparison of the O.D.$^{260}$ and radioactivity profiles.

An example of a separation of bulk RNA from *B. megaterium* is shown in Fig. 11. The profile is similar to those obtained for *E. coli* (23) except that the 16S region appears to be partially resolved into two components.

The 23S region indicated by the arrows in Fig. 11 was chromatographed repeatedly, and the profile on the fourth column is shown in Fig. 12A. Here, the arrows denote the region pooled and concentrated for experimental use. Figure 12B shows the size distribution in a sucrose gradient. As can be seen, the purified labeled component is confined to the 23S region of the bulk *E. coli* RNA added as a size marker.

The 16S component of Fig. 11 was similarly treated; Fig. 13A shows a representative profile on an MAK column. Again, the arrows indicate the region pooled, concentrated, and analyzed for size. Figure 13B shows the size distribution of this region compared to *E. coli* marker RNA. Although of interest, the abnormal shape seen on the radioactivity profile is not at present directly pertinent, and discussion of it will be deferred until later. Comparison of Figs. 13A and 13B indicates that the asymmetry in the chromatographic profile is not due to significant contamination with 23S RNA. All preparations used in the experiment to be described were examined before use in sucrose gradients for evidence of cross-contamination or breakdown. Samples showing evidence of either were discarded. We now consider the three types of experiments.

*Saturation Plateaus.* The saturation plateau for each ribosomal RNA subclass was determined with heat-denatured DNA having an $S_{20}$ of 21.8 and an estimated molecular weight of $7.3 \times 10^6$. The results are

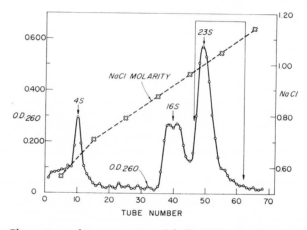

TUBE NUMBER

Fig. 11. Chromatographic separation of bulk RNA. *Bacillus megaterium* RNA was uniformly labeled with $H^3$-uridine. The column was equilibrated at 0.66 M NaCl; the RNA was loaded at 50 μg/ml in 0.66 M NaCl and eluted with a 360-ml linear gradient running from 0.66 M to 1.25 M NaCl; 5-ml fractions were collected (Yankofsky and Spiegelman, 57).

summarized in Fig. 14, in which it is clear that the 23S RNA reaches a plateau when approximately 0.18% of the DNA is occupied, while 0.14% is capable of complexing with the 16S RNA. In six repetitions, mean values of 0.179 ± 0.0072 and 0.136 ± 0.014 were obtained for the respective saturation values of 23S and 16S. The fact that the saturation plateaus for the two are different supports the conclusion that the two types of RNA are complementary to different regions of the DNA.

*Additivity.* It will be noted from Fig. 14 that, for 50 μg of DNA, saturation for the 23S RNA is achieved at 3 μg/ml, whereas 2 μg/ml is saturating for the 16S component. We now inquire whether the addition of both at saturating levels increases the amount of complex observed, and if so to what extent. The results of such an experiment are presented in Table II. Addition of the values obtained when saturating amounts of

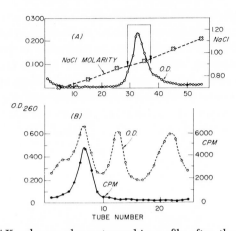

FIG. 12. A, MAK column: chromatographic profile after the fourth chromatography of the 23S region shown by the arrows in Fig. 11. The column was equilibrated at 0.68 M NaCl; 600 µg RNA was loaded at 50 µg/ml in 0.68 M NaCl and eluted with a 320-ml linear gradient from 0.72 to 1.22 M NaCl. B, sucrose density gradient centrifugation. An aliquot (0.5 µg RNA, 60,000 cpm) of the pooled tubes indicated by the arrows in (A) was used; 0.6 mg E. coli bulk RNA was added as O.D. marker; 1.2-ml fractions were collected, and 0.3-ml samples from each tube were plated for radioactive counts. The O.D. profile identified the known components in the added carrier material. The first major peak on the left is the 23S, the second the 16S, and the last corresponds to the 4S component (Yankofsky and Spiegelman, 57).

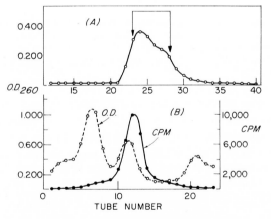

FIG. 13. A, MAK column: chromatographic profile of B. megaterium 16S-RNA (steady-state P[32] label) after third chromatography. The column was equilibrated at 0.6 M NaCl; 700 µg RNA was loaded at 50 µg/ml in 0.6 M NaCl and eluted with a 340-ml linear gradient from 0.6 M to 1.2 M NaCl. B, sucrose density gradient centrifugation: analysis of an aliquot (0.5 µg of RNA, 80,000 cpm) from the pooled tubes shown under the arrows in (A); 0.6 mg of E. coli bulk RNA was added as O.D. marker. All other details as in Fig. 12B (Yankofsky and Spiegelman, 57).

each RNA subclass are complexed alone (mixture 1 + mixture 2) indicates that 0.303% of the DNA would be hybridized. The amount of complex formed when both are incubated together is within 4% of this value. These results are difficult to reconcile with a common origin but are clearly consistent with the existence of distinct complementary regions. We come now to the final experimental test.

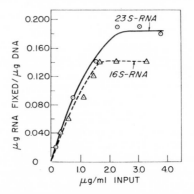

FIG. 14. Saturation plateaus: saturation curves of *B. megaterium* 16S and 23S RNA hybridized with 50 μg *B. megaterium* heat-denatured DNA per milliliter. Each point represents RNase-resistant counts found in the DNA region after CsCl equilibrium density gradient centrifugation (Yankofsky and Spiegelman, 57).

TABLE II

TEST FOR ADDITIVITY DURING HYBRIDIZATION AT SATURATION LEVELS OF
16S AND 23S RNA

| Mixture[a] | Contents | RNase-resistant hybrid (μg RNA fixed/100 μg DNA) |
|---|---|---|
| 1 | 50 μg/ml 1XDNA + 3.06 μg/ml 23S RNA | 0.186 |
| 2 | 50 μg/ml 1XDNA + 2.21 μg/ml 16S RNA | 0.117 |
| | | Sum = 0.303 |
| 3 | 50 μg/ml 1XDNA + 3.06 μg/ml 23S RNA + 2.21 μg/ml 16S RNA | 0.291 |

[a] The addition mixture (3) contained the same DNA and RNA preparations as the control mixtures (1 and 2). All three mixtures were annealed under identical conditions and centrifuged together, and the raw hybrids were tested for RNase resistance with the same enzyme preparation (Yankofsky and Spiegelman, 57).

*Competitive Interaction.* The principle here is the same as in the test designed to distinguish between the sequences of ribosomal and mRNA. Two identifying isotopes, $P^{32}$-16S RNA and $H^3$-23S RNA, are used. It is important in such experiments to make certain that one of the pair is held at its saturation value with respect to the DNA, so that if the other does complex with the same sites it will exclude the first. Accordingly, increasing amounts of P³²-labeled 16S RNA were incubated in three tubes, each containing 50 μg of denatured DNA and H³-23S RNA at its saturation level (3.0 μg). With the aid of the identifying isotopes, it was possible to determine the per cent hybrid formed by each ribosomal class in the three mixtures. From the results shown in Fig. 15, it is evident that each

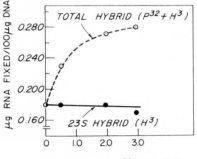

Fig. 15.  Competitive interaction: tests for competitive interactions between mixtures of 23S-H³-RNA and 16S-P³²-RNA from *B. megaterium* complexed with homologous heat-denatured DNA. All mixtures contained 50 μg DNA and 3 μg purified 23S-H³-RNA per milliliter (see Fig. 12) and the indicated concentrations of purified 16S-P³²-RNA (see Fig. 13) (Yankofsky and Spiegelman, 57).

subclass behaves as though the other were not present. Addition of more 16S RNA does not significantly influence the amount of 23S hybrid structure formed. There is no significant displacement of the H³ from the complex as the P³² enters into it. Finally, as more 16S RNA is added, the total hybrid approaches a level of saturation close to that expected from the sum of the two subclasses when incubated alone. Within the sensitivity of the test there is clearly no evidence that 16S and 23S ribosomal RNA molecules are competing for common DNA sites. We conclude that each class is distinct and is derived from a unique sequence in the DNA.

The experiments we have thus far described with bacteria settled a number of basic issues with respect to ribosomal RNA. They established with three organisms (*E. coli*, *Ps. aeruginosa*, and *B. megaterium*) that DNA contains complements of ribosomal RNA. They further demonstrated that the sequences of the 16S and 23S species were different. Finally, in the three organisms examined, the DNA complements of ribosomal RNA constituted 0.3% of the genome. This latter number implies a multiplicity of sites, which raises interesting implications of ribosomal heterogeneity. These and related questions are more readily discussed with the aid of information derived from higher forms which possess larger genomes. However, before considering experiments of this nature, it is desirable to discuss recent developments in the methodology of hybridization.

## Methods of DNA–RNA Hybridization and Detection

The usefulness of hybridizations between DNA and radioactive RNA as a test for complementarity has stimulated the search for procedures which combine reliability and convenience. Initially, Hall and Spiegelman (19) used annealing in solution and equilibrium density gradient centrifugation (31) in preparative rotors for hybrid detection.

To exploit this technique for the identification of small (less than 0.1%) complementary segments, ribonuclease treatment was introduced (55-57) to eliminate low levels of adventitious contamination. Here, advantage is taken of the ribonuclease resistance of RNA extensively complexed to DNA. It was this device which made possible the experiments with ribosomal RNA and also led to a similar detection of the DNA complements of the sRNA molecules (Giacomoni and Spiegelman, 14; Goodman and Rich, 16).

All the above studies used density gradient separation of hybrids which required lengthy centrifugations. The full realization of the potentialities of the hybridization technique clearly required the design of a procedure less costly in time and expensive equipment. The first success came with the introduction by Bautz and Hall (2) of nitrocellulose columns to which glucosylated DNA was attached. This method was quickly generalized by Bolton and McCarthy (6), who recognized that mechanical immobilization per se would suffice, and from this concept they developed agar columns containing denatured DNA trapped in the solidified gel. Most recently, the ultimate in convenience and capacity for handling many samples was provided by the discovery (Nygaard and Hall, 35) that nitrocellulose filters strongly adsorbed single-stranded DNA along with any hybridized RNA.

To appreciate the purpose of the present discussion it is important to recognize that hybridization involves both hybrid formation and hybrid detection. Except for the two-column procedures, all the methods described anneal the DNA and RNA in solution and then assay the amount of hybrid complex. Hybridization in solution has one obvious disadvantage stemming from the fact that RNA–DNA formation must compete with the re-formation of the DNA–DNA complexes. The existence of these competitive interactions can introduce serious errors, particularly in experiments determining saturation plateaus.

In certain instances, the complications of annealing in solution can be surmounted by incubating at temperatures well below the melting temperature ($T_m$) of the DNA, a strategy used by Yankofsky and Spiegelman (55-57). However, low temperature is not a universally available solution. RNA molecules possessing an extensive secondary structure will not hybridize until their own melting temperature is approached, a situation encountered with sRNA (14).

In principle, immobilization of the DNA during the hybridization provides a logical method of avoiding these unwanted interactions. The obvious answer (Gillespie and Spiegelman, 15) was to fix the denatured DNA irreversibly to nitrocellulose membrane filters and carry out the hybridizations on them. This should serve to eliminate, or greatly reduce, DNA–DNA interactions while retaining the almost indispensable convenience of the filter method. To these advantages can be added RNase treatment to eliminate low levels of contamination with unpaired RNA, which can become crucial in many types of investigations.

After exploration of several more involved procedures (for example, ultraviolet irradiation), it was discovered that irreversible fixation of DNA to nitrocellulose membranes was readily achieved by thorough drying at moderate temperatures. The result is a simple and conveniently flexible method of hybrid assay possessing a vanishingly small noise level combined with high accuracy.

## Hybridization with Membrane-Immobilized DNA

The procedure, in outline, consists in (a) binding the DNA to nitrocellulose membrane filters, (b) hybridizing the RNA to the fixed DNA, and (c) removing RNA "noise"—that is, unpaired RNA and RNA complexed over short regions. The details of each step are presented below.

*Step I—Immobilization of Denatured DNA on Nitrocellulose Membrane Filters.* The denatured DNA is dissolved in 6 × SSC at a concentration between 5 and 10 µg/ml and passed through a membrane filter (presoaked in 6 × SSC for 1 minute and washed with 10 ml of the same buffer). The filters loaded with DNA are subsequently dried at room temperature for at least 4 hours and at 80°C for an additional 4 hours in a vacuum oven. Prior drying at low temperature was instituted to avoid renaturation of the DNA in the early stages. When monitored with radioactive DNA, no detectable loss (less than 1%) is observed during any of the subsequent steps of the procedure.

*Step II—Hybridization.* Hybrids are formed by immersing the DNA filters in scintillation vials containing 5 ml of P³²-RNA in either 2 × SSC or 6 × SSC as specified. Annealing is generally carried out at 66°C without shaking, after which the vials are chilled in an ice bath.

*Step III—Elimination of RNA "Noise."* The filters are removed from the hybridization fluid, and *each side* is washed with 50 ml of 2 × SSC by suction filtration. Any remaining RNA not completely complexed is destroyed by immersing the filters for 1 hour at room temperature in 5 ml of 2 × SSC containing heated pancreatic RNase (20 μg/ml). After RNase treatment, the vials are again chilled and the filters rewashed on each side. Finally, the filters are dried and counted in a Packard Tri-Carb scintillation counter.

It should be remarked that the RNase treatment must be carried out in 2 × SSC, whereas the other steps may be carried out at the higher (6 × SSC) buffer concentration.

An obvious advantage conferred by prefixing the DNA on the filter is

TABLE III
ELIMINATION OF RNA NOISE[a]

| Sample | Salt | Cpm remaining | Per cent input cpm remaining |
|---|---|---|---|
| 1 | 2 × SSC — | 13,838 | 1.8 |
| 2 | 2 × SSC wash | 290 | 0.059 |
| 3 | 2 × SSC wash; RNase; wash | 25 | 0.0033 |
| 4 | 6 × SSC wash; RNase; wash | 108 | 0.0076 |
| 5 | 6 × SSC wash; RNase; wash (50 μg DNA; 0°C; 6 hr) | 99 | 0.0066 |
| 6 | TMS[b] — | 81,038 | 10.0 |
| 7 | TMS[b] wash | 23,528 | 2.9 |

[a] Unloaded or DNA-containing filters were immersed in buffer containing 2 μg RNA (400,000 cpm/μg) for 24 hours at 53°C, except for samples 4 and 5. These latter samples were incubated in buffer containing 10 μg RNA (100,000 cpm/μg) for 6 hours at 66°C. All filters were removed from the RNA solutions, and some were washed and/or treated with RNase (Gillespie and Spiegelman, 15).

[b] TMS = 0.3 M NaCl; 0.005 M MgCl$_2$; 0.001 M Tris; pH 7.3.

the ease with which contaminating RNA is removed. As may be seen from Table III, simply lifting the membrane out of the hybridizing mixture leaves 98% of the noncomplexed RNA behind. The washing procedure brings the contamination down to 0.06% of the input, and the RNase treatment reduces this further to 0.003%. Fixed DNA on the filter has no effect on the ability to remove nonhybridized RNA. It should be noted from samples 6 and 7 of Table III that the presence of magnesium is to be avoided if low contamination levels are desired.

A comparison was made of the counts which survive the purification procedure at different levels of RNA and DNA inputs held for various times and temperatures. Less than 100 cpm were found, with input counts ranging from 2 × 10$^5$ cpm to 5 × 10$^6$ cpm. Increasing the input of RNA by 25 resulted only in a 2.5-fold increase in residual counts. The presence of DNA at noncomplexing temperature does not increase the contamination. The procedure is clearly effective in eliminating noncomplexed RNA.

## MODIFICATION OF THE NYGAARD-HALL TECHNIQUE TO LOWER NOISE LEVELS

We wanted to compare hybridizations carried out with DNA in solutions with others in which DNA is immobilized. The Nygaard-Hall (35) method omits RNase and, depending on the amount of RNA, has a noise level ranging between 0.1% and 1% of the input. Their experiments involved comparatively massive amounts of hybrid formation, and this amount of contamination was not important. It was, however, too high for our purpose, and we consequently introduced the RNase step *after* collecting the hybrids formed in liquid on the membrane. Table IV shows that this modification lowers the noise level from 0.08 to 0.003%.

TABLE IV
RNA NOISE LEVEL OF LIQUID HYBRIDIZATION TECHNIQUES[a]

| Sample | Method for RNA noise elimination | Per cent of input RNA remaining |
|---|---|---|
| 1 | No RNase | 0.0718 |
| 2 | RNase before filtration | 0.2005 |
| 3 | RNase after filtration | 0.0034 |

[a] Reaction mixtures containing 50 µg DNA and 50 µg RNA (600,000 cpm/µg) were made up at room temperature in 2 × SSC, and collected by filtration on nitrocellulose membrane filters. Treatment with RNase (20 µg/ml) was carried out at room temperature for 1 hour. All filters were washed with 100 ml 2 × SSC after collection of the reaction mixtures. Sample 3 was additionally washed with 100 ml 2 × SSC after RNase treatment (Gillespie and Spiegelman, 15).

Another useful fact is recorded in Table IV. Note that RNase treatment *before* collection of the complex on the filter increases the "noise" from 0.08 to 0.2%. The RNase, being a basic protein, tends to remain on the membrane when the treated complexes are filtered and adsorb small core fragments of RNA core which would otherwise be washed away. The presence of *any* basic protein (methylated albumin, lysozyme, etc.) at the filtration step causes the same difficulty.

## SATURATION PLATEAUS ATTAINED WITH IMMOBILIZED DNA

The availability of a method which avoids competition with DNA–DNA interaction gave us an opportunity to check our previously obtained saturation plateau values for ribosomal RNA, and the *B. megaterium* system was chosen. Comparisons were made between annealing ribosomal RNA (16S and 23S) with DNA in solution and with membrane-fixed DNA. To minimize interference with DNA self-annealing, the liquid hybridizations were carried out at 43°C as had been done previously. In all cases, the ratio of RNA to DNA employed was sufficient to attain the saturation plateau, and the times required were determined from preliminary kinetic experiments. Table V summarizes the results obtained with dissolved and immobilized DNA, the values representing the average of three determinations. The saturation value obtained previously (Table II) by the CsCl density gradient method with the same biological

TABLE V

AVAILABILITY OF DNA FOR HYBRIDIZATION[a]

| Hybridization technique | Average cpm complexed | Per cent DNA hybridized ($\bar{x} \pm 2\sigma$) |
|---|---|---|
| DNA in solution | 11,711 | 0.314 ± 0.027 |
| Membrane-fixed DNA | 1,702 | 0.315 ± 0.008 |
| CsCl | | 0.303 |

[a] The annealing in liquid was carried out in 6 × SSC, with 40 μg H³-DNA (5,000 cpm/μg) and 40 μg P³²-RNA (100,000 cpm/μg) in 1.5 ml. Hybridization was performed at 43°C for 12 hours.

The membrane-fixed DNA technique employed a filter containing 5 μg DNA (5,000 cpm/μg) in a 6 × SSC solution containing 10 μg RNA (100,000 cpm/μg). Hybridization was carried out at 66°C for 8 hours. Each number is the average of three experiments ± 2σ (Gillespie and Spiegelman, 15).

materials is also recorded. The average plateau values of all four are in agreement, indicating that the earlier values obtained by low-temperature annealing in liquid were not seriously in error owing to DNA–DNA interaction. However, this is not the case when the temperatures are close to the $T_m$ of the DNA, as will be seen in the next section.

### A Comparison of Plateau Stability in Liquid and Immobilized DNA Hybridization at High Temperatures (65°)

Figures 16 through 19 give some typical kinetics of hybridizations carried out at various input ratios of RNA to DNA. We may first focus attention on the results obtained with immobilized DNA. Figures 16 and 17 reveal, not unexpectedly, that the rate of approach to the plateau is influenced by the concentration of RNA. At 10 μg of RNA the hybridization reaches the expected plateau in 5 hours, a value not attained in 15 hours at 2 μg. On the other hand (Figs. 18 and 19), the kinetics of complex formation is very slightly influenced by increasing the amount of DNA fixed to the membrane.

Comparison of these findings with the results obtained with DNA in

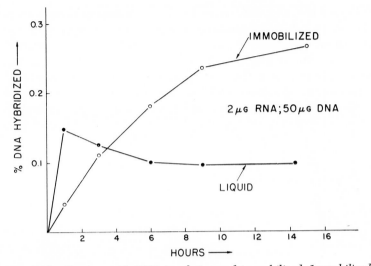

FIG. 16. Hybridizations with DNA in solution and immobilized. *Immobilized-DNA technique:* DNA filters containing 50 μg DNA were prepared by using 6 × SSC and were immersed in 5 ml of 6 × SSC solution containing 2 μg RNA. Hybridization was carried out at 66°C without shaking. *Liquid technique:* Reaction mixtures containing 50 μg DNA and 2 μg RNA in 1.5 ml were made up in 6 × SSC. The mixtures were held at 66°C, after which the hybrids were purified by the modified Nygaard-Hall technique (Gillespie and Spiegelman, 15).

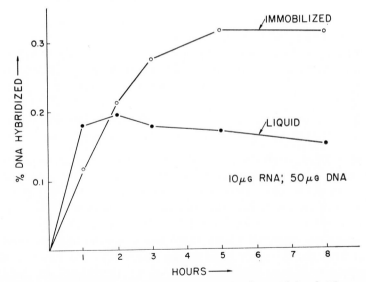

FIG. 17. Hybridizations with DNA in solution and immobilized. The procedures are the same as those described in the legend for Fig. 16, except that 50 μg DNA was hybridized with 10 μg RNA (Gillespie and Spiegelman, 15).

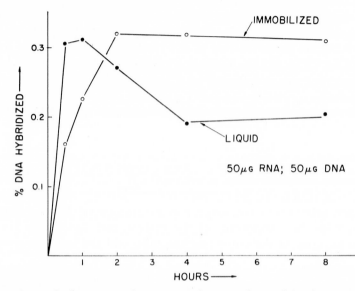

FIG. 18. Hybridizations with DNA in solution and immobilized. The procedures are the same as those described in the legend of Fig. 16, except that 50 μg DNA was hybridized with 50 μg RNA (Gillespie and Spiegelman, 15).

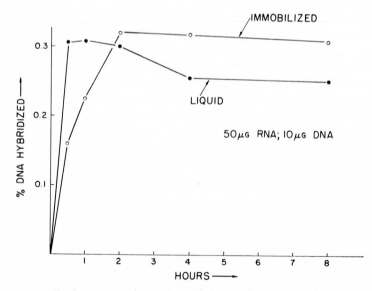

FIG. 19. Hybridizations with DNA in solution and immobilized. The procedures are the same as those described in the legend for Fig. 16, except that 10 μg DNA was hybridized with 50 μg RNA (Gillespie and Spiegelman, 15).

solution dramatically illustrates the advantages of using immobilized DNA. We see (Fig. 16) that, at the lower input of RNA, the plateau value of 0.31% is never reached in the liquid hybridizations. At a level of 50 μg RNA (Fig. 18) the saturation plateau is almost attained within a few hours, but this is followed by a decomposition of formed hybrid, a phenomenon reported by Nygaard and Hall (36). In general, this loss of complexes during liquid hybridization increases in severity with the concentration of DNA present.

## SOME GENERAL PRECAUTIONS IN HYBRIDIZATION EXPERIMENTS

It may be useful to others if we explicitly record here some of the complications which can be encountered in carrying out hybridizations and the precautions we have adopted as a consequence. In most instances they center on the components of the system, and the details are best discussed in terms of the individual reactants and the steps involved.

### DNA Preparations

The DNA used must be completely available for hybridization if saturation plateaus are to be interpreted with confidence. It follows that the denaturation of the DNA employed must be shown to be complete.

A difficulty commonly encountered with DNA preparations is contamination with ribonuclease, a protein well known for its ability to bind to DNA and for its resistance to inactivation. The usual preparative procedures rarely provide DNA completely free of ribonuclease. Passage through an MAK column is extremely helpful, since RNase remains behind. A useful supplement is to incubate the DNA with pronase to destroy residual RNase activity. The pronase can then be removed by deproteinization with phenol. It is advisable first to subject the pronase to "self-digestion" to remove any nucleases it might contain. In any case, no DNA preparations should be employed which have not been assayed for ribonuclease activity for the time periods and under the conditions employed for hybridization. DNA from bacteria was isolated according to Marmur (28) whereas that from insects was prepared according to Mead (30).

### RNA Preparations

Assay for and removal of nuclease activity is, of course, equally important in the case of RNA. A frequently encountered difficulty is contamination with DNA fragments resulting from incomplete removal or digestion. This is true for RNA labeled with either $P^{32}$ or uridine, since many cells can convert the latter to thymine. It is a particularly serious complication with glucosylated DNA (for example, cells infected with T2, T4, or T6 bacteriophages), since it is much more resistant to enzymatic digestion. The DNase treatment must be continued until the residue of alkali-stable counts is at an acceptable level. Even small amounts of contaminating labeled DNA can destroy the interpretability of many kinds of hybridization experiments.

### Enzymes

The RNase and DNase preparations used must be assayed to be certain that each is free of significant contamination by the other. DNase can be readily freed of ribonuclease activity by column chromatography on DEAE (Polatnick and Bachrach, 40). Deoxyribonuclease activity in RNase is readily destroyed by heating a solution adjusted to pH 5.0 to 90°C for 10 minutes. Assays for contaminating enzymes must be of a duration comparable to that employed in the relevant hybridization step. The use of radioactive polynucleotide as substrate makes it possible to achieve the necessary level of sensitivity in the assay for contaminating activity.

### Enzymatic Elimination of Unpaired RNA

One of the most common pitfalls stems from the use of commercial RNase without checking for DNase contamination. No resistant plateaus of hybrid are observed if DNase activity is detectable. The other is the failure to treat the hybrid under conditions specified for stability. Although stability may vary, in our experience temperatures above 37°C and salt concentrations below 0.25 $M$ should be avoided. We reproducibly obtain an absolutely resistant hybrid fraction when enzyme treatments are carried out with 10 µg of RNase per milliliter at 30°C in 0.3 $M$ NaCl. Wherever possible, internal controls of free RNA appropriately labeled with an identifying radioactive isotope should be included to be certain that the ribonuclease is functioning properly.

### Presence of Basic Proteins in the Hybridizing Mixture

Basic proteins adsorb RNA molecules and small core fragments liberated by enzyme digestion. They are also retained very efficiently during filtration through nitrocellulose membranes. The net result is to increase "noise" levels by several orders of magnitude. Unless the columns are exhaustively washed before use, nucleic acid preparations purified on MAK are likely to contain enough methylated albumin to cause this sort of trouble. For the same reason, excessive (more than 20 µg/ml) amounts of RNase should not be used in the elimination of unpaired RNA.

### METHODS OF HYBRID DETECTION AND ASSAY

Of the available methods of hybrid detection, two permit the actual isolation of the complex and allow its further characterizations. These involve the use of equilibrium density gradients of CsCl or $Cs_2SO_4$ and the more recently developed chromatographic separations on MAK columns (Hayashi et al., 22). The latter method has the advantage in both capacity and convenience. Further, it has been shown in the same study that the column fractionates hybrids on the basis of the ratio of RNA to DNA in the complex.

The agar (Bolton and McCarthy, 6) and nitrocellulose columns (Bautz and Hall, 2) are particularly useful for preparative fractionation of complementary RNA. The membrane filter is clearly the method of choice when large numbers of assays for complementarity are required.

Comparative experiments at high temperature clearly establish that hybridizations with immobilized DNA are superior to those carried out in solution, conferring certainty and accuracy by avoiding DNA–DNA interactions. Hybridizations at elevated temperatures ($> 50°C$) in liquid which are not monitored by a kinetic analysis are likely to be in error. If they are extended, they are almost certain to yield low estimates.

The introduction by Nygaard and Hall (36) of membrane filters for hybrid detection greatly expanded the number of samples it was feasible to analyze. The use of membrane-fixed DNA both for annealing and for detecting the hybrid product generates still other advantages of convenience.

The technique is inherently flexible and can be adapted to almost any volume. For example, one need not use the entire filter, since, after a specified amount of DNA is fixed, circular subsections of known area (or weight) can be punched out and employed. Further, more than one filter can be placed in the same hybridization mixture, and, if desired, individual ones can be removed at suitable intervals and analyzed. Alternatively, a loaded filter can be left in for a fixed time, then removed and replaced by a new one to allow further hybridization, permitting a simple search for heterogeneity in hybridizability. In addition, with the DNA immobilized, a wide temperature range is available, uncomplicated by DNA renaturation. One can thus study the hybridization of molecules possessing high degrees of secondary structure and requiring elevated temperatures for annealing.

The RNA hybridized to the fixed DNA can be recovered for further study by elution at elevated temperatures and low ionic strength. Finally, the combined use of RNase and the membrane-immobilized DNA makes it possible easily to push the "noise" level down to almost any desired level, and it does not require extraordinary effort to achieve levels corresponding to 0.003% of the input RNA.

The availability of this method made it feasible to proceed in our analysis of the ribosomal cistrons by examining the situation in biological material more suitable for the next stages of the investigations.

## The Problem of Localization of the Ribosomal RNA Cistrons and the Function of the Nucleolus in Higher Organisms

The existence proof of DNA complements of ribosomal RNA in bacteria encouraged others to look at this problem in more complicated organisms. The methods developed with microorganisms sufficed to establish that a similar situation exists in higher plants (5, 11), mammals (29, 39, 45), and insects (51).

The proportion (0.3%) of the total genome involved was constant in the bacteria examined and indicated the presence of a multiplicity of sites for each of the two ribosomal components. The densities of the DNA–RNA hybrids suggested (56) that the multiple sites were clustered rather than scattered throughout the genome. However, the bacteria were not convenient material for a more detailed attempt at illuminating the relation of these cistrons to each other and to the rest of the genome.

The genomes of higher organisms are larger than those of bacteria by several orders of magnitude. If the proportion of the DNA complementary to ribosomal RNA was kept reasonably constant, the redundancy would be much greater and, therefore, easier to examine in higher organisms. Further, properly chosen material would permit the correlation of cytogenetic and cytochemical information with data derived from molecular hybridization. Thus, diverse observations implicate the nucleolus with protein synthesis (10, 9, 52), ribosomes (4, 41, 25, 5), and ribosomal RNA formation (12, 37, 38), the most striking finding being the absence of ribosomal RNA synthesis in a lethal anucleolate mutant of the aquatic toad, *Xenopus laevis* (8).

In summary, the available facts are consistent with the hypothesis that identifies the nucleolus as the site of ribosomal RNA synthesis. They do not, however, eliminate the alternative possibilities that it is a repository for RNA synthesized elsewhere or that the nucleolus serves some other indirect function in the assembly of ribosomes. Nevertheless, if we adopt it as a working concept, the notion of a nucleolar location for ribosomal RNA formation leads to some interesting and experimentally testable predictions.

The nucleolus characteristically occupies a specific position (the nucleolar organizer, or "NO," segment) in the chromosome complement. This invariant relation between the nucleolus and a particular chromosomal locus suggests the obvious possibility that the DNA complements which generate the ribosomal RNA strands are confined to the nucleolar organizer region. Confirmation would simultaneously resolve the question of nucleolar function and decide between scattered versus clustered distributions of the multiple ribosomal RNA cistrons.

A direct attack requires a reliable method for isolating pure nucleoli still attached to their chromosomal segments and uncontaminated by other chromatin fragments. Comparative hybridizations could then be carried out between ribosomal RNA and "nucleolar DNA" versus "nonnucleolar DNA." Two attempts (5, 29) to carry out such experiments have yielded contradictory results, and it is apparent from both investigations that neither had available "nucleolar chromatin" of sufficient purity to permit a truly decisive experiment. Under the circumstances, it seemed worth while to consider other experimental approaches which bypass the limitations of physical separations by employing biological devices to achieve the desired end result.

Mutants of *Drosophila melanogaster* are known (7) which contain inversions involving (46, 48, 33) the "NO" region of the X chromosomes and others which contain useful linked markers (1, 34). Stocks can be derived from these possessing duplications or deletions of the "NO" region, making it possible to construct (13) by suitable crosses strains which have from one to four doses of the nucleolar organizer region. Hybridization experiments between DNA derived from these stocks and isotopically labeled ribosomal RNA should, in principle, provide a precise answer to the following question: *Are the DNA complements of the ribosomal RNA confined to the nucleolar-organizer region?* An affirmative answer would be indicated if the amount of RNA hybridizable per unit of DNA is directly proportional to the dosage of "NO" per genome. The absence of proportionality would indicate that the ribosomal RNA cistrons are not localized in the chromatin region contained in the deleted and duplicated regions.

### Nature of the Stocks and the Source of the DNA

The steps involved in the production of the stocks from the original inversion mutants are summarized diagrammatically in Fig. 20. The deletion and duplications arise as complementary products of the cross between the two inversions. Thus, the segment appearing as a duplicate in one is equivalent to that deleted in the other. The deletion extends from the proximal break of inversion *scute⁴* to the proximal break of inversion *scute⁸*, encompassing the nucleolar organizer and the *bobbed* locus.

Four different stocks of *Drosophila* were used in the present studies to prepare DNA containing various proportions of the "NO" region. One is the Standard (7) Urbana wild type. Individuals of this strain carry one "NO" region on each X and one on each Y chromosome; hence both

males and females carry two. The DNA derived from this stock is designated either ♂ (2) or ♀ (2). Another is the G-21 of the Oak Ridge National Laboratory, which has the following relevant genetic constitution:
$In(1)$ $sc^{4L, 8R}$, $y$ $sc^4$ $^{+ 8}$ $cv$ $v$ $f/RA$, $yf/y$. The males of this line lack the
"NO" region on their X but carry one on the Y. The corresponding DNA
preparations are designated in the text as ♂ (1). The third is G-31 from
the Oak Ridge National Laboratory, which has the following genetic
constitution: $In(1)$ $sc^{81L, 4R}$, $sc^{81}$ $v$ $B/RA$, $yf/B^sY$. The males of this stock
carry two "NO" regions on the X and another on the Y chromosome, mak-
ing three in all. DNA preparations from the males of this stock are, therefore, designated as ♂ (3). The fourth stock was designed to provide a

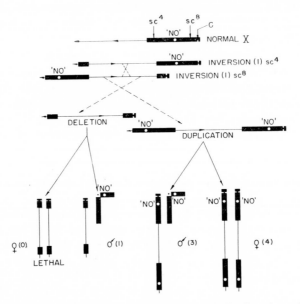

Fig. 20.   Origin and construction of stocks. The symbols identify nucleolar organizer (NO), centromere (C), $scute^4$ ($sc^4$), and $scute^8$ ($sc^8$). A cross between the
two inversions yields the desired deletion and duplication from which the various
stocks can be developed (Ritossa and Spiegelman, 42).

DNA containing four "NO" regions per genome. To obtain it, males of
G-31 were crossed with wild-type females. The females of the F1 were
back-crossed with the males of stock G-31. From these, females were
selected exhibiting, because of homozygosity, the genetic markers, $B$,
$sc$, $v$. Here advantage was taken of the presence of the inversion in the X
chromosome which, by suppressing crossing over, permits use of the
markers linked to "NO" to select the proper combinations with respect
to "NO." The females chosen necessarily contain two X chromosomes, both

of which carry two doses of the nucleolar organizer region. The stock was maintained with males of G-31 which, of course, also possess duplicates of "NO" on their X. DNA derived from the females of this stock is designated by ♀ (4).

## Numerical Details of a Saturation Experiment

To exemplify the absolute amounts of materials and radioactivity levels being dealt with, a typical experiment is detailed in Table VI. H³-labeled *Drosophila* ribosomal RNA at the indicated concentrations is incubated with a constant amount of ♂ (1) DNA. The internal "noise"

TABLE VI
DETAILS OF A SATURATION EXPERIMENT[a]

| *Drosophila* DNA | H³-RNA | E. coli P³²-RNA | H³ (cpm) | P³² (cpm) | H³ noise | Per cent of genome |
|---|---|---|---|---|---|---|
| 36.5 | 0.7 | 1 | 3284 | 10 | 83 | 0.113 |
| 37.3 | 1.4 | 2 | 4283 | 11 | 91 | 0.145 |
| 37.1 | 2.1 | 3 | 4838 | 15 | 124 | 0.164 |
| 37.3 | 2.1 | 3 | 4680 | 16 | 132 | 0.157 |
| 37.3 | 2.8 | 4 | 4609 | 20 | 166 | 0.154 |
| 37.3 | 3.5 | 5 | 4923 | 23 | 190 | 0.164 |

[a] Incubations were carried out in 4 ml of 2 × SSC at 65°C. The indicated amounts of ♂ (1) DNA were prefixed on the membrane filters. The specific activities of the H³-RNA of *Drosophila* was 77,285 cpm/μg, and that of P³²-RNA of *E. coli* was 9200 cpm/μg. Irrelevant RNA was removed by washing and RNase treatment. H³ "noise" is calculated from the finally observed P³² counts corrected for difference in specific activities. All recorded counts are corrected for background. Numbers in the first three columns refer to micrograms of nucleic acid added (Ritossa and Spiegelman, 42).

control is provided by including P³²-ribosomal RNA of *E. coli* in quantities which approximate the H³-marked RNA from *Drosophila*. "Noise" correction is made by subtracting from the H³ counts the proportion of P³² counts observed which survive the purification of the Gillespie and Spiegelman (15) hybridization procedure. It is evident from Table VI that the contamination is negligible compared to the counts hybridized, a fact which is even more strikingly obvious from Fig. 21, in which are plotted the actual H³ counts observed and the estimated "noise" from the P³². The H³-RNA in true complex plateaus at 4750 cpm, and the internal controls, corrected for specific activity, are all below 200 cpm.

## Saturation Curves with DNA Containing Various Dosages of the Nucleolar Organizer Region

The four types of DNA carrying different proportions of "NO" were subjected to saturation curves, and the results obtained are described in

Fig. 22. A majority of these experiments contained internal "noise" controls, but they are not recorded, since they all yielded results identical to those shown in Fig. 21.

We may first focus our attention on the results with wild-type DNA [curve labeled ♀ (2), ♂ (2)], since they settle an issue which could have complicated numerical interpretation of the outcome. It has already been noted that males of some stocks and females of others were employed to achieve the desired dosage of the "NO" region. Consequently, we had to know whether the nucleolar organizer segments on the X chromosome and the Y chromosome contribute equally to the observed proportion of

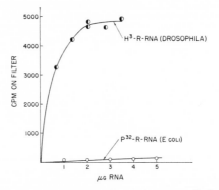

FIG. 21.   Observed saturation plateau of ♂ (1) DNA. All details are as described in Table VI. Note that the actually observed P³² counts of the control heterologous RNA were less than those plotted by a factor of 8.3. The latter represent estimated noise in the H³-cpm (Ritossa and Spiegelman, 42).

complementarity between DNA and ribosomal RNA. For this purpose, wild-type male and female DNA were tested in separate hybridization experiments. It is clear that the open circles ( ♀ ) and the half-shaded circles ( ♂ ) fall on the same curve and approach the same plateau of 0.27%.

Since the XY and XX combinations contribute equivalently to the DNA which is complementary to ribosomal RNA, we can with confidence estimate expected plateaus without regard to sex. We now assume that the plateau attained by the wild type represents a dose of two "NO" segments, from which we can predict the plateaus which should be achieved by the others, *if all the DNA complements of the ribosomal RNA are confined to the "NO" segment*. These predictions are indicated by the solid horizontal lines of Fig. 22. The corresponding numerical values are recorded on the right-hand ordinate.

Comparison of the observed and predicted plateau values of Fig. 22

suggests that experimental support has been provided for the assertion that the DNA complementary to the ribosomal RNA is confined to the region of the nucleolar organizer.

It would have been interesting to test a DNA completely lacking in nucleolar organizer. With *Drosophila*, death occurs rather early in the

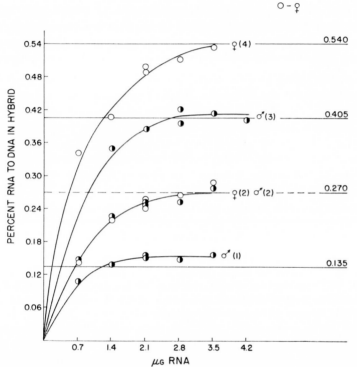

FIG. 22. Saturation levels of DNA containing various dosages of nucleolar organizer region. The dosage of "NO" is indicated by the number in parentheses. The dotted horizontal line at 0.270 is assumed to be a correct estimate for a dosage of 2, and the solid horizontal lines represent predicted plateaus for dosages of 1, 3, and 4, respectively. The numerical values of the plateaus are given on the right. Replicate determinations are indicated by multiple points at the same input level. All hybridizations and subsequent RNase and washing treatments were carried out (Ritossa and Spiegelman, 42).

development of stocks homozygous for the deletion, making it difficult to obtain DNA uncontaminated with cytoplasmic DNA of maternal origin. The anucleolate mutant of *Xenopus laevis* (8) ultimately may furnish more suitable material, providing it is a deletion and not an operator mutation.

The multiplicity of ribosomal cistrons can be estimated from the saturation plateau and the DNA content of a haploid genome which lies between 0.2 and $1 \times 10^{-12}$ g (43, 49). Conversion of the lower (43) value to equivalent molecular weights yields $1.2 \times 10^{11}$ daltons, which must be divided by 2 for our purpose, since available evidence (17, 21, 50) indicates that RNA is found complementary to only one of the two DNA strands in any given region. Thus a wild-type haploid genome contains $1.6 \times 10^8$ daltons of DNA complementary to ribosomal RNA, which is equivalent to about 100 stretches for each of the two ribosomal RNA components. If the higher estimate of the genome is taken, this number becomes 500.

It is interesting to note that plateau values clustering around 0.3% of the genome for the ribosomal RNA cistrons have been found for several bacteria (56, 57), for a higher plant (5, 11), and now for an insect (51). The only published value considerably below this (about 0.01%) for HeLa cells (29) is suspect on several grounds. In particular, the conditions of hybridization (60°C for 24 hours) used are known (15, 36) to give low hybrid yields. Further, the choice of HeLa cell DNA as the challenging material was not a happy one. The presence of aneuploidy and nonviable cells lacking particular chromosomes makes it uncertain that a proper sample of the genome was being examined.

## IMPLICATIONS AND CONCLUDING REMARKS

The fact that approximately 0.3% of the DNA is set aside for ribosomal RNA complements in genomes varying over several orders of magnitude poses an interesting problem. It may, however, be worth pointing out that the 0.3% value may turn out to be a simple numerical consequence of supply and demand. Ribosomal RNA constitutes the bulk of cellular RNA (85%) in bacteria. If we assume a half-life of 2 minutes for mRNA, the ribosomal RNA cistrons must turn out as much RNA per generation as all the other cistrons put together. If this is the situation at some point in the development of all organisms, and no cistron can be made to work more than three hundred times as fast as the average, about 0.3% of any genome would have to be set aside for ribosomal cistrons.

The experiments reported with *Drosophila* locate all the DNA complementary to both 18S and 28S ribosomal components in the region of the nucleolar organizer. They, therefore, decide the issue in favor of a clustered rather than a disperse distribution. The data further specify a location of the relevant DNA templates which supports the notion that the nucleolus is the site of ribosomal RNA synthesis.

The considerable multiplicity of ribosomal RNA cistrons in complex organisms generates some interesting implications. For example, the question immediately arises whether the several hundred stretches found for *Drosophila* are all of identical sequence. It seems likely that, if they have existed for some time, accumulating mutations could have resulted in some sequence differences. This in turn implies that the ribosomes of an organism may not all be identical. If they are dissimilar, one is inclined to inquire whether their differences have been used to some advantage. One obvious possibility is to specialize certain ribosomal types for the preferential acceptance of certain classes of messages. The fact that ribosomes will accept synthetic messages, or ones foreign to the cells from which they are derived, does not establish that they are completely indifferent and will translate all messages with equal facility. Such questions can be examined only in experiments exposing ribosomes to mixtures of homologous and heterologous messages so that a choice can be detected, if one exists.

In any event, the existence of multiplicity makes it mandatory to reopen the possibility of ribosomal differentiation. The availability of the genetically rich *Drosophila* material makes possible a host of potentially informative experiments on these and other issues.

## References

1. AGOL, I. J., *J. Exptl. Biol.* (*Russian*), **5**, 84 (1929).
2. BAUTZ, E. K. F., AND HALL, B. D., *Proc. Natl. Acad. Sci. U.S.*, **48**, 400 (1962).
3. BELOZERSKY, A. N., AND SPIRIN, A. S., *Nature*, **182**, 111 (1958).
4. BERNHARD, W., AND GRABOULAN, N., *Exptl. Cell Res.* Suppl. 9, 25 (1963).
5. BIRNSTIEL, M. L., CHIPCHASE, M. I. H., AND HYDE, B. B., *Biochim. Biophys. Acta*, **76**, 454 (1963).
6. BOLTON, E. T., AND MCCARTHY, B. J., *Proc. Natl. Acad. Sci. U.S.*, **48**, 1390 (1962).
7. BRIDGES, C. B., AND BREHME, K., *Carnegie Inst. Wash. Publ.*, **J62** (1944).
8. BROWN, D. D., AND GURDON, J. B., *Proc. Natl. Acad. Sci. U.S.*, **51**, 139 (1964).
9. BUSCH, H. P., BYORET, P., AND SMETANA, K., *Cancer Res.*, **23**, 313 (1963).
10. CASPERSSON, T., *Cell Growth and Cell Function*, Norton, New York, 1950.
11. CHIPCHASE, M. I. H., AND BIRNSTIEL, M. L., *Proc. Natl. Acad. Sci. U.S.*, **50**, 1101 (1963).
12. EDSTROM, J. E., GRAMPP, W., AND SCHOR, N., *J. Biophys. Biochem. Cytol.*, **11**, 549 (1961).
13. GERSHENSON, S., *J. Genet.*, **28**, 297 (1934).
14. GIACOMONI, D., AND SPIEGELMAN, S., *Science*, **138**, 1328 (1962).
15. GILLESPIE, D., AND SPIEGELMAN, S., *J. Mol. Biol.*, in press.
16. GOODMAN, H. M., AND RICH, A., *Proc. Natl. Acad. Sci. U.S.*, **48**, 2101 (1962).
17. GREENSPAN, C., AND MARMUR, J., *Science*, **142**, 387 (1964).
18. GROS, F., GILBERT, W., HIATT, H. H., ATTARDI, G., SPAHR, P. F., AND WATSON, J. D., *Cold Spring Harbor Symp. Quant. Biol.*, **26**, 111 (1961b).
19. HALL, B. D., AND SPIEGELMAN, S., *Proc. Natl. Acad. Sci. U.S.*, **47**, 137 (1961).

20. HAYASHI, M., AND SPIEGELMAN, S., *Proc. Natl. Acad. Sci. U.S.*, **47**, 1564 (1961).
21. HAYASHI, M., HAYASHI, M. N., AND SPIEGELMAN, S., *Proc. Natl. Acad. Sci. U.S.*, **50**, 664 (1963b).
22. HAYASHI, M., HAYASHI, M. N., AND SPIEGELMAN, S., *Biophys. J.*, **5**, 231 (1965).
23. KANO-SUEOKA, T., AND SPIEGELMAN, S., *Proc. Natl. Acad. Sci. U.S.*, **48**, 1942 (1962).
24. KURLAND, C. G., *J. Mol. Biol.*, **2**, 83 (1960).
25. LAFONTAINE, J. G., *J. Biophys. Biochem. Cytol.*, **4**, 777 (1958).
26. LERMAN, L. S., *Biochim. Biophys. Acta*, **18**, 132 (1955).
27. MANDELL, J. D., AND HERSHEY, A. D., *Anal. Biochem.*, **1**, 66 (1960).
28. MARMUR, J., *J. Mol. Biol.*, **3**, 208 (1961).
29. McCONKEY, E. H., AND HOPKINS, J. W., *Proc. Natl. Acad. Sci. U.S.*, **51**, 1197 (1964).
30. MEAD, C. G., *J. Biol. Chem.*, **239**, 550 (1964).
31. MESELSON, M., STAHL, F. W., AND VINOGRAD, J., *Proc. Natl. Acad. Sci. U.S.*, **43**, 581 (1957).
32. MONIER, R., NAONO, S., HAYES, D., HAYES, F., AND GROS, F., *J. Mol. Biol.*, **5**, 311 (1962).
33. MULLER, H. J., AND PROKOFYEVA, A. A., *Dokl. Akad. Nauk SSSR*, **4**, 74 (1934).
34. MULLER, H. J., RAFFEL, D., GERSHENSON, S. M., AND PROKOFYEVA-BELGOVSKAYA, A. A., *Genetics,* **22**, 87 (1937).
35. NYGAARD, A. P., AND HALL, B. D., *Biochem. Biophys. Res. Commun.*, **12**, 98 (1963).
36. NYGAARD, A. P., AND HALL, B. D., *J. Mol. Biol.*, **9**, 125 (1964).
37. PERRY, R. P., *Proc. Natl. Acad. Sci. U.S.*, **48**, 2179 (1962).
38. PERRY, R. P., HALL, A., AND ERRERA, M., *Biochim. Biophys. Acta,* **49**, 47 (1961).
39. PERRY, R. P., SRINIVASAN, P. R., AND KELLEY, D. E., *Science,* **145**, 504 (1964).
40. POLATNICK, J., AND BACHRACH, H. L., *Anal. Biochem.*, **2**, 161 (1961).
41. PORTER, K. R., *Proc. 4th Intern. Conf. Electron Microscopy, Berlin*, Vol. 2, p. 186. Springer, Berlin, 1960.
42. RITOSSA, F. M., AND SPIEGELMAN, S., *Proc. Natl. Acad. Sci. U.S.*, **53**, 737 (1965).
43. RUDKIN, G. T., *Proc. 11th Intern. Congr. Genet.*, in press, and personal communication.
44. SAGIK, B. P., GREEN, M. H., HAYASHI, M., AND SPIEGELMAN, S., *Biophys. J.,* **2**, 409 (1962).
45. SCHERRER, K., LATHAM, H., AND DARNELL, J. E., *Proc. Natl. Acad. Sci. U.S.*, **49**, 240 (1963).
46. SIDOROV, B. P., *Proc. 4th Congr. Zool.*, Vol. 20, p. 251 (1930).
47. SPIEGELMAN, S., *Cold Spring Harbor Symp. Quant. Biol.*, **26**, 75 (1961).
48. STURTEVANT, A. H., AND BEADLE, G. W., *Genetics*, **21**, 554 (1936).
49. SWIFT, H., personal communications.
50. TOCCHINI-VALENTINI, G. P., STODOLSKY, M., AURISICCHIO, A., SARNAT, M., GRAZIOSI, F., WEISS, S. B., AND GEIDUSCHEK, E. P., *Proc. Natl. Acad. Sci. U.S.*, **50**, 935 (1963).
51. VERMEULAN, C., AND ATWOOD, K. C., *Biochem. Biophys. Res. Commun.*, **19**, 221 (1965).
52. VINCENT, W. S., *Intern. Rev. Cytol.*, **4**, 269 (1955).
53. WATSON, J. D., AND CRICK, F. H. C., *Nature*, **171**, 964 (1953).
54. WOESE, C. R., *Nature*, **189**, 920 (1961).
55. YANKOFSKY, S. A., AND SPIEGELMAN, S., *Proc. Natl. Acad. Sci. U.S.*, **48**, 1069 (1962a).

56. YANKOFSKY, S. A., AND SPIEGELMAN, S., *Proc. Natl. Acad. Sci. U.S.*, **48**, 1466 (1962b).
57. YANKOFSKY, S. A., AND SPIEGELMAN, S., *Proc. Natl. Acad. Sci. U.S.*, **49**, 538 (1963).
58. YANKOFSKY, S. A., AND SPIEGELMAN, S., in press.

# The Evolution of Polynucleotides

Bill H. Hoyer, Ellis T. Bolton, Brian J. McCarthy,[1]
and Richard B. Roberts

U.S. Department of Health, Education, and Welfare, Public Health Service,
National Institutes of Health, National Institute of Allergy and
Infectious Diseases, Laboratory of Biology of Viruses,
Bethesda, Maryland, and Carnegie Institution of Washington,
Department of Terrestrial Magnetism, Washington, D.C.

## Introduction

Comparisons of amino acid sequences, enzymatic activities, and immunological properties of macromolecules show only a few of the many attributes of the organisms under consideration. Pictures of systematic relationships and evolution, as derived from such features, may be said to be painted with a very finely tipped brush. Details are observable which may involve only single amino acid changes, or determinants, or reactive sites in proteins. The field of vision is too narrow to include some parts of the general evolutionary picture which might be seen from a vantage point providing broader perspective. Of course, as studies of individual macromolecules from a variety of sources become more complete and involve a greater proportion of the constituent molecules of organisms, the picture of relationships and evolutionary trends may well expand into a more general view.

Our approach has been to paint a picture of certain animal relationships with a broad brush. The method involves a quantitative study of the recombination of separated strands of deoxyribonucleic acid (DNA). Inherent in the philosophy of the approach is the assumption that the total molecular composition of living materials is determined by the nucleotide sequences in DNA. Specific affinities observable among various DNA's are indicative of qualities of the whole organism.

In this presentation the findings described will be mainly restricted to the DNA–DNA relationships among vertebrates with emphasis on the primate group. The primates were chosen as an example because of the active interest in their relationships and because of the backlog of information concerning this group from a variety of studies which range from the molecular to the sociological.

---

[1] Present address: Departments of Microbiology and Genetics, University of Washington, Seattle, Washington.

## Methodology

Rather extensive descriptions of the DNA–agar procedure and some of its uses are already published (1, 2, 8). A description of the procedure as applied to the animal DNA systems has also appeared (5). We will not attempt to detail the procedure but, instead, indicate its properties, advantages, and pitfalls as we now recognize them.

### History

A matrix provided by an agar–agar gel was found to be capable of entrapping high molecular weight DNA in its "melted," single-stranded form (1). The DNA strands (molecular weight $> 10^7$) were mixed with melted agar and rapidly cooled. The slab of DNA–agar was sieved, washed with double strength SSC (SSC is 0.15 $M$ NaCl plus 0.015 $M$ Na citrate), and freed of excess water to provide uniform gel particles which contained single-stranded high molecular weight DNA.

Although high molecular weight DNA remained in the agar matrix, smaller molecules such as polyribonucleotides (RNA) could freely enter and leave the gel. When appropriately incubated together under conditions favoring DNA–RNA binding, RNA molecules which had become located on their complementary DNA sites remained in the agar gel despite extensive washing. Incubation temperatures were chosen which would minimize adventitious binding. The bound RNA could be recovered by elution at higher temperature and in lower salt concentrations.

This DNA–RNA interaction method has provided information on the relationships and characteristics of RNA's from bacterial viruses (1), bacteria (7), and animal cells (4, 9).

It became necessary to determine the availability of the complementary sites on *Escherichia coli* DNA embedded in agar for binding its homologous RNA. Molecules known to be complementary to both strands of the embedded DNA and representative of the total genome were required. Such molecules also must be able freely to enter and leave the agar gel. All of these requirements were met by DNA fragments (molecular weight about $0.5 \times 10^6$) prepared by shearing DNA in a pressure cell at about 10,000 p.s.i. When melted to form single strands and incubated with homologous DNA agar, these fragments were found to saturate about 90% of the complementary sites immobilized in the agar (8).

Sheared, melted DNA fragments were then put to use to establish relationships among a group of Gram-negative bacteria (7) and between lambda bacteriophage and either lysogenic or nonlysogenic bacteria (3). Relationships among the bacteria established by the DNA–agar procedure were the same whether DNA–DNA or DNA–RNA interactions were used as criteria. This similarity is the result of the genome's being completely expressed in a culture of exponentially growing bacteria.

A hint that extensive cross relationships might exist among the DNA's of animals was obtained when rapidly labeled RNA isolated from mouse liver bound about 25% as well to calf thymus DNA–agar as to mouse DNA–agar, but bound not at all to *E. coli* DNA–agar (4). This hint was amplified when radiolabeled human DNA fragments were bound to mouse DNA–agar about 20% as well as to the homologous human DNA–agar. More extensive observations confirmed the cross relationships among a variety of animal DNA's and detailed the characteristics of these relationships (5).

Relationships determined by DNA–DNA and DNA–RNA comparisons among animals need not yield similar results, as they do in bacteria. Different portions of the genome may be expressed in the various tissues of the same animal and it is likely that certain portions of the genome are expressed only during morphogenesis, and others not at all.

### Advantages and Disadvantages of the DNA–Agar Method

Whenever DNA–DNA or DNA–RNA interactions are examined in free solution, the complementary DNA strands are free to interact. The embedded high-molecular-weight DNA strands with which we are here concerned are physically restrained from interaction in the agar system. These embedded strands may be supplied at high concentration while the RNA molecules or DNA fragments may be used at relatively low concentrations. This combination allows the investigator to observe the binding of a radiolabeled complementary nucleic acid strand to the embedded DNA under incubation conditions stringent enough to minimize adventitious reactions. The relative simplicity of the method is an obvious advantage when a series of nucleic acids from different sources are investigated. In addition, bound molecules may be readily recovered and used again for other experiments.

High-molecular-weight DNA strands must be used, or considerable leaching of the embedded strands may occur during incubation. It may be difficult to prepare DNA–agar from a series of DNA's and be assured of comparable binding characteristics among the preparations. Animal DNA, despite its potential high molecular weight, must be prepared with care so that it will ultimately yield DNA–agar with good binding properties. If equal amounts of double strength SSC and DNA–agar (usually 0.50 g agar and 0.50 ml of $2 \times$ SSC) are incubated overnight at 60°C with radiolabeled homologous DNA fragments at a ratio of about 50 to 100 µg embedded DNA to 1 µg fragments, 30 to 40% of the labeled fragments will bind to satisfactory agar preparations. The embedding procedures are unsuitable for DNA which is naturally of molecular weight less than about $10^7$.

Thus far, cells radiolabeled biologically in tissue culture have been the source of labeled DNA fragments. It is not practical to label biologically all specimens of interest; a suitable chemical or physical labeling procedure would be very desirable.

## RESULTS AND DISCUSSION

As has been well documented, melted animal DNA does not return to its original state as evidenced by studies of ultraviolet absorption (6). This observation might lead to the premature conclusion that adequate comparisons of animal DNA's cannot be made by comparisons of the binding properties of DNA's, one to another. However, it has already been indicated that comparisons of relationships of animal DNA's are, indeed, possible by use of the DNA–agar procedure. Evidently, perfect rematching is not required. Some of the tests of specificity and other observations made with various animal DNA's are presented below.

### Specificity of the Reaction

Labeled DNA fragments from either human or rhesus monkey bind almost equally well to human or rhesus monkey DNA embedded in agar. A comparison of these binding capacities indicates an 85 to 90% relationship between these DNA's (5). A more stringent test of the specificity of the reaction was made by mixing $P^{32}$-labeled rhesus and $C^{14}$-labeled human DNA fragments. This mixture was melted and incubated with human DNA–agar in the presence of increasing amounts of either human or rhesus unlabeled melted DNA fragments. Should the reaction lack specificity, increasing excesses of the closely related rhesus monkey fragments would continue to interfere with the binding of the $C^{14}$-labeled human DNA fragments until the binding became indistinguishable from that of the $P^{32}$-labeled rhesus monkey DNA fragments. Figure 1 clearly indicates that the binding of human DNA fragments to human DNA–agar continues even in the presence of a 600-fold excess of rhesus monkey fragments. This excess of unlabeled rhesus monkey DNA, thus, did not interfere with the binding of a fraction of human DNA fragments which must represent sequences for which there exist no homologues in the rhesus DNA. By comparison, the unlabeled human DNA fragments effectively competed with either labeled rhesus or human DNA fragments for binding to *human* DNA–agar. Thus, under identical conditions of incubation and elution, the specificity of the animal DNA–DNA interaction is evident.

Another indication of the specificity of these nucleic acid interactions is shown by the result presented in Fig. 2. For these experiments, a mixture of P³²-labeled mouse DNA fragments and C¹⁴-labeled human DNA fragments from HeLa cells was incubated overnight at 60°C with agar containing either mouse DNA or human DNA. The agar containing human DNA bound 19.5% of the human DNA fragments, as compared to 4.6% of the mouse fragments. Conversely, 4.4% of the human DNA fragments and 18.3% of the mouse DNA fragments were bound to agar containing mouse DNA. The relative extents of the heterologous and

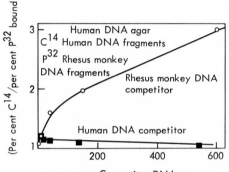

FIG. 1.   Ratios of binding of a mixture of melted C¹⁴-labeled human DNA fragments and melted P³²-labeled rhesus monkey DNA fragments to human DNA–agar in the presence of increasing amounts of either rhesus or human melted unlabeled DNA fragments. A mixture of equal quantities of C¹⁴-labeled human DNA fragments and P³²-labeled rhesus monkey DNA fragments was melted and rapidly cooled. This mixture (0.5 μg of each fragmented DNA) was added to portions of double-strength standard saline citrate (0.50 ml) which contained no competitor or increasing amounts of unlabeled melted fragments of either human or rhesus monkey DNA. These mixtures were incubated at 60°C overnight, and the unbound fragments were washed free with double-strength standard saline citrate at 60°C. The bound fragments were eluted at 75°C in standard saline citrate diluted 100-fold with distilled water. The ratios of the percent of the C¹⁴-DNA bound to P³²-DNA bound were determined with each competitor.

homologous reactions in the two experiments are in good agreement. Thus, these two species appear to have in common some 20 to 25% of their polynucleotide sequences. It is worth noting that such agreement between reciprocal reactions can occur only where the amount of DNA indicative of a haploid set of genes is very similar in the two species. In this connection it is of interest that reciprocal tests also agree quantitatively among enterobacteria (7) where the genomes are represented in giant molecules of DNA known to be similar in molecular weight.

## Competition Reactions

Base sequence complementarity among nucleic acid molecules can be studied by means of competition reactions as described for the experiments shown in Fig. 1. Similarity is measured by the extent of interference (with a homologous reaction) resulting from the presence in the reaction mixture of an excess of unlabeled heterologous nucleic acid (5). This approach has two great practical advantages: study of a series of

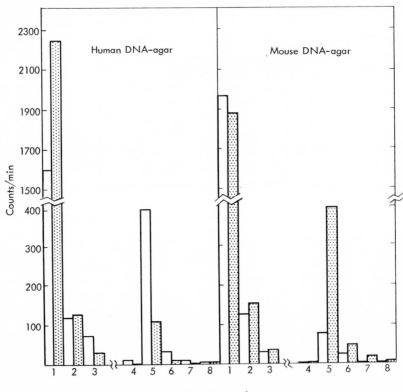

FIG. 2. Reaction of a mixture of $P^{32}$-labeled mouse DNA fragments and $C^{14}$-labeled human DNA fragments with either mouse DNA–agar or human DNA–agar. The mixture of radiolabeled fragments was melted, rapidly cooled, and added in 0.50 ml double-strength standard saline citrate to either 0.50 g mouse (466 µg/g) or human DNA–agar (656 µg/g). The mixtures which contained 10 µg human DNA fragments and 25 µg $P^{32}$-labeled mouse DNA fragments were incubated at 60°C overnight. The unbound fragments were washed free with double-strength standard saline citrate at 60°C for fractions 1 to 4; at fraction 5, the temperature was raised to 72° to 73°C, and the standard saline citrate concentration was reduced 100-fold. The radioactivity in each fraction was determined. The stippled bars represent the radioactivity of mouse DNA and the open bars the radioactivity of human DNA.

genetic relationships requires only a single labeled nucleic acid preparation and a single preparation of DNA–agar. The advantage of eliminating some of the labeled DNA's is obvious, but perhaps equally important is the possibility of making comparative studies with aliquots of a single DNA–agar preparation. Much of the variability in the quality of the data obtained results from the number of different DNA–agar preparations used, each containing different amounts of trapped DNA, itself of variable molecular weight, and each subject to more or less loss of DNA during incubation. Although these effects can be maintained within acceptable limits by careful control of the preparation of DNA and DNA gels, it is nevertheless true that the most highly reproducible results are obtained with a single batch of DNA–agar.

The competition reaction has been used in the further study of the cross reaction noted earlier between the DNA's of widely different vertebrates. The relationship of several of these DNA's to rhesus monkey DNA has been measured from the extent of competition exhibited in the homologous rhesus DNA reaction. A series of 0.50-g aliquots of a single preparation of agar containing rhesus DNA were incubated with 0.5 μg of fragments of $P^{32}$-labeled rhesus DNA in the presence of various amounts of unlabeled DNA fragments prepared from various sources. The percentage of the labeled DNA fragments forming duplexes under these conditions is given in Fig. 3. Even large amounts of chicken DNA, whose base composition resembles that of mammalian DNA, inhibit the homologous reaction only slightly. There is thus no obvious nonspecific effect even where the competing DNA is several thousand times more abundant than the labeled component. On the other hand, the presence of large quantities of unlabeled rhesus monkey DNA greatly reduces the amount of the labeled component bound.

Competing DNA's of other primates and mammals yield results which are arranged in a series lying between these extremes and which progresses according to the generally accepted taxonomic ranking of the species examined. The taxonomic separations between the rhesus monkey and the other species are indicated on the right-hand side of Fig. 3. Evidently, these data provide a "yardstick" for a quantitative evaluation of the extent of genetic diversity indicated by the various taxa of vertebrates. Whether the measure shown in Fig. 3 is quantitatively applicable within other orders of mammals must await more data. However, it would seem that a means for evaluating the extent of genetic diversity within taxa and among corresponding taxa of organisms is at hand. In this connection it has already been commented that "the genetic diversity among families of bacteria is relatively greater than the genetic diversity among all the major vertebrate classes" (5).

## Evolution of Polynucleotides

Moreover, similarities in polynucleotide sequences may be related to the time at which the lines of organisms we examine in the present diverged from one another in the geologic past. The result is presented in Fig. 4. It is immediately apparent that the data show systematic rela-

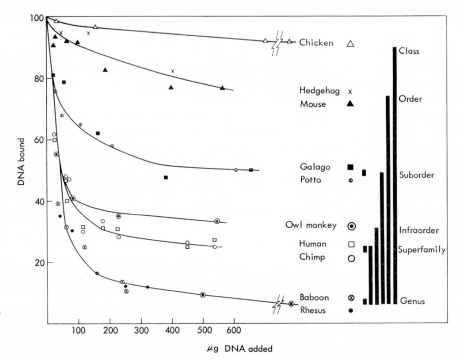

FIG. 3. Competition by unlabeled DNA fragments in the reaction between P³²-labeled rhesus monkey DNA fragments and rhesus monkey DNA–agar. One-half microgram of P³²-labeled rhesus monkey DNA fragments was incubated with 0.50 g of agar containing 130 μg of rhesus monkey DNA in the presence of varying quantities of unlabeled DNA fragments from the source indicated. The reaction volume was 1.00 ml. The amount of labeled DNA bound relative to the homologous reaction in the absence of competitor is plotted against the amount of unlabeled DNA present in the reaction mixture. The vertical bars on the right relate the taxonomic separation between the rhesus monkey and the other groups to the quantitative differences among their nucleotide sequences.

tionships that any adequate theory of evolution must explain. At first glance there appears to be a random "decay" process, the correspondence between genes decaying exponentially with a half-life of one hundred million years. However, when several distantly related species of mammals are examined, it is found that the fraction in common to any two is common to all. This fraction includes the smaller fractions common to birds and fishes (5). If the changes occurred at random throughout the genome, there could be no large fraction common to a diverse group. It is clear that this group of genes had some special characteristic that enabled it to resist change over periods of hundreds of millions of years.

Any detailed interpretation of Fig. 4 must await knowledge of the intimate physical chemistry of the nucleic acid interactions under study.

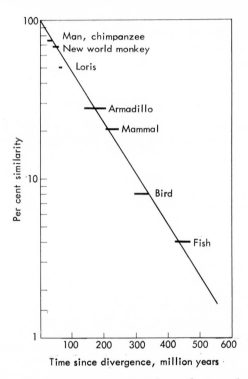

FIG. 4.   Relationship between polynucleotide similarity and time of evolutionary divergence.

However, it is tempting to speculate. One possibility is that the curve results from the *distribution of mutability* in the genome. That is, given the right combination of rates of mutation for the various components of the vertebrate genome, such a simple exponential curve could be constructed. On the other hand, the decay of similarity between genes resembles the "single-hit curve" familiar for radiation effects wherein a single event is sufficient to bring about a change. Thus, rather than a very special distribution of mutability, it may be that common genes are lost in single events as by deletions or their equivalent. If this be the case, then the DNA lost in the process must be replenished in order to conserve the size of the vertebrate genome. Several mechanisms for this can be envisioned: existing DNA could be duplicated, giving mutliple copies of certain genes; DNA could be added by "end addition," a process that has been observed *in vitro;* and new DNA could be introduced as by virus infection in the germ-line followed by integration of parts of the viral DNA into the host genome.

The implications of the data presented above for understanding the mechanism of organic evolution urge experiments which can distinguish between these possibly alternative interpretations of evolutionary divergence or assess their relative importance should they both be applicable. In principle, at least, the tools and materials appear now to be available for this purpose.

## Acknowledgments

We would like to thank Dr. Arthur J. Riopelle, Director of the Delta Regional Primate Research Center, for supplying primate tissues, and Dr. Morris Goodman, of Wayne State University, for his valuable collaboration.

## References

1. Bolton, E. T., and McCarthy, B. J., *Proc. Natl. Acad. Sci. U.S.,* 48, 1390 (1962).
2. Bolton, E. T., and McCarthy, B. J., *J. Mol. Biol.,* 8, 184 (1964).
3. Cowie, D. B., and McCarthy, B. J., *Proc. Natl. Acad. Sci. U.S.,* 50, 537 (1963).
4. Hoyer, B. H., McCarthy, B. J., and Bolton, E. T., *Science,* 140, 1408 (1963).
5. Hoyer, B. H., McCarthy, B. J., and Bolton, E. T., *Science,* 144, 959 (1964).
6. Marmur, J., Schildkraut, C. L., and Doty, P., *in* "The Molecular Basis of Neoplasia," Univ. of Texas Press, Austin, 1962.
7. McCarthy, B. J., and Bolton, E. T., *Proc. Natl. Acad. Sci. U.S.,* 50, 156 (1963).
8. McCarthy, B. J., and Bolton, E. T., *J. Mol. Biol.,* 8, 184 (1964).
9. McCarthy, B. J., and Hoyer, B. H., *Proc. Natl. Acad. Sci. U.S.,* 52, 915 (1964).

# On the Evolution of Genetic Systems

RUTH SAGER

*Department of Zoology, Columbia University, New York, New York*

The analysis of nonchromosomal heredity has represented a tantalizing problem in biology ever since the discovery of the first nonchromosomal gene by Correns in 1908. Until recently most of the experimental information has indicated the widespread distribution of nonchromosomal genetic factors, especially in microorganisms and higher plants, but has not provided much insight into their chemical nature, cellular location, or mode of action. Within the past few years, a number of new findings have been reported which are beginning to illuminate these questions and to raise other questions of some evolutionary significance.

The new findings come from two different lines of investigation, one genetic and the other biochemical. In the past, genetic evidence of nonchromosomal inheritance had been based almost exclusively on single-factor crosses, since more than one nonchromosomal factor had rarely been found in the same organism. The new genetic evidence is based upon studies of an extensive series of nonchromosomal gene mutations induced by streptomycin in the alga *Chlamydomonas* (Sager, 4; Sager and Ramanis, 6). Some of the mutations result in loss of photosynthetic activity and therefore probably affect the chloroplast, while other mutations, to streptomycin resistance or dependence, poor growth, and tiny colony formation, probably do not involve the chloroplast. By following the distribution of these nonchromosomal genes in multifactor crosses, we have for the first time been able to study recombination of nonchromosomal genes.

The importance of recombination analysis in genetics lies in its power to provide information about the organization of genetic material obtainable in no other way at this time. In classical genetics, recombination analysis provided the basis for distinguishing genes on different chromosomes which showed unlinked or random recombination from those which were linked on the same chromosome. Linked genes remained preferentially associated in their parental combinations among the progeny of crosses, and the frequency of their recombination provided the basis for mapping them in a linear array along the chromosome. More recently, it has become possible to map the linear array of nucleotides

591

within a gene by the same basic method of recombination analysis, as shown most elegantly by the work of Benzer (1). The molecular events responsible for linked recombination are not fully understood at this time, but it is clear that a close and precise pairing of homologous genes must be involved, followed either by breakage and exchange between old strands, or by replication of new material containing sequences recombined from the two parents.

We have begun to use the classical method of recombination analysis to explore the organization of nonchromosomal genes. This paper will summarize the information so far available. We have found unlinked recombination between two different nonchromosomal (NC) genes, suggesting that they are carried on different linkage groups. And we have found recombinant genes, which we interpret to be derived from intragenic recombination between allelic homologous nonchromosomal genes coming from the two parents. The occurrence of intragenic recombination provides the first evidence that nonchromosomal genes, like the chromosomal ones, are capable of precise pairing, followed by some kind of exchange.

Of all the cell constituents, the nucleic acids are the only ones known to possess the physical properties making possible this kind of intramolecular event. Consequently, we interpret our results as providing the first evidence of the nucleic acid composition of nonchromosomal genes.

The data to be described in this paper are derived from genetic analysis of crosses involving two pairs of nonchromosomal genes. The fundamental difference in transmission between chromosomal and nonchromosomal genes in the sexual green alga *Chlamydomonas* is shown diagrammatically in Fig. 1. Chromosomal genes show classical 2–2 segregation among the progeny in each tetrad, while as a rule the NC genes show what we call 4–0 segregation. That is, the NC genes from the female (or mating type plus) parent are transmitted to all of the progeny of each zygote, while the corresponding NC genes from the male parent are lost in the zygote and do not reappear in any of the progeny. This is maternal inheritance and is the characteristic pattern of inheritance of NC genes in most organisms.

The pattern of maternal inheritance is not invariant. Many of the organisms which show maternal inheritance also show occasional exceptions to the rule in which NC genes from the male parent are transmitted to the offspring. In *Chlamydomonas,* we have found that exceptional zygotes exist in which the male NC genes persist and are transmitted to the offspring together with female NC genes. We have been able to study the segregation and recombination of NC genes as it occurs in the progeny of these exceptional zygotes.

The method of analysis consists, first, in selecting exceptional zygotes by germinating them under conditions in which one of the NC genes from the male parent must be present for survival of the progeny. As shown in Fig. 2, in the cross $sd\,ac_1\,mt^+ \times sr\,ac_2\,mt^-$, the female parent ($mt^+$) is streptomycin-dependent ($sd$), requiring streptomycin for growth, while the male parent ($mt^-$) is streptomycin-resistant ($sr$). The

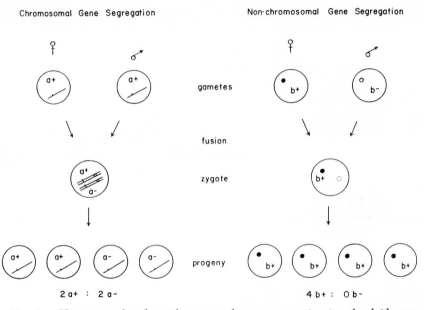

FIG. 1. Chromosomal and nonchromosomal gene segregation in a haploid organism. The segregation of chromosomal gene $a$, present as the $a+$ allele in the female parent and as the $a-$ allele in the male parent, depends on the mechanics of chromosome duplication and segregation at meiosis. Each chromosome duplicates, and the homologous chromosomes from the two parents pair, giving rise to four strands for each chromosome of the haploid set. In meiosis the strands are distributed equally to the four progeny cells. In the same cells, the nonchromosomal genes, represented as $b+$ in the female and $b-$ in the male, enter the zygote, but the $b-$ complement is generally not transmitted to the progeny. After Sager (5).

parents are also segregating for a second pair of NC genes $ac_1$ and $ac_2$. These mutations block photosynthetic activity, and the mutant strains require acetate for growth. Each of the progeny after meiosis is haploid for the chromosomal markers but still contains the NC genes from both parents. The $sr$ gene is apparently dominant, in the sense that cells containing both $sd$ and $sr$ genes will grow with or without streptomycin. In our experiments, the progeny are allowed to grow for a few vegetative multiplications, and then each cell is classified for all of its segregating

markers, both chromosomal and nonchromosomal. The chromosomal
genes segregate normally in all of our crosses.

The classes of progeny, with respect to NC genes, recovered from the
cross diagrammed in Fig. 2, are given in Table I, in terms of their frequency distribution. Several conclusions can be drawn from these data.

1. The unselected acetate-requiring markers, $ac_1$ and $ac_2$, segregate
1–1 on the average among the progeny. We interpret this result to mean
that the parental strains contribute equal numbers of $ac_1$ and $ac_2$ deter-

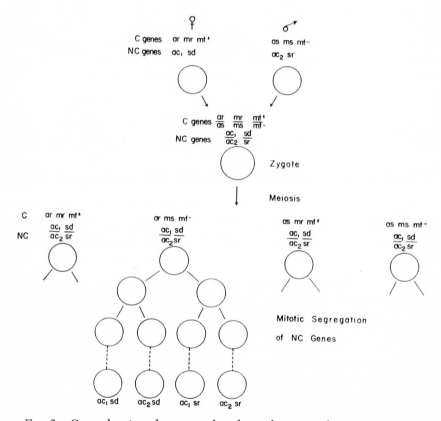

FIG. 2. Cross showing chromosomal and nonchromosomal gene segregation in
exceptional zygotes of *Chlamydomonas*. In this cross the female parent differs from
the male by three pairs of unlinked chromosomal (C) genes and two pairs of nonchromosomal (NC) genes. The zygote is diploid, containing all the genes from both
parents. In meiosis the C genes segregate as determined by chromosome behavior,
giving rise to four genetically different products. The NC genes do not segregate in
meiosis, and in these exceptional zygotes the haploid progeny initially still contain
NC genes from both parents. NC gene segregation occurs in the mitotic divisions of
each vegetative clone after meiosis. After Sager (5).

minants. Segregation begins in the first few divisions after meiosis, indicating that the number of copies of each gene is very low; it may even be one. A detailed analysis of the segregation pattern is still in progress. The ratio of $sd$ to $sr$ progeny is far from 1–1, but selective conditions may have distorted these data, and this question requires further study.

2. Both the $ac_1/ac_2$ pair and the $sd/sr$ pair begin to segregate early, but they do not always segregate at the same division. As shown in Table I, after four to five mitotic doublings, there are equal numbers of the parental types $ac_1 sd$ and $ac_2 sr$, and of the nonparental or recom-

TABLE I

RECOMBINATION OF NC GENES[a]

|        | $ac_1$ | $ac_2$ | $ac^+$ | $ac$-mixed | Total |
|--------|--------|--------|--------|------------|-------|
| $sr$   | 6.6    | 5.2    | 1.1    | 24.2       | 37.1  |
| $sd$   | 3.3    | 4.1    | 1.0    | 14.8       | 23.2  |
| $ss$   | 1.8    | 1.6    | 0.45   | 2.4        | 6.2   |
| New types | 0.8 | 1.6    | 0.3    | 4.0        | 6.7   |
| Mixed  | 4.6    | 4.0    | 0.45   | 17.1       | 26.1  |
| Total  | 17.1   | 16.5   | 3.30   | 62.5       | —     |

[a] Forty-one exceptional zygotes were selected after germination on medium without streptomycin when zygote colonies contained 16 to 64 cells (two to four doublings of each zoospore product of meiosis); 22 of them were analyzed on medium without streptomycin, and 19 on medium with streptomycin; 71% of the zygotes contained all four chromosomal marker types, 20% contained three types, and 9% contained two types. In all, 648 progeny were analyzed, representing 148 zoospore clones. Every progeny cell from each zygote was classified for all segregating markers, both chromosomal (actidione resistance and sensitivity, methionine sulfoximine resistance and sensitivity, and mating type) and nonchromosomal (acetate requirement, streptomycin resistance or dependence). Yield of exceptional zygotes was 0.02% of total zygotes. Data from the two sets (with and without streptomycin) were normalized to 100% and pooled to provide the average frequencies shown in the table.

binant types $ac_1 sr$ and $ac_2 sd$. Thus, the two NC gene pairs segregate independently both in time and in space. It is possible that random assortment could result from the two pairs' being located very far apart on the same linkage group, as sometimes occurs with long chromosomes, but it seems more likely that they are carried on different particles.

3. In addition to the four expected classes of progeny discussed above, we also recover novel classes of progeny, including $ss$ and $ac^+$ types, indistinguishable from the wild-type ancestors of the $ac$ and $sd$-$sr$ parents; and new mutant types with altered levels of streptomycin resistance, dependence, or acetate requirement, different from the parents. Several lines of evidence support the hypothesis that these novel types result from a process of intragenic recombination.

The evidence includes the demonstration that these novel types are not pre-existing in the population before the cross is made, either as novel cells or as novel particles or genes present in masked form in the parental cells. During vegetative growth of the progeny clones, novel types continue to arise anew from any cells which are still mixed, containing both $ac_1$ and $ac_2$ and/or $sd$ and $sr$. The novel types, both the wild-type $ss$ and $ac^+$ and several of the altered mutant types, have been further studied by test crosses which show that they are stable in replication and transmission. We do not yet know whether the recombination process is a reciprocal one, in which both a wild type and a double mutant arise in the same event. No double mutants have yet been found, but this work is still in progress.

These results represent the first genetic evidence of recombination of nonchromosomal genes and, as such, provide the first steps toward a new understanding of the organization of genetic information in cells.

These genetic data correlate very well with recent demonstrations of high-molecular-weight DNA in chloroplasts and mitochondria (Chun, Vaughan, and Rich, 2; Sager and Ishida, 7; Luck and Reich, 3). Although no definitive experiment has yet shown that organelle DNA carries genetic information, it seems a reasonable guess that some nonchromosomal genes will in time be localized there. Thus, both the genetic and the biochemical evidence to date supports the view that chloroplasts and mitochondria carry some primary genetic information in the form of DNA. These results do not preclude the possibility that cells contain additional genetic systems, perhaps in other organelles and not necessarily composed of DNA.

In speculations about the origin of life, geneticists have stressed replication, while physiologists have stressed energy as the primary requirement. Recent evidences of the universality of the genetic code, and of the intimate role of RNA in protein synthesis, have strengthened the view of a primeval association of nucleic acid-like and protein-like molecules. In such an association, the nucleic acid would code for the protein, and the protein would help to replicate the nucleic acid, with energy and building blocks coming initially from the environment. Addition to this nucleoprotein of an energy-generating system, such as a primitive photosynthetic or chemosynthetic apparatus, would have provided a molecular aggregate with considerable evolutionary stability.

If aggregates of this sort represented the origin of cellular organelles which later coalesced to form cells, then genes would clearly have arisen in the cytoplasm in association with these organelles. A subsequent line of development would have led to the origin of chromosomes, with the transfer of primary genetic information from RNA to DNA and from cytoplasm to nucleus. Classically, chromosomes have been viewed as the solution to the problem of segregation and recombination. But, if so, why do modern cells still contain cytoplasmic genetic systems?

I think the answer may be found in the regulatory functions of genes. Evidence is rapidly accumulating of regulatory devices at the chromosome level which control the time and the rate of gene action. It now seems likely that regulatory genes, which function to control the expression of other genes, represent a large fraction of the total genome. Indeed, regulatory requirements probably provided a strong selective pressure in the evolution of chromosomes. Although the mechanism of this regulatory action is not yet fully understood, the molecular organization of the chromosome is probably the key to the problem. By analogy, the continuing presence of DNA in organelles probably indicates the importance of permanent structural association of some sort.

If organelle DNA does carry genes, its replication would have to be carefully regulated. As has been shown with many organisms, chromosome replication is rigorously geared to the cell cycle to ensure that chromosome reproduction keeps pace with cell division. However, the limited evidence so far available suggests that the growth of organelles is not geared to the cell cycle in the same way, but that mitochondria and chloroplasts may proliferate under environmental stresses independent of cell division. If so, their DNA must also replicate in response to signals different from those that trigger chromosomal replication.

Thus the cytoplasmic genetic systems, far from representing a vestige of early evolution, may be of continuing importance in providing flexibility for organelle growth in response to a changing environment and independent of the cellular division cycle.

## ACKNOWLEDGMENTS

This work was supported by a grant from the National Institutes of Health. The efficient and enthusiastic collaboration of Mrs. Zenta Ramanis is gratefully acknowledged.

## REFERENCES

1. BENZER, S., *Proc. Natl. Acad. Sci. U.S.*, **47**, 403 (1961).
2. CHUN, E. H. L., VAUGHAN, M. H., JR., AND RICH, A., *J. Mol. Biol.*, **1**, 130 (1963).
3. LUCK, D., AND REICH, E., *Proc. Natl. Acad. Sci. U.S.*, **52**, 931 (1964).
4. SAGER, R., *Proc. Natl. Acad. Sci. U.S.*, **48**, 2018 (1962).
5. SAGER, R., *New Engl. J. Med.*, **271**, 352 (1964).
6. SAGER, R., AND RAMANIS, Z., *Proc. Natl. Acad. Sci. U.S.*, **50**, 260 (1963).
7. SAGER, R., AND ISHIDA, M. R., *Proc. Natl. Acad. Sci. U.S.*, **50**, 725 (1963).

# Discussion of Part IX

R. D. Hotchkiss, E. K. F. Bautz, V. Bryson, P. Siekevitz, V. Moses

Chairman Hotchkiss: Late as it is, I would not want to have this go without an opportunity for discussion.

Dr. Bautz: I should like to make a comment on Dr. Demerec's paper. He mentioned the difference between Dr. Marmur's futile attempts to hybridize *Salmonella* DNA with *Escherichia coli* DNA and the experiments by Bolton and McCarthy, who found 70 percent homology between the two DNA species.

I think the difference in these two experiments is that Dr. Marmur had in his experiment both *E. coli* DNA as well as *Salmonella* DNA to compete for the *E. coli* DNA sites, whereas in Bolton and McCarthy's experiment there was no free *E. coli* DNA to compete with the *Salmonella* DNA.

I don't think you need perfect homology in order to get double strands. As far as our experience with synthetic polynucleotides goes, 10 percent mispairing will lower the $T_m$ by as little as 6°C.

Dr. Bryson: Perhaps there is a certain homology between inversion, which does not seem to occur, and the production of small replicons which does occur in some enteric bacteria. It will be interesting to learn whether the lack of inversions in *E. coli* is related to a repair mechanism that favors the alternative formation of small closed loops as the end product of breakage and reunion. Replicons so formed may contain only part of a gene complex, but their survival would result from facile transmission and, more significantly, from their existence as additive rather than substitutive genetic information in the usual bacterial host.

Chairman Hotchkiss: I never fail to marvel at how Dr. Demerec has so often in his career managed to be doing the most interesting and modern things and often in the most biologically significant way.

For discussion, I suppose an interesting aspect would be the relation between these genetic homologies and the molecular ones that have been underlying the thinking of the papers just before and after. Also, I think the geneticist has to be interested in the very fact that these non-homologies are influencing the rates of exchange in their regions; so we must re-examine the basis for assuming that recombination rates reflect distances.

Dr. Siekevitz: I wonder, in these days of messenger RNA, whether we might not still look for some other explanation for some experimental results. I wanted to ask Dr. Moses whether it is not possible that he could explain his results by postulating a low amino acid concentration in the starved cells. What he is doing when adding a thing like carbohydrate source is to "save" the amino acids. That is, the carbohydrates are being used for energy instead of amino acids.

As soon as he puts the cells into a fresh medium, the amino acids are used not for energy but for protein synthesis.

DR. MOSES: I do not see why this should affect the time for the galactosidase to be synthesized compared with other proteins, why a differential discrimination against β-galactosidase should arise. The saving phenomenon suggested by Dr. Siekevitz would presumably favor the synthesis of all proteins. Two other inducible enzymes, D-serine deaminase and L-tryptophanase, behave in exactly the same way as β-galactosidase.

CHAIRMAN HOTCHKISS: The audience and speakers have been so patient and done so well, I think we should thank all of them, and finally thank Dr. Vogel, Dr. Lampen, Dr. Braun, and Dr. Bryson for the excellent arrangements they have made, and the Institute of Microbiology staff for being such excellent hosts.

Dr. Bryson has some concluding remarks in behalf of the Institute.

DR. BRYSON: It is now time to bring these proceedings to a close. My colleagues and I thank you for your participation and enthusiasm. Perhaps a few years from now we can meet again to survey the vast domain of evolution from the vantage point of biochemistry and genetics. If so, we hope that you will join us again to renew old friendships and to form new ones.

# Author Index

Numbers in parentheses are reference numbers and indicate that an author's work is referred to although his name is not cited in the text. Numbers in italics show the page on which the complete reference is listed.

601

# Subject Index